Shorts
Aircraft

since 1900

Manx Airlines' Shorts 360 G–ISLE at Luton International Airport in November 1985 while operating night mail services. (*Gordon Roberts*).

Shorts Aircraft
since 1900

C H Barnes

Revised by Derek N. James

PUTNAM

By the same Author
BRISTOL AIRCRAFT SINCE 1910
HANDLEY PAGE AIRCRAFT SINCE 1907

First published 1967

This edition published in Great Britain 1989 by
Putnam Aeronautical Books
an imprint of
Conway Maritime Press
24 Bride Lane, Fleet Street
London EC4Y 8DR

British Library Cataloguing in Publication Data
Barnes, C. H.
Shorts aircraft since 1900. —2nd rev. ed.
1. Short Brothers aeroplanes, to 1982
I. Title
629.133'34

ISBN 0–85177–819–4

Typeset by Hope Services, Abingdon
Printed and bound by Richard Clay Limited, Bungay

IN TRIBUTE TO

Horace Leonard Short, 1872–1917
Albert Eustace Short, 1875–1932
Hugh Oswald Short 1883–1969

the First Aircraft Manufacturers in the World,
coupled with the name of

John Lankester Parker, 1896–1965

'I do not think . . . aeronautics will ever come into play as a serious modification of transport and communication.' H. G. WELLS (1901)

'Hindsight is always 100 per cent.'
B. S. SHENSTONE (1966)

Contents

Foreword

Although the author was never employed by Short Brothers, his admiration for their products began during his early schooldays at Felixstowe, when his enlightened headmaster (the late F. J. Cawthorne), having declined to allow his boarders to roam the Promenade on Whit-Monday 1921, arranged for them to be guests for the day of the local Royal Air Force Station, where they were allowed to climb all over many stored obsolescent seaplanes (including Short 184s and F.3s) and to see the process of launching and beaching Short-built F.5 flying-boats. So, although this book has been actually written in less than two years' spare time, it contains the essence of more than 45 years of intermittent personal contact with Short Brothers' aircraft, including some insight into the wartime repair on site of Sunderlands at Alness and Stirlings at Chedburgh during civilian attachment to No. 43 Group. Consequently the subject was the obvious, indeed only, choice for a companion volume to *Bristol Aircraft since 1910*; it was intended to be no more than that, but the author looked forward to the help of John Lankester Parker, O.B.E., who in July 1965 signified his willingness to collaborate in what he described as 'this worthy venture'. John Parker's sudden death on 22 August, 1965, seemed at first to have frustrated the project, but in subsequent months the company's Chairman, Mr C. E. Wrangham, and Mrs Parker both very generously agreed to make available all relevant documents at Belfast and Worlington and to give every facility to enable the work to proceed; since no single volume of reasonable size could do justice to the full biographical, commercial and technical aspects of the company's history since the turn of the century, it was agreed to concentrate on the aircraft themselves, arrayed against a background of people and places concerned with their evolution and operation.

During several 'marathon' visits to Queen's Island, the author has been granted exceptional facilities to explore the photographic, inspection and design archives and to obtain reminiscences from long-service members of the company's senior staff, some of whom he had already met ten years earlier in connection with Britannia production. Their enthusiasm, like their hospitality, has been unbounded and inspiring and indeed the book has virtually written itself; inevitably a few anecdotes of the Rochester saga have had to be excluded as being irrelevant to the chosen theme within the space available; it is to be hoped that some of these will be recorded by Mr Oswald Short himself in the family biography on which he has been engaged for many years, and the author is particularly grateful to him for his loan of unpublished memoirs and his scrutiny and constructive criticism of the narrative here presented. Amongst Shorts' former employees, much help has been given by R. Beaney, T. W. Brooke-Smith, H. G. Conway, G. T. Gedge, R. J. Heathcote,

ix

E. A. Hyde, Professor D. Keith-Lucas, R. C. Kemp, C. P. T. Lipscomb, J. H. Lower, R. R. Rowett, L. Stedman, J. Strong, S. H. Swayland, and M. W. West. Outside the company, generous assistance, as always, has been given by the librarians of the Royal Aeronautical Society and the Royal Aero Club, and by the staffs of the Science Museum, Imperial War Museum and editorial and photographic departments of *Flight International*, *The Aeroplane*, *Air Pictorial* and *Flying Review International*; from farther afield the author's helpers include Hugo T. Byttebier of Buenos Aires, A. E. Flanders of Mosman Park, W. Australia, and Vice Admiral T. Kuwabara of Tokyo, to all of whom he is most grateful; of his long-term collaborators, A. J. Jackson had the enterprise to fly the author from Southend on a low-level reconnaissance of Sheerness, Queenborough, Eastchurch, Rochester and Grain one fine Sunday morning, and C. F. Andrews, J. M. Bruce, H. F. Cowley, G. S. Leslie, J. D. Oughton, H. J. Penrose and J. W. R. Taylor have all contributed— sometimes unwittingly. The whole work has rested and relied on the sure foundation provided by Frank Kelly, Geoffrey Norris and Herbie Edgar at Belfast, and by Miss Sally Parker from her father's logbooks and memoirs at Worlington; the final edifice has been embellished and enhanced by L. E. Bradford's accurate line drawings.

Last, but not least, the author acknowledges his debt to his wife for tolerance, moral support and clerical assistance; to Dr Mariko Yasugi of Bristol University for translation from Japanese; to the literary executors (whom he has been unable to trace) of the late H. M. Schofield for a brief quotation from *The High Speed and Other Flights* in the Crusader chapter; and to Air-Britain for the use of information collated in their publications but not readily accessible elsewhere.

Kendleshire, Bristol, July 1967. C.H.B.

Foreword to Second Edition

The second edition of this splendid work by Chris Barnes has been long awaited by a new generation of those interested in British aviation history. Its publication in response to their demands will bring much pleasure to the Author. On his behalf I must thank a number of people who have provided updated information and help with this new edition. They are Gregory Webb, a one-time member of the Shorts design team; Jack Bruce, the eminent aviation historian; Peter Smith, Project Manager of Sunderland Ltd; and Peter Rooley, Manager–Personnel and Administration with HeavyLift Cargo Airlines. I am most grateful to Marnie O'Neill, Public Relations Manager, and Kate Mullen of Short Brothers; Norman Barfield, Public Relations Manager, British Aerospace, Weybridge; Gordon Roberts and Michael Hooks for their help with photographs. My special thanks go to John Stroud for his continuing help and patient guidance during the updating of this book.

Barnwood, Gloucester, January 1989. D.N.J.

The First Torpedo Drop

When Chris Barnes was writing this book he did not have available to him the text of the diary-form notes written by the late Air Chief Marshal Sir Arthur Longmore, GCB, DSO, who, as Lieutenant (later Squadron Commander) Longmore, RN, had been in command of Calshot Naval Air Station in the summer of 1914, while early experiments in flying with and dropping torpedoes from seaplanes were being conducted. He had, moreover, personally and specifically responded to a request made by the First Lord of the Admiralty (then the Rt Hon Winston Churchill) for an acceleration of the torpedo experiments: Longmore told Churchill that '. . . if I could retain a certain Short 160 Gnome seaplane, I would undertake within a short time to carry and successfully release a 14-inch torpedo which weighed some 900 lb.' (*From Sea to Sky*, by ACM Sir Arthur Longmore; Geoffrey Bles, 1946).

The account of the first successful airborne drop given on pages 95–97 of this book attributes the feat to Gordon Bell, and was based on the personal recollections (*c* 1936) of the late Oswald Short. Longmore's holograph diary notes are held in the Fleet Air Arm Museum, and suggest a different history of the event. In particular, they record that the Short Folder No. *121*, which had been at Calshot since 11 July, 1914, was officially taken over by Calshot (from Grain) on 23 July, on which day 'Shorts men arrived at 4.30 p.m. to carry out necessary alterations to No. *121* to fit her for torpedo'. Not until the afternoon of 27 July did Longmore record *121* as ready, when Lieut. R.P. Ross, RN, made unavailing attempts to take off with torpedo slung. The engine was not delivering full power, and the men of RNAS Calshot 'worked late on engine'.

This is substantially different from Oswald Short's recollection, which suggests that *121* had to be erected 'in a few hours' and was ready for flight all in one day, and that there was then time only for Gordon Bell to fly it late that evening. It seems highly unlikely that Longmore's knowledge of and notes on the activities of 27 July, 1914, could have excluded full awareness of a late evening flight and successful drop, using one of his station's aircraft and one of the Royal Navy's torpedoes, yet he recorded no such thing. Nor was there any hint of such awareness in his diary note for 28 July, 1914: 'I took *121* out with torpedo and managed to get off the water and fire it successfully; torpedo made a good run.'

J. M. Bruce

Origin and History of the Company

The Short family came originally from Berwick-upon-Tweed, where they were well established in the eighteenth century as millers. With the coming of the Industrial Revolution they migrated south, and Samuel Short, born at East Holywell, Northumberland, in 1840, was one of six brothers, all of whom were apprenticed as engineers to Robert Stephenson & Co at Newcastle-upon-Tyne, where the eldest, John, assembled the first steam locomotive for the Russian railways; the other brothers all took up mining, and William sank the first two shafts at Newcastle, New South Wales, when coal was discovered in Australia, naming them Hetton and Chilton after his home collieries. Samuel Short himself sank the shaft and later became manager at Little Chilton Colliery, Co. Durham; he married Emma Robinson from Ashover in Derbyshire and their eldest son Horace Leonard was born on 2 July, 1872. While still in infancy, Horace met with a head injury resulting in meningitis followed by abnormal brain development, which fortunately made him a genius to compensate for his loss of good looks. Soon after this accident the family moved to Derbyshire, where Samuel became chief engineer to the ironworks at Stanton-by-Dale, where the second boy, Albert Eustace, was born in June 1875 and the youngest, Hugh Oswald, in January 1883. By this time Horace had shown his extraordinary aptitude as a scholar and soon outstripped his teacher's ability to construe Latin and solve mathematical problems at sight. For five years he was employed at the Stanton Ironworks, but in 1890 he determined to see more of the world he had read so much about and set out by sailing ship to visit his uncle in Australia.

With physical strength to match his intelligence and a ferocious mien which nevertheless could change instantly to a welcoming smile of great charm, he found no difficulty in working his passage by a leisurely route, which included a first look at the Nile and a call on his cousin in Shanghai; thence he headed for Sydney via Samoa, where in 1891 he met Robert Louis Stevenson. He was taken captive by cannibals on another island of the group; these worshipped him as a king and taught him their language and pearl-fishing, but refused to let him leave them. After several months, he managed to escape one night in a dug-out canoe and reached a German mission station on another island. On arrival in Australia, he wrote home a full account of his adventures, not knowing that his father, consumptive for many years, had died in 1891, leaving the family nearly penniless. In 1893 his letter was published in a Chesterfield newspaper and the sum of £19 was raised to enable Eustace to go and find him, but by then he had moved on to South America and disappeared without trace. Eventually he turned up in Mexico, having apparently trekked on foot from the River Plate to the Amazon. Eustace went steerage from Liverpool to

1

Key West, Florida, then worked for a druggist for some weeks to replenish his exhausted funds, and finally reached Mexico, where Horace had already become a legend as the giant English silver-mine manager, whose convoys the bandits dared not attack. Eustace hired a muleteer and rode 300 miles over the mountains till he found Horace in a rocky eyrie commanding a constant view of the only two entrances to the mine-workings; Horace had let it be known to the bandits that both entrances were booby-trapped with dynamite and that any interference with silver-ore convoys would reap the direst retribution; he made the most of his terrifying physiognomy, and the local peons credited him with divine powers and omniscience, so his silver consignments always reached the coast unmolested.

Horace Short in 1900, aged 28, with the Auxetophone invented and patented by him two years earlier.

When Eustace arrived on mule-back, Horace was assembling a steam engine and boiler to drive his machinery. His first words to Eustace were, 'What the bloody hell are *you* doing here?' and he gave him a job to do at once, without enquiring his mission till some time later; Eustace told him of their mother's plight and implored him to come home as head of the family; but Horace could not leave the silver-mine to the mercy of the bandits, so he gave Eustace £500 and promised to return later; this was in 1895, and Oswald was supposed to be at school, although in fact he was working as an errand-boy to help his mother. On getting back to England, Eustace invested Horace's money in a coal-merchant's business, and next year Horace came home, having invented

2

a sound-amplifying device that he wanted to patent. The Short family moved to London, where Eustace saw balloons being flown with coal-gas and in 1897 was able to buy a Spencer balloon very cheap at a second-hand sale. Eustace and Oswald read all they could lay hands on about ballooning, including James Glaisher's *Travels in the Air*, which they found in a local library; they repaired the Spencer balloon, and Eustace persuaded Horace to accompany him on an early ascent, during which they travelled 40 miles in 47 minutes and landed very abruptly; this experience only confirmed Horace's conviction that balloons were dangerous vessels, incapable of being steered and to which no power plant could be safely attached because of the proximity of a large volume of inflammable gas; he was anxious about Oswald ('The Kid') risking his life in such a useless contraption and declined to join in his brothers' proposed balloon-making partnership. Instead, having patented his Auxetophone, a device for magnifying sound by means of steam or compressed air, he accepted an offer by Col Gouraud (Thomas Edison's agent in Europe) to equip a laboratory at Hove, Sussex, for further acoustic experiments. At the Paris Exhibition of 1900 he installed an auxeto-gramophone in Gustave Eiffel's octagonal room at the top of the Eiffel Tower, whence he broadcast pre-recorded arias sung by the stars of the Paris Opera, which could be heard all over the city.

Eustace and Oswald also visited the Exhibition but, having already begun making their first new balloon, were more interested in the method of making truly spherical envelopes developed by Édouard Surcouf at the Société Astra. On returning home, they revised their design to incorporate Surcouf's ideas, which were a great improvement on the somewhat rough-and-ready standards which satisfied the fairground showmen who were the Spencers' principal customers. Horace allowed them to use the loft above his laboratory, and in 1902 they completed and successfully flew their first spherical balloon of 33,000 cu ft capacity, although they had very little money left by then. Soon afterwards Horace was approached by the Hon Charles Parsons, who was experimenting on similar lines at Newcastle-upon-Tyne, and in 1903 Horace sold him the Auxetophone patents and contracted to become his personal experimental engineer on steam-turbine development, for a term of five years. On moving to Newcastle he gave up the Hove premises and his brothers were left without a workshop, but eventually they rented two arches of the L.B.S.C. Railway at Battersea Park, next to the gas-works, a location advantageous both to Eustace's business for buying coke and for filling balloons with coal-gas; soon they became proficient enough to take up passengers for trips over London from Battersea gas-works.

In 1904 Eustace secured Horace's brief collaboration in a project for a high-altitude hydrogen balloon of no less than 625,000 cu ft capacity, having a pressure-tight cast aluminium spherical gondola; for this Horace designed an ingenious ventilating and pressurising system having two piston-pumps coupled to a handwheel, one bringing in fresh air at 10 lb/sq in while the other scavenged stale air; under favourable conditions of differential pressure and temperature (and, of course, low enough friction losses) this machine could become self-sustaining and was potentially the first 'boot-strap' air-conditioning unit in aeronautical history. Although Eustace and Horace described this project to the Aeronautical Society in July 1904, they could find no one to finance its construction, but it was a remarkable forecast of Auguste Piccard's 500,000 cu ft balloon in which he attained 51,776 ft in May 1931, an event which rekindled Eustace's enthusiasm for a similar scheme, on which he was working when he died in 1932.

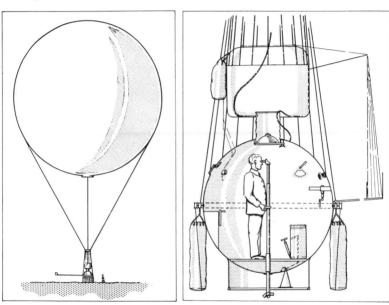

Horace Short's proposed stratospheric balloon 1904.

In 1905 Eustace and Oswald replied to a War Office advertisement in *The Times* and won a contract to supply three reconnaissance balloons for the Indian Army; their high quality was commended by Col Templer, Superintendent of the Balloon Factory at Farnborough, who introduced the two to the Hon Charles Rolls, a well-known aeronaut and racing motorist, who commissioned the 78,500 cu ft *Britannia* for the first Gordon Bennett balloon race in 1906; this had alternative cars, to carry two men for racing or ten for touring, and in the race Rolls, with Col Capper as his 'aide', achieved a flight of over 26 hours from Paris to Norfolk, being out-distanced only by the American winner, Frank P. Lahm, who reached Yorkshire. They also built the *Venus* of 45,000 cu ft for a syndicate composed of Rolls, Warwick Wright and J. T. C. Moore-Brabazon, and the 77,000 cu ft *Zephyr* for Professor A. K. Huntington, all of whom were active members of the Aero Club of the United Kingdom. They showed a balloon at the Aero Club's exhibition at the Agricultural Hall, Islington, in April 1907, winning a gold medal for excellence of

4

manufacture and appointment as official Aeronautical Engineers to the Club. For Griffith Brewer they rebuilt Santos-Dumont's 1906 Gordon Bennett balloon as the 75,250 cu ft *Lotus II*, which he test-flew from Battersea to Rayleigh, Essex, on 25 August, 1907, with the Hon Claude Brabazon and Eustace and Oswald as passengers; in October Brewer and Brabazon competed with *Lotus II* in the 1907 Gordon Bennett race at St Louis, Missouri, whence they travelled 350 miles in 25 hours to within 20 miles of Dayton, Ohio. Also in 1907 they built the 45,000 cu ft *Mercury* for another syndicate and the *Nebula* of similar size for the only certificated woman member of the Aero Club, the Hon Mrs Assheton Harbord, to whom they supplied the *Valkyrie* of 60,000 cu ft and *Vivienne* of 75,000 cu ft in 1908. With plentiful supplies of

Battersea balloon works in 1909, with *(left) Venus* and *(right) Continental No. 2* ready for launching.

coal-gas at hand, Short Brothers could store Aero Club members' balloons and have them laid out and filled for an ascent by day or night within an hour of receiving a call on '788 Battersea'.

Meanwhile in America the Wright brothers had made over 150 flights since their first in December 1903, and in 1907 were ready to demonstrate flying publicly for the first time, little notice having been taken of their progress at Dayton, Ohio, during 1904 and 1905. Neither the United States nor British Governments would negotiate terms for the use of their invention, but Hart O. Berg, their European agent, and Griffith Brewer, who looked after their patents in the British Empire, had invited them to come to Europe as soon as possible. Having at length agreed a contract with Lazare Weiller, Wilbur Wright duly arrived in France in August 1908 and began giving demonstrations and passenger flights near Le Mans, moving south to Pau when the winter set in. On 8 October his passengers were Griffith Brewer, Charles Rolls, Frank Hedges Butler and Major B. F. S. Baden-Powell. Their

5

enthusiastic accounts of this experience caused Oswald Short to exclaim to Eustace, 'This is the finish of ballooning; we must begin building aeroplanes at once, and we can't do that without Horace!' So Oswald went to Newcastle to ask him once more to join them, and this time Horace replied, 'Yes, but you'd better be quick; I'll be with you in three days, and if you aren't ready by then I'll start without you.' He had just renewed his contract for another five years, but Parsons released him, saying, 'You can't hold a good man with a piece of paper.' The new partnership of Short Brothers was registered at Battersea in November 1908 with a capital of £600, subscribed in equal shares by the three brothers; they had not at that point actually seen the Wright Flyer, but in the same month Eustace visited Le Mans twice, and on the second occasion Wilbur Wright took him up, also Roger Wallace, Professor A. K. Huntington and Frank McClean, all of the Aero Club. Immediately afterwards, Horace began designing a glider for Rolls (based on photographs of the Flyer) and an original biplane for Frank McClean.

Interior of Battersea works in 1909, with Short No. 1 biplane under construction. (*Flight.*)

Many of Wilbur Wright's passengers begged him to sell the Flyer or replicas of it, but he had neither manufacturing facilities nor, indeed, any drawings. He therefore agreed to let contracts to responsible craftsmen for replicas to be built under licence and, on Brewer's advice, assigned the British rights to Short Brothers, for an initial batch of six, all of which were already bespoken by members of the Aero Club; in February 1909, Horace Short, having already begun building both the glider for Rolls and Short No. 1 for

Pioneers at Mussel Manor, 4 May, 1909: (*left to right—back row*) Oswald, Horace and Eustace Short, Frank McClean, Griffith Brewer, Frank Hedges Butler and Dr Lockyer; (*front row*) J. T. C. Moore-Brabazon, Wilbur Wright, Orville Wright and Charles Rolls. (*Flight.*)

McClean, accompanied Eustace to Pau by motor-car, to make detailed sketches of the Flyer, from which were prepared the first official working drawings. Meanwhile Griffith Brewer, looking for an unobstructed flying area for Frank McClean, had discovered a tract of level marshland between Leysdown and Shellness on the Isle of Sheppey in Kent; he informed the Shorts, who at once bought a site on which to erect a new factory for assembling the Wright machines; half a mile away was a small farmhouse, Mussel Manor, which McClean purchased for use by the Aero Club, together with the flying rights over several hundred acres of the adjacent marshes, known as Shellbeach. By August the payroll at the new factory had risen to eighty, who included Short Brothers' first foreman William George Bell, always

Leysdown factory on 4 May, 1909; on the right is Charles Rolls' own Rolls-Royce, with the owner at the wheel, Orville Wright beside him, and (*left*) Griffith Brewer and (*right*) Wilbur Wright in the back seat. (*Flight.*)

7

known as 'Father Bell' to distinguish him from his son Howard ('Dinger'), who was the first apprentice in the aircraft industry, having commenced with Shorts on 10 July, 1909; another employee was Percy Muir Jones, the first draughtsman in the aircraft industry, who had begun working for Eustace at Battersea in 1907. The Wrights' contract with Short Brothers was indeed the first aircraft production contract ever awarded and established Shorts as the first aircraft manufacturers in the world, for at that date neither the Wrights nor anyone else had built any aeroplanes for sale as proprietary articles.

Wilbur and Orville Wright visited Leysdown on 4 May, 1909, to inspect the Short-Wright Flyers and were well satisfied with their quality and materials. They flew well, but McClean's Short No. 1 was unsuccessful, and Horace then built a new machine, Short No. 2, more on Wright lines, to the urgent order of J. T. C. Moore-Brabazon, who flew it on 30 October, 1909, to win the *Daily Mail*'s £1,000 prize for the first flight in England of one mile in a closed circuit by an all-British combination of pilot, aircraft and engine. Next came the smaller Short No. 3 for Charles Rolls and two others to the designs of J. W. Dunne, but by this time the Leysdown dykes had taken their toll in crashes and McClean had found a smoother flying ground at East-church, to which the Aero Club moved early in 1910 and was followed by Short Brothers, who already needed a larger factory with room for future extensions. Here in April 1910 was built the first of the Short Farman-Sommer-type biplanes, which quickly superseded the Wright type and were produced in some numbers, the final developed version being reordered for school work as late as 1915. There were many variants of this type, among them the first two successful twin-engined aeroplanes in England; they were followed by a series of simple but sturdy tractor biplanes, one of which also had two engines in tandem.

Horace Short's preoccupation with aeroplanes at Sheppey did not preclude Eustace and Oswald from continuing their balloon interests at Battersea; in January 1909 they signed an agreement with Paul Brodtmann of Hanover to build balloons of his 'Continental' rubberised fabric, the first of which, *Continental No. 2* of 50,250 cu ft, was test-flown by Charles Rolls in May, along with *Continental No. 1*, which was German made. In March 1908 they had made a lightweight two-man varnished silk balloon of only 17,500 cu ft, the *Imp*, for Rolls, who already owned an even smaller one, the *Midget* of 11,000 cu ft, which could carry a solo pilot for 12 hours or more when inflated with hydrogen, but this seems to have been made originally by Percival Spencer; Griffith Brewer had made his first solo in it as early as 1 August, 1892, so it may have been repaired by Short Brothers before coming into Rolls' hands. The largest of Short Brothers' range was represented by Mortimer Singer's 79,000 cu ft *Planet*, in which he and Frank McClean competed in the 1909 Gordon Bennett race from Zürich to Poland; others built the same year were Baroness Heeckeren's *L'Espérance* and John Dunville's *La Mascotte*, both of 50,000 cu ft, and Mortimer Singer's smaller

8

Satellite of 28,000 cu ft; in this last Singer won a 'Hare and Hounds' race from Hurlingham on 17 July, 1909, in which Rolls, solo in *Imp*, acted his customary role of 'Hare'. At the beginning of the year Short Brothers had lent one of their older balloons, complete with car and net, to the London Balloon Company, R.E., T.F., for drill purposes. In May 1909 the Admiralty invited tenders for materials and components for Rigid Airship *No. 1* (nicknamed *Mayfly*), being built by Vickers Ltd at Barrow-in-Furness, and Shorts'

Naval airship *No. 1* at Barrow-in-Furness in August 1911; note the triple elevators and quadruple rudders designed and made by Short Brothers, together with the outer covering, gas-bags and valves.

quotation for the design and supply of the gas-bags, Parseval-type valves, outer cover and control surfaces was accepted. The Admiralty had decided against lining the gas-bags with gold-beater's skin (prepared ox-gut, which was almost impermeable to hydrogen), so the seventeen bags were made up from laminated cotton-and-rubber fabric, while the 66,000 sq ft outer cover was made from silk waterproofed by the 'Ioco' process; the control surfaces also were covered with two-ply proofed silk; this was a very substantial order for such a small firm, but was executed punctually during 1910. Short Brothers found rubberised fabric adequate for normal balloon flights, which were usually of short duration followed by immediate deflation, but when the *Mayfly* was launched in August 1911 her gas-bags had deteriorated during storage after delivery and leaked so badly that the full capacity of 706,000 cu ft had to be replenished every four days. This convinced Oswald Short that gold-beater's skin was essential for rigid airships, which were required to remain serviceable for long periods with the minimum of topping-up with gas. A few weeks later the *Mayfly* was wrecked while being man-handled into

9

(*Left*) Eustace Short; (*right*) Griffith Brewer's *Bee* being filled with hydrogen at Knowles' Oxygen Works, Wolverhampton, in 1911.

her shed in a high wind, and airships were temporarily abandoned by the Navy. In 1911 Shorts made the *Bee* of 18,000 cu ft for Griffith Brewer, having an equatorial suspension band instead of the usual all-over net, and intended specifically for inflation with hydrogen instead of coal-gas; the *Bee* was very successful and was purchased by the Admiralty on the outbreak of war in 1914, when Brewer took charge of Naval balloon training at Roehampton and used the *Bee* to teach free ballooning to future airship pilots and kite-balloon observers; Short Brothers made no more free balloons after 1914, but the Battersea works were kept busy with orders for airship and kite balloon valves and other gear.

In authorising the construction of Naval Airship *No. 1*, the Admiralty had virtually excluded any financial provision for naval aeroplanes, a reasonable enough decision in 1908 but no longer valid in 1910. The protection of dock-yards and arsenals was obviously the Navy's affair, and the possibility of attack by enemy airships was foreseen to the extent that anti-aircraft defences were recommended; in November 1910 the Royal Aero Club (as it had become) offered the Admiralty free instruction for Naval officers by one of its members, Cecil Grace, on aeroplanes lent by another member, Frank McClean. The offer was accepted in February 1911, by which time Grace had been lost at sea

10

Charles Samson strapped into S.28 before starting a practice flight at Eastchurch in May 1911; obviously he expected to walk away from his landing.

and his place was taken by another member, George Cockburn. Out of over 200 eager volunteers, four were chosen to be the pioneers of the Royal Naval Air Service; they all qualified in April and May 1911 and were succeeded by others in turn. Each received six months' technical instruction from Horace Short, for which the Admiralty paid £20 plus breakages. The first to qualify, Lieut Charles Rumney Samson, was appointed to a technical sub-committee of the Committee of Imperial Defence and, together with Lieut Arthur Longmore (second to qualify), began experiments with Oswald Short to improve the usefulness of aeroplanes at sea. Oswald designed pneumatic

Eastchurch factory photographed from the air by Dr Lockyer in July 1912, with Royal Aero Club sheds in the foreground and Frank McClean's house, 'Stonefitts', on the far left.

11

S.38 and S.41 stowed on the runway of H.M.S. *Hibernia* at Weymouth in May 1912. (*Flight.*)

flotation bags for emergency descent on the water, and in January 1912 Samson took off from a staging erected over the fore-deck of H.M.S. *Africa* while at anchor at Sheerness, landing dry on the Isle of Grain. He repeated this exploit from H.M.S. *Hibernia* while steaming at 15 kt during the Naval Review at Weymouth in May 1912. Samson also flew the first Short monoplane, which was less successful than a seaplane conversion of a tractor biplane. The latter (dubbed by the Press of the day 'H.M.S. *Amphibian*') was the ancestor of some thousands of single-engined twin-float seaplanes built to Horace Short's designs and used for naval reconnaissance in all theatres of the First World War.

In 1913 the expansion of seaplane work made Eastchurch inconvenient as

The original Short 184 (S.106) before its first launching at Rochester early in 1915; in the background the frames of No. 2 Shop are being erected. (*Flight.*)

well as inadequate, so a new factory was built at Rochester on the right bank of the Medway, and Oswald Short took charge of seaplane production there. After the outbreak of war many other firms, mainly in the wood-working and light engineering industries, were given Admiralty contracts to build seaplanes to Short designs; they included Fairey, Mann Egerton, Parnall, Phoenix Dynamo (later English Electric), Sage, Saunders, Supermarine (Pemberton-Billing), Westland (Petters) and J. Samuel White, all of whom set up design teams of their own, and some of whom have survived, in tradition if not in

Assembly of Dover-type Short 184 *N1636* in the Phoenix Dynamo factory at Bradford in 1917. (*Courtesy G. S. Leslie.*)

name, to this day. Early in the war, the Admiralty Air Department realised the urgent need for a heavy bomber and ordered a suitable twin-engined type from Handley Page; as this could not be ready for some months, Short Brothers improvised a single-engined bomber from a standard Sunbeam-engined seaplane with a wheeled undercarriage and extended wings and tail. For the use of the Short designs by all other Admiralty contractors during the war period Short Brothers eventually received cash compensation of £20,000, but most of this was swallowed up by the cost of excavating chalk for factory extensions in 1918.

In February 1915 the need for anti-submarine patrol airships became urgent, and the Submarine Scout type was quickly improvised by hanging an obsolete B.E.2c fuselage from a spare Willows envelope; this was done by the R.N.A.S. at Kingsnorth, and on seeing the result for the first time Horace Short, already noted for his very apt and original vocabulary, named it 'Blimp', adding, 'What else could you call it?' Several firms made prototypes, of which the Short-built *SS3* proved very successful, but Shorts did not undertake any later contracts for complete 'blimps'.

13

In July 1915 Shorts were invited to tender for two rigid airships to an Admiralty design based on the Vickers-designed *No. 9*, for which they had already designed and made the multiplane control surfaces. Their tender was accepted in January 1916 (for *Nos. 31* and *32*), and a contract was arranged whereby Shorts would receive £110,000 on loan for the purchase of land and erection of a 700 ft airship shed, together with factory buildings, at Cardington near Bedford; this loan was repayable by way of return of half the profits, and it was intended to make the arrangement permanent. Short Brothers also submitted proposals of their own for a 700 ft long wooden rigid airship of 2,077,000 cu ft, which the Admiralty examined but turned down in favour of a similar design based on the ideas of a Swiss engineer named Müller; this was 594 ft long and used constructional methods derived from German Schütte-Lanz practice, of which Müller possessed expert knowledge. The final design, approved by the Director of Naval Construction in May 1916, owed nothing to the destruction of *SL11* at Cuffley, which occurred over four months later and yielded no information, since the wreckage had been totally consumed by fire. Short Brothers took up rigid airship construction with enthusiasm, Horace's misgivings having yielded to wartime expediency, and relaxed none of their customary quality control; in particular, Oswald Short insisted on three layers of gold-beater's skin for lining the gas-bags after the *Mayfly* débâcle; in later years, when invited to view *R101* while under

Cardington airship factory in August 1918, with *R31* on test and *R32* under construction.

14

construction at Cardington, he expressed extreme dismay on finding that only a single layer was specified, and foretold the extent of the hydrogen leakage which did in fact occur and contributed to the loss of the airship. *R31* was launched at Cardington in August 1918, but suffered from various teething troubles and had only logged 9 hours by November, when, during her delivery flight to East Fortune, some of her glued joints began to crack and she had to be hurriedly docked at Howden in a shed whose roof had been burned out when *R27* caught fire three months earlier. A few days later the war ended and *R31*'s exposure to wet weather was forgotten until too late, by which time she had warped beyond repair. Her sister ship *R32* was more fortunate and reflected great credit upon Shorts' workmanship. Commissioned in September 1919, she was based at Howden and used for experimental work with the National Physical Laboratory until October 1920; thereafter she became a training ship until April 1921 for the U.S. Navy crews assigned to *R38*; finally, after logging 260 hours, she was tested to destruction on 27 August by bursting No. 18 gas-bag; the remains were broken up, but like *R31* (sold for £200 to an unlucky coal merchant who thought he had a bargain in firewood) she was fully fire-proofed and steadfastly refused to burn.

Short Brothers began building two more rigid airships at Cardington after completing *R31*. The first was *R37* (sister ship to the Beardmore-built *R36*), of which the duralumin girders had been fabricated by Vickers at Walney Island but not assembled because the necessary large shed at Flookburgh was cancelled through shortage of steel for its construction. *R37* was transferred to Cardington late in 1917 and a second larger airship, *R38*, was ordered from Shorts in September 1918, both being designed by a Royal Corps of Naval Constructors team headed by Commander C. I. R. Campbell. After the Armistice, Short Brothers sought assurances from the Government that airship construction would continue in peacetime; at that time the Admiralty were proposing to take over the factory as a Royal Dockyard for airships, leaving Shorts in charge and intending to order new airships on a regular programme for civil operation. In January 1919 Shorts asked for improved financial terms in any new contract, whereupon the order for *R38* was peremptorily cancelled and on 17 February Oswald Short was called to the Admiralty and informed by Sir Vincent Raven that Cardington was being nationalised under the Defence of the Realm Act and that this decision was irrevocable; the Company were entitled to compensation assessed at £40,000 in addition to £34,000 for work completed but not yet paid for. So Short Brothers had to relinquish Cardington in April 1919, when it became the Royal Airship Works, in whose favour the *R38* contract was reinstated; however, a group of Shorts' draughtsmen under C. P. T. Lipscomb stayed on at Cardington to assist the Air Ministry designers until completion of *R38* in June 1921. Paradoxically the neighbourhood is still called Shortstown, and the revised title of the company, Short Brothers (Rochester & Bedford) Ltd, applied for in 1916, was first registered on 28 May, 1919, with a capital of £150,000.

15

Whether Horace Short would have fared any better than his young brother is open to doubt, because Sir Vincent Raven's chief at the Admiralty was the formidable Sir Eric Geddes, whose notorious 'Axe' was to fall so heavily on the Royal Air Force and the industry alike in 1922, but unhappily Horace had been taken ill and died at Eastchurch on 6 April, 1917. Eustace, full of ideas and as keen as ever on practical flying, was very much bound up with the balloon side of the business at Battersea, fulfilling orders for both Cardington and Kingsnorth, and it was Oswald with whom Horace had always discussed technical and administrative problems; so Oswald took charge at Rochester, making it the firm's headquarters and transferring the Eastchurch premises to the R.N.A.S. later in the year. The Shorts had always been very good friends with the early naval airmen, particularly Samson and Longmore, and seaplane development owed much to this partnership. Notable improvements due to Horace included folding wings and the first practicable scheme for carrying and launching a full-size torpedo, while Oswald had originated sprung floats and buoyancy bags; but Horace had obstinately refused to take any part in the development of flying-boats in spite of progress by Glenn Curtiss, John Porte and Linton Hope. After his death, however, Oswald Short accepted Admiralty contracts for F.3 and F.5 boats designed by Porte

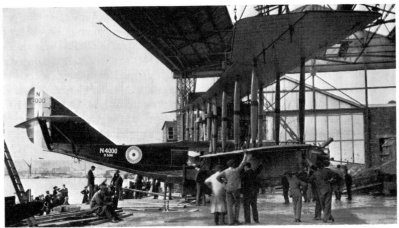

Short Brothers' first F.3 flying-boat, *N4000*, ready for launching on 15 May, 1918: No. 3 Shop was incomplete, and its slipway had not yet been built, so the crane had to be used.

at Felixstowe, and 50 of them were being built at Rochester when war ended. Their obviously superior seaworthiness in the larger sizes induced Oswald Short to submit a tender in 1918 for a twin-engined long-range patrol flying-boat designed for co-operation with the Grand Fleet; a contract for three prototypes was awarded, being reduced after the Armistice to one, which eventually flew in 1921 as the Cromarty. Other designs originated by Oswald Short and detailed by Francis Webber were the second Scout seaplane (the last prototype to be built at Eastchurch), the N.2B and the Shirl deck-landing torpedo-plane. Unfortunately, Horace Short's death had coincided with other changes affecting seaplane design policy, not least of which was Murray Sueter's posting away from the Admiralty Air Department to command the R.N.A.S. in the Mediterranean, so Oswald Short was deprived of his advice and support just when he needed it most. The situation was not made any easier by the formation first of the Ministry of Munitions and then of the Air Board, resulting in delays and anomalies in contract negotiations; in particular, Oswald found the appointment of Alec Ogilvie as Controller of Technical Design at the Air Board very irksome, because Ogilvie seems to have been unsympathetic to Short Brothers ever since Horace's refusal in 1910 to build the improved Wright instead of developing the Farman-Sommer type; in this Horace's judgment had been proved correct. Ogilvie had always been friendly with C. R. Fairey and his later co-directors Dawson and Maurice Wright during their undergraduate days at Eastchurch, and recognised the Fairey Campania and its successors as having more development potential than the Short 184, however blatantly they may have copied it in the first place. Possibly Horace would have pulled a brand-new winner out of the bag had he lived longer and so shared with Fairey an equal proportion of the small post-war market for seaplanes for the R.A.F., but Oswald was a victim of circumstances beyond his immediate capacity to control, both at Rochester and at Cardington. Having been refused permission by Ogilvie to test the N.2B with a Rolls-Royce Eagle, he 'borrowed' one from the Air Ministry allocation for flying-boats and satisfied himself that his seaplane was as good as the Fairey IIIC, but of course he could not prove it officially without admitting his 'crime'. This decided him to strike out on his own with duralumin construction in spite of official opposition.

Through his experience of airship construction at Cardington, Oswald Short had had unusual opportunities for comparing wood and duralumin in airframe applications, and saw the unfortunate demise of *R31* as conclusive evidence against the continued use of wood and glued joints for components exposed to water or climatic extremes of humidity. In 1916 he had designed and tested the first duralumin wing ribs with some success, and he realised how metal-skinned seaplane floats and hulls would avoid the weight penalty caused by water soakage. By 1919 the vagaries of duralumin, particularly the importance of close control of heat treatment, were better understood, and the early researches of Bengough and Stuart at the National Physical Laboratory offered some hope of combating corrosion, so he extended the scope of his structural tests to duralumin monocoque specimens. From the first he relied on close-pitched ring frames for reinforcement and only later conceded the need for stringers; even then the frames were never cut or notched, but longitudinal stiffening was provided by short intercostals cleated to the frames at each end. The first complete aircraft built on this principle was the private-venture Silver Streak, which made a profound impression in July 1920 at Olympia, contrasted with an all-wood seaplane, which it was hoped would attract former naval pilots. Only one seaplane was sold, and although the

Silver Streak attracted much interest from American visitors to the show, it was finally bought by the Air Ministry for evaluation at Farnborough; as it was an unproved structure, R.A.F. pilots were forbidden to fly it, nor were Shorts allowed to demonstrate it, and after only a few early flights it spent the rest of its life as a test specimen behind locked doors. Eventually two prototypes of a two-seat fighter derivative, the Springbok, were ordered, and these were delivered in 1923.

Meanwhile the firm kept their work-people busy building motor-boats, ship's lifeboats, barges and other vessels, in which Eustace took a substantial interest; they ranged from luxurious silent electric canoes ('lined throughout with Wilton Carpet') to the sea-going motor-barge *Rochester Castle* with a cargo capacity of 500 tons. The barge-yard was located downstream from the seaplane works, and its near-aeronautical products included airscrew-driven hydroplane craft or skimmers. Eustace later designed an ingenious lightweight rubber mooring buoy for seaplanes which was virtually the hydraulic analogy of a spherical balloon; this was highly commended by Sqn Ldr Maycock of Felixstowe, and adopted as standard equipment for R.A.F. flying-boat units; for use in the Nile, these buoys had to be coloured bright red to discourage the crocodiles from eating them; dozens of them are still being used in the Medway today. Oswald Short claimed that, unlike many aircraft firms threatened with closure when war ended, he never had fewer employees at any time after the Armistice than he had during the peak war years. Finances became critical in the depression of 1923–4, and disaster was averted only by a

Rochester Seaplane Works in 1919, showing Nos. 1, 2, 3 and 4 Shops, which remained unchanged in area until 1936. No. 5 Shop is out of the picture.

18

successful tender to supply lightweight omnibus bodies for London General's and Thomas Tilling's new covered-top fleets; this production line continued for many years, and Short Brothers became a household name to straphanging commuters who had little to entertain them in rush hours apart from the small print displayed around the lower deck. The bus-body contracts originated from a chance remark by Harry Harper of the *Daily Mail* to Oswald Short that the London General Omnibus Co. were losing three-halfpence a mile because of the legal limitations on axle loading in London.

Oswald then went to see the L.G.O.C.'s chief engineer (Mr Shave) and offered to build a lightweight body which would permit more passengers to be carried for the same maximum axle load; on completion this bus could carry five extra passengers, and during the period 1925-7 over 2,000 similar bodies were supplied to the L.G.O.C. alone, with many more to Tillings, East Kent, Maidstone & District, Scottish Motor Traction, Southdown, Wilts & Dorset and United (Lowestoft); also the municipal undertakings of Belfast, Birmingham, Bristol, Hull, Morecambe, Nottingham and Norwich; finally, this department, managed by W. P. Kemp, undertook production of complete trolley-buses to the designs of Railless Ltd until 1933. One of the first operators of Short-built trolley-buses was Oldham Corporation, in whose service a number of rear-axle shaft failures occurred; naturally Oldham Corporation sought redress from Railless Ltd, who passed the buck to Short Bros, but Kemp suspected fatigue failure, and Oswald Short commissioned Professor A. M. Low to conduct a technical enquiry into the case. Low proved that the failures were due to torsional resonance at much less than the static design load, and so the responsibility rested with the designers at Railless Ltd, who had neglected to take account of dynamic effects, Short Bros having adhered strictly to the drawings provided. Bus bodies were also exported, including 100 to Athens. The income from road vehicles carried two-thirds of the overhead cost of the whole of Rochester works, which required an annual turnover of £400,000; during the period 1918-25 the total net profit on aircraft work was only £12,878, which was rather less than the actual loss for 1924-5 alone; during this period Oswald Short fixed his salary as head of the firm at £700 per annum.

Meanwhile, the only Air Ministry work obtainable, after completion of the two Springboks, was a series of small contracts for renovating D.H.9A airframes stored since 1918 and now required for service in Iraq and India. After repeated refusals by the Air Ministry to order more metal prototypes from Shorts, two designs, a twin-engined twin-float biplane and an all-metal version of the Cromarty, were shown to the U.S. Navy, who offered to buy them if an American manufacturer would take up a licence, but none came forward at that time, although some years later a licence was negotiated with the Keystone Division of Curtiss-Wright Corporation. Last-minute aid came from the Air Ministry in the shape of an order for a duralumin hull to suit an F.5 flying-boat, with the promise of a follow-up order for a metal Cromarty if the F.5 hull proved successful.

Short Brothers had hoped to obtain orders for civil conversions of F.3 and F.5 boats, but had to compete with the rock-bottom prices quoted by the Aircraft Disposal Company. They did in fact convert and sell one F.3 as a luxury cabin cruiser to Lebbaeus Hordern of Sydney, N.S.W., and reconditioned another for Portugal in 1920. More than a thousand seaplanes of Shorts' design had been built during 1914–18 by other contractors, but Shorts themselves had built only 150 aircraft (D.H.9s and Porte boats) not of

Short-built F.5 of the Imperial Japanese Navy at Yokosuka in 1922. (*Courtesy Vice-Admiral Kuwabara.*)

their own design. They supplied seaplane conversions to pioneer operators in many parts of the world and eventually built ten more F.5s for the R.A.F. and 12 for the Japanese Navy; on the strength of the metal hull order they put in hand as a private venture one of the smallest flying-boats ever built, the Cockle, powered by two motor-cycle engines with a combined output of 32 hp; this was successfully flown in 1924 and sent to Felixstowe for appraisal of its duralumin hull. For the Air Ministry's light aeroplane trials in 1923 for single-seaters, a wooden monocoque monoplane of only 16 hp, the Gull, was built to the design and private order of Oscar Gnosspelius, a pioneer of hydroplanes, who in 1919 joined Shorts' experimental department as manager and remained later as a consultant. For the two-seater competition in 1924 the Satellite monoplane with a metal monocoque fuselage and fabric-covered wings was built and flown. On completion, the F.5 with metal hull was found very satisfactory and a large new all-metal flying-boat, the Singapore I, similar in size to the Cromarty, was ordered, together with three more improved Springboks. With the initiation of subsidised light aeroplane clubs in 1925, a new two-seat light monoplane was built, primarily as a twin-float seaplane; this was the Mussel, named in memory of the Royal Aero Club's first headquarters on Sheppey. Although built to test many experimental features and not intended for production, it was an excellent *ab initio* trainer and its floats set the standard for most seaplane conversions of the day, being adopted as they were for Moths and in larger sizes for bigger aircraft, following Alan Cobham's choice of them for the D.H.50 in which he flew to Australia and

20

back in 1926. Eustace Short was delighted with the Mussel, and John Lankester Parker, Shorts' test pilot, taught him to fly on it, sending him solo in October 1927; Eustace enjoyed flying it in all kinds of weather, but in 1928 he hit a barge mast with his wing-tip while landing and crashed. He was not hurt, and in 1929 a second improved Mussel was built, mainly to test a novel amphibian landing gear; needless to say, Eustace flew it almost daily, but on 8 April, 1932, he had just made a perfect landing when the Mussel was seen to taxi away upstream, eventually running aground; when retrieved, it was found that Eustace Short had died of heart failure at the moment of touch-down and had been unable to switch off.

In addition to testing prototypes both in flight and in the structural laboratory, Oswald Short had installed a seaplane tank, to save the cost and delay of taking models to the William Froude tank at Teddington. Its length, limited to 350 ft by cost considerations, proved restrictive in later years, but it was justified by the success of the Singapore, whose hull was designed by Arthur Gouge from measurements of resistance and stability made in the tank by himself and Oscar Gnosspelius; they designed the travelling carriage and balances to suit their own specialised requirements, including simulated wing-lift as take-off speed was approached; this was difficult to arrange in the Froude tank, which was intended for and usually occupied by ship models

Oscar Gnosspelius and John Parker with Gull and dog at Lympne in May 1923.

21

In the Calcutta at Westminster in August 1928 (see also *Frontispiece*): Winston Churchill and John Lankester Parker in the pilots' seats, with Oswald Short explaining design features from the bow mooring cockpit.

whose waterline drag was the prime consideration. To assist Gouge in running the tank and calculating the results, Jack Lower was recruited from Chatham Dockyard, being the first of many from 1924 onwards who came to Short Brothers on completion of four years' technical training in H.M. Dockyard Upper School during apprenticeship; they were the 'brains' of the future

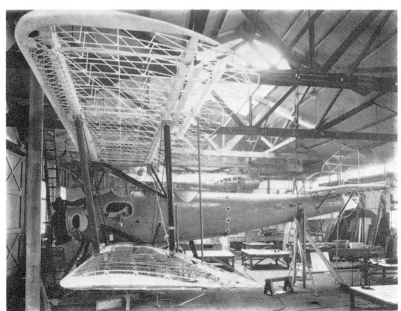

Two early examples of Short duralumin monocoque construction—the Sturgeon in No. 1 Shop at Rochester, with the Satellite stored in the rafters, in 1927.

design organisation and included Rupert Beaney, Bob Boorman, Walter Browning, Bill Hambrook and Percy Lewis, to name only a few; all were imbued with the shipbuilding tradition which distinguished Short Brothers' constructional methods from those of most other aircraft manufacturers; guiding them into the unknown jungle of aeronautics were C. P. T. Lipscomb (a Woolwich Arsenal graduate) and A. W. S. (Nobby) Clarke, both of whom had joined the company in 1914.

The Singapore I flew from the Medway in August 1926, and after proving trials at Felixstowe, including participation in a cruise round the Baltic, it was lent to Sir Alan Cobham for a 23,000-mile survey flight round Africa on behalf of Imperial Airways, who in 1927 ordered two prototypes of the three-engined Calcutta, the first truly commercial flying-boat to go into airline service. Five more Calcuttas were built, three for Imperial Airways and two for the French

Inside No. 3 Shop in August 1930, with Rangoons and K.F.1 under construction.

Government; the French Navy were so impressed by it that a licence for its manufacture in France was granted to Breguet, who built four more at Le Havre together with the Breguet Bizerte and Saïgon, which had Short-type hulls. Among the smaller aircraft of this period was the Crusader racer for the 1927 Schneider Trophy contest; there were also the Chamois and the Sturgeon, derived from the Springbok. The Singapore I was not adopted for R.A.F. squadron service because its original Condor engines were obsolescent, but the Calcutta, with its better take-off capability and roomy well-ventilated hull made an excellent military boat for service in the Persian Gulf, and six of this variant, the Rangoon, served in this role for six years from 1930. In 1927

Shorts built the Gurnard for a two-seat Fleet Fighter competition; it was a complete breakaway from the main line of monocoque development, having a welded steel-tube fuselage with large removable side fairing panels for easy maintenance on board ship. Two were built and proved satisfactory on trial, but no production order followed, although one was lent to Shorts for further experiments with amphibian gear. Next the Singapore II was ordered, with four engines in tandem pairs; this was flown in 1929 and underwent service trials for three years, after which the developed Singapore III was adopted for R.A.F. service overseas and 37 were supplied. In 1930 a large three-engined twin-float monoplane, the Valetta, was built for the Air Ministry, for comparison with the Calcutta of the same size, and was lent to Sir Alan Cobham for a 12,300-mile survey and route-proving flight along the Nile to Central Africa and back in 1931. Also in 1930 was built in great secrecy an enlarged version of the Singapore, with three Buzzard engines, for the Japanese Navy, four more being built under licence by Kawanishi in Japan.

All three Kents and Calcutta *G-EBVH* in Alexandria harbour in 1932.

To supplement and eventually replace the five Calcuttas, Imperial Airways ordered three of a larger four-engined version, the Kent, which entered service in 1931. Like the Calcuttas, these remained out in all weathers and showed no signs of corrosion in five years of exposure to extremes of climate. In 1934 Imperial Airways ordered two landplane variants, *Scylla* and *Syrinx*, having the same wings and engines but with wheeled landing gear and cabins for 39 passengers; these reinforced their busy cross-Channel fleet and gave reliable, if unspectacular, service until 1940. Shorts' development of large biplane flying-boats culminated in June 1932 with the launching at Rochester of the Sarafand, powered by six Buzzard engines totalling 5,000 hp. It was followed just over a year later by the little six-seat Scion cabin monoplane with two Pobjoy engines totalling 180 hp, of which 22 were sold, two being still airworthy in Australia 30 years later. Concurrently an experimental twin-engined gull-wing monoplane flying-boat, nicknamed the Knuckleduster,

24

was launched, with cantilever wings of great torsional stiffness and a flat-sided hull of low drag; although not adopted for R.A.F. squadron service, it provided a great deal of valuable data for the design of the outstandingly successful Empire Boats, ordered by Imperial Airways for the implementation of the Empire Air Mail Scheme agreed between the Air Ministry and the Commonwealth Postmasters-General.

Canopus on test over Rochester in July 1936. (*Flight.*)

Experimental air mail services had been flown between London and Australia in April and May 1931, but an attempt to expedite the Christmas mail in this way was dogged by misfortune. The cost of operating mail-only aeroplanes, as in America, was uneconomic over the long sea and jungle crossings of the route, particularly during the monsoons, but K.L.M. and the Netherlands Post Office had satisfactorily combined passengers and mail on their Amsterdam–Batavia route, so it was decided that Imperial Airways should operate similarly. The Australian Government agreed to be responsible for the Singapore–Brisbane sector and the Government of India for the Karachi–Rangoon sector, Qantas Empire Airways and Indian Trans-Continental Airways being formed for this purpose. Services began in December 1934 in fierce competition with K.L.M., and it soon became obvious that new aircraft with much higher performance were needed to match the DC-2s with which K.L.M. had replaced their traditional Fokkers. At the same time there was a persistent demand for a Bermuda–New York flying-boat service, to be shared equally with Pan American Airways, who had already surveyed a transatlantic route via Bermuda and the Azores.

In 1933 Short Brothers were asked to submit proposals for a flying-boat basically suitable for both short-range and transatlantic operation, according to the fuel tankage and accommodation installed. It was here that Shorts' long-term programme of step-by-step research paid off, and when, in 1935, a four-Pobjoy ten-seat version of the Scion took the air it was at once apparent that a geometrically similar flying-boat of twice the linear size would meet both E.A.M.S. and Bermuda requirements in every way. So confident were Imperial Airways of Shorts' competence and so urgent was their need that they ordered the whole fleet of 28 Empire Boats without waiting for the first to fly, which it did in July 1936 with complete success. Two of them were equipped with long-range fuel systems for transatlantic trials and three more were ordered by Qantas Empire Airways. At the same time the Air Ministry ordered two development prototypes, one a military version which became the Sunderland, and the other the Mayo Composite, comprising a heavily loaded high-speed mail-carrying seaplane carried for take-off on the back of a suitably adapted and lightly loaded Empire Boat. Major Robert Mayo, whose scheme

The second separation of *Mercury* from *Maia* over Rochester, on 23 February, 1938. (*B.O.A.C.*)

this was, had been Imperial Airways' consulting engineer for many years, and the cost of this experiment was equally shared by Imperial Airways and the Air Ministry. Alternative schemes for overcoming the take-off problem for transatlantic operation were refuelling in flight and catapult launching, the former being advocated by Sir Alan Cobham and the latter being demonstrated with some success by both German and French air mail operators, using catapults mounted on ships. Short Brothers submitted proposals for both methods, but themselves preferred an enlarged version of the Empire Boat, capable of normal take-off with enough fuel for the longest stage as well as an adequate payload; three of these, known as G-Boats, were ordered,

Oswald Short in his Hampstead garden in 1936, with his Amazonian parrot Laura; she refused to talk but sang soprano arias very beautifully in Portuguese.

together with eight more specially strengthened Empire Boats which began regular flight-refuelled Atlantic crossings on the eve of war in 1939.

Shorts' achievement in designing the Empire Boat was matched by their ingenuity in building it in series at Rochester. For the first time the long-established nucleus of skilled craftsmen had to undertake the training of un-skilled recruits as well as the normal intake of apprentices. It was found that the many coachbuilders hitherto employed on bus-bodies took readily to hull assembly; in fact, Arthur Gouge (himself originally a 'chippie') always claimed that carpenters made the best sheet-metal workers. But however many more hands were trained on shore, only one man was in charge once a flying-boat was afloat; this was George Wadhams, the head waterman, whose family had for generations been Freemen of the River Medway; trained from childhood to recognise every whim of tide, wind and current, his authority on the water was absolute and his skill uncanny. Parker trusted him implicitly and obeyed his instructions exactly when being taken in tow; often Wadhams would seem to charge his motor-boat head-on at a taxying flying-boat, missing its bows by inches and taking the line almost from the pilot's hand; on other occasions he was to be seen drifting down the evening tide in a dinghy, his oars shipped and his eyes closed, with £40,000-worth of Empire Boat secured alongside only by a lanyard held in one hand as he changed it from one moor-ing to another. Oswald Short would watch him, knuckles white from apprehension, muttering, 'Doesn't he know how much it has cost to build?', but no boat ever missed its buoy or ran aground while in Wadhams' care.

By 1936 it was evident that large-scale production of Sunderlands and

27

other types for the R.A.F. expansion programme could not be undertaken at Rochester in addition to the further civil aircraft already on order. Production of Scions was sub-contracted to Pobjoy Airmotors, in whom Shorts took up a substantial shareholding, and a survey in 1936 of possible sites for a new factory indicated Belfast as an excellent location. Here a new airfield was being made at Sydenham adjacent to Harland & Wolff's shipyard and deep-water dock, with unrestricted access to open water in the Lough. Following discussions with the Northern Ireland Government, Belfast Harbour Commissioners and the local authorities, the Air Ministry agreed to build and equip an aircraft factory on Queen's Island to be managed by a new company, Short & Harland Ltd, jointly owned by Short Brothers and Harland & Wolff. This factory began production in 1938 with 'learning' contracts for 50 Bristol

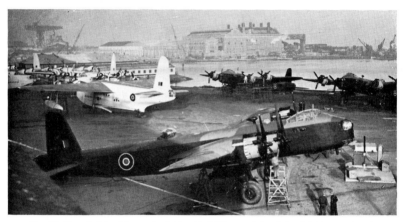

Outside Queen's Island factory in 1943, with Stirlings and Sunderlands being completed.

Bombays followed by 150 Handley Page Herefords. Meanwhile Rochester had gained orders for two prototypes of the first four-engined heavy bomber for the R.A.F., the Stirling, together with three orders for an even larger civil airliner, the S.32, although the latter were cancelled when war began. A wooden half-scale Stirling model was flown late in 1938 and the first Stirling prototype in May 1939, followed by the first G-Boat in June, too late to share the Atlantic service with Pan American's Boeings of similar size. At that time Gouge was already planning an 80-ton six-engined flying-boat, and foresaw a future development of it with submerged power plants and pressurised passenger cabins. Although frustrated by the war, this idea was to mature six years later as the Saro Princess, which resulted from the pooling of Gouge's ideas with Henry Knowler's. Gouge was a convinced protagonist of very large flying-boats for long-range Empire communications, but did not foresee the drastic changes brought about by the world-wide construction of long, strong concrete runways whose ready-made availability alone made land-based airliners more economical to operate than boats after the war: of the operators consulted by the Brabazon Committee in 1943 only British South American Airways Corporation and R.A.F. Transport Command showed interest in the Princess.

In spite of an accident to the first Stirling on landing at Rochester Airport after its maiden flight, production at both Rochester and Belfast was not delayed, and was supplemented later by Austin Motors at Longbridge, Birmingham. Sunderland production began at a new Clydeside factory operated jointly by Blackburn Aircraft and Denny Brothers at Dumbarton; a Sunderland production line also grew up beside the Stirlings at Belfast. New projects begun by the Rochester design office included a very large ocean patrol flying-boat to specification R14/40, of which two prototypes were eventually completed and flown as the Shetland, and its landplane equivalent, the B8/41 'Super-Stirling', which was not built. Rochester works felt the strain of war early and acutely, being in a very exposed location during the Battle of Britain. The seaplane works, though well equipped for building flying-boats by traditional methods, were not adaptable to Stirling assembly, which had been started in a new factory on the eastern boundary of Rochester Airport. It was still not completely tooled-up when, on the formation of the Ministry of Aircraft Production in May 1940, the industry was forced to concentrate on fighter output, priorities for Stirlings were reduced and difficulty arose in getting delivery of machine tools, forgings, castings, extrusions and power plants. When at last the assembly line got under way, it received a direct hit in an air raid on 9 August which destroyed six nearly completed Stirlings and caused severe dislocation. Similar damage was done at the Belfast factory on 15 August, while the Treasury's authorisation of large credit facilities was not accompanied by priorities for the release of urgently needed materials. The Stirling design office and part of the production line were immediately dispersed to Kidderminster, and new assembly lines were initiated at Hucclecote and Swindon to replace the lost capacity at Rochester. After several changes of policy on the Stirling programme during 1941 the situation in Shorts was being somewhat unfavourably contrasted with rationalised production methods and lower unit costs achieved elsewhere.

Short Brothers did their best to meet the Ministry's fluctuating demands, but soon after Sir Stafford Cripps became the third Minister of Aircraft Production to assume that office in 1942, matters came to a head. Oswald Short's health had suffered from the continual strain, and in January 1943 he resigned from the Chairmanship, remaining in Short Brothers as Honorary Life President. His eventual successor was Sir Frederick Heaton, Chairman of the Tilling group of transport companies, to whom Shorts had in the lean years supplied many hundreds of bus bodies. Gouge (who had been General Manager as well as Chief Designer since 1930) made strenuous efforts to meet the accelerated Stirling programme now demanded by Bomber Command, but, being used to shipyard methods, lacked the imagination necessary to embark on really massive production, as was being done in the motor-car

One of No. 218 Squadron's Stirlings ready for a sortie in 1942. (*I.W.M.*—*Crown Copyright.*)

industry under the direction of Patrick Hennessy of Fords; on 23 March, 1943, he resigned, the Government having already taken over the full management of Short Bros under Defence Regulation 78, the whole share capital of £447,493 being transferred to the Treasury Solicitor.

Gouge became Vice-Chairman of Saunders-Roe Ltd at Cowes, to whom the detail design and manufacture of the wing and power plant group of the Shetland flying-boat had already been sub-contracted; thus he was able to continue technical supervision of the Shetland, which was launched at Rochester in October 1944 and was the biggest flying-boat ever to take off from the Medway. It is evident that Gouge must have come into head-on collision with Sir Stafford Cripps, who arrived at Rochester on the fatal day at an hour's notice, called an immediate meeting of all personnel and was accompanied on the platform only by the Shop Stewards' Convenors, the management being left standing on the floor; this could hardly have been a tactless oversight on the part of anyone as intelligent as Sir Stafford, and was consequently interpreted as a deliberate snub, much resented by the majority of long-service employees, who knew from experience that Oswald Short's

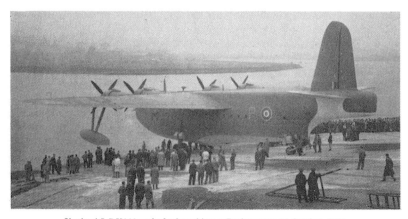

Shetland I *DX166* ready for launching at Rochester on 24 October, 1944.

30

rigid discipline and autocratic rule were tempered by his generous humanity and innumerable acts of unsolicited kindness to any of his people in need or distress, about whom he was always kept promptly informed by his secretary.

After Gouge left, the design team at Rochester was headed by C. P. T. Lipscomb, ably supported by 'Nobby' Clarke as Chief Engineer. As more Lancasters became available, Stirlings were withdrawn from Bomber Command and modified into glider tugs and paratroop transports, taking a major part in the Normandy and Arnhem landings; production of this version was also undertaken by new factories at Aldergrove and Meghabery as well as at Rochester. Sunderland production was supplemented by a new factory at Windermere, and a developed version, originally the Sunderland IV but later renamed Seaford, was flown at Rochester three months before the Shetland. The design office by this time was busy with a new carrier-borne twin-engined strike monoplane, Sturgeon 1, to a stringent Naval specification, of which the prototypes were built at Rochester, with production scheduled for Belfast. Meanwhile the Empire Boats, which had maintained B.O.A.C.'s 'Horseshoe Route' between Durban and Sydney since 1940, had been seriously depleted by accidents and Japanese attacks, and civil conversions of the Sunderland had been supplied to reinforce B.O.A.C.'s fleet. When war ended, these were brought up to peacetime airliner standard as Hythes, and many new conversions were produced at Belfast as Sandringhams. Similar treatment turned the Seaford into the Solent and enabled the second Shetland to be completed as a civil transport; the last aircraft to be built and flown from Rochester Seaplane Works was a Solent (*G-AHIY*) on 8 April, 1948, the sixteenth anniversary of Eustace Short's death. The Seaplane Works main gate finally closed in July 1948, when some of the older staff elected to retire instead of moving to Belfast; among them was P. M. Jones, the world's first aircraft draughtsman, who had detailed the original Short-Wright drawings for Horace Short at Leysdown in 1909; in the late 1930s he had become the firm's librarian at Rochester and was one of those presented to the King and Queen during their visit on 14 March, 1939. Shorts retained a service department hangar and ferry flight at Rochester Airport for a further five years, but all the factory premises both at the Airport and on the waterfront were in due course re-let to firms in light industries. Apart from the names of the present occupiers, the Seaplane Works have changed their appearance little, but the M2 motorway viaduct now spans the Medway at Cuxton Reach, the fairway used for so many famous maiden flights by John Lankester Parker, who came to Shorts at Eastchurch as a part-time test pilot in 1916, became Chief Test Pilot in 1918 and a Director in 1943; he continued flying until 1945, when he was succeeded by his deputy since 1940, Geoffrey Tyson. Parker had flown every Short type since the single-engined Bomber and had made the first flight in every prototype from the Shirl to the Shetland, covering a range of size from 560 lb to 130,000 lb; in 1946 Tyson joined Saunders-Roe, to be succeeded by Harold Piper, who was followed in 1948 by Tom Brooke-Smith, on whose retirement in 1960 Denis Tayler was appointed Chief Test Pilot.

31

In November 1947 Short Brothers (Rochester & Bedford) Ltd and Short & Harland Ltd were merged to form a new company, Short Brothers & Harland Limited, registered and wholly based at Belfast, with Oswald Short remaining Life President. Harland & Wolff retained their original holding of £360,000, and the balance of £640,000 was subscribed by the Government through S.B. (Realisations) Ltd. In 1948 the capital was doubled by means of a Treasury grant, and in July 1954 a further increase of £360,000 was subscribed by The Bristol Aeroplane Company, who were seeking a second-source production line for Britannias and whose engines had been extensively employed in Shorts' airframes since the Springbok; the relative holdings then became 69½ per cent by the Government and 15¼ per cent each by Harland & Wolff and The Bristol Aeroplane Co, in a total of £2,360,000. The company built many Canberras and Britannias under sub-contract, and designed important variants of them, but continued vigorously to develop its own projects; these

New Seamews and a refurbished Sunderland in the Queen's Island factory in 1956.

included target-tug and anti-submarine versions of the Sturgeon, the Sperrin four-jet heavy bomber and the Seamew anti-submarine spotter, together with the Seacat, Tigercat, Blowpipe, Javelin and Starstreak anti-aircraft guided missiles, Stilleto and Skeet aircraft targets, and the Skyspy remotely-controlled aerial reconnaissance vehicle. Experimental prototypes included the Sherpa and S.B.5 research monoplanes and the pioneer S.C.1 jet-lift VTOL aircraft, with its highly developed auto-stabilisation and blind-landing systems. In the civil field, 24 Sealand light amphibians were produced and sold overseas between 1948 and 1953, while the two freighters in production in 1966, Belfast and Skyvan, presented the same dimensional contrast as did the *Golden Hind* and Scion at Rochester in 1938. Although the Belfast failed to attract export orders, the Skyvan appealed to operators in undeveloped territories as a practical and versatile aerial two-ton truck, with notable economy and short-field capability in all climates.

From the Skyvan a family of twin-propeller-turbine regional airline aircraft was developed which have sold widely, principally in export markets. Conceived in 1971 the first was the SD3–30, a 30-seat aircraft which was still in production in 1988 with 120 built. Two variants introduced in 1982 were the military utility tactical transport (UTT) and a freighter version, the Sherpa, both of which attracted only limited sales. During July 1980 Shorts announced a stretched version of the SD3–30; this was the 36/39-seat SD3–60 which has become another market success with over 80 operating in the United States out of a world-wide total of some 150. It was against this background of success that in early March 1988 the company disclosed first details of the Shorts FJX, a purpose-designed 44-seat twin-turbofan regional airliner aimed at the growing and new commuter aircraft markets of the 1990s.

Shorts also became important partners in international contracts, beginning with the manufacture of outer wings for the Royal Navy's McDonnell Phantoms and the design and sole-source production of complete wings for, first, the Fokker F.28 Fellowship and its U.S. derivative the Fairchild–Hiller F–228, then the Fokker 100. This was followed in 1969 by production of Lockheed L1011 TriStar ailerons, wingtips, spoilers and main undercarriage doors: later Shorts also became the sole-source of Boeing 747 main undercarriage doors.

In 1989 the company's programme of work on airframe components included those for the Boeing 737–300 and 757; engine nose cowls for the Rolls–Royce RB.211 turbofan in Boeing 747, 757 and 767; complete nacelle systems for the BAe 146 and, in collaboration with Rohr Industries, International Aero Engines' V2500 turbofans in the Airbus A320. Although this work is a valuable element of Shorts' total production effort it is unlikely to outweigh the company's traditional aircraft manufacturing activities. The Shorts 330 and 360 seem destined to carry on a noble tradition of service to isolated communities undreamed of in the days when Horace Short was held captive in Samoa. The outcome of the Government's privatisation plans for the company, after some 45 years of State ownership, can only be enhanced by the Tucano production programme and, of more importance, the £500 million FJX project which is seen as a key factor in Shorts' future. In December 1988 it was announced that British Airways, having joined British Midland Airways in backing this project, was to buy at least 20; however, the Government stated that it would only consider providing launch aid for the FJX after Shorts had been transferred to private ownership.

The three Short brothers, first manufacturers of aircraft in the world, are assured of a place of honour in the annals of aviation, and this book is intended as a tribute to their courage and imagination; it also commemorates the faithful partnership in their enterprise of John Lankester Parker, the premier flying-boat test pilot of all time.

Short-Wright Glider, as first tried without rudders, July 1909. (*Courtesy J. H. Blake.*)

Short-Wright Biplanes

Wilbur Wright's demonstrations of flying the improved Wright Model A biplane at Hunaudières and Camp d'Auvours, near Le Mans, in August 1908, created unprecedented enthusiasm, with spectators and would-be passengers flocking from all over Europe to see him. After taking up numerous passengers in September and October, including leading members of the Aero Club of the United Kingdom, Wilbur Wright was bombarded with requests for replicas of the Flyer; Charles S. Rolls was among the first to place an unconditional order for one. But the demonstration Flyer was only the fourth powered machine the Wrights had constructed, and their contract with Lazare Weiller, promoter of their European tour, provided for his ultimate retention of it, after completion of an agreed programme of demonstrations, including tuition for not more than three pupils. It was the first of its particular type, and the Wrights had not intended to put it into production, so they had never made any complete working drawings. However, they agreed to allow copies of the Flyer to be built under licence by approved constructors, and in France these were to be Chantiers de France at Dunkerque and the Société Astra at Billancourt; during his first visit to France in 1907, Wilbur Wright had arranged for a firm of precision engineers, Bariquand & Marre of Paris, to build spare Wright engines, and in 1908 he was so cordially welcomed at Le Mans by Léon Bollée, who put a bay of his well-equipped automobile factory at Wilbur's disposal, that Bollée also was awarded a licence to make Wright engines. All sales in France were handled by Weiller's firm, Cie. Générale de Navigation Aérienne, but all the British Empire rights were held by Griffith Brewer, who managed the Wrights' U.K. patents.

Brewer was a well-known balloonist, and from his experience of the work of the Short brothers had no hesitation in recommending them as competent to manufacture the Flyer in England; by February 1909 Eustace Short had made a contract with Wilbur Wright to construct six aircraft at a total price of

£8,400; all were already bespoken by members of the Aero Club, the first being reserved for Charles Rolls in accordance with his original order of the previous September. Rolls was impatient to begin learning to fly, and since Wilbur Wright declined to take on any more pupils in addition to the three (Comte Charles de Lambert, Paul Tissandier and Capt Lucas de Girardville) already nominated in France, he recommended Rolls to start practising with a glider of the type already described in the patent of 1906, and gave Short Brothers permission to construct one apart from the Flyer contract. On completion of his flights at Le Mans in December 1908, Wilbur Wright moved to Pau in the warmer south on 14 January, 1909, accompanied by Orville Wright and their sister Katharine, who had just arrived from the United States. Horace Short spent several days with Eustace at Pau in February measuring and sketching every aspect of the Flyer, and soon after his return to England he and his assistant, P. M. Jones, had produced the first complete set of working drawings ever made of any Wright biplane. Meanwhile, the Aero Club had established its new flying ground at Shellbeach on Sheppey, and half a mile away Short Brothers built a new factory in which to assemble the six Short-Wright Flyers; work on details began at Battersea, but the railway arches were too cramped for final erection of aeroplanes. The first building, a corrugated-iron shed 100 ft long by 45 ft wide, was put up by Harbrow of Bermondsey early in March 1909, and by May Horace was already lamenting its inadequacy and planning extensions; by August a second shed was in use and Short Brothers were employing 80 men. Horace Short designed and manufactured the Short-Wright glider at Battersea in four weeks during the spring of 1909, taking it to Shellbeach in June for fabric covering and final rigging; Rolls attempted his first launch, unsuccessfully, on 1 August and achieved his first glide the following day. Thereafter he practised regularly and with increasing proficiency till 10 October.

The Short-Wright glider had plain rectangular warping wings, with a forward biplane elevator and twin aft rudders exactly similar to the Wright glider of 1902–3, except that the pilot sat upright with a control lever in each hand; the left-hand lever moved fore-and-aft to control the elevator, and the right-hand lever moved sideways for warping and fore-and-aft to control the rudder. It was hand-launched from a trolley on a rail laid downhill on a slight eminence near Leysdown, and Rolls achieved soaring flights of several hundred yards in suitable weather. Rolls did not dispose of his glider until March 1910, when he offered it for sale in good condition, together with its shed and rail and the lease of the site.

The Wrights visited Battersea on 3 May and Shellbeach the next day, and were well pleased with the quality and progress of the six Flyers under construction. As at first built, they were exactly similar to Wilbur Wright's demonstration Flyer, and only the last two ever incorporated later improvements. The two-spar wings had neither dihedral nor stagger and were wire-braced, with the two outer bays on each side arranged to warp. The main chassis comprised a pair of forward elevator outriggers combined with landing skids. An additional small feature, peculiar to Short-built Flyers, was a projecting wing-tip skid at each end of the lower leading edge, introduced by Horace Short because of frequent damage on the rough ground at Shellbeach. The biplane elevator incorporated an ingenious linkage for reversing the camber to match the angle of attack, so that when incidence was negative the camber was inverted. The parallel rudders were boxed together and pivoted on a central vertical axis carried by a single pair of upper and lower booms braced by wires to the rear spars. The pilot and passenger sat side-by-side on the left-hand half of the lower wing between the chassis frames, with the engine beside them on their right; they had separate seats with back-rests and a common fixed foot-rail. The pilot usually sat on the right, with a fore-and-aft elevator lever in his left hand and a universally pivoted lever in his right hand, which moved fore-and-aft to control the rudder and sideways to control the warp; thus the functions of 'balancing' and 'steering' were psychologically separated, while the use of rudder to counteract warping drag became instinctive with the right hand, leading naturally to the Wrights' elegant banked turns, previously thought to be a highly dangerous manoeuvre in spite of its universal and age-old use by birds and bats!

The 27 hp four-cylinder water-cooled vertical engine of the Wrights' own design drove, through separate chains in guide tubes and sprockets giving a reduction ratio of 9:32, a pair of two-bladed propellers mounted outboard just behind the wings with their thrustline at half-gap; their tips rotated outwards at the top, so creating a resultant upwash in the middle of the slipstream, the longer left-hand chain being crossed to produce counter-rotation. The standard method of take-off was from a trolley on a launching rail laid to face into wind, with assistance from a rope hooked to the trolley and pulled by a falling weight previously raised on a portable derrick located downwind of the rail. This was a nuisance in variable wind conditions and a source of trouble whenever the rope jammed in a pulley, which happened rather often. Occasionally, in a steady light breeze, the Flyer could take off without external assistance, and later in 1909 some of those built in France appeared with wheels attached to the skids.

Although the first four Short-Wright Flyers were completed by July 1909, they were kept waiting for their engines, which had originally been ordered from Léon Bollée for all six; only two Bollée engines were finally delivered, and Bariquand & Marre were substituted in the others, but none was ready for Orville Wright to test personally in August as intended. As a temporary expedient, Frank McClean installed the engine out of his Nordenfelt car in his Short-Wright (No. 3) and was launched from the rail, but failed to sustain flight; two Bollée engines eventually arrived and early in October Charles Rolls made a few brief hops in his Short-Wright (No. 1), but came to grief; after repairs to the minor damage incurred, he began flying steadily on 1 November, and his proficiency was such that before the day was out he had covered $1\frac{1}{2}$ miles, thereby winning the first of four Aero Club prizes of £25 for a flight of 250 yards and the David Salomans Cup and £105 for a flight of half

Frank McClean being launched on Short-Wright No. 3 at Leysdown late in 1909.
(Courtesy J. H. Blake.)

a mile out and half a mile back without landing. Three days later he won the first of three Aero Club prizes of £50 for flying one mile in a closed circuit at Shellbeach, which he accomplished at a height of 60 ft. Alec Ogilvie took delivery of Short-Wright No. 2 at his private flying ground at Camber Sands, near Rye, Sussex, on 3 November, 1909, when he flew for nine minutes. Next day he made two more flights of ten minutes each, but allowed enthusiasm to outrun caution; after attaining 50 mph (as shown by an air-speed indicator of his own design and later improved and patented by him) his Léon Bollée engine seized, but he made a safe forced landing. On 20 November Rolls flew from Shellbeach to the Aero Club's new flying ground at Eastchurch, over an indirect course of 5½ miles, but two days later he, too, suffered engine failure after covering seven miles. On the same day Frank McClean took delivery of the third Short-Wright, after installation of its Bariquand engine, making initial flights up to 400 yards in length, and continued to make steady if unspectacular progress whenever the weather permitted, attaining four miles by 17 December (the sixth anniversary of Orville Wright's historic 'first ever' powered flight). McClean had not had as much prior experience as Rolls and Ogilvie, for the latter had purchased a Wright glider from T. W. K. Clarke of Willesden in August and had soared it for 350 yards after less than a fortnight's practice. By 21 December Rolls had achieved a 15-mile cross-country flight over Sheppey and the fourth Short-Wright had been delivered to Maurice Egerton. On New Year's Day 1910 Frank McClean flew from Eastchurch to Short Brothers' works and back, and Rolls, after a solo flight of nearly an hour, took up Cecil Grace as his first passenger. During the next few weeks Rolls flew frequently with passengers, including Ogilvie, whose own machine was back at Shellbeach for repairs, and on 12 February Maurice Egerton flew over to Shellbeach to win both the third £25 and the second £50 Aero Club prizes.

The last two Short-Wright Flyers, ordered originally by Percy Grace and Ernest Pitman, incorporated an improved four-boom tail outrigger with a single fixed tailplane behind the rudders. Both were flown for the first time on 14 February, the former by Cecil Grace, who covered 300 yards (after earlier practice on Moore-Brabazon's Voisin *Bird of Passage*) and the latter by

Cecil Grace on Short-Wright No. 5 at Leysdown, showing the revised double tail-boom.

Charles Rolls, who had bought it from Ernest Pitman before completion; after a spectacular high flight in his new machine on 25 February, Rolls towed his old Flyer behind his Silver Ghost tourer to London for exhibition on the Royal Aero Club's stand at Olympia, after which he presented it to the Balloon Company, Royal Engineers, at Aldershot; subsequently he gave ground instruction to Army officers on it at Farnborough, and later it was kept at Hounslow Barracks, but there is no record of its ever being flown again. On 24 March Rolls collected his new Flyer from the works at Shell-beach and flew it thence all round Sheppey for 26 miles, attaining 1,000 ft over Queenborough before landing at Eastchurch. On the same day Cecil Grace won the remaining £25 and £50 prizes at Shellbeach; he went on to make regular flights throughout April, culminating in a 46-minute flight over Sheerness at 1,500 ft, in the course of which he dropped a packet of letters, all of which were posted by their finders and reached their destinations. Meanwhile Rolls had bought a new French-built Wright with a wheeled chassis, which he flew at the Nice International Meeting as one of the Royal Aero Club's representatives; on his return he kept this machine for competition purposes, while his second Short-Wright was dismantled to donate its wings, elevators and empennage to his experimental Rolls Power Glider, or R.P.G., which also employed the wheeled chassis and 35 hp Green engine from the unsuccessful Short No. 3 biplane (q.v.). Consequently, he used his French Wright at the Wolverhampton meeting, having previously flown it on 2 June from Dover to Sangatte and back without landing, a feat which won him the Gold Medal of the Royal Aero Club and other awards. Ogilvie flew his Short-Wright (No. 2) at Wolverhampton, and a fortnight later he and Rolls both entered the same machines in the Bournemouth meeting, where Rolls

38

met his death on 12 July while making a second attempt to win the alighting competition. Horace Short, who examined the wreckage, concluded that the tail-boom was not stiff enough to carry the controllable aft elevator which Rolls had fitted only five days earlier, and had deflected far enough to touch the tip of one propeller, with catastrophic results.

After Rolls' death Short Brothers bought back Short-Wright No. 6 from his executors, reassembled it and sold it, less engine, to Alec Ogilvie, who had already fitted wheels to his first Flyer with some success. This encouraged him to make a series of modifications to No. 6, with a view to competing in all-British events, including the de Forest prize and the British Michelin Cup, for which Bollée and Bariquand & Marre engines were ineligible. He first considered fitting a 50 hp E.N.V., but the British-built model of this engine was not yet available, so he chose a new 50 hp V-4 two-stroke supercharged N.E.C., which he installed in September 1910; then he went to New York as the Royal Aero Club's entry in the Gordon Bennett Race at Belmont Park in October. His mount was a Wright C-type racer, with wheels but no front elevators, whose performance so impressed him that on his return to England in December he tried hard to persuade Horace Short to accept the Wrights' offer to extend Shorts' manufacturing licence to include the later models; Horace refused to do so, and Ogilvie thereupon went off, apparently in rather

Alec Ogilvie flying his modified Short-Wright No. 6 at Camber in October 1910.

a huff, to Camber, where he proceeded to convert the sixth Short-Wright to the latest Dayton standard, with the tailplane turned into an aft elevator, the front elevators deleted, the skids shortened and the 'blinkers' placed low on them. He also incorporated Orville Wright's improved steering control, comprising a fore-and-aft lever for the right hand, operating rudder and warp together, with a sideways-hinged handle at the top, whereby a limited amount of differential movement could be interposed between rudder and warp controls. The N.E.C. engine rotated the opposite way to the Wright, and with a rear elevator this was found to be an advantage because it gave pitch-up with engine on and pitch-down with engine off, so improving longitudinal stability and making the machine less tiring to fly.

With these modifications, Ogilvie flew 142 miles in just under four hours on 28 December, 1910, in an attempt to win the British Michelin Cup, terminated prematurely by a radiator leak. In May his lease of the Camber ground expired and he flew back to Eastchurch on 2 May, 1911, and remained there; in later months he modified his machine even more, bringing the engine forward and placing the pilot's and passenger's seats behind it, the whole being enclosed in a nacelle. This improved performance as well as comfort, and on 29 June, 1912, he took off at Eastchurch with three passengers in addition to his own not inconsiderable weight; still later he tried it on floats at Leysdown, but found it unseaworthy. Ogilvie's modified Short-Wright was still being regularly flown right up to the outbreak of war in August 1914, and its N.E.C. engine survives in the Science Museum, South Kensington, London, together with the Wright-Bollée engine and one propeller from Short-Wright No. 2. One of the Bariquand & Marre engines, almost certainly that first installed in Short-Wright No. 6, was stored successively at Eastchurch and Rochester and was later restored and placed on permanent exhibition at Queen's Island, Belfast; incidentally, Bariquand & Marre's London agency, Barimar Ltd, became world-famous as exponents of machinery repairs by welding and now, based at Newcastle-upon-Tyne, occupies a leading place in shipbuilding and heavy steel fabrication.

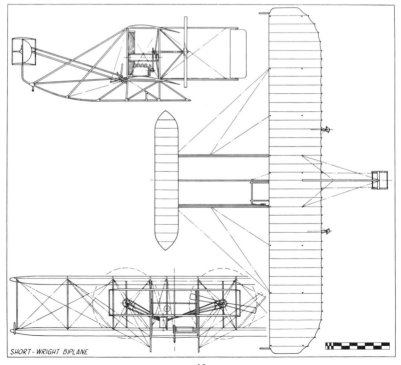

SHORT - WRIGHT BIPLANE

Alec Ogilvie in his rebuilt Short-Wright with positions of pilot and engine revised and enclosed in a nacelle; Eastchurch 1913.

Glider—Span 32 ft 10 in (10 m); length 18 ft (5·5 m); area 325 sq ft (30 m²).
Flyer—Span 41 ft (12·5 m); length 29 ft (8·8 m); area 515 sq ft (47·8 m²); empty weight 885 lb (401 kg); loaded weight 1,200 lb (545 kg); speed 50 mph (80 km/h).

Frank McClean on Short No. 1 at Leysdown in September 1909.

Short Biplane No. 1

Immediately after his flight with Wilbur Wright at Le Mans in November 1908, Frank McClean had to go to China to observe a solar eclipse; from his ship he wrote to Horace Short (whom he had met only once), saying, in effect, 'Build me an aeroplane' with no other conditions stipulated. Frank McClean was a leading light in the Aero Club, and his very generous patronage was a principal source of the Shorts' early business. Even before the Wright brothers awarded their licence, Horace Short began designing Short No. 1 at Battersea, and after only four weeks of manufacturing effort enough progress had been made for the uncovered airframe to be exhibited in March 1909 at the first Aero and Motor Boat Show at Olympia. Although superficially similar to the Wright Flyer, it differed in principle and in detail, having a rigidly braced three-bay cellule with flexible trailing-edge extensions at the outer bays, where the chord was increased from 6 ft 6 in to 10 ft 6 in over a span of 6 ft at each wing-tip. The mainplanes were slightly staggered and double-surfaced, with sharp leading edges and pronounced camber, the profile being derived from steam-turbine experience. A similarly cambered biplane elevator was carried in front and there was no tail; instead, there was a central fixed fin between the front elevators, and four rudders were pivoted in pairs from the wing-tip extensions. Control was by two hand levers and a foot bar, the left-hand lever controlling the elevator, the right-hand the rudders and the foot control warping the flexible wing extensions. The single engine drove two 10 ft diameter laminated spruce propellers mounted aft of the

Frank McClean after an attempted flight on Short No. 1 at Leysdown in September 1909.

wing through a chain drive; at first it was intended that the port chain should be crossed to effect counter-rotation, as in the Wright system, but this could not easily be done without infringing the Wright patents. The landing-gear comprised a pair of robust skids carried by numerous struts; the chassis had no wheels, and a starting rail was used for take-off. The uncovered airframe was inspected by the Prince of Wales (later King George V) when he visited Short Brothers' stand at Olympia on 26 March, 1909.

Except for the ash skids, the machine was built entirely of spruce, and the spars incorporated bolted flitch joints to enable the wing assembly to be dismantled into three sections for transport; the covering was 'Continental' balloon fabric, already rubberised, but difficulty arose in attaching it to the concave undersurfaces, and covering was still unfinished at Shellbeach in May. A Wright-type Bariquand & Marre engine of 30 hp was on order, but had not been delivered by July, when Frank McClean got back from China, and he was so anxious to begin flying that he bought a second-hand Nordenfelt car from which he removed the engine; this was rated at 30 hp, but weighed over 600 lb when installed, and in the first trials in September it failed to propel the biplane even as far as the end of the starting rail, after which it was transferred to Short-Wright No. 3, but with no better success. The Bariquand & Marre engine arrived in October, and with this McClean almost got No. 1 airborne during three attempts on 2, 3 and 6 November, but on the last occasion he pulled up the elevator to its limit and the machine stalled in a nose-up attitude off the end of the rail, slewed sideways, demolishing its chassis, and fell over backwards, so breaking both propellers. It has been suggested that it was repaired and successfully flown later with a 60 hp Green engine, but in later years this report was denied by both Sir Francis McClean and Lord Brabazon. Virtually nothing was recorded about Short No. 1 in the Press of the day because, to quote the editor of the first edition of the *Aero Manual*, published in 1909: 'Messrs Short Bros are pursuing a policy of reticence, and up to the time when this book has gone to press have asked us not to make public any information about their aeroplanes.'

Span 40 ft (12·2 m); length 24 ft 7 in (7·5 m); area 576 sq ft (53·5 m²); loaded weight 1,200 lb (545 kg).

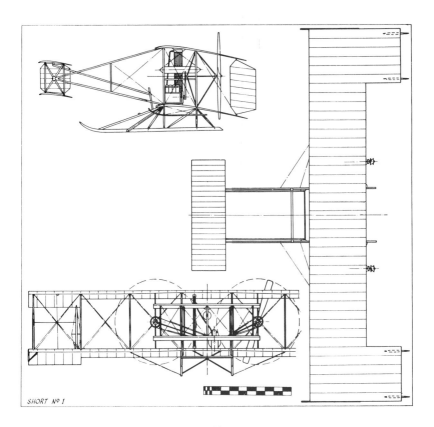

SHORT Nº 1

J. T. C. Moore-Brabazon on Short No. 2 in November 1909.

Short Biplane No. 2

The second biplane designed by Horace Short was ordered in April 1909 by J. T. C. Moore-Brabazon, specifically for his attempt to win the *Daily Mail*'s prize of £1,000 for the first flight of one mile in a closed circuit by a British pilot in an all-British aeroplane. Moore-Brabazon had built himself a biplane as early as 1907, for which Short Brothers had manufactured various components, although they had no part in its design. When it failed to fly at Brooklands, on the meagre power of a single 12 hp Buchet engine, he abandoned it and went to France, where he bought three Voisins in succession, the third being the E.N.V.-engined *Bird of Passage*, which he brought to Shellbeach in the spring of 1909; on this he became the first Englishman to fly in England, at the end of April. The *Daily Mail*'s prize was announced just previously, on 7 April, and had to be won within one year from that date, so Moore-Brabazon was naturally keen to add to his laurels.

By this time Short Brothers' works at Shellbeach were in commission and Horace Short had become familiar with the details of the Wright Flyer and indeed critical of some of its design features. It was by no means certain that any British engine of more than 30 hp would be available, but a 50–60 hp Green was ordered, although delivery from the Aster works, where they were being made, was at that time very slow. Moore-Brabazon had salvaged the Vivinus

44

engine originally fitted to his second Voisin, and this was available for practice flights, although ineligible for competition, because of its Belgian origin.

Short No. 2 incorporated a great deal of Wright practice, but differed in several important respects. The biplane wings and front elevators were somewhat similar to the Wrights', but of higher aspect ratio. The chassis comprised a pair of strongly trussed girders shaped like a sleigh to ride across the Leysdown dykes in a forced landing; each girder consisted of upper and lower longerons, parallel below the wings but curved upwards at the front to meet at the elevator pivots, separated by nine vertical struts braced by diagonal steel strips in each bay, the strips being twisted so as to lie flat where they crossed each other. Like Short No. 1, both of No. 2's propellers turned the same way, being driven by uncrossed chains. The elevators were of wide span and narrow chord and gap, with square tips, and incorporated a new type of camber-changing linkage (patent No. 23,166/09) which avoided infringement of the Wright patent (No. 16,068/09). The mainplanes were rigidly braced throughout their span, warping being replaced by differentially linked 'balancers', or mid-gap ailerons, for lateral control; these were of very low aspect ratio, and each comprised a pair of forward and aft 'sails' carried on a centre-pivoted boom mounted just above the middle of the outermost wing strut; the fabric of each sail was stretched on its frame by tension springs along the trailing edge so that the surface took up a camber appropriate to its angle of attack. The balancers were controlled by a centre-pivoted foot-bar with stirrups at each end, while the pilot had also two hand-levers, the right for the elevator and the left for the rudder, both moving fore-and-aft. The pilot's seat was mounted on the lower leading edge to starboard, with the engine on the centre-line farther aft, leaving space for a passenger's seat on the port side, if required. The single rudder was a tall narrow rectangle carried on short outriggers immediately aft of the elevator assembly, and a large vertical fin was carried by a pair of booms behind the wings. Horace Short was convinced that a large fixed fin surface in the slipstream was necessary to counteract yaw due to warping or aileron drag; he had argued unsuccessfully to this effect with the Wright brothers, who preferred their fixed keel area ('blinkers') forward and their rudders aft.

J. T. C. Moore-Brabazon flying the Vivinus-engined Short No. 2 at Leysdown late in September 1909. (*Flight.*)

45

Short No. 2 was completed during September 1909, but the Green engine had not been delivered by then, so the Vivinus was installed for preliminary trials; in spite of being underpowered with this rather heavy engine, Moore-Brabazon succeeded in flying nearly a mile after being launched by derrick and rail on 27 September; he made a second flight of about 400 yards on 30 September, but landed heavily and damaged the port wing-tip. This was repaired, and the Green engine, which had just arrived, was installed, giving a larger reserve of power. Notice was given to the *Daily Mail* and the Aero Club that all was ready for the attempt on the £1,000 prize, and Lord Northcliffe sent Charles Hands to observe the flight; at once the weather became unsettled and remained so for a fortnight, but at last the day came; Moore-Brabazon rounded a mark-post half a mile away and landed back beside the starting rail, in an undulating flight varying in altitude from 20 ft to a few inches, but without actually touching the ground; he had won the prize, and the date was 30 October, 1909. This was two days before Charles Rolls made his first true flight on the first of the Short-Wright Flyers, and Moore-Brabazon could have claimed the David Salomans Cup also, but very sportingly waived his claim to it provided Rolls could himself qualify for it

J. T. C. Moore-Brabazon flying Short No. 2 at Leysdown in November 1909 after the Green engine had been installed.

within one week, which he did. Moore-Brabazon's prize-winning flight was followed by appropriate celebrations at Mussel Manor, during which he was challenged to take up a piglet to disprove the adage that 'pigs can't fly'; this he did in style on 4 November with a $3\frac{1}{2}$ miles cross-country flight outside the Shellbeach ground; on 7 January, 1910, he flew $4\frac{1}{2}$ miles from Shellbeach to the new flying ground at Eastchurch, after first winning the second of the Aero Club's £25 prizes for an observed flight of 250 yards. Before leaving Shellbeach a larger cruciform tail, carried on four booms, had been fitted to No. 2, to improve stability for an attempt on the British Michelin Cup. Moore-Brabazon began practising in earnest for this competition, which closed on 31 March, 1910, and made four short flights on 12 February, followed by one of eight minutes on the 14th, carrying 20 gallons of petrol. All was ready for a serious attempt on 1 March, and he had covered 19 miles

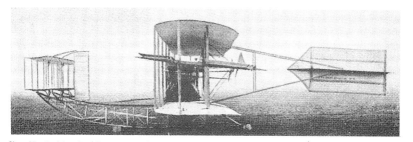

Short No. 2 with enlarged empennage (inscribed 'J. T. C. Moore-Brabazon No. 5') at Eastchurch early in 1910. The drawing below shows the original design before modification.

in 31 minutes before his crankshaft broke as a result of running continuously at maximum power. A spare engine was available and was fitted two days later, but then No. 2 was due to be exhibited on the Royal Aero Club's stand at Olympia. After the show, No. 2 was taken back to Eastchurch, where the empennage was raised 21-in to a position level with the upper wing; Moore-Brabazon flew it once in this condition on 25 March, finding no improvement in control, but knew by then that nobody else with an all-British machine had a chance of beating his earlier performance, and in April he was adjudged the

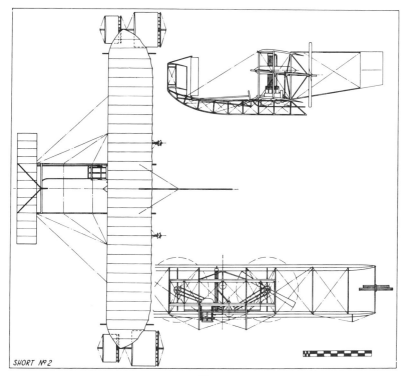

SHORT Nº 2

winner of the Cup; much longer distances had been flown by Rolls in his Short-Wright, but this was ineligible because of its French engine. After this Moore-Brabazon ordered one of the newer Farman-type biplanes that Horace had begun building after moving his works to Eastchurch and No. 2 was not flown again; there is an excellent $\frac{1}{10}$ scale model of it in the Science Museum at South Kensington.

Span 48 ft 8 in (14·9 m); length 32 ft (9·75 m); area 450 sq ft (41·8 m²); loaded weight 1,485 lb (674 kg); speed 45 mph (72·5 km/h).

Short Biplane No. 3

Like the Wright Type A, the Short No. 2 biplane was handicapped by its dependence on rail and derrick launching, quite apart from its general instability and unorthodox control system. Horace Short was well aware of these disadvantages and discussed them at length with members of the Aero Club at Mussel Manor. Late in 1909 he designed and built to Charles Rolls' order an improved lightweight biplane, Short No. 3, which was completed in time for the next Olympia show in March 1910. It was much smaller than No. 2, although similar in layout, and had four wheels which could be held down below the skid runners for taxying and take-off, and retracted by springs before landing. The engine, a 35 hp Green, was mounted high up, with a direct-drive propeller, permitting the use of widely spaced booms to carry a fixed cruciform tail. Improved balancers with spring-tensioned fabric, as in No. 2, were operated by a right-hand lever with sideways movement only; the left-hand lever moved fore-and-aft to control the elevator, and there were foot pedals for direct control of the rudder, which was rubber-sprung to return to neutral if released. Thus the control system more nearly conformed to the single lever and rudder-bar system evolved by Esnault-Pelterie and popularised by Blériot and Farman. The fixed tail comprised a low aspect ratio fin mounted centrally on a high aspect ratio tailplane, whose incidence could be adjusted on the ground through a limited range. The front rudder was larger than No. 2's and the front elevators had no camber. Horace Short was anxious to find alternative means of lateral control at low speeds and took out several further patents for both leading-edge spoilers and trailing-edge intercostal vents or valves, to act as 'lift dumpers' on one side at a time. These are described in patents Nos. 2,613–5 of February 1910, but were not tested in flight, so far as is known. The chassis construction was generally similar to No. 2's, with the same twisted-strip cross-bracing, and the wheel retraction device allowed the wheels to remain in use for landing if preferred, when they were sprung so as to bring the skids into play if the landing was too hard.

Five replicas of No. 3 were ordered even before the show opened, but in spite of its excellent workmanship, it was obviously out-of-date by comparison with the robust and uncomplicated Farman type, whose latest development by Roger Sommer had just been bought by Charles Rolls and was also on view.

Two views of Short No. 3 as shown at Olympia in March 1910. (*Flight.*)

The Rolls Power Glider constructed by combining the wings and control surfaces of Short-Wright No. 6 with the chassis and engine of Short No. 3, at Eastchurch in May 1910.

After the show ended, Rolls had only a few days to spare before taking part in the International Meeting at Nice, where he flew the French-built Wright on which he was killed at Bournemouth in July. When Short No. 3 failed to fly in its original form it seems that Rolls dismantled it and combined its chassis members with the wings, elevators and tail-booms of Short-Wright No. 6, as a prototype of his own design, called the Rolls Power Glider; this name indicates that he aimed to fly on as little power as possible at a low wing-loading. In the R.P.G. the 35 hp Green engine was installed on the starboard side, as in the Wright, but drove uncrossed Renolds chains, so that both propellers turned the same way; to compensate for the higher offset engine weight, the flat rectangular radiator was placed outboard of the port propeller shaft and was connected to the engine water jacket by long pipes. Apparently Rolls hoped to develop this contraption into a saleable article, but it was unfinished at his death, and the Wright components were retrieved by Short Brothers, who paid Rolls' executors £200 for the dismantled No. 6, but could find no bidder for the remains of Short No. 3. The other five replicas of No. 3 were never started, and the only other aeroplanes built at Shellbeach were two designed by J. W. Dunne, one of them being Professor Huntington's and the other the D.5 tailless biplane for the Blair Atholl Syndicate; it is not known whether these received Short constructor's numbers, but the remaining c/ns up to 25 were not used, and a fresh start was made at Eastchurch with S.26, the first of the Short–Farman–Sommer boxkites.

Span 35 ft 2 in (10·7 m); length 31 ft (9·45 m); area 282 sq ft (26·1 m²); empty weight 657 lb (296 kg); loaded weight 860 lb (390 kg); estimated speed 45 mph (72·5 km/h).

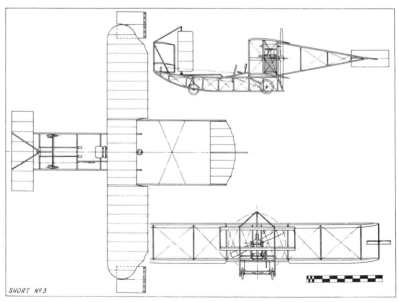

SHORT Nº 3

Cecil Grace flying S.27 at Dunstall Park, Wolverhampton, in June 1910.
(Courtesy Royal Aeronautical Society.)

Short Pusher Biplanes (1910–14)

On 15 February, 1910, H.M. King Edward VII granted the prefix 'Royal' to the Aero Club of the United Kingdom, in recognition of the growing importance of aviation and of the Club's contribution to the art of flying. Many new members were attracted, some of whom might earlier have doubted the respectability of a movement so near the 'lunatic fringe', and a London headquarters had been opened at 166 Piccadilly. This was well patronised, although the hardier members preferred to spend their time at Mussel Manor, their Club-house at Shellbeach, near Leysdown, Sheppey; but the adjacent flying ground was small and much restricted by numerous dykes and rough areas. Horace and Eustace Short owned an ancient 7 hp Panhard car which apparently took such obstacles in its stride, and in this they explored the entire Isle of Sheppey, eventually discovering 400 acres of excellent level grassland adjoining Stamford Hill near Eastchurch, about four miles east of Leysdown. Frank McClean then purchased this as an auxiliary flying ground and invited Short Brothers to move their works to it. The Leysdown works were still completing the last two Short-Wrights and Short No. 3, but only Charles Rolls and Alec Ogilvie still thought this type had any future after having seen the standard Farmans flown at Reims in August 1909 by Henry Farman, George Cockburn and Roger Sommer. Horace Short considered the Wright to be 'a beast that needs some handling', and he and Frank McClean readily accepted the view of George Cockburn and Cecil Grace that the Farman was easier to fly, cheaper to construct and maintain, and had more development potential, particularly when allied with the 50 hp Gnome rotary engine. By March 1910 Rolls, too, had come to the same conclusion, for he had bought one of the latest Sommer biplanes, which he showed at Olympia and flew briefly at Eastchurch in April, before going to Nice.

In May 1910, having completed the sixth Short-Wright at Leysdown for Rolls, Short Brothers moved their factory to Eastchurch, where they had

51

plenty of room for future expansion, and began production of a batch of bi-planes designed by Horace Short on the basis of both the standard Farman and Sommer's derivative of it. The first four were similar, two having 40 hp Green engines, for Frank McClean and J. T. C. Moore-Brabazon respectively, one having a 60 hp E.N.V. for Cecil Grace and one being a reserve airframe. The works Nos. were S.26 for McClean, S.27 for Grace and S.28 for Moore-Brabazon, but they were generically called the 'S.27 type', because Cecil Grace was their foremost exponent at flying meetings. The wings were of equal span, with four uncompensated ailerons, and the front elevator was in two parts joined to a central lever directly connected by wires to the pilot's control lever; the span of the front elevator extended beyond the pivots carried by the front booms. The tail-booms were parallel in plan, but slightly conver-gent rearwards in side view, as in the Sommer, and carried a cambered mono-plane tail having a narrow-chord inset elevator linked to the front one, with a square rudder pivoted centrally below; this single rudder was adequate for the Green-engined version, but Grace preferred to augment it by a similar rudder above the tailplane when using the E.N.V. The landing-gear, like Sommer's, was simpler than Farman's, with the skids wire-braced laterally, carrying only a single wheel inboard of each skid. The wheels were mounted on a long rubber-sprung cross-axle, which was soon found to be too flexible and was thereafter stiffened by an ingenious truss of kingposts and bobstays. As in the Sommer, malacca cane half-hoops below each lower tail-boom formed the tailskids.

Although the exact first flight date of the new Short biplane is not on record, it is known that both S.26 and S.27 were being flown on 19 June, 1910, the former by G. C. Colmore, a beginner with only 20 minutes taxying time to his credit; nevertheless, his first flight covered 11 miles in 20 minutes, and the next day he completed the tests for his pilot's certificate (No. 15), which the Royal Aero Club granted on 21 June, 1910. Cecil Grace began flying S.27 about the same time, and on 20 June flew for 45 minutes over Sheerness, circling above the battleships *Bulwark* and *Victorious* and reaching a height of 1,180 ft, a new British record; he reported that the ailerons designed by Horace Short were quite as effective as the Wright warping system, thus resolving a doubt which had hitherto existed. At the Midland Aero Club's meeting at Dunstall Park, Wolverhampton, from 27 June to 2 July, he gave a brilliant display of manoeuvrability for half an hour, finishing with a dead-stick landing from 150 ft. Moore-Brabazon took delivery of S.28 during the last week of June and flew it once or twice at Eastchurch. He had entered it for the Bournemouth meeting on 11 July, but did not fly there, although both Colmore and Grace took part on S.26 and S.27. After the death of Rolls on 12 July Moore-Brabazon was persuaded by his wife to give up competitive flying and S.28 was stored for the time being at Eastchurch. Colmore flew S.26 in the Lanark meeting, where he covered the flying kilometre at 52·75 mph, but in trying to improve on this on 13 August he came to grief in a young fir plantation. After repairing the damage, McClean had a 50 hp Gnome fitted to S.26; at the same time a flat tailplane with a larger aft elevator was fitted and the front elevator was reduced in span, with levers at each side to carry the control wires linking the two elevators; this arrangement became standard on all future Short biplanes of this type. McClean flew S.26 thus modified on 31 August and made rapid progress. Completing his tests for R.Ae.C. certificate No. 21 on 19 September he made several cross-country flights, but damaged S.26 in a heavy landing on 30 September; a stronger chassis with diagonal struts was fitted, together with stronger tailskids, and he was flying again on 15 and 16 October, watched by a party of Naval officers from Sheerness, whose interest had been aroused by Cecil Grace's exploits; on 22 October McClean took up as his first passenger Dr W. J. S. Lockyer, his old friend and colleague in astronomy, who was also a keen balloonist and a pioneer of aerial photography.

McClean next bought S.28 from Moore-Brabazon and had it fitted with a 50 hp Gnome, flying it in this form on 15 November, 1910. After two weeks' flying he substituted a 60 hp Green engine, so as to make it an all-British aeroplane and thus eligible for the de Forest Prize of £4,000, which was on offer till the end of 1910, for British subjects on British aircraft only, for the farthest distance flown from a starting-point in England to a point on the

Cecil Grace about to start from Dover in S.29 on 22 December, 1910.
(*Courtesy C. F. Andrews.*)

Continent. By coincidence, Baron de Forest's announcement of this prize had been sent to the Aero Club on 25 July, 1909, the day Louis Blériot flew the Channel, but before the news of Blériot's feat had reached London. Cecil Grace, too, was competing in S.29, which had been completed with a 60 hp E.N.V. engine and a number of other modifications, including flotation air-bags and extensions to the upper wing-tips. Grace flew S.29 to his starting-point at Dover on 5 December, but McClean had engine trouble with S.28 and abandoned his attempt on 18 December, when the weather became very rough. Grace decided to discard the flotation bags and took off from Dover on the 22nd, making an excellent flight to Les Baraques in spite of bad weather; he decided to fly back at once to make another attempt and was heard near the North Goodwin lightship in fog, but never reached Dover, nor was ever seen again.

A few weeks earlier Frank McClean, through the Royal Aero Club, had offered the Admiralty the free use of two Gnome-engined Shorts (S.28 and S.29), and Cecil Grace had offered to give free tuition on them. This offer was to remain open for six months, during McClean's absence, as a representative of the Norman Lockyer Observatory, with a Government Solar Eclipse Expedition to Fiji and Tasmania; Dr Lockyer was in charge of the party, which sailed on 31 January, 1911, in the cruiser *Encounter* and was due to return in July after recording the eclipse on 28 April. On 5 December, 1910, in a General Fleet Order, Admiral Sir C. C. Drury, C.-in-C. The Nore, invited applications from Royal Navy and Marine officers to join the flying course, and 200 volunteers sent in their names. After Cecil Grace had been presumed dead, George Cockburn offered to take his place as instructor, and a new biplane, S.34, was built to replace S.29. The first four officers selected for the first course were Lieuts C. R. Samson, A. M. Longmore and R. Gregory of the Royal Navy and Lieut G. V. Wildman Lushington of the Royal Marine Artillery. Cockburn began instructing Samson on S.28 on 15 March, but Lushington was on sick leave, and his place was taken by Lieut E. L. Gerrard, Royal Marine Light Infantry. Samson and Longmore qualified for R.Ae.C. certificates on 24 April, and Gregory and Gerrard on 1 May; all four were airborne on 11 May when Prince Louis of Battenberg (commanding Reserve Fleet, Sheerness) paid the first of many visits to Eastchurch. At the start of the course McClean's S.26 had also been made available for instruction, but it was found sluggish compared with the later machines and was only used for preliminary taxying lessons; it was known as 'The Dud', and when S.28 ('Little Willy') began to accumulate flying time it was deemed wise to have another machine in reserve, so a new biplane, S.38, similar to S.34, was built to replace S.26 and was first flown by Samson on 24 May, 1911. Like S.34, its upper wing spanned 46 ft and it had top and bottom ailerons. The bottom ailerons had been deleted at Cecil Grace's request on S.29, because of flexibility in the bottom wing spars, but Horace Short had found an answer to this problem by means of kingposts in the inner bays above the spars and in the centre bay below the spars; at the same time the whole wing truss had been strengthened by solid compression ribs below the lower surface of the upper wing, between the interplane strut top sockets. Thus the 'improved S.27', as it was known, was notable for its robust construction, although its open accommodation, with the passenger behind and above the pilot, was spartan in the extreme.

In July both S.34 and S.38 were prepared for maximum duration flying, and S.34 was equipped with extra large tanks for 28 gallons of fuel and 13 gallons of oil. S.38 had been built with tankage for four hours, but this was supplemented by a gravity tank mounted fore-and-aft above them; S.38 also sported fabric wheel covers at this stage of its career. On 17 August Lieuts Gerrard and Lushington flew S.34 for 4 hours 13 minutes, then landing only because of dusk, with over two hours' fuel remaining. Two days later Samson flew solo in S.38 for 4 hours $58\frac{1}{2}$ minutes to set up a new British duration record. During this flight his watch stopped, so he circled the flying ground calling in a stentorian voice for a time-check, which was thereafter displayed at five-minute intervals, chalked large on a blackboard. When the six months' agreement expired on 31 August, 1911, it was reckoned that 'Little Willy' had flown 4,000 miles, and S.34 and S.38, 3,000 and 2,000 miles respectively; the total breakage bill incurred was only £25.

While the four Naval airmen were perfecting their skill, two more variants of the 'improved S.27' appeared from the works. The first of these was S.35, built to the private order of Maurice Egerton, who liked a modicum of comfort, especially in winter. S.35 had a neatly streamlined nacelle for pilot and passenger in tandem, terminated by a square-section combined fuel and oil tank, wedge-shaped in plan. It had a 50 hp Gnome and, like S.29, had a central Farman-type sprung tailskid and no bottom ailerons. Its owner first

S.35 as built with nacelle for Maurice Egerton, at Eastchurch in 1911. (*Flight*.)

flew it on 9 March, 1911, and it was so successful that when S.28 went into the works in December 1911 for overhaul it was rebuilt to the same standard, but retained its original ailerons and double tailskids. It was too popular in this form to escape damage by over-enthusiastic pupils and was wrecked on 13 January, 1912, by Lieut J. W. Seddon, who misjudged his landing run and crashed into the closed doors of a hangar, demolishing the aircraft and breaking his own left leg.

The second S.27 variant was S.32, which was ready for Frank McClean on his return from Tasmania; he made the first flight on it on 29 July, 1911. This biplane had begun in November 1910 as a tractor design for Cecil Grace, but had been set aside after his death and then completed as a pusher at McClean's request. It had a 70 hp Gnome and was the first Short biplane to feature side-by-side seats with full dual controls; this made it particularly suitable for school work and, following the success of the Naval pupils,

McClean offered similar free tuition on this machine and another like it, S.33, to volunteers from the London Balloon Company, R.E., T.F. In November 1911 the first 'Terrier' pupils began flying lessons under Jack Travers, one of Shorts' draughtsmen, who had already gained his pilot's certificate at Brooklands; the first to qualify was V. A. Barrington-Kennett (whose more famous brother was a few months later to become the first Adjutant of the Royal Flying Corps); he went solo on 6 December and gained his certificate (No. 198) on 5 March, 1912. By this date, however, the War Office was committed to expand the Air Battalion, R.E., into the Royal Flying Corps, and ruled that members of Territorial Balloon Companies were not to indulge in aeroplane pilotage, so McClean had to end the free training scheme,

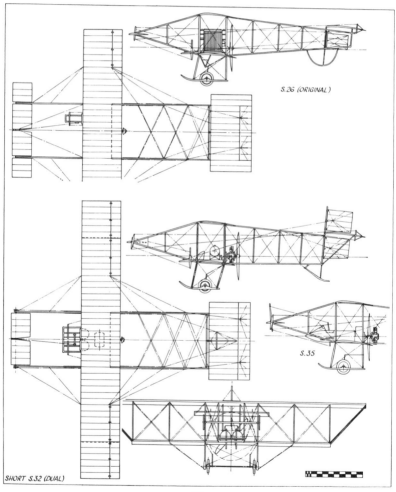

S.26 (ORIGINAL)

S.35

SHORT S.32 (DUAL)

56

S.43, one of the two side-by-side dual-control biplanes supplied to the Central Flying School, Upavon, in 1912.

but not before three more 'Terrier' pilots, including Tom O'Brien Hubbard, had won their brevets. Two more dual-control school biplanes, S.43 and S.44, were built for the new Central Flying School at Upavon, being tested by McClean at Eastchurch early in June 1912 and delivered to Upavon in July, after official scrutiny and acceptance at Farnborough; they were serialled *401* and *402*. Although their discomfort made them unpopular, their indestructibility earned them respect, and they were still in daily use late in 1914.

After the Territorial scheme ended, Frank McClean converted S.33 into a twin-float seaplane, which he began flying from the Swale at Harty Ferry on 31 May, 1912, mainly to obtain data for Horace Short on the design and rigging of floats to get the best take-off performance. The floats were flat-bottomed pontoons without steps, having wooden frames covered with waterproofed canvas and internally braced with piano wire; at first they were reluctant to unstick from smooth water, but soon the correct setting was discovered, and by 9 June McClean had learned the knack of taking off even with a passenger aboard. On 10 August the *Daily Mail* had widely advertised their arrangements for the arrival on a French seaplane of the famous Lieut de Conneau, who was to have become the first aviator to fly up the course of the Thames through the City of London, to a reception at Carmelite House; special permission had been obtained by Lord Northcliffe, and reporters and photographers were posted at all vantage points to record the event. Unfortunately Conneau was delayed at Boulogne with a recalcitrant engine, but

57

Frank McClean flying through Tower Bridge in S.33 on 10 August, 1912.

at 6.30 am McClean slipped quietly away from Harty Ferry in S.33 and touched down between Charing Cross and Westminster bridges just after 8 am. Following the river closely, he found himself unable to climb above the top of Tower Bridge, and took the only possible course by flying through the opening between the footbridge and the road span, to the astonishment and delight of the photographers on the spot. He skimmed through all the other bridges just above water level, but the police forbade him to repeat the performance on the return journey next day and insisted on his taxying all the way to Shadwell Basin. There he attempted a take-off, but the wind was across the fairway, and in attempting a sharp avoiding turn, he side-slipped and damaged one float, so the machine was brought ashore and dismantled for return to Eastchurch by road. This bold flight was quite a feather in the cap of the British flying fraternity, who had become somewhat annoyed latterly by the championship by the Press of foreign pilots, while their own abilities were either overlooked or disparaged. S.33 hit the headlines only briefly, however, and it fell to S.38 to make history in a parallel direction—as a Naval deck-flyer.

When the agreement between the Royal Aero Club and the Admiralty expired in August 1911 it was not to be expected that Their Lordships would have created a dangerous precedent by being ready with a permanent scheme for the continuance of Naval aviation, but in the event the hiatus was not as long as it might have been. After some pressure by Samson and Longmore, the Admiralty agreed in October to set up a Naval Flying School at Eastchurch on ten acres of land leased from the Royal Aero Club, to purchase S.34 and S.38 and to appoint four more officers for training in succession to the first four; the School was to be borne on the books of H.M.S. *Actaeon* at Sheerness, which meant that the officers could live at Eastchurch. McClean

58

generously offered several more of his own aircraft on loan on the same terms as before, and Samson and Longmore were permitted to collaborate with Horace and Oswald Short in various experiments. They began by fitting three streamlined air-bags to the chassis and tail of S.38; these had been designed by Oswald for the de Forest competitors as a safety precaution, but were now fitted lower down so as to prevent the aeroplane from becoming waterlogged. On 1 December, 1911, Longmore made a successful descent on the Medway off the Isle of Grain, and was towed ashore by a Naval picket boat; after a short drying-out period he took off from the beach and flew back to Eastchurch. Phase 2 of the experiment began on 10 January, 1912, when Samson flew S.38 from Eastchurch to the Isle of Grain, landing just inside the sea-wall at Cockleshell Hard. It was then man-handled over planks across the sea-wall and on to a coal lighter, from which it was hoisted by topping lift on to a wooden runway built out over the fore gun turret of H.M.S. *Africa*. Half an hour later Samson gave the signal to let go and roared down the platform, just clearing the bows, then climbed slowly to 300 ft and flew back to Eastchurch. This made a great impression at Sheerness, and next day the Naval Flying School was visited by Admiral Sir Richard Poore, C.-in-C. The Nore, who was taken up in S.38 and expressed great satisfaction with all he saw. Fortunately he was well out of the way when Seddon flew into the hangar doors two days later.

After a further spell of school work, S.38 was again made amphibious and a 70 hp Gnome was installed to improve take-off. On 1 May it was taken to

S.38 being hoisted aboard H.M.S. *Hibernia* at Weymouth in May 1912.

59

Commander Samson flying S.38 off the forecastle of H.M.S. *Hibernia* at Weymouth in May 1912.

Sheerness by lighter and hoisted aboard H.M.S. *Hibernia*, to which *Africa*'s runway had been transferred, *en route* for the Naval Review at Weymouth the following week. It was put ashore by lighter on 3 May and flown by Gregory on the day of the Royal Review, 8 May, when he dropped a dummy bomb of 300 lb from 500 ft and also spotted a submarine while submerged to periscope depth. The next day was foggy, but S.38 was put aboard *Hibernia* once more, and late in the afternoon, when the fog cleared, Samson took off from the platform while *Hibernia* was making 15 kt, and landed back at the flying field at Lodmoor; after this it was shipped back to Eastchurch, but reappeared in the same role on 3 July, when Samson flew it from Eastchurch on to the water alongside H.M.S. *London* at Sheerness, which had been equipped with a flying-off platform; she hoisted S.38 aboard and proceeded to the Portsmouth Naval Review and manoeuvres, and next day, still 19 miles from land, Lieut C. J. L'Estrange Malone took off into a 20-kt wind while the ship was steaming at 12 kt; apparently S.38 lifted off without any forward run and in spite of a bumpy trip Malone landed at Eastney Barracks without difficulty. In view of events some 50 years later, 4 July, 1912, should be remembered as the date on which the first vertical take-off was made (though not by design) by a Short Brothers aeroplane. Malone made one more flight from H.M.S. *London* on 9 July, but later that day S.38 was wrecked while being hoisted aboard from its lighter in a choppy sea.

The remains were returned to Eastchurch and emerged from the factory in August completely rebuilt to a new standard, with a nacelle similar to, but longer than, that of Egerton's S.35, and with the engine raised, the chassis shortened, the gap reduced and the span increased to 52 ft. The new wing extensions were set at a slight dihedral angle and braced by kingposts and wires instead of struts. The tailplane and rear elevator were enlarged and set

Commander Samson in rebuilt S.34 at Dover in September 1912. (*Courtesy G. S. Leslie.*)

high, with twin rectangular rudders below, and the front elevator, though carried on the original booms, was much smaller than before. The rudders carried the Naval serial *2* already allotted in June (originally as *T.2*, while S.34 became *T.1* at the same time). In its revised form, S.38 was first flown, with a 70 hp Gnome, by Samson on 30 August, when it climbed to 1,000 ft in eight minutes and subsequently took off with two passengers in addition to the pilot. Thus rebuilt, S.38 became the prototype of a new production series, the 'S.38-type', whose works numbers ran from S.54 to S.62. In the production version the wing extensions were slightly tapered (the leading edge being swept back), the front elevator booms were deleted and the elevator was carried on an outrigger on the nose of the nacelle. S.54 was first flown on 4 November by Lieut Wilfred Parke and received the Naval serial *19* on acceptance; the next two became *28* and *34* and were followed by S.57–8 and S.60–1, serials *62–65*; all these were retained at Eastchurch by the Naval Flying School, but S.62, built in March 1913, was delivered on 19 July to the C.F.S., Upavon, as *446*; it was from this machine that on 3 October, 1913,

S.62 at Hendon *en route* to Farnborough in July 1913. (*Flight.*)

61

Major Merrick fell to his death through not being strapped in during a steep dive; S.59 remained Short Brothers' property for a time and was occasionally flown by Maurice Egerton and others. In July 1913 the S.38-type's landing gear was revised to the latest Henry Farman pattern, comprising two separate units, each with a short skid and two wheels on a short rubber-sprung cross-axle. The earlier machines were revised as they came in for repair and overhaul, and both *1* and *2* had acquired paired wheels and full dual controls by

Winston Churchill and his flying instructor, Capt Wildman Lushington, in S.38 at the Naval Flying School, Eastchurch, in November 1913.

29 November, 1913, when Winston Churchill, First Lord of the Admiralty, paid one of his frequent visits to Eastchurch and was given nearly an hour's flying lesson in *2*; unfortunately his instructor, Capt G. V. Wildman Lushington, was killed three days later when his Maurice Farman side-slipped out of control while coming in to land. Both *1* and *2* remained in regular use at the Naval Flying School at least until August 1914 and probably for several months later. Another veteran was S.28, already once rebuilt after being wrecked by Seddon in January 1912 while still on loan from McClean, which was further modified into an S.38-type without front elevator, as the 'Eastchurch Gun Machine', serial *66*; this was used for armament trials with a Maxim machine-gun pivoted on a pillar on the nacelle nose, while the pilot occupied the rear cockpit; *66* was first flown on 24 September, 1913, and remained in service for over two years, being shown to Winston Churchill when he visited Eastchurch on 15 May, 1915.

Two other types of pusher biplane deserve notice. One was a startling metamorphosis of the original Triple-Twin, S.39, which reappeared on test by Sydney Pickles on 24 July, 1913, as a neat two-seat tandem pusher without a front elevator. It had constant-chord wings of improved profile with struts

S.39, formerly the Triple-Twin, rebuilt as a pusher (RNAS *3*) at Eastchurch in 1914.

of oval steel tube and the landing gear and tail unit of a late production S.38-type, with balanced rounded rudders; it still retained its original serial *3*, which was almost its only link with the past. Lighter in weight than a standard S.38-type, it had a very lively performance, with a top speed of 65 mph and the then exceptional rate of climb of over 600 ft/min; its ceiling was better than 9,000 ft. It was a favourite mount of Samson's, and he used to fly it at night; he took Winston Churchill up in it during his visit to Eastchurch on 24–25 October, 1913. Finally, it joined the scratch squadron which Samson took to Flanders early in the war and was based at Poperinghe in October 1914, but was never armed and only used as a communications hack. The second pusher variant was a 'sociable' version of the S.38-type, with side-by-side seats and full dual controls in a single cockpit; two of this type first flew in the spring of 1914 and had probably been rebuilt from McClean's S.33 and Egerton's S.35; they were taken on charge by the Naval Flying School as *152* and *190* and had 80 hp Gnome engines; a third was flown as a test-bed for a four-cylinder Austro-Daimler engine of 90 hp and may have been built new as S.67; its serial was *145*. In September 1914, *152* was sent to Great Yarmouth for coast patrol duties; it crashed there soon after arrival, but was apparently rebuilt and returned to service at Eastchurch, where it remained till 1916. Of the production S.38s, *19* was Winston Churchill's mount during his visit to Eastchurch in May 1915; *28* visited Great Yarmouth in June 1913 and was still flying at Eastchurch in 1916; *34* specialised in bombing and armament training, and *62*, having survived many rebuilds after crashes, was still in service at Eastchurch in 1916. In September 1913, *64* and *65* took part in the Army manoeuvres, being based at Lilbourne, near Rugby, where *3* was also flown. In June 1914, *65* was converted into a twin-float seaplane and equipped with a retractable version of the Gregory–Riley–White beaching gear for experiments at the Isle of Grain; *62* to *65* inclusive were all fitted with balanced rudders when they entered service.

Early in 1913 Frank McClean and an explorer, J. H. Spottiswoode, decided to organise a seaplane expedition up the River Nile to see the Aswan Dam and

Frank McClean's S.32 rebuilt with wings of 70½ ft span, at Eastchurch in May 1913.

investigate the cataracts between there and Khartoum. Realising that high power and low wing-loading were essential for take-off in the hot Sudanese climate, McClean had his old school biplane S.32 rebuilt to the S.38-type standard, but with an extra bay inserted on each side in both upper and lower wings, increasing the span to 70 ft 6 in; the extra bay and overhung extension formed a single unit, with dihedral and taper on both upper and lower wings. This machine, though intended as a seaplane ultimately, was first flown at Eastchurch in May 1913 as a landplane, using its original two-wheeled cross-axle undercarriage and a 70 hp Gnome engine; it seems to have incorporated components discarded from other early biplanes, including S.33 and S.34,

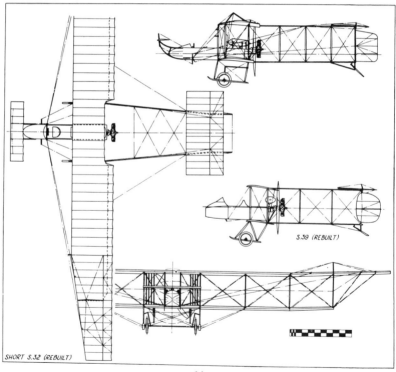

S.39 (REBUILT)

SHORT S.32 (REBUILT)

which has confused its provenance, but it evidently contained more parts from S.32 than from elsewhere. With a wing-loading of little more than 2 lb/sq ft, it flew easily but was very slow and could make no headway against any appreciable wind, so it was obviously unfit for development, even with twice the power; furthermore, its tandem nacelle provided too little stowage space for the expedition's needs. So McClean ordered a new seaplane specially designed for the purpose, with a wide nacelle having two pairs of seats side-by-side; this was the Nile Seaplane, S.80. It had constant-chord wings of 67 ft span, 5 ft chord and 5 ft 3 in gap, with strut-braced extensions, parallel ailerons and folding gear; to clear the uprights in the tail-boom structure when folded, the upper wings had small hinged flaps in the trailing edge resembling inset ailerons. The two-row 160 hp Gnome engine drove a massive two-bladed propeller, and the two main pontoon floats were carried on three pairs of struts beneath the nacelle; twin air-bags were attached under the lower tail-booms, and these were far enough apart to render wing-tip floats unnecessary for lateral stability on the water.

(*Left*) Frank McClean and Alec Ogilvie in the Nile Seaplane, February 1914; (*right*) Gordon Bell at Eastchurch in 1914. (*Courtesy J. H. Blake.*)

S.80 was first flown as a seaplane at Leysdown on 2 October, 1913, by Gordon Bell; on 19 November, with Frank McClean as pilot, it proved its weight-lifting ability by taking off from Harty Ferry with Alec Ogilvie, Horace Short, Charles Samson and Ivor Courtney as passengers. McClean asked Samson to be his co-pilot on the Nile venture so as to have at least one Gnome expert in the crew, but Samson could not get leave, and Ogilvie took his place. S.80 was shipped to Alexandria in the *Corsican Prince*; it arrived on

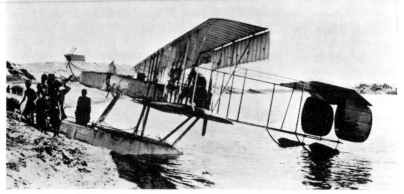

S.80 beached for engine repairs during Frank McClean's flight up the Nile in 1914.

27 December and was re-erected at the Naval Dockyard by McClean, Ogilvie and Horace Short and their mechanic Gus Smith, assisted by Anna McClean, who had charge of the party's domestic affairs. On 2 January, 1914, the sea-plane was launched by being carried bodily into the water by a gang of Dock-yard workers, and next day McClean, Ogilvie, Horace Short and Smith flew the 160 miles to Cairo in just under three hours, but this was the limit of its range, and Spottiswoode had to lay down fuel dumps at 120-mile intervals all along the route, which fortunately kept close to the railway except for the gap between Wadi Halfa and Aswan. After a few days the party started off again, but soon began to have trouble with overheating of the rear bank of cylinders, and after take-off from the Aswan Dam the performance fell off so quickly in the first 40 miles that McClean returned to the Dam, mostly on the water, and the engine was found to require four new cylinders; these were cabled for from Paris, and a fresh start was made on 16 February, when the seaplane flew 192 miles up-river to Wadi Halfa, on the Sudan frontier. From there McClean had been recommended to follow the railway direct across the desert to Abu Hamed, substituting wheels for floats, but he preferred to stay with the river round the Dongola Bend in order to see the second, third and fourth cataracts. After two days' rest the seaplane was flown, with two refuelling stops, 245 miles to Argo, where McClean found they were being pursued by a gigantic 'haboob' and had to alight abruptly, breaking off the port lower wing-tip. This was patched up and the flight continued to Merowe, where the Governor of Dongola Province, Col Jackson, entertained the party in royal style; after several more stops with minor engine trouble they reached Abu Hamed, but an hour (45 miles) later an oil pump broke and they had to come down on the rock-strewn river and taxi three miles to Shereik, where they beached and encamped till a spare pump could be sent from Atbara by rail to Shereik station, six miles away. Next day they had flown for only an hour when both oil pumps failed together, and in the ensuing 'dead-stick' landing one float and two of its struts were damaged; local tribesmen beached the

66

machine near Gananita Island, with a station only three miles away, and the Sudan Railway sent a wagon-load of spares from Atbara, together with a carpenter and a mechanic. After ten days the engine had been rebuilt and damage to the floats and tail-booms repaired; they left Gananita on 14 March and arrived at Atbara in under an hour, but next day, after flying a similar distance to Kabushia, a connecting-rod broke and wrecked the engine, which had to be taken out yet again and sent back to the railway workshops at Atbara. On 22 March they took off once more, and this time, with the help of a strong tailwind, reached Khartoum in under two hours; after a day giving joy-rides at Khartoum S.80 was dismantled and crated for return to England via Port Sudan and the Suez Canal, somewhat to the relief of all concerned.

At Eastchurch it was found that the centreplane top rear spar was fractured, so the seaplane was extensively rebuilt, with new wings, new tail-booms slightly convergent in plan (bringing the rudders closer together) and a new tailplane of reduced chord. The front elevator (which McClean agreed did no useful work but was there 'for company' at his request) was removed and the nacelle was revised to a dual-control Sociable layout, with the fuel tank

S.79 in its final form as dual-control trainer *905* at Grain in 1915. (*Major W. G. Moore.*)

lowered into the space formerly occupied by the two rear seats. There was a proposal to adapt S.80 as a torpedo-carrier for H.M.S. *Hermes*, but this plan was dropped; McClean flew it again for the first time at Harty Ferry on 13 July, and later made several trips with passengers to Westgate and back. Finally, when war was seen to be imminent, he flew it across to the Isle of Grain on 1 August as a gift to the Admiralty, and four days later was himself gazetted in the R.N.A.S. as a Flight Lieutenant, afterwards commanding the Naval Flying School at Eastchurch. In October 1914, S.80 was re-engined with a more reliable 100 hp Gnome-Monosoupape driving a four-bladed propeller, also acquiring a central rectangular fixed fin and larger rudders; it carried early Naval red circles on the wings but no other markings, although

S.32, finally converted to a standard 52-ft span trainer, at Hendon in 1915 as *904*.
(*Courtesy G. S. Leslie.*)

the serial *905* was allotted. It remained at Grain in 1915, but could not take off
from calm water in zero wind with its lower-powered engine, so it was only
used for seaplane practice by aeroplane pilots. McClean also presented his
70 hp wide-span S.32 to the Admiralty; this became *904* in the R.N.A.S., and
after being rebuilt with standard 52-ft-span wings and double landing wheels
was used as a trainer at Hendon.

S.81, with 1½-pounder Vickers gun, at Calshot during the Naval Review in July 1914.

Short Brothers' final pusher design was a twin-float seaplane, S.81, generally
similar to S.80, but with rubber-sprung floats (introduced by Oswald Short)
and a strengthened nacelle designed by the armament specialist Arthur
Camden Pratt to mount a 1½-pounder Vickers shell-firing gun. It was a
logical development of the Maxim-armed *66* and was ordered specifically for
aerial gunnery trials at Calshot by Lieut Clark-Hall. S.81 had a 160 hp Gnome
and four-bladed propeller, also wing-tip floats were provided because the

raised centre of gravity due to the gun increased the tendency to roll while moored out or taxying. S.81 was first flown in the spring of 1914 at Calshot; the gunnery trials were not very successful, and the gun was later passed to the R.F.C. for testing over land, but S.81 received the Naval serial *126* and took part in the Spithead Naval Review in July. Later it was sent to Great Yarmouth, where in March 1915 it was equipped with a 6-pounder Davis recoilless gun, with which scheduled trials were successfully completed in April, but this unwieldy weapon was not adopted for active service, being outclassed by the advent of synchronised machine-guns which could more

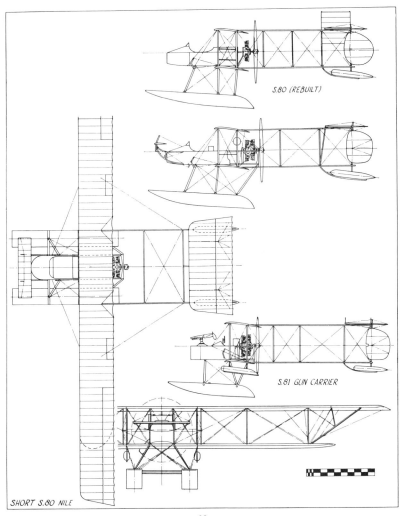

S.80 (REBUILT)

S.81 GUN CARRIER

SHORT S.80 NILE

effectively be installed in high-performance tractor biplanes. Although S.81 was the last pusher biplane built by Short Brothers, the S.38-type dual-control school biplane was produced by sub-contractors throughout 1914 and 1915, 12 being built by Pemberton-Billing Ltd at the Supermarine works at Woolston, Southampton, and 24 by White & Thompson Ltd and their successors The Norman Thompson Flight Co Ltd at Middleton-on-Sea, Bognor, Sussex; the last were delivered in June 1916, and all were flown at the Eastchurch and Chingford Naval Flying Schools until superseded by Avro 504s.

Production-type S.38 trainer built by Norman Thompson Flight Co in 1915.
(*Courtesy G. S. Leslie.*)

S.26–28 (original)—Span 34 ft 2 in (10·3 m); length 40 ft 6 in (12·3 m); area 480 sq ft (44·6 m²); empty weight 1,000 lb (454 kg); loaded weight, 1,400 lb (635 kg); speed 40 mph (62·9 km/h).

S.29, S.32–35, S.38, S.43–44—Span 46 ft 5 in (14·1 m); length 42 ft 1 in (12·8 m); area 517 sq ft (48 m²); empty weight 1,100 lb (500 kg); loaded weight 1,540 lb (700 kg); speed—50 hp Gnome, 39 mph (62·8 km/h); 70 hp Gnome, 45 mph (72·5 km/h).

Standard S.38-type—Span 52 ft (15·84 m); length 35 ft 6 in (10·8 m); area 500 sq ft (46·5 m²); empty weight 1,050 lb (476 kg); loaded weight 1,500 lb (680 kg); speed 58 mph (93·4 km/h); duration 5 hr.

S.32 (rebuilt)—Span 70 ft 6 in (21·5 m); length 35 ft 6 in (10·8 m); area 725 sq ft (67·4 m²); loaded weight 1,540 lb (700 kg); speed 38 mph (62·6 km/h).

S.39 (rebuilt)—Span 52 ft (15·84 m); length 29 ft (8·85 m); area 500 sq ft (46·5 m²); empty weight 1,000 lb (454 kg); loaded weight 1,500 lb (680 kg); speed 65 mph (104·6 km/h).

S.80–81—Span 67 ft (20·4 m); length 33 ft 9 in (10·2 m); area 540 sq ft (50·2 m²); empty weight 2,200 lb (1,000 kg); loaded weight 3,600 lb (1,635 kg); speed 60 mph (96·6 km/h).

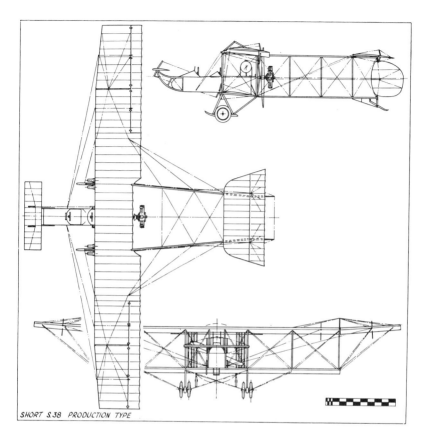

SHORT S.38 PRODUCTION TYPE

Postscript. As this book went to press, confirmation arrived from Mr Gascoyne (formerly of the E.N.V. Co.), via Mr H. F. Cowley, that the French-built 60 hp E.N.V. engine (Type F, series 1, No. 4), discovered in 1964, was indeed the engine originally installed in S.27 and flown by Cecil Grace at Wolverhampton and Bournemouth in 1910. This engine had been stored since 1914 at the Chequers Inn, Eltham, Kent, and was in running condition when found by a Mr Tagg. Only British-built E.N.V.s were eligible for the de Forest competition, and it was one of the first of these that was lost in Grace's S.29; two others were installed in T. O. M. Sopwith's winning Howard Wright and in Grahame-White's unlucky Bristol Boxkite.

71

Close-up view of S.39 in its original form with equal-span wings; Eastchurch, September 1911.

Short Twin-Engined Biplanes (1911–13)

Short Brothers were not the originators of the twin-engined aeroplane, as has sometimes been claimed, for both Hiram Maxim in 1894 and Clément Ader in 1897 had used two steam engines, because they needed twice the output of the only available power units; for the same reason Col Capper installed two 12 hp Buchet engines in the Dunne D.4 in 1908 and J. W. Seddon used two N.E.C.s in his fantastic steel-tube tandem biplane in 1910; neither of these left the ground, but on 27 September, 1910, Roger Sommer made the first successful twin-engined flight in a biplane of his own design. About the same time Horace Short, in his search for better controllability at low speeds, conceived the idea of placing all the control surfaces in the slipstream and took out a master patent, No. 1,223 of January 1911, covering all practicable arrangements, including outboard airscrews in front of the ailerons and a central airscrew or propeller ahead of the tail surfaces. As a first application of the principle, he designed and built a variant of the S.27-type with two engines which could be shut down independently; this biplane, S.39, could maintain flight on either one of its two engines and was thus the first example in the world of twin engines being used to enhance safety.

S.39 was structurally the same as the improved Farman-Sommer-type Short biplane of 1911 apart from the nacelle and power plant arrangement; it had a stronger chassis laterally braced by struts, three rudders below the tailplane and a front elevator carried on inset pivots by booms pitched closer together than normal. The nacelle contained a cockpit with two seats side-by-side and carried a 50 hp Gnome engine and propeller on a standard overhung pusher mounting at the back; another 50 hp Gnome was mounted at the front, rotating in the opposite direction so that gyroscopic moments cancelled out when both engines were running. The forward engine drove two wing-mounted tractor airscrews through Wright-type Renold chain gears, the port chain being crossed to obtain counter-rotation, and the 'bent-end' airscrews were exactly like those made for the Short-Wright biplanes. S.39, known as the Triple-Twin, was first flown on 18 September, 1911, by Frank McClean; he made a brief solo flight, then, with Samson as passenger, flew eight wide circuits of Eastchurch aerodrome, throttling back each engine in turn and experiencing for the first time the luxury of an ample speed range while flying a level course. The effect of the outboard slipstream on lateral control was not up to Horace Short's expectations, but he was pleased with the Triple-Twin's overall performance and next decided to try the effect of co-axial

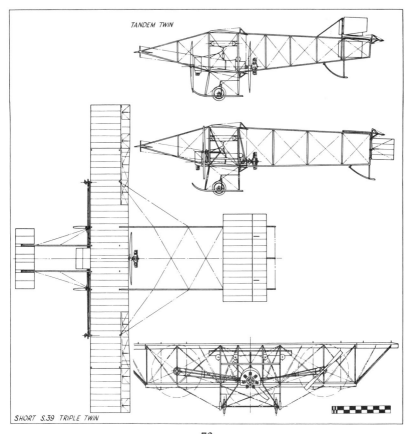

TANDEM TWIN

SHORT S.39 TRIPLE TWIN

Frank McClean about to start in the Tandem-Twin S.27.

counter-rotation on stability. The first step was to convert Cecil Grace's old S.27 to a similar twin-engined layout, but with the front engine direct-coupled to an airscrew, as shown in patent No. 22,675 of 1911.

This version was called the Tandem-Twin, or, less formally, the *Gnome Sandwich*, and retained the original S.27 wings and cambered tail unit unchanged except for the addition of two extra top rudders. The chassis was strengthened in the same way as for S.39, and the existing front elevator and booms were retained, since they allowed adequate clearance for the central airscrew. The Tandem-Twin was flown by McClean on 29 October, 1911, without any preliminary taxying; after a short flight at 100 ft he landed and expressed even more satisfaction than with the Triple-Twin; he spent the rest of the day taking up various passengers to test their reactions to the slipstream and to the location of the rear propeller only 10 in behind their heads. The draught in the cockpit was quite powerful and the Tandem-Twin soon acquired yet another soubriquet—*The Vacuum Cleaner*—and was credited with the ability 'to pull the hairs out of a fur coat'; this was mainly due to the

S.39 after its first revision, with extended upper wing but original fuel system. (*Flight.*)

open hole in the floor, which was the only means of access. The Tandem-Twin could maintain height with either engine throttled back, but was unstable in every direction, due to insufficient aileron power and to unpredictable variations in torque reaction with the rear propeller working in the wake of the front one. Horace Short investigated this effect very thoroughly and deduced design rules for the relative diameters and pitches of tandem airscrews which were still valid 20 years later.

He also designed a larger biplane with two central engines of 120 hp each, driving four propellers arranged in tandem pairs in the wings, with independent chain gears for the front and rear engines. He obtained a number of patents (Nos. 8,108, 8,394 and 22,750 of 1911) for co-axial and interconnected airscrews, but the four-screw aeroplane was never built; however, Maurice Egerton apparently had his S.35 biplane converted into a Triple-Twin and

S.39 in its later form, with four fuel tanks. (*Courtesy J. D. Oughton.*)

flew it regularly from April 1912 onwards. Both S.39 and S.27 were flown at first without wing extensions, and on 21 November, 1911, they were raced by Longmore and Gerrard respectively; both did better than 55 mph, but S.39 seemed to have the edge over S.27. In December, S.39 was fitted with extensions and double fuel capacity; in February 1912, S.39's extensions were removed and fitted to S.27, and in October 1912, S.39 was temporarily given equally extended upper and lower wings of 50 ft span, which further top extensions later increased to 64 ft. S.39 was purchased by the Admiralty in June 1912 and given serial *T3*, later simplified to *3*; in the spring of 1913 it was returned to the works for overhaul and completely remodelled as a two-seat tandem pusher with new wings and no front elevator, as already described. The Admiralty declined to buy the Tandem-Twin, which remained McClean's property (it was No. 11 in his private fleet list), but he lent it to the Naval Flying School without charge, and it was eventually crashed by Samson;

Egerton's S.35 appears to have been dismantled and probably formed the basis of one of the Sociables of early 1914. The final development of the triple-twin theme was the Triple-Tractor S.47, which is described in a later chapter.

Triple-Twin—Span 34 ft (10·3 m), later 50 ft (15·3 m); length 45 ft (13·7 m); area 435 sq ft (40·4 m²), later 500 sq ft (46·5 m²); empty weight 1,800 lb (816 kg); loaded weight 2,100 lb (953 kg); speed 55 mph (88·6 km/h).

Tandem-Twin—Span 34 ft 2 in (10·4 m), later 50 ft (15·3 m); area 480 sq ft (44·6 m²), later 517 sq ft (48 m²); otherwise as for Triple-Twin.

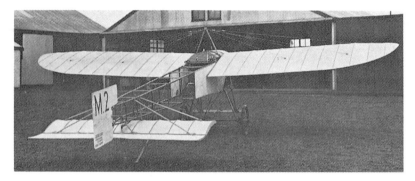

Monoplane *M2* at Eastchurch in 1912.

Early Short Monoplanes (1912)

In the summer of 1911 E. V. Sassoon's Universal Aviation Co Ltd of Brooklands produced their one and only monoplane, a close copy of the Blériot Type XI, from which it differed in appearance only in its semicircular elevators and the overhung mounting of its 50 hp Gnome rotary engine. It was flown in the *Daily Mail* Circuit of Britain race by H. J. D. Astley, who started well but dropped out at Harrogate. Later in the year it was entered for the 1911 British Michelin Cup competition, for which purpose it was fitted with a 40 hp water-cooled A.B.C. engine; it made only a brief appearance at Brooklands during October, again flown by Astley, and soon afterwards the firm went bankrupt and its assets were sold; the monoplane, by then nicknamed the *Birdling*, was bought by Frank McClean and taken to Eastchurch, where it became No. 9 in his private list. He had it overhauled and partly rebuilt by

Short Brothers, and with a new airscrew it was found to perform quite well. McClean lent it to the Naval Flying School, and Samson and Longmore began flying it regularly in November 1911. Samson was very keen on it, in spite of several shortcomings, but on 20 July, 1912, Spenser Grey taxied it across a rough patch and several longerons broke; its remains were deposited by Frank McClean on loan to the Science Museum, where a permanent aviation exhibition opened in January 1913.

Commander Samson about to take off from Eastchurch in *M2*. (*Courtesy C. F. Andrews.*)

Horace Short took note of Samson's early enthusiasm for the *Birdling*, and in January 1912 built a completely new 50 hp Gnome-engined monoplane of similar but more robust design. The Short monoplane had warping wings of the Blériot pattern and a rectangular cambered tailplane with a rear-hinged elevator. The engine was in line with the leading edge of the wing on an over-hung mounting attached to a strong rigid chassis, with truncated skids carry-ing a pair of wheels on a rubber-sprung cross-axle; the rear fuselage carried a long sprung tail skid and the rudder was square with a small forward balance area. It was first flown by Samson on 24 February, 1912; he remained up for an hour and reported on landing that it needed no adjustments; his speed at 1,400 ft was 65 mph. At first it was flown with the rear fuselage uncovered, in the usual Blériot style, and was allotted the temporary Naval serial *M2*, which was painted on the rudder. It was taken to Weymouth for the Naval Review in May 1912, and Samson flew it from the flying field at Lodmoor on 4 and 6 May, but damaged it on landing after the second flight; it had by then had its rear fuselage covered, and this may have altered its handling. It was repaired at Eastchurch and was flying there again on 9 July, with Lieut Gordon at the controls; it was again flown on 14 September, by Wilfred Parke; after then no more is heard of it and it was probably condemned, along with the *Birdling*, not because of the 'monoplane ban', which did not apply to Naval pilots, but rather because of a general mistrust of warping wings as speeds increased. It is believed to have been allotted serial *14* in the November 1912 numbering scheme.

The second monoplane built by Short Brothers was ordered by the Admir-alty as serial *12*, and was an extension of the earlier successful experiments

77

with twin engines and with deck launching. Unfortunately no drawings or photographs of it have survived, and available descriptions are sketchy. It had rigidly braced wings with ailerons, and was described as being intended 'for water work only', although all its recorded flights were made from land. The two 70 hp Gnome engines drove a tractor airscrew and a propeller, mounted, as in the Tandem-Twin biplane, at each end of a short nacelle containing a central cockpit with two seats side-by-side; both occupants were exposed to a fierce castor-oil-laden slipstream, which soon earned the mono-plane the nickname of *Double-Dirty*. The tail surfaces were mounted on open braced booms of normal pusher type, and the landing gear carried stream-lined pneumatic flotation bags, which, however, would not have permitted take-off from the sea; thus the intention must have been to fly it off a runway on board ship, as had been so successfully demonstrated with S.38. Samson flew the *Double-Dirty* for the first time on 21 October, 1912, and made two more flights on the 23rd, with E. Featherstone Briggs as passenger on the last occasion. On 5 November Samson flew it to Isle of Grain, where he landed and flew back to Eastchurch the same day; he flew it twice more that week, but then it went back into the works for modification and seems not to have reappeared or been accepted for Naval service. No doubt the modifications to

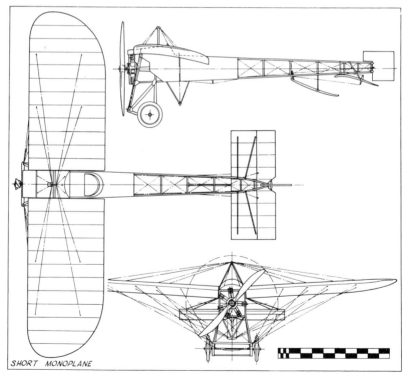

SHORT MONOPLANE

suit it for stowage aboard ship included the provision of folding wings (patent No. 16,973 of 1913), and it seems to have been Short Brothers' counterpart of the Bristol-Burney hydrovane flying-boat, with the same operational requirements in view. Horace Short's own interest in hydrovanes is shown by patents Nos. 22,407 and 22,408 of 1911, but his proposal to scoop up water into an aft ballast tank while alighting, to counteract the overturning moment of the front hydrovanes, seems to have been more ingenious than practical.

Span 29 ft 3 in (8·9 m); length 25 ft (7·6 m); area 165 ft (15·4 m²); weights not recorded; speed 55 mph (88·6 km/h); no data available for Twin Monoplane.

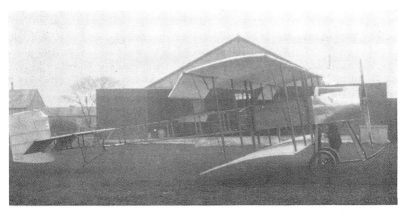

S.36 as originally built with open rear fuselage. (*Courtesy C. F. Andrews.*)

Short Tractor Biplanes (1910–12)

After flying a Blériot monoplane at the Blackpool meeting in 1910, Cecil Grace asked Horace Short to consider developing a tractor biplane having a comparable performance, and work was begun in December on a tractor version of the S.27-type, with a 60 hp E.N.V. engine, allotted works No. S.32. Then Grace had flown to his death in the de Forest contest and S.32 was completed as a normal pusher training biplane. From January to July 1911 Frank McClean was absent from Eastchurch on the Fiji eclipse expedition, but on his return Horace Short showed him a revised design for a 70 hp Gnome-engined tractor biplane, and McClean ordered one for his private use. Details of the geometry were discussed at some length, and Horace Short insisted that the thrust and drag should be made to coincide so as to minimise change of trim with engine on or off, using a flat tailplane, so he located the fuselage midway between the wings. The biplane, S.36, was finished late in 1911, and McClean flew it for the first time, very successfully, on 10 January, 1912.

As built, S.36 had standard two-bay wings with strut-braced extensions on the upper wing and no bottom ailerons. The middle bay struts embraced the

79

fuselage sides and there was a central gap in the lower wing. The fuselage was a simple square-section wire-braced girder of four straight longerons, converging slightly from nose to tail, with plywood covering along the sides of the two tandem cockpits and aluminium panels enclosing the tanks and overhung engine mounting; a simple twin-skid chassis, with two wheels on a rubber-sprung cross-axle, was carried by the bottom longerons between the wing leading edge and the engine front bracket. The non-lifting tailplane carried divided elevators, and a partly balanced rectangular rudder was hinged to the vertical sternpost; there was a sprung trailing tailskid, and the rear fuselage was at first left uncovered, as in the Blériot monoplane. With a 9-ft airscrew, S.36 had a quick take-off and a speed of 60 mph. McClean immediately lent it to the Naval Flying School, and on 11 March, 1912, Lieut Longmore, with his mechanic, E. R. A. O'Connor, as passenger, flew it 172 miles in four hours, thereby winning the Royal Navy Mortimer Singer prize of £500. S.36 was intended only as an experiment, and was not offered for sale to the Admiralty, who were sufficiently impressed to order two more tractor biplanes, suitable for use from either land or water by exchange of landing gear. One was to have a 100 hp two-row Gnome engine and the other a 70 hp Gnome like S.36. The larger of these, S.41, was completed in March 1912, and there is some evidence to show that two separate fuselages were supplied for it, one with wheels and the other with twin floats. Its first flight, on wheels, was made by Samson on 2 April, 1912, with a more extended flight on 5 April, when he reached 60 mph without difficulty.

Apart from its more robust engine mounting, with front cross-bearer and round-topped cowl, S.41 was generally similar to S.36, except that the fuselage was slightly lower relative to the wings; this increased the ground clearance of the lower wing; as built, both the upper and lower centre-sections were open. S.41 was next converted into a seaplane, with two main floats pitched fairly close together and three streamlined air-bags, one under each wing-tip and one under the rear fuselage. The main floats were plain pontoons (steps were tried briefly but soon abandoned) and were placed well forward with a flat board between them to protect the airscrew. After satisfactory water take-off and alighting trials at Shellness, S.41 was flown to Sheerness, hoisted aboard H.M.S. *Hibernia* and taken to Weymouth for the Naval Review; on arrival on 3 May, Samson was lowered overboard in it and flew to a slipway at Portland, whence Longmore flew it on test next day; on 6 May Samson flew out 12 miles to meet the Fleet and escorted the flagship into Weymouth bay. There is no evidence that S.41 ever flew off the runway on *Hibernia*, which was used only by S.38, although the spare (wheeled) fuselage was available on board. On 10 May S.41 was hoisted aboard *Hibernia* and stowed on the runway ahead of S.38 and the ship sailed for Sheerness that night; early next morning, off Dover, Samson and S.41 were once more hoisted out and he took off, but had to come down off Westgate with engine trouble, being then taken in tow to Sheerness by the torpedo-boat *Recruit*.

Meanwhile the second Naval tractor biplane, S.45, had been completed and,

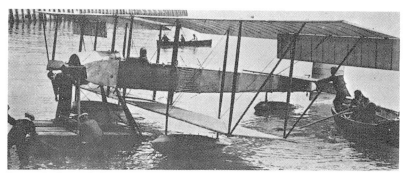

Commander Samson in S.41 at Dover on 13 July, 1912, during his flight from Portsmouth to Harwich.

profiting from Samson's experience with S.41, both S.45 and McClean's S.36 had their fuselages rigged lower, so as to increase wing-tip ground clearance; at this stage both had their rear fuselages covered with fabric, to increase directional stability, particularly necessary if floats were to be fitted. S.45 had two fewer ribs in each wing than S.36, so that its span was slightly less and the ailerons were set farther inboard. The extension struts were attached to the top end ribs of S.45, which was almost the only visible difference from S.36 after the fuselage modifications. S.45 was first flown as a landplane by Lieut Spenser Grey on 24 May, 1912, and he twice flew to Margate and back with Lieut Sheppard as passenger on 30 and 31 May. On acceptance, S.45 received the serial *T5* and continued to carry this even after conversion to a seaplane, when officially the serial should have become *H5*.

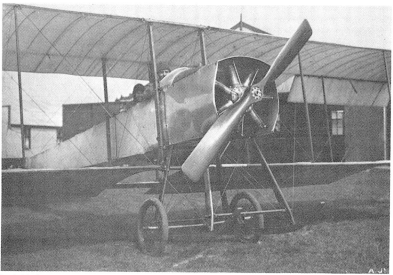

Frank McClean and his sister Anna in S.36 at Eastchurch in 1912; the rear fuselage has been covered and set lower relative to the wings.

81

On 3 June, 1912, having had an engine overhaul, S.41 was flown by Samson from Burntwick Island, Sheerness, to Harwich, to explore the Orwell and Stour estuaries and decide on the best site for a new seaplane station; after inspecting Shotley and Mistley, Samson recommended the Suffolk shore between Felixstowe Dock and Landguard Point, and this was how the Felixstowe Air Station, afterwards for so many years the home of the Marine Aircraft Experimental Establishment, originated. Samson flew back to Sheerness without incident on 14 June and then supervised the installation of a float chassis on S.45, which was in the works being repaired after a forced landing in fog. S.45 was given a single central pontoon, again with no step, and was stabilised at rest by two streamlined air-bags set low under the inner pair of wing struts. The main float was long enough to keep the seaplane's tail clear of the water, and the original tailskid was left *in situ*, but later an air-bag was packed close under the rear fuselage to prevent the tail being submerged while on tow. When tested at the end of June by Samson, S.45 reached 62 mph as a seaplane, while carrying a passenger.

S.45 at Portsmouth during the Naval Review in July 1912.

During this time McClean had been engaged in a maritime exercise of his own in S.36. On 17 June he flew to Eastbourne to attempt to photograph the submerged wreck of the P & O liner *Oceana*, which had sunk off Beachy Head. After a few trial runs he took off on 21 June with photographer Charles Cusden of *The Sphere* in the rear cockpit and made successive passes over the wreck at 900 ft, 700 ft, 500 ft and finally 300 ft; in the last run his airscrew picked up a little blown spray but was not damaged. He started home on 2 July, but flew into rain and fog, so he landed at his family home near Tunbridge Wells, the biplane returning to Eastchurch by road. The wings were found to be so waterlogged that they had to be renewed, but McClean was flying S.36 again by 21 July.

Both S.41 and S.45 were flown to Portsmouth for the Naval Review in July. Samson, flying solo in S.41, covered the 194 miles round the coast from Eastchurch to Eastney in 195 minutes, most of the way at 2,000 ft.

S.45 being beached at Eastney on 5 July, 1912, after being flown from Sheerness by Lieuts Spenser Grey and Sheppard. (*Courtesy G. S. Leslie.*)

Spenser Grey and Sheppard on S.45 had to alight at Newhaven for engine adjustments, but were not much delayed. Both flew over the Fleet on 9 July, and on 13 July Samson flew S.41 back to Dover, moored in the harbour overnight and, with E. R. A. O'Connor as passenger, flew on to Harwich next day, a total distance of 250 miles. On the strength of these performances, the Admiralty ordered two more 100 hp Gnome tractor seaplanes, with minor improvements but substantially similar to S.41. The 70 hp seaplane was not so successful, and on 25 July reappeared on wheels, when Spenser Grey flew it to Dover, returning to Eastchurch next day. Although its single-row engine was reliable by current standards, its single float made it difficult to handle on the water. The next line of experiment was the S.47 Triple-Tractor with two separate 50 hp Gnomes mounted in tandem in a tractor fuselage extended forward, with the front engine driving a direct-coupled airscrew and the rear engine, facing backwards so as to rotate the opposite way, driving wing-

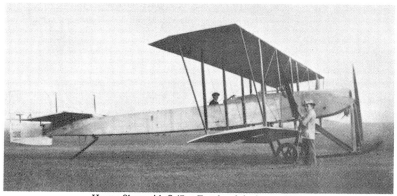

Horace Short with S.47 at Eastchurch in August 1912.

83

mounted, counter-rotating airscrews through Wright-type chain gears; the Triple-Tractor had a single cockpit with two seats side-by-side. Frank McClean flew S.47 for the first time on 24 July, 1912, and Lieut C. J. L'Estrange Malone flew its official acceptance tests on 22 August, when it received serial *T4*. It performed well apart from its propensity for generating heat under its 16 ft long cowling, which earned it the soubriquet of *Field Kitchen*. It was used for a variety of experiments, including the early trials of the first Rouzet wireless transmitter, whose signals were picked up at a range of 30 miles.

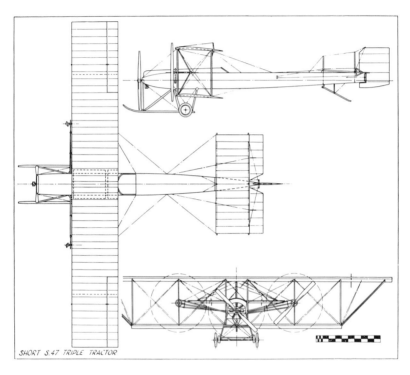

SHORT S.47 TRIPLE TRACTOR

On returning to Sheerness from Harwich on 27 August, after another of Samson's coastal survey flights, S.41 was converted to a landplane for participation in the Army autumn manoeuvres in East Anglia. All three of the Naval Short tractors took part, Samson on S.41 setting out first on 5 September, but having to land near Bishop's Stortford with engine trouble. Malone left Eastchurch in S.47 on 7 September and arrived before Samson at the rendezvous at Hardwicke, near Cambridge; finally, Gordon flew S.45 to Hardwicke on the 13th, and all three returned to Eastchurch on the 20th. The Triple-Tractor then went into the works for overhaul and the other two for modification and reconversion to seaplanes. S.41 emerged with little visible change

S.45, with revised wings and cockpit coaming, at Carlingnose in October 1912
shortly before capsizing.

except that its wings could now be folded back alongside the fuselage to econo-
mise deck or hangar space; the gaps in the upper and lower centreplanes were
filled in and the rudder carried the new serial *10*. S.45, however, was more
drastically altered; the wings did not fold, but now had compensated ailerons
acting up as well as down, and the extensions were braced by wires and king-
posts instead of struts. The floats were unchanged, but the engine cowling
was square-framed at the front, continuing the line of the fuselage longerons,
with local bulges in the panels to afford clearance for the engine; a faired
coaming was added to the top decking around the two cockpits, and the
rudder carried the simplified serial *5*. In this form S.45 became the prototype
of three similar landplanes with dual controls (S.48–50), ordered by the War
Office for use at the newly established Central Flying School at Upavon on
Salisbury Plain. Both S.41 and S.45 were shipped to Carlingnose, near
Rosyth on the Firth of Forth, which was opened as a temporary Naval Air
Station on 2 October; it was not a good location for a seaplane base, and on
4 October, *5* capsized on landing after a flight by Lieut Gordon; it was towed
ashore for repairs, but is not recorded as having flown again.

S.49 at Eastchurch in January 1913 before delivery to the Central Flying School.

85

On 10 October Capt Gerrard ferried S.48, serial *413*, from Farnborough to Upavon, and it was flown on each of the next two days by Capt J. M. Salmond, who found it rather underpowered by C.F.S. standards. Nevertheless, it was flown fairly regularly, and on 28 November Lieut Smith Barry took it up to 7,000 ft, but this minor triumph was short-lived, for on 3 December Lieut Hubbard, with a passenger, stalled while approaching to land and wrecked it completely, though without injury to themselves. The other two S.45s already ordered arrived at Upavon in February 1913; Gerrard ferried *424* from Farnborough on the 17th in a gale and, after a good landing in difficult conditions, had the misfortune to be overturned by a gust while taxying in; he was luckier when he brought in *423* on 22 February, and this was used for instruction for about a month, but then disappears from the record. Then, to the surprise and confusion of historians, both *423* and *424* returned to service in the spring of 1914, but had become B.E.8s! This was an example of a trick of War Office accounting which permitted the identity of an aeroplane to be vested in its original engine, regardless of the extent of 'repairs' made to its airframe, and was a subterfuge to which Col Seely resorted to avert a scandal when called to account in Parliament by Joynson-Hicks and other M.P.s over the alleged deficiency of service-

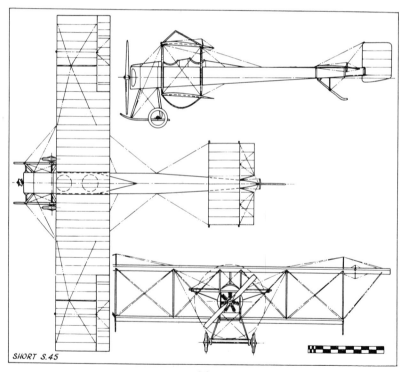

SHORT S.45

86

able aircraft available to the Royal Flying Corps. The two Short tractors, *423* and *424*, having donated their identities and Gnome engines to two new Royal Aircraft Factory-built B.E.8 airframes, became surplus to War Office requirements; they were transferred to the Admiralty in August 1914 and, repaired and re-engined with 100 hp Clerget rotaries, flew again at Eastchurch as *1268* and *1279*. No more Short tractor biplanes were built primarily as landplanes until the Bombers of 1915–16, and for the remaining years of peace all new Short designs were seaplanes.

S.41 as a landplane with experimental folding wings at Eastchurch in November 1913.
(Courtesy J. H. Blake.)

S.36—Span 46 ft 5 in (14·1 m); length 35 ft 6 in (10·8 m); area 515 sq ft (47·9 m²); empty weight 850 lb (380 kg); loaded weight, 1,300 lb (590 kg); speed 60 mph (96·6 km/h).

S.41—Span 50 ft (15·3 m); length 36 ft 6 in (11·15 m) as landplane, 39 ft (11·9 m) as seaplane; area 450 sq ft (41·8 m²); empty weight 1,100 lb (500 kg); loaded weight 1,600 lb (726 kg); speed 60 mph (96·6 km/h); duration 5 hr.

S.45, S.48–50—Span 42 ft (12·8 m); length 35 ft 6 in (10·8 m); area 450 sq ft (41·8 m²); empty weight 1,080 lb (490 kg); loaded weight 1,500 lb (680 kg); speed 60 mph (96·6 km/h).

S.47 Triple-Tractor—Span 48 ft (14·6 m); length 41 ft (12·5 m); area 500 sq ft (46·5 m²); weights not recorded; speed 60 mph (96·6 km/h).

RNAS *20* coming ashore at Great Yarmouth during trials of the G.R.W. beaching gear in July 1914.

Short Tractor Seaplanes (1912–14)

When Winston Churchill became First Lord of the Admiralty in the autumn of 1911 the Royal Naval Air Service already existed in embryo, but lacked the means and authority to achieve legitimate birth. The Admiralty had opted three years earlier to spend all its available resources on a rigid airship, leaving no provision for aviation in the naval estimates. The *Mayfly*, built at Barrow-in-Furness, had come to grief before it ever left its dock, and only the munificence of Frank McClean (through the Royal Aero Club) and the voluntary services of George Cockburn had combined to make free flying instruction available to the first four Naval volunteer pilots. The value of aeroplanes to the Navy had been conclusively proved by April 1912, when the first all-service Royal Flying Corps, with Naval and Military Wings, came into being. Although both Wings combined to operate the Central Flying School at Upavon, the Naval Flying School at Eastchurch was allowed to continue in parallel, with a strong emphasis on experimental flying and fleet co-operation. By the end of 1912 the feasibility of seaplanes had been accepted, and, when the Weymouth Review ended, the Board of Admiralty authorised the purchase of no fewer than 25 new seaplanes, an unprecedented expansion at that date. Not all were to be of British origin, but the products of Short Brothers had shown their merit and were hardly challenged at home except by Sopwith, who was a newcomer to the industry. So Eastchurch works became steadily busier, and the demand was almost exclusively for twin-float seaplanes, strongly advocated by Horace Short.

The Short S.41, serial *10*, had put up some notable performances in the hands of Charles Samson, and two more of the same type had been ordered, as already stated. These differed visibly from S.41 only in having an improved wing section, king-posts instead of strut bracing for the extensions, double-acting ailerons with return cables, and smaller lateral floats at the extreme wing-tips. They were ready for test by Easter 1913 and were ferried from Harty Ferry to Isle of Grain after being flown and passed by Gordon Bell on 23 April; on acceptance there, they received serials *20* and *21*. Bell had become Short Brothers' first staff test pilot, though only part-time, in December 1912, when Frank McClean found this duty too exacting to be continued on an honorary basis. Bell remained a freelance pilot, filling in with ferrying and demonstration flights for other firms, but gave Shorts first call on his services. On 13 June, 1913, he narrowly escaped death in a crash at Brooklands in a Martinsyde monoplane, in which his passenger, Capt J. R. B. Kennedy, was killed; later the Royal Aero Club censured him for reckless flying on this occasion, but he had learned his lesson and his certificate was not suspended.

Before this mishap, however, he had test-flown another new Short seaplane, a private-venture design exhibited at the Olympia show in February 1913. It incorporated many of Horace Short's latest design features, such as manganese-steel tube struts instead of wood, improved main and tail floats, seats for two passengers side-by-side in front of the pilot and turning gear for starting the engine from the cockpit. The single-row 80 hp Gnome engine was neatly cowled and was carried on front and back bearings, with an under-

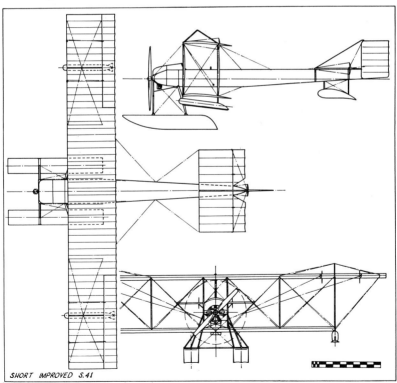

SHORT IMPROVED S.41

shield intended to protect the engine from sea-water, although this caused overheating and was soon removed. The wings, though of improved profile and construction, did not fold and their extensions were strut-braced; also the ailerons (on the upper wing only) were of the trailing uncompensated type.

RNAS *42* at Leven, Fifeshire, in July 1913.

On acceptance, this seaplane became serial *42* and was taken to Leven, on the Firth of Forth, in July 1913; while there it was flown by Gordon, Travers and Babington. Its floats were somewhat less robust than needed in tidal waters and, after having them stove-in more than once, *42* was converted into a land-plane by the substitution of skids with wheels on a cross axle. A small fixed fin had been added, and with the floats removed *42* became a 'lodger' at the R.F.C. establishment at Montrose; during 1914 it returned to Eastchurch, whence it was taken to France in August with Samson's Eastchurch Squadron. A month later it was the sole aeroplane possessed by Headquarters Flight, Morbecque, where on 28 September, 1914, Samson wrote it off in a tree when its engine failed just after take-off.

Nos. *20* and *21* at Grain were used for experiments in wireless telegraphy, under the supervision of Lieut Raymond Fitzmaurice, who persuaded the Admiralty to buy four lightweight transmitters from Lucien Rouzet, engineer in charge at the Eiffel Tower, Paris. Flown by Babington, *20* could transmit messages up to 20 miles, and was the first aircraft to signal a salute to King George V, on his return from the Schelde in the royal yacht *Victoria and Albert*. In July, *20* was sent to Great Yarmouth, where it was to remain until scrapped in 1915. This station, on the unsheltered tidal beach of the South Denes, posed particularly difficult beaching problems, and *20* was used to pioneer the G.R.W. (Gregory–Riley–White) gear, comprising pairs of wheels which could be quickly attached to or removed from seaplane floats so that the aircraft could be taxied into or out of the sea under its own power. Both *20* and *21* suffered, like *10*, from the unreliability of the two-row Gnomes, mainly due to the crude induction system from the carburettor via the hollow crank-shaft and piston-crown inlet valves; this worked well enough in single-row engines, but was a haphazard arrangement for double-rows, where the rear cylinders always tended to receive too rich a mixture while the front ones were starved; inevitably the rear sparking plugs oiled up while the front ones overheated and misfired.

Gordon Bell's accident came at a time when important new designs were taking shape at Eastchurch, and his place was filled temporarily by Sydney Pickles, also a well-known freelance test pilot. Three new types of tractor seaplane were on the stocks, two for the Admiralty and one as Frank McClean's private entry in the 1913 Circuit of Britain seaplane race. First to be completed was a large patrol seaplane, with a two-row 14-cylinder Gnome engine of 160 hp. Two of these had been ordered, plus seven with 100 hp Gnomes. They were developed from Horace Short's original *42*, modified in accordance with naval requirements resulting from the previous year's service trials. Wing area was increased, stronger and larger rubber-sprung floats gave a reserve of buoyancy and the balanced rudders had triangular fixed fins in front. The roomy front cockpit provided ample stowage for wireless and other gear, and the pilot occupied the rear cockpit. The high aspect ratio wings were of the latest type with steel-tube struts, originally in two bays, with strut-braced upper extensions and uncompensated wide-span ailerons.

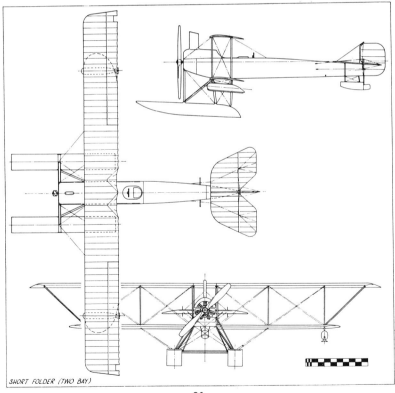

SHORT FOLDER (TWO BAY)

The first seaplane with 160 hp Gnome (S.63, serial *81*) was accepted after test flights by Samson (in Bell's absence) on 17 July, 1913, and taken aboard H.M.S. *Hermes*, the Navy's new depot ship, at Sheerness. Samson continued to fly *81* throughout the Naval manoeuvres, which lasted from 24 July till 1 August, with Fitzmaurice as his observer; *Hermes* was based on Great Yarmouth, and *81* was lowered overside whenever the rather heavy swell permitted, and flew successfully on 26, 27 and 31 July, reporting back the positions of ships by means of a Rouzet transmitter. On 1 August, *81* flew about 50 miles out, but on the return trip part of the cowling came adrift and cut several of the sparking-plug leads, stopping the engine; *Hermes* came to the rescue and found the drifting seaplane near its last reported position. It appears that *81* had been fitted with folding wings before taking part in this exercise, but they could only have been simply hinged, needing man-handling and locking from outside. It was decided soon afterwards that *Hermes* should be permanently equipped as a seaplane carrier, and for this purpose wing-folding became a necessity for all but the smallest scouts carried aboard her. The second 160 hp seaplane (S.64, serial *82*) was completed in March 1914, and was followed by two more (S.65–6, *89* and *90*), after a mechanical folding gear, operated from the cockpit, had been devised and tested. The development of this gear, covered by patents Nos. 1,792, 15,727 and 28,610 of 1913, was worked out on the original S.41, which was extensively rebuilt and re-appeared, bearing its old serial *10*, in November 1913, being among the 22 aeroplanes inspected at Eastchurch by Winston Churchill on 29 November. It had its original two-wheeled landing gear with skids, and the original fuselage had been reconditioned, with reinforced engine bearers, but the wings and tail surfaces were completely new and resembled those of *81*, with two bays and steel struts; the wings were folded back for inspection by the First Lord, and it was flown by Gordon Bell later in the day.

Gordon Bell had made a good recovery and returned to duty at Eastchurch during September, just in time to take the place of his erstwhile deputy Sydney Pickles, who, by an unhappy coincidence, had been the victim of an accident similar to Bell's. This time it was not due to reckless flying, for the rudder-bar became jammed on the Champel biplane he was flying at Hendon on 20 September, causing him to spin in out of control; this time, too, his passenger (Mrs de Beauvoir Stocks) did not die, although her injuries prevented her from resuming her career as one of the few British women pilots of that time. Pickles himself returned to Eastchurch in April 1914, intending then to fly only his own Blériot for pleasure, but five months later he volunteered for war service, and thereafter became a much sought-after seaplane test pilot, doing valuable work at Rochester and elsewhere. Rochester works were built between October 1913 and January 1914 on a site beside the Medway upstream from the bridge, this location being chosen partly because of the difficulty of testing seaplanes built at Eastchurch (they had to be taken along narrow roads to either Sheerness or Leysdown and there rigged before launching) but more because of the plentiful labour available in the Chatham district.

After *81*'s early debut the next tractor seaplane due out of Eastchurch was S.68, Frank McClean's entry for the 1913 *Daily Mail* Circuit of Britain seaplane race. It was basically similar to the 100 hp Gnome seaplanes already in production, but was to have a 100 hp Green water-cooled six-in-line engine. Its wing-span was over 60 ft, and at first the lower wing was shorter than the upper, but later it appeared necessary to reduce the wing-loading, so a new set of wings with equal upper and lower spans, reduced gap and slightly wider chord was made. By mid-August the aircraft was complete, but the engine vibrated badly, causing the radiator to leak and the water to boil away so quickly that, on one engine run, a piston seized and a new cylinder was needed. Eventually it was flown for about half an hour, but found to be too slow and under-powered for racing, so the entry was scratched at the last moment.

S.68, Frank McClean's ill-fated entry for the 1913 *Daily Mail* seaplane race, in its initial form before the wing area was increased. (*Courtesy J. H. Blake.*)

Non-folding 100 hp seaplane, RNAS 75, at Spithead in July 1914. (*Courtesy G. S. Leslie.*)

93

Winston Churchill as Commander Samson's passenger in RNAS *76* at Grain in 1914.

The production batch of 100 hp Gnome seaplanes for the Navy reached completion at the end of 1913. Somewhat lighter and of less wing area than *81*, they had three-bay non-folding wings, being intended for coastal patrol from shore stations. The first of them, S.69, was test-flown by Gordon Bell on 4 and 7 January, 1914, C. R. Fairey being observer on the first occasion and Maurice Wright on the second, which included the delivery flight to Grain, where it received the serial *74*. Bell tested S.70, the second of the batch, on 16 January, taking up both Fairey and Wright together on one flight. Four more (S.71–74) were tested during the last week of January, and the last (S.75) was flown straight to Grain without landing on 1 February. It is not clear from the records whether these seven aircraft were test flown from Leysdown or Sheerness, but the latter seems probable because there was a crane there for launching after rigging the floats and wings on the pierhead; the 'folders' could, of course, be taken from Eastchurch to the pier by road without dismantling. These seven non-folding seaplanes (*74–80*) were shared between the air stations at Grain (with detachments at Clacton and Westgate) and Dundee, and the latter provided a flight of four for the Spithead Royal Naval Review on 18–22 July, 1914. On the same occasion were flown four of the latest 160 hp 'folders' (S.82–85, serials *119–122*), which had gone into service at Grain in May and June. Their double-row engines still gave trouble and old No. *10* had been fitted with a similar 140 hp Gnome in May for Samson to experiment with; overheating had been reduced by fitting large vertical exhaust stacks in the tops of the cowlings, discharging over the upper wings clear of the crews; in true nautical style, these funnels were deco-

RNAS *82*, the second two-bay 'folder', at Spithead in July 1914.

94

Gordon Bell flying RNAS *89*, the first three-bay 'folder', at Leysdown in March 1914.

RNAS *120* being launched at Westgate in August 1914. (*Courtesy G. S. Leslie.*)

rated with one, two, three and four white rings to identify the four 'folders' which took part in the Review. These four and a fifth (S.86, *186*) differed from the first four in having longer fuselages and larger fins to match their three-bay wings of increased span, but *89* and *90* had three-bay wings of the same span as the two-bay *81* and *82* and retained the original fuselage length and fin area. Four more non-folding seaplanes similar to *74* were assembled at Eastchurch in July 1914, apparently from spares, and became *180–183*; of these, *181* had an 80 hp Gnome and the others 100 hp Gnome-Monosoupapes.

On 15 June, 1914, the Calshot seaplane station, commanded by Longmore, had been inspected by the Board of Admiralty, including Prince Louis of Battenberg (First Sea Lord) and Winston Churchill (First Lord). The latter asked Longmore whether torpedo-dropping experiments already started by Flt Lieut Hyde-Thomson at Calshot could be speeded up; Longmore said they could if he were permitted to retain a certain 160 hp Short seaplane (which was *121*), when he would undertake at an early date to carry and

95

One of the last batch of 160 hp three-bay 'folders' newly launched at Sheerness Pier in July 1914.

release a 14-in torpedo weighing 810 lb, which he had not so far been able to do with the Sopwith seaplane specially built for this task. This was agreed and (in Oswald Short's own words):

'Horace at once put in hand two new main float cross-bars, bent upward in the middle to allow the torpedo to be swung between the main floats clear of the water, and fitted a quick release catch [designed by Hyde-Thomson] to release the torpedo. With the late Gordon Bell, who was our test pilot, and Mr Bibby, one of our foremen, I went to Calshot Seaplane Base and erected the machine in a few hours. As I was talking to [Long-more] at his office door he received a telegram. He opened it and, having read it, remarked "We were nearer to war in 1911 than we are now", but I did not know to what he was referring. . . . By the time the machine was ready to take off it was already dusk. There was much activity too with the Sopwith torpedoplane which had been specially constructed for the pur-

121, the first British seaplane to launch a torpedo; here seen at Grain in 1915.
(*Courtesy Major F. B. Fowler.*)

pose. It was at the water's edge and mechanics were working on the engine. At Bell's first attempt to take off, the Short seaplane did not gain enough speed even to straighten out the ailerons. I heard one of the rival mechanics say, "Safe as a house!" Gordon Bell returned to shore and reported one cylinder missing; this was soon put right and at the next attempt the seaplane took off, the torpedo was dropped and a magnesium flare attached to it enabled it to be found and picked up. It was now dark. This was the first torpedo taken up and launched from a seaplane in Great Britain, only a few days before war broke out.'

In fact, the date was 27 July, 1914, and from this account it is clear that, even though Longmore flew *121* with a torpedo next day, it is to Gordon Bell that the credit of having made the first drop should go. With such a load the aircraft was flown solo and could only carry fuel for about 30 minutes; even so, it was loaded well beyond the stress limits permissible even in 1914 for regular service, so it was far from being an operational weapon; in spite of this, the other four 160 hp 'folders' were later equipped with torpedo gear and carried on *Engadine*, one of three converted cross-Channel steamers, but no torpedo was ever launched by them in action. In March 1915, *120–122* were shipped to Durban on the armed liner *Laconia* and thence taken on 23 April to Niororo Island; there they were intended to assist the Navy in flushing the German light cruiser *Königsberg* from deep cover in the Rufiji delta, but their performance in that hot, humid climate was totally inadequate.

The unreliability of the double-row Gnome led to alternatives being sought; in the case of the 100 hp seaplanes the remedy was found by replacing the original ten-cylinder two-row Gnomes by nine-cylinder single-row Gnome-Monosoupapes, and this may have been done at Grain before entry into service. An alternative to the 160 hp Gnome was more difficult to find, but the new range of water-cooled radial Canton-Unné engines produced in France by Salmson seemed promising. They were to be built under licence in England by the Dudbridge Ironworks of Stroud, Glos., and were already in use in the larger Farman, Sopwith and Wight seaplanes.

In September 1913 the Admiralty ordered two similar prototype Short seaplanes, one with the single-row Salmson of 135 hp and the other, slightly larger, with the double-row version rated at 200 hp. These were built at Eastchurch during March and April 1914 and resembled the 160 hp 'folder', but had stronger two-bay wings with strut-braced extensions and inversely tapered ailerons. Entirely by coincidence, the smaller seaplane was allotted the serial *135* and the larger *136*; they were delivered to Grain in July and September 1914 respectively. On Christmas Eve they formed part of the complement of nine seaplanes, seven of them Shorts, aboard the three carriers *Engadine*, *Empress* and *Riviera*, which sailed with an escort from Harwich in an attempt to bomb the Zeppelin base at Cuxhaven. Early on Christmas Day all seven Shorts, which included also the 160 hp 'folders' *119* and *120*

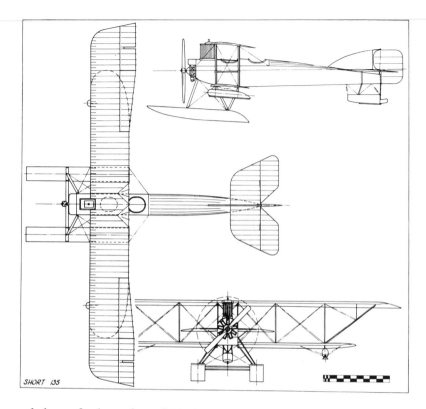

SHORT 135

and three of a later class of 100 hp Mono-Gnome 'folders' (*811*, *814* and *815*), got off the water with their bombs at a point 12 miles north of Heligo-land; they failed to find the airship shed, but attacked other targets along the Kiel canal; three of them, including *136*, returned to their flotilla after 3 hours, but *135* had engine failure and the pilot, Flt Lieut F. E. T. Hewlett (flying solo), was rescued by a Dutch fishing vessel, interned in Holland and later repatriated as a 'shipwrecked mariner'. The other three sea-planes alighted near Norderney and their pilots were picked up by the submarine *E11*, but the aircraft had to be sunk to avoid capture. *136* was later allotted to the newly commissioned seaplane-carrier *Ark Royal*, which sailed from Harwich on 1 February, 1915, for the Dardanelles, arriving at Tenedos on 17 February. *136* was reported to be 'the most valuable and only rough-weather seaplane on board the ship', but was shot at by Turkish gun-fire during a reconnaissance on 27 April, which damaged the floats and chassis and caused it to sink on alighting; it was hoisted aboard and patched up, but the engine never recovered from its immersion, and *136* had to be condemned on this account.

816, one of the eight Improved Type 74 seaplanes built at Rochester in 1914; they were basically Type 830, with 100 hp Mono-Gnomes substituted because of a shortage of Salmsons, and smaller fins. *(Courtesy Major F. B. Fowler.)*

RNAS *20–21*—Span 50 ft (15·3 m); length 39 ft (11·9 m); area 450 sq ft (41·8 m²); empty weight 1,100 lb (500 kg); loaded weight 1,600 lb (726 kg); speed 60 mph (96·6 km/h); duration 5 hr.

RNAS *42*—Span 48 ft (14·6 m); length 35 ft (10·6 m); area 390 sq ft (36·2 m²); empty weight 1,200 lb (545 kg); loaded weight 1,970 lb (895 kg); speed 65 mph (104·6 km/h).

S.68—Span 61 ft (18·6 m); length 40 ft (12·2 m); area 600 sq ft (55·8 m²), later 660 sq ft (61·4 m²); weights and speed not recorded.

RNAS *74–80*—Span 57 ft (17·35 m); length 39 ft (11·9 m); area 580 sq ft (54 m²); empty weight 2,100 lb (952 kg); loaded weight 2,700 lb (1,225 kg); max speed 65 mph (104·6 km/h); duration 5 hr.

RNAS *81–82*—Span 56 ft (17·05 m); length 40 ft (12·2 m); area 550 sq ft (51·1 m²); empty weight 2,400 lb (1,089 kg); loaded weight 3,100 lb (1,407 kg); max speed 78 mph (125·5 km/h); duration 5 hr.

RNAS *89–90*—Span 61 ft (18·58 m); length 40 ft 6 in (12·3 m); area 610 sq ft (56·7 m²); empty weight 2,500 lb (1,133 kg); loaded weight 3,400 lb (1,542 kg); max speed 78 mph (125·5 km/h); duration 5 hr.

RNAS *119–122, 186*—Span 67 ft (20·4 m); length 42 ft (12·8 m); area 690 sq ft (64·2 m²); empty weight 3,050 lb (1,385 kg); loaded weight 3,500 lb (1,589 kg); max speed 78 mph (125·5 km/h); duration 5 hr.

RNAS *135*—Span 52 ft (15·84 m); length 37 ft (11·43 m); area 530 sq ft (48·3 m²); empty weight 2,700 lb (1,225 kg); loaded weight 3,400 lb (1,542 kg); max speed 65 mph (104·6 km/h); duration 4·5 hr.

RNAS *136*—Span 54 ft 6 in (16·6 m); length 40 ft (12·2 m); area 570 sq ft (53 m²); empty weight 3,000 lb (1,361 kg); loaded weight 3,700 lb (1,679 kg); max speed 72 mph (116 km/h); duration 4 hr.

166 on *Ark Royal*'s steam crane at Mitylene in 1916. (*I.W.M.—Crown Copyright.*)

Short Seaplanes (1914–16): Admiralty Types 166, 827 and 830

The first proposal for an aircraft carrier was submitted to the Board of Admiralty by the Air Department in December 1912, based on a design by Beardmores of Dalmuir; but it was not accepted, because the Admiralty had already decided to equip the cruiser *Hermes* as a seaplane depot ship. *Hermes* was commissioned in May 1913 and carried Short seaplane *81* and a Caudron seaplane during the manoeuvres in July, in the course of which the Caudron was flown off a forecastle platform, as S.38 had done from *Hibernia* a year previously. The Caudron was considered too small for operational use, but the Short, the first to have folding wings, was highly commended. Subsequent production of the 160 hp 'folder' has already been described, together with the operational use of the two Salmson-engined prototypes *135* and *136*.

The reserve of power of *136* suggested its possible use as a torpedo-carrier, while *135*, though underpowered, had established the basic reliability of the 135 hp Salmson engine. The Air Department therefore ordered small production batches of folding seaplanes with both types of engine, the lower-powered type being somewhat smaller to reduce stowage space on seaplane-carriers, the first of which, *Ark Royal*, was bought late in 1913 from the Blyth Shipbuilding Co, Sunderland, while still building as a tramp steamer. After extensive redesign and conversion she was still not ready when war broke out and was in fact not commissioned till 9 December, 1914, too late to be used in the famous Cuxhaven raid on Christmas Day. For this operation, as already related, only the makeshift converted Channel packets *Empress*, *Engadine* and *Riviera* were available to serve as seaplane-carriers, but they proved so successful that they were joined later by the Isle of Man packets *Ben-my-Chree*, *Manxman* and *Vindex*. All these ships had hangars, cranes for hoisting outboard and very limited workshop equipment; only the last two had small forward flying-off decks. The seaplanes initially tailored to fit the *Ark Royal* proved to be well suited to the converted packets, as the Cuxhaven raid and Gallipoli campaign showed.

The production version of the larger prototype, *136*, was generally similar except that the wing extensions were braced by king-posts and cables instead of lift struts. This saved weight at the expense of a small increase in drag, but the practical advantages were that the sloping lift struts were all too easily damaged because of their small clearance from the tailplane when folded, and the stranded cables that replaced them were a normal product of seafaring skill, whereas the repair of struts was a specialised workshop job; at little increase of drag the cables could be duplicated, giving a valuable 'fail-safe' advantage under enemy fire. The first production batch of six 200 hp seaplanes (S.90–95), known as Short Type A, was already in hand at Eastchurch when war broke out; they received serials *161–166* and were referred to in Admiralty records as Type 166, in accordance with the early system of naval nomenclature. They were embarked in *Ark Royal* in November 1915 and acquitted themselves well at Salonika, bombing enemy batteries and spotting for the guns of the monitors *Raglan* and *Roberts*. They never carried torpedoes, although equipped to do so, and later in the campaign *163* and *166* were flown as landplanes from the R.N.A.S. airfield at Thasos. No further production of Type 166 was ordered from Short Brothers, but a batch of 20 (*9751–9770*) without torpedo gear was built by the Westland Aircraft Works, Yeovil, and of these *9754* also became a landplane at Thasos. They were delivered to Hamble by rail in July 1916 and test-flown there by Sydney Pickles; they were fitted to carry wireless and three 112-lb bombs, and the observer in the rear cockpit was armed with a Lewis gun. Somewhat similar in dimensions and role to Type 166 was the prototype Type B ordered as *178* but cancelled after war began, and so never built. This was an attempt to improve the crew's view by placing them ahead of the wings and moving the engine aft to maintain balance, driving the airscrew through a long shaft; the engine proposed was a 200 hp Le Rhône two-row rotary, and some indication of the layout is given in patent No. 13,021 of 27 May, 1914.

The smaller seaplanes, at first known at Eastchurch as Short Type C, were more numerous than Type 166 and went farther afield. Originally they had constant-chord ailerons and a span of 52 ft 4 in, but both the span and the aileron area were increased before they were flown. They were the first to be built at Rochester seaplane works when production there began in April 1914. Salmson engines were scarce at that date, and the first eight out of Rochester

had to be completed with 100 hp Gnome-Monosoupapes; somewhat mis-
leadingly, the Admiralty called them Improved Type 74, but they were
identical in design to the Salmson seaplanes except for the deeply cowled
overhung engine mounting and a much smaller fixed fin. These eight (*811–
818*) were all assigned to *Empress, Engadine* and *Riviera*, and *811, 814* and *815*
took part in the Cuxhaven raid, flown by Edmonds, Gaskell Blackburn and
Oliver respectively. 135 hp Salmsons were available for the next six off the

S.41 in its final state as a Type 830 landplane with No. 2 Wing, RNAS, at Imbros in 1915; it has the same
small fin as the Improved Type 74. (*Copyright W. Pollard.*)

Rochester line, and the old S.41 was rebuilt to the same standard to serve as a
development prototype, still with its original serial No. *10*; finally, it saw
active service with No. 2 Wing, R.N.A.S., as a landplane at Imbros in
1915. Meanwhile a promising new alternative engine had come into production—the 150 hp Sunbeam V-8 water-cooled engine, later named Nubian.
Its makers, John Marston & Sons Ltd of Wolverhampton, were originally
bicycle manufacturers, who added motor-cars to their products early in the
20th century and soon earned a name for quality; in 1909 they engaged as
chief engineer Louis Coatalen, who designed a 3-litre Sunbeam racing car
which won the Coupe des Voiturettes at Dieppe in 1912. Combining two
banks of the racing car engine to make a V-8 aero-engine, Coatalen installed it
in a Maurice Farman, which was flown for long periods at Brooklands by
Jack Alcock during the summer of 1913. Having demonstrated its reliability,
it was adopted by the Admiralty, together with a V-12 development of 225 hp,
for both seaplanes and airships.

The smaller Short seaplane was readily modified to take the Sunbeam
engine, and its performance was enhanced by an extra 15 hp for the same
installed weight as the Salmson. After the early difficulties with the radiator
on the 1913 Circuit of Britain seaplane, Horace Short had decided that only

a robust unit of rectangular formation would stand up to severe vibration, so he based his design on marine condenser practice, with vertical spiral tubes assembled into flat elements arranged in four rows edge-on to the slipstream and to the pilot's line of sight. This highly individual design remained a constant feature of Short seaplanes for several years, and has sometimes been disparaged as clumsy and unsightly, but in fact it was efficient and reliable, did not seriously interfere with the pilot's vision and helped to keep the crew warm in winter; being located above the engine, its circulation was assisted by the natural thermosiphon effect, so that engine cooling was not wholly dependent on water-pump efficiency; in a hot climate, if (as it frequently did) the water boiled away, the cylinders remained immersed for as long as possible, and forced landings were more often averted. Introduced on *135* and *136*, this block radiator was a standard unit for either the 135 hp Salmson or the 150 hp Sunbeam in one size, or for the 200 hp Salmson and 225 hp Sunbeam in a larger size. So of the remainder of the first production batch at Rochester, six (*819–821* and *828–830*) were built with Salmsons and were called Type 830, while *822–827* had Sunbeams and were called Type 827; *827* itself, however, was tested with both engines in turn at Rochester. Since the engine weight was less than in the 200 hp seaplane, the observer was moved forward to a point above the c.g., which also made ballast unnecessary for solo flying; the cockpit under the centre-section required a longer fuselage bay than the wing-spar pitch, so the rear struts had to be raked instead of vertical; all the wing struts were of oval-section steel tube without additional fairings and the ailerons were inversely tapered with straight trailing edges. Only one other batch of Type 830 was built, comprising *1335–1346*, which followed *161–166* at Eastchurch; after war began all these seaplanes were camouflaged before being taken by road to Queenborough Pier, where they were lowered into the water by crane for flight test; this pier, built for the Queenborough–Flushing railway steamers, was commandeered by the Admiralty to avoid having to take seaplanes to Sheerness for launching.

Eastchurch-built Type 830 *1335* at Queenborough Pier in 1915.

After satisfactory trials with *824* and *826* from H.M.S. *Campania* in June 1915, Type 827 was adopted for wider production, 30 (*3063–3072/3093–3112*) being built at Rochester, while 72 were subcontracted, 20 each to the Brush Electrical Engineering Co Ltd, Loughborough; Parnall & Sons Ltd, Bristol, and the Sunbeam Motor Car Co Ltd, Wolverhampton; also 12 to the Fairey Aviation Co Ltd, Hayes, Middlesex, a new aircraft company set up in 1915 by C. R. Fairey, who had been Short Brothers' works manager and assistant designer at Eastchurch, after previously working there for the Blair Atholl Syndicate. These arrangements resulted from the vastly increased demand for seaplanes after war began, far beyond the combined resources of East-church and Rochester, to meet which a number of Admiralty contractors without aircraft experience were asked to undertake seaplane manufacture under Short Brothers' supervision, for which they were entitled to claim an agreed royalty after the war was over. Type 827 was the standard equipment from 1915 onwards of many R.N.A.S. coastal stations, including Grain, Calshot, Dundee, Killingholme and Great Yarmouth, for both patrol duties

Type 827 *8229* being launched at Calshot in 1916. (*Courtesy G. S. Leslie.*)

and training; *3063, 3064, 3106* and *3107*, allotted to Grain in April 1916, were still there in the Nore Patrol Flight in April 1918. On 25 April, 1916, Yar-mouth, Lowestoft and Southwold were shelled by battleships of the German High Seas Fleet, which in turn were bombed by R.N.A.S. seaplanes, including *3108* flown by Flt Sub-Lts Hall and Evans from Great Yarmouth. Three 827s were sent to Mombasa on the armed liner *Laconia* in July 1915 to help the monitors *Severn* and *Mersey* to destroy the *Königsberg* in the Rufiji delta, but arrived too late to participate in the final action and were sent on in August to Mesopotamia; there they proved unable to take-off from the Shatt al Arab at Basra because of the heat and limited clear fairway; two were converted into landplanes and pressed into service as bombers against the Turkish advance on Kut-al-Amara in December 1915. Four more 827s equipped No. 8 Squadron R.N.A.S. when it arrived at Zanzibar on the *Laconia* in March 1916 and were flown from Chukwani Bay, their limited range being later increased by carrying one on board each of the three ships in the area, *Laconia, Himalaya* and *Manica*. They spotted for the guns of the monitor *Severn* at

Lindi and reconnoitred enemy positions to assist British landings. Finally, these four (Short-built *3093–3095* and Parnall-built *8219*) were handed over in March 1916 to the Belgian volunteer force opposing the Germans on Lake Tanganyika. Shipped in crates from Zanzibar to Matadi, they were transported up the Congo and overland to Lukuga (Albertville) and finally reerected on the shore of Lake Tongwe at Mtoa, whence the first seaplane was flown on 14 May, 1916; this feat was a tribute to both the endurance of the party and the relative ease of assembly of the seaplane with only the crudest of skill and facilities. In spite of their marginal performance in that climate, two of the seaplanes bombed the German lake cruiser *Graf von Goetzen* in harbour at Kigoma on 23 July, and three days later the town surrendered. Two more 827s, *3097* and *8218* were sent to Zanzibar as replacements for use on *Manica* and were supplemented by Sunbeam-built *8641–2* shipped from Grain on 29 May, 1916; *8641* was still on *Manica* in February 1917. Other 827s served in the Mediterranean, at Otranto and on *Ben-my-Chree*; Parnall-built *8251* was sent to Grain for gunnery trials as late as April 1918, no doubt for use as a target, but in October 1918 three survived at home stations and one at Otranto. They were flown also as dual-control trainers at Windermere, and at least one of these had small boat-built wing-tip floats in place of the usual air-bags.

Single examples of both Type 827 and Type 830 were modified by R.N.A.S. stations for their own purposes. On one of the latter, whose identity has not been ascertained, the wings were modified to a constant-chord plan-form, with stiff trailing edges, parallel ailerons and elliptical wing-tips; this may have been connected with experiments on new aerofoil sections by the Admiralty Board of Invention and Research. The 827, Brush-built *8237*, was more drastically altered at Calshot in 1917 and was flown with equal-span constant-chord three-bay wings, with strut-linked ailerons and wing-tip floats mounted directly on the lower surface; these features were typical of Howard T. Wright's designs for J. Samuel White & Co of Cowes, and may have been suggested as a means of combining the best Short and Wight design features in one seaplane. The purpose of this modification seems to have been to adapt Type 827 as a trainer reproducing the handling characteristics of the Short 184.

8237, the Type 827 rebuilt at Calshot with equal-span wings, flying at Lee-on-Solent in 1918.
(I.W.M.—Crown Copyright.)

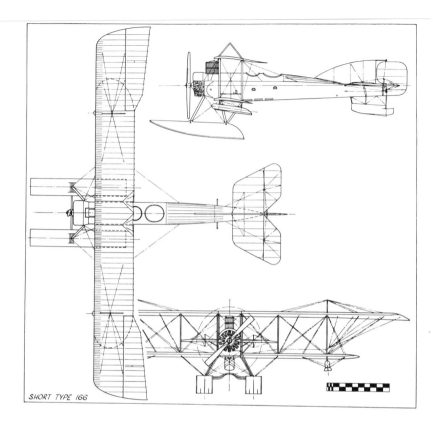

SHORT TYPE 166

Type 166—Span 57 ft 3 in (17·45 m); length 40 ft 7 in (12·4 m); area 575 sq ft (53·5 m²); empty weight 3,500 lb (1,589 kg); all-up weight 4,580 lb (2,080 kg); max speed 65 mph (104·6 km/h); duration 4 hr.

Type 827—Span 53 ft 11 in (16·4 m); length 35 ft 3 in (10·75 m); area 506 sq ft (47 m²); empty weight 2,700 lb (1,225 kg); all-up weight 3,400 lb (1,542 kg); max speed 62 mph (100 km/h); duration 3·5 hr.

Type 830—Dimensions and area as for Type 827; empty weight 2,624 lb (1,192 kg); all-up weight 3,324 lb (1,510 kg); max speed 70 mph (113 km/h); duration 3·5 hr.

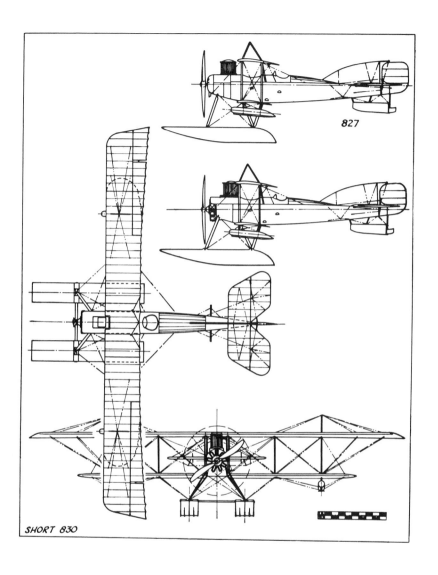

827

SHORT 830

Ten later Salmson-engined Short seaplanes, S.301–310 (*9781–9790*), were built at Rochester in 1916, primarily for training duties at Calshot. They were a hybrid design, with the wide-span wings and long fuselage of Type 166, and the straight-edged ailerons and forward observer's position of Type 830. The power plant was a 140 hp single-row Dudbridge-built Salmson and the top centre-section was left open to afford easy access for slinging; the seaplane was unarmed, but carried a rack for practice bombs. The long fuselage enhanced its appearance and doubtless improved its flying qualities, but by the time this variant appeared, the earlier Short seaplanes had been almost superseded by the larger and sturdier Type 184 with 225 hp Sunbeam, which became the best-known and most numerous of all the seaplanes of the First World War.

S.301–310.—as for Type 830 except length 40 ft 7 in (12·3 m).

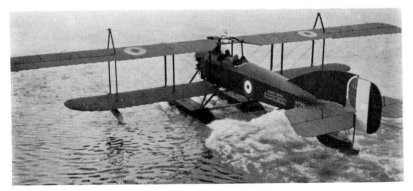

S.310 (*9790*) starting on a test flight from Rochester in 1916.

S.106 (*184*) in original condition before launching at Rochester in March 1915. (*Courtesy G. S. Leslie.*)

Short Admiralty Type 184 Seaplanes

The failure of the Green-engined Circuit of Britain seaplane in 1913 must have been a great disappointment to Horace Short, not so much because it had to be scratched from the race but because Short Brothers were more concerned with the improvement of the art than with public acclaim and never allowed their products to compete in events unless there was some experimental value in doing so. In modifying the special seaplane for Frank McClean to fly in the *Daily Mail*'s competition, Horace Short had introduced several new features, the most striking being the arrangement of high aspect ratio equal-span wings with an unusually small gap. Although he employed the same camber for upper and lower wings, it seems probable that he intended later to try the effect of reducing nose camber on the lower wing, as proposed in patent No. 23,708 of 20 October, 1913; such an arrangement offered in theory less interference between the planes, and consequently lower drag. The usual way of minimising interference was by staggering the planes, but this conflicted with easy wing-folding. Horace's views on high aspect ratio no doubt stemmed partly from observations of the albatross during his early voyages in the Pacific, and also from his experience in designing cascades of blades for Parsons steam turbines; he would not have overlooked the space saving afforded by narrow-chord wings when folded, particularly on a seaplane-carrier.

The fatal vibration encountered when the 100 hp six-cylinder Green was run at full power was partly due to its insufficiently stiff crankcase, and it was otherwise a sound design which later won the first prize of £5,000 in a rigorously supervised competition at Farnborough in 1914; no doubt the massive test bench masked resonance peaks which showed up in a much less rigid airframe installation. At all events, the Air Department of the Admiralty was not discouraged from developing six-in-line engines, and William Beardmore & Co took up the licensed manufacture of the very successful 120 hp Austro-Daimler (designed by the eldest Ferdinand Porsche) some months before war began; the Royal Aircraft Factory had specified it for their R.E.5 biplane, and

109

the Admiralty had gained a good impression of the smaller 90 hp four-in-line version in several prototypes, including a trial in the Short Sociable pusher *145* at Eastchurch. About the same time Louis Coatalen began work on the 12-cylinder version of his 150 hp V-8 engine, and Capt Murray Sueter, Director of the Air Department, saw this as an excellent power plant for a long-range torpedo-carrier, with a substantially better performance than the 200 hp Salmson could offer. Capt Sueter, with Lieut Hyde-Thomson, had drawn up a detailed specification for a seaplane to carry a 14-in Whitehead torpedo, with a crew of two and wireless, and the Short Type 166 and Sopwith Type C seaplanes had shown this task to be too much for the Salmson. So in September 1914 a revised specification based on the 225 hp Sunbeam was drafted for issue to Short Brothers, Sopwith and J. Samuel White, each of whom was invited to submit proposals. When Murray Sueter first explained his requirements to Horace Short, the latter replied, 'Well, if you particularly wish this done, I will produce a seaplane that will satisfy you', and on the strength of that statement two prototypes were ordered, for which serials *184* and *185* were reserved; from this the type became officially known as the Short Type 184 Seaplane, though quite as frequently called the Two-Two-Five from the horsepower of its engine.

The Short 184 was a direct development of the 1913 Circuit seaplane, strengthened but not much enlarged, with its weight-lifting ability enhanced by a robust engine of more than twice the power. It had the block-type radiator introduced for the 200 hp Salmson, equal-span wings of small chord and gap, improved wing-folding arrangements designed by Horace Short and large compartmented sprung twin floats designed by Oswald Short. Not only could the wings be swung and locked into flying position by means of a cockpit windlass but the front spar lock was a splined and threaded spigot and socket, locked or unlocked by a quarter-turn like the breech-block of a field-gun (patents Nos. 5,290/14 and 20,537/14); when folded, the wings were supported and locked by a cross-shaft in the rear fuselage with upturned ends engaging in slots in the rear middle wing struts; these ends could be rotated, after engagement, by a lever in the cockpit, so that the whole operation could be done single-handed by the pilot (patent No. 9,276/15). The usual cylindrical air-bags served as wing-tip floats, and the wooden tail-float was supported on struts which permitted a limited fore-and-aft movement as well as rotation about a transverse axis, both movements being restrained by rubber cords. The small water-rudder at the stern of the tail-float was actuated from the main rudder through sliding telescopic torque-tubes of oval section. The float chassis comprised a pair of main struts attached to the front cross-tube and two pairs to the rear cross-tube; the cross-tubes were arched in the middle to accommodate the torpedo crutches, and their centres were braced by auxiliary struts to the bottom longerons, the torpedo release strop being mounted on the rear tube centre. A feature peculiar to this and one other type of Short seaplane was that the rear main struts did not meet on the centre-line of the float but straddled it, relying on the stiffness of the cross-tube to take care of the eccentric loading; thus both resilience and redundancy were obtained without weight penalty at a highly stressed point where a collapse due to a single failure could not be risked; it also simplified assembly and repair by avoiding a built-up V-strut. The floats themselves were slotted to move vertically relative to the cross-tubes and were suspended on rubber cords.

The wings were braced in three bays by stranded cables, with jury-struts at the front spar root-ends to maintain tension while folded. In the outermost bays the anti-lift cables were deflected upwards by bobstays to clear the tail-plane and elevators when folded; this requirement had not arisen in earlier designs, whose outer bays when folded did not enclose the tailplane. The lower wing had constant chord and no ailerons; the upper wing was inversely tapered from the root to two-thirds of the semi-span and parallel from there to the tip. The ailerons were of wide span and uncompensated, and the wing struts were of round steel tube with wood and fabric fairings. The fuselage was a conventional four-longeron wire-braced girder, entirely of spruce with manganese-steel fittings of high strength. The longerons were spindled-out where possible to save weight and were carried forward to the front of the engine, which was mounted on separate bearers carried by pressed-steel transverse frames, thus providing a stiff and accessible installation. The engine cowling was readily detachable and also had large side doors for daily servicing, the magnetos and carburettors being easily reached without risk of contact with hot spots such as the exhaust manifolds; since the exhaust ports faced inwards, the manifold lay centrally between the cylinder banks and the exhaust pipe was swept down the front of the engine to terminate just outside the bottom cowling panel. The remainder of the fuselage was fabric-covered, and alongside the cockpits the bottom longerons were reinforced on both sides by side-plates having foot-steps cut in them. The tail unit was of standard Short pattern, with a balanced rudder and a large dorsal fin. The pilot's controls, with a handwheel for the ailerons, were in the front cockpit, with the fuel tank in the next bay forward; the rear cockpit contained the observer's seat and stowages for all his varied gear, including the W/T transmitter and receiver, signalling lamp, smoke flares, Very pistol, sea anchor and basket of pigeons, to which were later added a Lewis gun with spare trays of ammunition and even two more small bombs, stowed loose.

Before the two prototypes flew, orders for trial batches of ten more seaplanes were placed with Short Brothers, similar orders being given also to Sopwith for ten of their Type 860 and to J. Samuel White for ten of the Wight Type 840 designed by Howard T. Wright. From the beginning the superiority of the Short design was obvious, and when the two prototypes (S.106–7) emerged at Rochester in the early spring of 1915 they certainly looked like redeeming Horace Short's promise to Murray Sueter. Furthermore, they were delivered punctually, and the initial order for ten (S.120–128 and 130, 841–850) was quickly followed by massive contracts (for those days) too big to be undertaken in Shorts' own two factories. So with Rochester fully occupied with a main order for 75 (S.173–247, *8031–8105*), a batch of 30 was ordered from S. E. Saunders Ltd of Cowes (*8001–8030*) and batches of 12 each from Mann, Egerton & Co of Norwich (*8344–8355*), the Westland Aircraft works of Petters Ltd of Yeovil (*8356–8367*), Phoenix Dynamo Co, Bradford (*8368–8379*) and Frederick Sage & Co, Peterborough (*8380–8391*), all for delivery in 1915. In fact, Sages, under the energetic direction of Eric Gordon England, got their first machine away in November, followed by Mann Egerton in December and Phoenix and Westland in January 1916.

This was a very stout effort, because early flights of *184* at Grain revealed the need for modifications, the most serious of these being to improve lateral control. The large uncompensated ailerons were unmanageable when taxying downwind and hardly adequate for control at low speeds; so balancing rubber cords were introduced above the top wing to hold them up in the neutral position, except when pulled down by the pilot's control, when each aileron moved separately in the downward direction only, because the design of the

184 with compensated ailerons at Grain in April 1915. (*Courtesy Major F. B. Fowler.*)

hinges did not permit up-float. Lateral control was still marginal, so next narrow-chord ailerons were added to the lower wings; these were linked to the upper ailerons by separate cables running in pulleys at the top and bottom of the middle and outer front struts and vertically down the front of these struts, the rubber cords being transferred from the upper wings to the top of the rear struts, from which they pulled up the bottom ailerons and maintained tension in the link cables; cumbersome though it appeared by comparison with the more orthodox closed spanwise circuit, it was preferred because it suited the existing folding gear, and the prevention of up-float probably reduced the risk of dropping the inside wing during a turn close to the sea. Later the aileron circuit was altered to the orthodox layout in a batch of Eastchurch-built 184s, but the old system was retained in the latest sub-contracted batches, even when they had been improved in many other respects. Incidentally, Sopwith was willing to pay a royalty to use the Short wing-folding patents, but Howard Wright designed a heavier and less-satisfactory worm-and-rack spar-locking device to avoid infringement; later on, the Short patents were successfully challenged on the grounds that gates had hinges and birds had folding wings, and it became unprofitable to contest infringements. Other modifications included bomb-racks and compressed-air starting; at some point in its career, *184* itself had its tail damaged and was repaired with the fin and rudder from a spare airframe (S.129), with the balance portion of the rudder deleted and the fin extended back to the hinge line, but this seems to have been an improvisation rather than a modification.

By the time Phoenix Dynamo began deliveries, on 21 January, 1916, a second round of orders had been placed for 20 each from Robey & Co, Lincoln (*9041–9060*), and Sage (*9065–9084*). Meanwhile the Short 184 had been in action and acquitted itself well. In October 1914 the original R.N.A.S. depot ship *Hermes* had been fully refitted as a seaplane-carrier, but within a few weeks of commissioning she was torpedoed and sunk in the English Channel. The stop-gap conversion of *Engadine*, *Empress* and *Riviera* and their exploits on Christmas Day 1914 have already been mentioned, and more extensive conversions were made of the old Cunard liner *Campania* and several Isle of Man packets. One of the latter, *Ben-my-Chree*, had been commissioned about the same time as the first flight of *184*, and on 21 May, 1915, left Harwich for the Dardanelles carrying *184*, *185* and one spare airframe (S.129) unassembled, together with two Sopwith Schneiders. She arrived at Mitylene on 12 June, and two months later both *184* and *185* launched their torpedoes in anger and with effect. Horace Short had just succeeded in meeting Murray Sueter's specification, but with insufficient margin to make up for the high temperature and humidity of the Aegean climate. When Flt Cdr C. H. K. Edmonds took off in *184* from the Gulf of Xeros on 12 August, 1915, he had to fly solo and with petrol for only 45 minutes. With his torpedo he could not climb above 800 ft, nevertheless he crossed the Bulair peninsular into the Straits, where he found an enemy transport off Gallipoli; coming down to 15 ft above the water, he launched his torpedo from 300 yards and scored a direct hit; later he was told the ship had already been crippled by a submarine, but on 17 August he repeated his exploit and torpedoed the middle one of three transport ships off Ak Bashi Liman, leaving her on fire. On that day Flt Cdr G. B. Dacre, who was flying *185*, had to alight in the Straits with a failing engine, but then saw an enemy tug which he torpedoed while taxying. Lightened of its load, the seaplane managed to take off, cleared Bulair very low and got back safely to *Ben-my-Chree*. These, however, were the only successes the 184 ever had as a torpedo-carrier, although trials continued with *8349* at Felixstowe during 1916 and 1917; this machine also was flown solo, with the rear cockpit stripped of equipment and faired over. Loss of power through low atmospheric density, oiled-up sparking plugs, burnt exhaust valves and boiling radiators in the Aegean environment made full-throttle sorties with torpedoes impracticable except with nearly new aircraft and engines, and all future attacks were made with two 112-lb bombs, which allowed a crew of two as well as a useful increase in range. Thus equipped on 8 November, 1915, Edmonds and Dacre flew their 184s more than 100 miles overland to bomb the Maritza railway bridge on the enemy's main supply route from Germany through Bulgaria. Less spectacularly, but more

Phoenix-built *8372* on *Manxman*'s topping lift, with four-bladed airscrew and torpedo, in the Eastern Mediterranean in 1918, possibly at the time of the *Goeben*'s mishap at Nagara Burnu.
(Courtesy G. S. Leslie.)

continuously, the 184s shared with earlier Short seaplanes the task of directing the gunfire of naval monitors, which shelled enemy shipping out of sight in the Straits with sufficient accuracy and persistence to persuade the Turks to stop reinforcing the Dardanelles forts by sea.

Nearer home, the enemy had begun to mount their U-boat blockade soon after capturing Ostend and Zeebrugge in October 1914, using them as bases for submarines built in the Antwerp shipyards. Short seaplanes of earlier types operated from new bases at Dover and Dunkerque, but were relatively ineffective, and 184s were brought in as soon as possible to take on longer-range patrols after the sinking of the *Lusitania* and *Arabic* in May 1915. Even in the cooler climate of the North Sea and English Channel, engine trouble occurred frequently, and forced landings were rarely successful in anything but a dead calm; in such events many crews owed their lives to the carrier pigeons always taken on patrol, whose prompt delivery of SOS messages was more reliable than W/T. 184s were included in the complement of most of the seaplane-carriers, from one of which, *Vindex*, three of them attempted on 25 March, 1916, to bomb the Zeppelin sheds at Tondern, but without success. Some of them led charmed lives, and *8086*, which had gone out from Grain on 1 March, 1916, to search for the Curtiss H.4 *1230* missing from Felixstowe, was still on the strength of the Nore Patrol at Grain in April 1918, together with *8354*. At Grain they were widely employed for armament experiments and in April 1916 *8364* undertook trials of a 2-pounder Davis gun fitted with a

114

Hamilton sight; six rounds were fired (on six successive flights, since the gun could not be reloaded in the air) with fair success at an obsolete Wight seaplane towed by two motor-boats; bombing trials were also made by 184s on an armoured roof target at Kingsnorth, on which a 500-lb bomb was dropped for the first time on 9 May, 1916, by *8052* from 4,000 ft using a C.F.S. bombsight designed by Bourdillon and Tizard. One was sent up from *Engadine* on 31 May, 1916, just before the Battle of Jutland, but on many other occasions, as on 18 August, the sea was too rough for take-off.

In home waters 184s could at least rely on being able to take-off from their base in fair weather, which was more than Cdr Samson found possible when he took *Ben-my-Chree* and two smaller seaplane-carriers to the eastern Mediterranean, Red Sea and Indian Ocean in 1916 and 1917. In May 1916 he had not previously flown the 184, and after some experience of its marginal performance in a hot climate, even with a four-bladed airscrew and a 240 hp engine, he decided to reduce the lower wing span and fin area of one of them, with encouraging results; in fact, he claimed to have gained 'six knots in speed and about 15 per cent in climb' with the 'Cut-Short', as Murray Sueter called it; this machine has not been positively identified, but may have been Rochester-built *8070*; apart from reducing the wing and fin area, Samson replaced the wing-tip floats by simple 'surf-boards', which saved a bit more

Samson's 'Cut-Short' (probably *8070*) in 1917. (*Courtesy G. S. Leslie.*

drag. In March Samson was ordered to Aden to seek out and destroy the German raider *Wolf* and took the 'Cut-Short' into the Indian Ocean on board the carrier *Raven II*, which he commanded after *Ben-my-Chree* was sunk at Castellorizo in January 1917. It made several patrol flights in the Laccadive Islands in search of *Wolf*, but finally its floats collapsed in a heavy swell off Kalpeni, and its crew were rescued just in time from shark-infested waters. Possibly as a result of Samson's earlier dispatches, the second batch of Short 184s ordered from Mann, Egerton & Co was required to incorporate a modified wing arrangement somewhat resembling that of Type 166; this was called 184 Type B, and Mann Egerton were asked to help in detailing and stressing the modifications, which comprised an increase in the upper wing span to 72 ft, new lower wings without ailerons, increased gap, raised engine bearers and deletion of torpedo gear. Known in Norwich as the Mann Egerton Type B, the first of these ten seaplanes (*9085–9094*) was delivered in

9085, first of ten 184 Type B seaplanes built by Mann, Egerton & Co at Norwich in 1916.
(*Courtesy G. S. Leslie.*)

mid-1916 from Norwich to Felixstowe, where it was test-flown by Sydney Pickles before being handed over to the Admiralty; according to Mann Egerton's aircraft manager, George Wilford, who was present on that occasion, it 'put up an exceptional performance, and subsequently broke the then existing records for seaplanes, both for climbing speed and height'. So evidently Samson had something when he increased the gap and reduced the aspect ratio, and although only these ten were built, one or two of this variant were still in service when the war ended.

The last three of the main Rochester batch were retained there and at Grain for experimental work. In July 1916, S.245 (*8103*) was converted into a single-seat bomber (known as Type D) with the front cockpit deleted and its space occupied by internal stowage for nine 65-lb bombs slung from their noses; this gave a useful reduction in drag, and a few others were similarly converted, but the variant did not go into production; possibly the real intention was to carry a 500-lb bomb internally as an insurance against late delivery of Handley Page O/100s. In January 1917, S.246 (*8104*) was flown with a 250 hp Rolls-Royce Eagle IV installed, which gave it an enhanced performance; the engine cowling was taller than normal, and side radiators were used instead of the central block; extra fuel was carried in a tank faired into the underside of the fuselage between the lower wing roots. Although tested with some success at Grain, it did not go into production. The last of the batch, S.247 (*8105*), eventually went into regular service at Great Yarmouth, but before delivery was tested at Rochester and Grain in July 1916 with a four-bladed airscrew and high chassis; in fact, it appeared somewhat higher than it actually was, because of the reduced diameter of the airscrew. Apparently the purpose of this installation was to compare the spray pick-up of two- and four-bladed

116

Ronald Kemp in 184 Type DS.245 (*8103*), at Rochester in July 1916.

airscrews in preparation for the standardisation of the 260 hp Sunbeam engine for final 184 production. Before this engine became available in quantity, a few 184s were fitted with 240 hp Sunbeams, while an interim variant produced in some numbers had the 240 hp Renault engine (dubbed 'Renault-Mercedes' because of a coincidental resemblance to the contemporary German Mercedes in the design of its cylinders and valve-gear). The Renault rotated the opposite way to the Sunbeam and had a bulbous central exhaust manifold with a stubby stack outlet; at first this installation had side radiators, but later the standard central block was reinstated; on some production lines a change was made from the Renault to the 260 hp Sunbeam before the latter installation had been finalised, and in these cases the Renault manifold had to be adapted to the Sunbeam, with the result that the radiator was raised higher than usual. The full 260 hp Sunbeam modification included

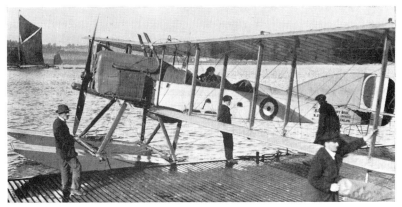

Ronald Kemp in S.246 (*8104*), fitted with Rolls-Royce Eagle IV, at Rochester in January 1917.

117

a level manifold with a sloping stack pipe forward of the radiator; both the Renault and later Sunbeam versions carried bombs on a long central rack under the fuselage and had a Whitehouse or Scarff ring for the observer's Lewis gun; the arched float cross-tubes for the torpedo gear had been replaced by straight tubes on production aircraft some time previously.

Twenty (S.314–333, N1080–1099) were built at Eastchurch early in 1917, and in N1089 the engine bearers were lightened and the tail-float was enlarged by 30 per cent and mounted closer to the fuselage; this form, with either

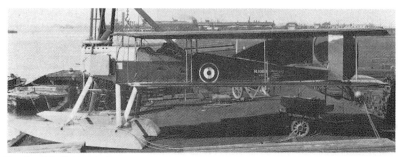

Eastchurch-built *N1084* with Renault engine and flank radiators, at Queenborough Pier in May 1917.

Improved 184 with Renault engine and top radiator, off Queenborough in June 1917.

engine, was officially called the Improved 184 and also had an orthodox aileron circuit and Rafwire bracing instead of stranded cables, but shortages inevitably brought about reversions to the older designs, of which there were plentiful supplies already in stock; sometimes this state of affairs was acknowledged in the contract papers by use of the term Intermediate Type 184, but there was considerable flexibility in determining the actual acceptance standard of each aircraft; S.332 (*N1098*) was evaluated with a neat 'car-bonnet' hinged cowling and frontal honeycomb radiator for its 260 hp Sunbeam, which drove a four-bladed airscrew, always used with this engine; those in-

118

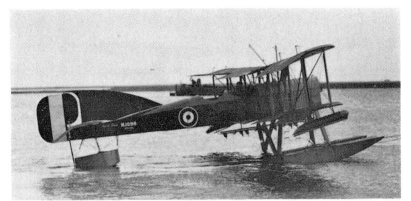

Eastchurch-built Improved 184 *N1098* at Queenborough in June 1917, fitted with 260 hp Sunbeam Maori I and experimental frontal honeycomb radiator.

tended to cope with the rough seas and heavy swells of the Dover Patrol stations at Newhaven and Cherbourg also had larger main floats and streamlined wing-tip floats and were known as the Dover Type 184. Only ten more 184s were built by Short Brothers (S.389–398, *N1580–1589*), and these all had Renaults, but production by other contractors continued up till the Armistice, when the total number built outside Rochester and Eastchurch amounted to 829; in addition to the firms already mentioned, the Brush Electrical Engineering Co of Loughborough built no fewer than 190 in five batches, and the Supermarine Aviation works built 15 at Woolston, Southampton; orders for a further 145 were cancelled after the Armistice.

Testing of 184s built at Rochester, or delivered there by sub-contractors, was normally done by Ronald Kemp, who had succeeded Gordon Bell in August 1914; Bell had become an official A.I.D. test pilot and was killed in France in July 1918 in this capacity. Ronald Kemp's elder brother, William

Phoenix-built Improved 184 *N1754* with 260 hp Maori I engine at Cattewater in 1918. (*Courtesy G. S. Leslie.*)

119

Brush-built Dover-Type 184 *N1670* taking off from the Firth of Tay at Dundee in 1918; this shows the high radiator position resulting from using a Renault exhaust stack with a Maori I engine.
(*Courtesy G. S. Leslie.*)

Pitcairn (invariably called Peter) Kemp was Admiralty overseer at several aircraft firms, including the Bristol Tramway works at Brislington; when Bristol Scout contracts were completed he came to Rochester and stayed on after the war as Oswald Short's works manager, although Ronald himself left the firm early in 1918. By 1916 Ronald Kemp was having to receive occasional help from other freelance pilots, including Sydney Pickles, Clifford Prodger and John Lankester Parker, all of whom tested aircraft at other factories and belonged to the Prodger–Isaacs Syndicate managed by Bernard Isaacs, pre-war manager of Hendon Aerodrome for Grahame-White; most of the 184s built at Eastchurch were first flown by Parker from Queenborough Pier. It was a tribute to Shorts' methods of manufacture and supervision that production could be so widely and successfully undertaken by firms entirely new to the aircraft industry; Short Brothers' own production of the 184 amounted to no more than 117, including the prototypes, but there were 312 on R.A.F. charge at the Armistice, all but 30 having 260 hp Sunbeams. They remained in service at least until the end of 1920, and Felixstowe still had several in store in 1921, but all had been struck off charge by the time of the Geddes 'Axe' Report in 1922. Short Brothers received a royalty of 3 per cent on all aircraft of their design built by other firms during the war, including spares supplied therewith; the agreement, drawn up by Horace Short, was intended to cover *all* spares, but when Oswald Short put in his claim after the Armistice the Treasury held that the words 'spares supplied therewith' meant only those supplied at the same time, and not subsequently; had the word been 'therefor' Short Brothers would have received a further £170,000 in royalties.

Short 184s served in all European waters on essential but unspectacular duties and penetrated to the Arctic Circle in the Archangel campaign of 1919, when they were embarked in the carrier *Pegasus*; at the other extreme they had carried supplies to the beleaguered troops in Kut-al-Amara in the Mesopotamian desert. After the Armistice they were mainly employed for spotting mines in the shipping lanes; many of the last deliveries were fitted with 275 hp Sunbeam Maori III engines, and in March 1919 *N9135* was flown at Grain with a 300 hp Sunbeam Manitou. A small number were sold abroad to Chile,

120

Estonia, Greece and Japan, and five came on to the British civil register after conversion to five-seaters for seaside joy-riding; all these had the latest Maori III engines with outside exhaust ports and were certificated for one year only; four were built by J. Samuel White (*G-EAJT, G-EBGP, G-EALC* and *G-EBBN*, ex *N2968, N2996, N2998* and *N9118* respectively) and one (*G-EBBM* ex *N9096*) by Brush. The eight supplied to the Estonian Air Force in 1919, also built by J. Samuel White, remained in service until November 1933, during which time only two were lost in crashes.

Samuel White-built improved 184 *N2987* with Maori III, showing the outside exhaust manifolds at Lee-on-Solent in 1918. (*Courtesy G. S. Leslie.*)

Nos. *40* and *41*, the last two of eight 184s supplied to the Estonian Air Force in 1919, survived till No. *40* crashed in the Gulf of Finland on 3 November, 1933, the crew being rescued after 19 hours in the icy water. (*Edgar Meos.*)

Excluding armament development and trials of experimental floats, there were only two major experimental variants of the Short 184. One was the use of a version of the G.R.W. wheel gear to permit take-off from the deck of an aircraft carrier, to avoid the danger from submarine attack incurred by stopping the ship to lower the seaplane overside. The first deck take-off with a 184 was made from *Campania* on 3 June, 1916, and in July 1917 flights were made from the fore-deck of *Furious* soon after she was commissioned as an aircraft carrier. At first the wheels remained attached to the floats and were jettisoned after take-off, but an improved scheme was devised whereby the wheeled trolley was retained in a slot in the deck with a buffer at the forward end; the pilot for these trials, which took place near Scapa Flow, was Flt Lieut

Gallihawk and the observer was Warr Off Flemming. The other experiment was the installation of Martin stabilisers on the upper wing-tips of *8076* at Grain; these were a form of pendulum control claimed by the American inventor to ensure automatic lateral stability, but were not a success.

The last surviving Short 184 was Westland-built *8359*, flown by Flt Lieut F. J. Rutland and Asst Pmr Trewin from *Engadine* at the beginning of the Battle of Jutland on 31 May, 1916, when three enemy cruisers and ten destroyers were spotted and reported shortly before action began; further reconnaissance was hampered by fog, which fortunately also prevented Admiral Scheer from getting any information from his Zeppelins. This seaplane was exhibited at the Crystal Palace after the war ended and was earmarked for permanent preservation in the Imperial War Museum, where it remained until 1940, when it was badly damaged during an air raid. After a survey it was decided that the remains could be restored but only the fuselage of *8359* is now exhibited in the Fleet Air Arm Museum at Yeovilton.

Type 184—Span 63 ft 6 in (19·7 m); length 40 ft 7 in (12·3 m); area 688 sq ft (64 m²); empty weight 3,500–3,800 lb (1,588–1,725 kg); all-up weight 5,100–5,560 lb (2,315–2,480 kg); max speed 75–88 mph (121–142 km/h); duration 4·5–2·75 hr.

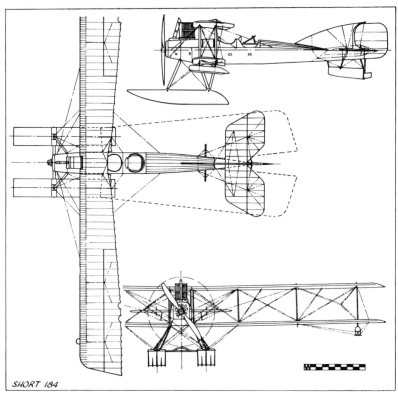

SHORT 184

Original two-bay Bomber prototype *3706* at Eastchurch in 1915, showing the proposed Lewis gun mounting, for which a retractable telescopic fairing was intended to protect the gunner while standing.

The Short Bomber (1915–16)

In the early days of aviation, though forced into a defensive role, the R.N.A.S. never lost sight of the aeroplane's potential as a long-range gun, and was more progressive than the Military Wing in developing basic bombing techniques. The functions of 'Britain's Sure Shield' have never been solely defensive, and have always included the ability to strike the enemy on his own doorstep. Consequently, one of the first objectives of the R.N.A.S. in August 1914 was the destruction of the German High Seas Fleet in its base at Kiel before it could begin to prey on our merchant shipping. Neither naval bombers nor torpedo-planes existed at that date which could tackle such a task, and we have seen how Capt Murray Sueter set about obtaining operationally capable torpedo seaplanes. At the same time he called for a long-range land-based bomber to carry six 112-lb bombs in addition to a crew of two, and specified two engines, partly from the safety viewpoint, but mainly because the task required 300–400 hp, and no engines of this power existed. As is well known, the design chosen was Handley Page's 'Bloody Paralyser', but this could not be produced before the end of 1915 and, after the fall of Antwerp, in October 1914, and the increasing U-boat and Zeppelin activity that followed, various stop-gap bombers were urgently pressed into service, beginning with the famous four Avros which raided the Friedrichshafen airship sheds on 21 November. The Short 184, with its big Sunbeam engine, was an obvious candidate for conversion into a landplane bomber, and a prototype was put in hand at Eastchurch concurrently with the emergence of *184* and *185* at Rochester, early in 1915.

The initial conversion was ready in only a few weeks, and the only alteration in the fuselage was the exchange of crew positions; the pilot's controls were in the rear cockpit and the observer sat in front and was expected to climb on to the decking to fire a Lewis gun on a pillar mounting above the upper wing. The floats were replaced by a sturdy four-wheeled undercarriage, with band-brakes on the rear wheels, which were larger than the front ones. The wings were entirely new and developed from those of the Type 166 seaplane; they had two bays with a large top wing overhang braced by cables over king-posts above the outer struts. The large ailerons, on the top wing only, were inversely tapered, but the lower wing and remainder of the upper wing had a constant chord of 6 ft. The gap was increased by 9 in to 6 ft 3 in and the standard wing-folding arrangements were unaltered; a simple rubber-sprung

123

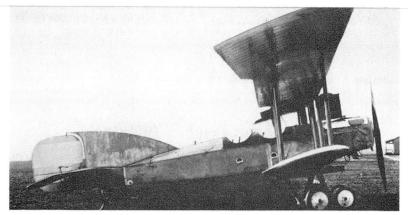

3706 with three-bay wings and experimental landing-gear.

tailskid replaced the tail-float. In this form the Bomber prototype (S.248, later *3706*) flew steadily but was unable to lift a full load of bombs in addition to a crew of two, so the next step was to insert an extra 6 ft bay in each side of the wing assembly. With the span thus increased from 72 to 84 ft, the Bomber could take off with full load, but was totally unstable in pitch and yaw, being very difficult to fly on a course even in fine weather. When Wing Cdr Longmore came over from Dunkerque to try the first production Bomber, he rejected it as hopeless for its role of night bombing in any kind of weather.

Kemp and Longmore knew that the cure was simply a longer tail arm, but Horace Short refused to make this change without restressing the whole airframe, and Longmore was anxious to get the German batteries silenced as quickly as possible. So he arranged for Horace to receive an invitation from the Admiral commanding Naval forces in Belgium to visit the R.N.A.S. base at Dunkerque and possibly, it was hinted, be flown as an observer over the German lines. This was a bait that Horace could not resist, and he set off

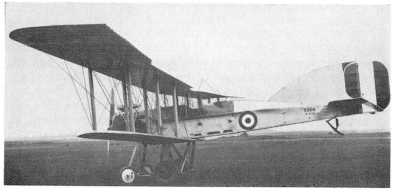

9306, the first production Short Bomber, was the subject of emergency surgery to lengthen its tail.

124

from Dover in high glee as an honoured guest on board a destroyer; immediately he had left Eastchurch, Longmore and Kemp got busy with handsaws, parted the longerons behind the rear cockpit and scarfed in a new parallel fuselage section of the correct length to permit normal wing folding, which proved to be 8 ft 6 in. They finished the job quickly, but when they wheeled the Bomber out for a test flight Horace Short's secretary sent him a telegram saying that 'monkey business' was afoot. Horace came back at the double, and when Kemp met his train at Sittingbourne station he was obviously very angry and refused to speak to him. On arriving at Eastchurch, he examined the unofficial modification very closely and stumped off into his office, still without a word to anybody. Next morning, Kemp and Longmore braced themselves for the explosion, but apparently Horace had stayed up all night checking the strength of the lengthened fuselage, and they were greeted with one of his broadest smiles and an announcement that the job was already cleared for production; Horace knew when he himself had been 'spike-bozzled'—a very rare occurrence.

Mann Egerton's first Bomber, *9476*, as originally built with short fuselage. (*I.W.M.—Crown Copyright.*)

Before this episode orders had been placed with Short Brothers for 50 Bombers (S.249–283, *9306–9355*), for which 250 hp Rolls-Royce engines were promised, and with the Sunbeam Motor Car Co of Wolverhampton for 20 (*9356–9375*) with 225 hp Sunbeam engines; soon more Rolls-Royce engines were released, and further orders were then placed with Mann, Egerton & Co of Norwich for 20 (*9476–9495*) and for ten each with Parnall & Sons, Bristol (*9771–9780*), and Phoenix Dynamo Co, Bradford (*9831–9840*), all with these engines. The first Sunbeam and Mann Egerton Bombers, like Shorts' own *9306*, were completed quickly early in 1916 to the unmodified drawings, and both were flown by Sydney Pickles, who agreed with Ronald Kemp that the tail was too short and refused to fly the first Parnall machine *9771* until it had been modified; all the fuselages were lengthened before acceptance, and at the same time the fin area of the Sunbeam-engined variant was slightly reduced by straightening the leading edge; this was also tried out on an early Short-built Rolls-Royce machine, but the latter was found to be better with the original fin unaltered. With the long fuselage, elevator control was powerful, and in conjunction with the four-wheeled undercarriage Kemp was able to taxi across

Sunbeam-built Bomber *9356* at Dunstall Park, Wolverhampton, after its fuselage had been lengthened, showing the straight-edged fin. (*Courtesy G. S. Leslie.*)

some of the deeper ditches in the outlying areas of Eastchurch aerodrome; he would approach the ditch with the control wheel hard back, apply the band-brakes on the rear wheels as soon as the front wheels were across, then with the control wheel fully forward, he would release the brakes and lift the rear wheels across with a burst of throttle.

All production Bombers reverted to the normal crew arrangement, because gun-rings had become available for the rear cockpit, which was built up above the decking. Dual control was installed and the main fuel tanks were protected by armour plate; in both engine installations fuel was pumped into a small streamlined gravity tank above the cowling. The radiators were flank-mounted, alongside the Rolls-Royce and a little farther aft for the Sunbeam, to give access to magnetos and carburettors in each case. The bombs were carried under the wing on four racks whose attachment lugs were braced by cables to the tops of the adjacent wing struts. The somewhat heavy Woolwich carriers were specified, but Short Brothers saved weight by hanging the bombs from nose-rings, which had little effect on aiming accuracy; skeleton carriers were later standardised, the designed maximum bomb load being eight 112-lb bombs, although 65-lb were usually carried instead to increase range.

In September 1915 the first Zeppelin raid was made on London, inflicting

Eastchurch-built Bomber *9315* with Rolls-Royce engine and lengthened fuselage; this was the first type flown by John Parker at Eastchurch in 1916.

unexpectedly high civilian casualties, and the demand for retaliation in kind, coupled with the more logical necessity of bombing the U-boat assembly yards at Antwerp, drew Parliamentary attention to the absence of effective R.N.A.S. bombers. Murray Sueter was continually pressed to confute the critics, and when at last the first long-fuselage Bomber arrived at Grain from Wolverhampton he had it photographed from a fixed point in four different locations on the aerodrome; a composite print gave the impression of four Bombers awaiting dispatch, and the photograph was circulated to M.P.s without comment, but was carefully kept from the Press; the deception was justifiable as a way of keeping up morale at a critical juncture, and disclosure could only have exacerbated the hostility between the Army and Navy supply departments, which came to a head in 1916 before the Bailhache and Burbidge Committees.

The Short Bomber deserves a place in history, if for no other reason, as the first big landplane flown by John Lankester Parker when, at Murray Sueter's suggestion, he came from Windermere to Eastchurch to take up part-time test-flying for Short Bros, as assistant to Ronald Kemp. At first Horace Short refused to allow 'that bit of a boy' to fly at all, but when in desperation Parker tendered his resignation, Horace pointed out six Bombers waiting to be tested and said, 'Go and break your bloody neck on those', then drove quickly away so as not to witness the ensuing disaster; but there was no disaster, and Parker flew three of the Bombers (*9328, 9329* and *9331*) that day (17 October, 1916) and the other three (*9326, 9327* and *9333*) the next day; while he was climbing the fourth machine to 6,500 ft in 21 minutes, Horace looked up in wonderment and conceded to Oswald, 'He's a first rate pilot!' He flew two more Short-built Bombers (*9332* and *9330*) on 28 October and then his first Sunbeam machine (*9361*) on 2 November. On 11 December he had to make two successive forced landings in *9362*, which developed a punctured carburettor float, and brought these off successfully, but on 13 December *9339* had engine failure at 5,000 ft and had to be put down outside the aerodrome, running into a ridge in the ground and breaking two chassis struts. This skilful 'dead-stick' landing considerably impressed his passenger, Lieut Wardle (the Admiralty acceptance officer), although Parker had expected a reprimand for not reaching the aerodrome from that height. Most new Bombers were first flown at Eastchurch, but a few were erected at Manston, where Parker tested Sunbeam-built *9366* on 7 December, Phoenix-built *9836* on 14 December and Parnall-built *9775* on 17 December.

Meanwhile, as Short Bombers were accepted for service, they had re-equipped No. 7 Wing, R.N.A.S., at Coudekerque and went into action as night-bombers on 15 November, 1916, when four of them, each with eight 65-lb bombs, raided submarine pens at Zeebrugge. Fifteen more were attached to the newly formed 3rd Wing, R.N.A.S., at Luxeuil, whose task was to carry the war into the Saar Valley; from this unit grew the Independent Force, R.A.F., of 1918, the lineal ancestor of Bomber Command. In June 1916 the R.F.C. itself was desperately in need of more aircraft for the Somme offensive, and General Trenchard had asked the Admiralty most urgently to release as many machines as possible; the Admiralty responded generously to this *cri-de-cœur*, even though this put back the 3rd Wing's own offensive till October; eventually 14 Short Bombers (*9315, 9319, 9320, 9325, 9476–9, 9482–5* and *9487–8*) were transferred to the R.F.C., in addition to one new Phoenix-built machine, *A3932*. With the arrival of Handley Page O/100 twin-engined bombers in November, the crisis was over and Short Bombers not yet delivered were cancelled, including the last 15 from Short Brothers, the last five from Sunbeam and the last four from each of the Parnall and Phoenix contracts, but Mann Egerton had delivered all their quota before the axe fell and these had been test-flown at Norwich by Clifford Prodger. A few Short Bombers remained with the 5th Wing at Dunkerque from January 1917 onwards, and on four successive nights in April they attacked the Zeebrugge Mole with 520-lb bombs in preparation for the famous naval raid on St George's Day. Apart from those transferred to the R.F.C., *9311* was presented to the French Armée de l'Air for evaluation against their standard

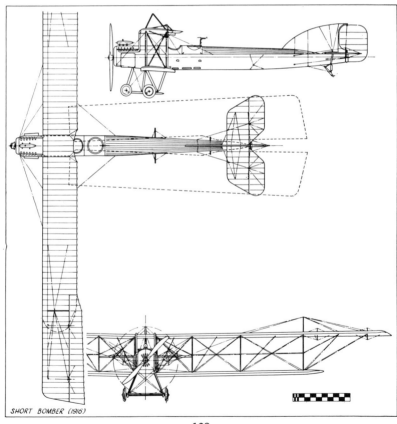

SHORT BOMBER (1916)

Caudrons and Breguets. One of the last Bombers on charge was the final one built by Shorts at Eastchurch, S.283 (*9340*), which was flown from Martlesham Heath to Grain on 9 November, 1917, but as late as April 1918 the first production Bomber S.249 (*9306*) was returned to Grain for gunnery trials, presumably as a target.

The Short Bomber came into existence only as a stop-gap; it did its job and, when no longer needed, bowed itself out and was gone. No further development took place, but apparently a twin-engined Short bomber had been contemplated in 1916, because serials *N507–8* were reserved for prototypes of this description; the engines were to have been 200 hp Sunbeams (Afridis or Arabs), but the project was cancelled before any work was done on it, probably because of Horace Short's death; it was possibly a landplane derived from the twin-fuselage tandem-engined seaplane depicted in Oswald Short's patent No. 3,203 of February 1915.

Span 84 ft (25·6 m); length 36 ft 6 in (11·15 m), later 45 ft (13·7 m); area 870 sq ft (80·9 m²); empty weight 5,000 lb (2,268 kg); all-up weight 6,800 lb (3,082 kg); max speed (Sunbeam) 72 mph (116 km/h), (R-R) 77 mph (124 km/h); duration 6 hr.

The prototype 310-A, S.299, at Rochester in July 1916, with Oswald Short at right.

Short 310 hp Seaplanes, 1916–19

When the Short 184 failed to repeat its first operational success as a torpedo-plane, due mainly to insufficient power in reserve to cope with both a torpedo and ample fuel, particularly in hot weather, Capt Murray Sueter and Lieut Hyde Thomson realised that they would have to face the complication of twin engines or wait for a power unit giving at least 300 hp, preferably at a weight no greater than that of current 200 hp engines. Early experience with the Wight twin-fuselage torpedo seaplane had provided only double trouble with no advantage in performance, plus an unnecessarily large aircraft for the task. Nevertheless, a twin-engined prototype torpedo-seaplane with 225 hp Sunbeam engines was ordered from the Blackburn Aeroplane Co and Louis Coatalen was urged to press on with the development of a 300 hp Sunbeam engine in competition with the rapidly improving Rolls-Royce Eagle; all supplies of the latter were already earmarked for bombers (D.H.4 and Handley Page O/100) and for Curtiss and Porte flying-boats which had begun to prove their ability to fight off and destroy Zeppelins at long range. The Admiralty's objectives of torpedoing the German and Austrian fleets in their respective anchorages at Wilhelmshaven and Pola had to yield priority to the urgent needs of the Western Front and North Sea battles, and consequently no Rolls-Royce Eagles could be spared for float seaplanes in 1916.

Meanwhile, Horace and Oswald Short prepared two designs based on the new Sunbeam engine; the first was a cleaned-up and strengthened torpedo-seaplane of almost the same size as the Mann Egerton Type B, with a roomier fuselage, increased chord and gap and similar wing arrangement; the second was a patrol seaplane with the same fuselage and chassis as the first, but having equal-span three-bay wings analogous to Type 184. Two prototypes of each were ordered as a batch of four, the torpedo-planes (310 Type A) being S.299–300 (serials *8317–8318*) and the patrol seaplanes (310 Type B) being S.311–312 (serials *8319–8320*); the latter were alternatively known as 'North Sea Scouts'. The Sunbeam engine, later named Cossack, was rated at 310 hp (normal) and 320 hp (maximum), but in production batches the normal rating was soon raised to 320 hp. Maximum priority was accorded to the torpedo version, once the engines were available, with a view to putting them to use in the Adriatic as soon as possible. General design features were similar to the 184's, but the 18-in Mark IX torpedo (weighing 1,000 lb against the 810 lb of the 14-in Whitehead) was carried close under the belly of the fuselage. The rear cross-strut of the float chassis was made detachable to permit a clear passage when the torpedo was launched, and extra struts were provided to secure the inner faces of the floats while the cross-strut was removed. The engine installation was generally similar to that of the 260 hp Sunbeam in the 184, with the same block radiator above and an auxiliary radiator and oil cooler on the port side of the fuselage between the wings; in later production batches the main radiator was enlarged and the auxiliary unit deleted. At first the central exhaust manifold had a downswept stack, but this resulted in fumes in the cockpit and only after various vertical and lateral pipes had been tried was the final stack, upswept and canted to port, found satisfactory; for a time the prototypes had a parallel pair of pipes close together. The prototypes had four-bladed airscrews, but two-bladers were standard on production aircraft. The pilot occupied the rear cockpit, to obviate the need for ballast under a variety of loading conditions, and the front cockpit provided all the normal stowages and equipment for the observer, including W/T; in later batches there was also a Scarff ring mounted on struts level with the upper-wing trailing edge, which gave the observer a clear field of fire for a Lewis gun, but was a position of great exposure for which no alternative could be found; however, the observer could not be carried at the same time as a torpedo.

The first prototype was ready for flight at Rochester in July 1916, and the

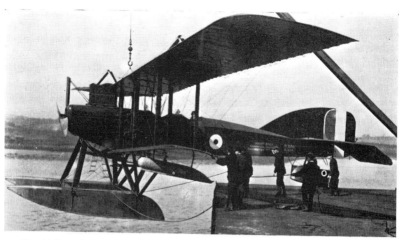

Ronald Kemp in *N1150* at Rochester in February 1917; note slender vertical exhaust stack.

second in August, both being first flown by Ronald Kemp. After acceptance, the two prototypes were urgently dispatched to the R.N.A.S. seaplane base at Otranto, where it was intended to station 12 of the type, but during early torpedo trials both seaplanes broke up in the air. At first it was thought that the rebound from suddenly releasing so great a weight might have been responsible for structural failure, but the defect was traced to the rear float attachment; this was redesigned with modified floats pitched farther apart and extra struts bracing the floats to the lower wings; the extra float struts were V-shaped welded tube assemblies which swung down when released for wing folding; a notice prominently painted on both sides of the fuselage read: '*Very Important: The Removable Rear Crossbar Must always be in Position Before the Wings are Folded*'; in this form the aircraft was designated the

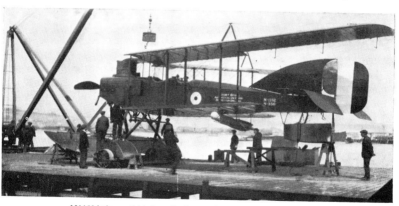

N1152 being unfolded on the jetty at Rochester in February 1917, showing alternative position of slender exhaust stack.

131

310-A4. The second 310-B (S.312) was converted during construction into an additional 310-A4 in February 1917 and renumbered *N1480*. Production had already begun at Rochester with a batch of 30 (S.354–363, *N1150–1159*, and S.334–353, *N1300–1319*) for urgent delivery to Otranto and Malta, to be followed by batches of 24 (S.365–388, *N1481–1504*) and 20 (S.399–418, *N1390–1409*). Concurrently a contract was placed with Sunbeam for batches of 30 (*N1360–1389*) and 20 (*N1690–1709*) respectively; it seems that the final batches from Short Bros and Sunbeam were exchanged, probably to ease temporary supply difficulties. No later production was undertaken because official policy had changed in favour of deck-landing torpedo-planes, following successful trials after the second refit of H.M.S. *Furious*. On its first operation the 310-A4 was robbed of success by a sudden gale which wrecked all six of those detailed for a torpedo attack on the night of 3 September, 1917, against a flotilla of enemy submarines off Cattaro in the Adriatic. To conserve fuel, they

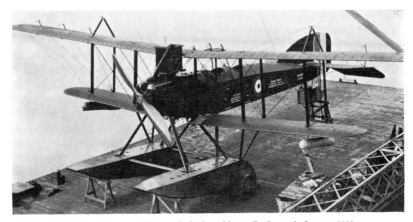

Production 310-A4 *N1397* ready for launching at Rochester in January 1918.

were towed on rafts to Traste Bay, where they arrived successfully but were capsized by a sudden storm at 4 am, just at zero hour for take-off; so the opportunity passed, and no other chance presented itself within the capability of the aircraft for several months. Then, in January 1918, the German cruiser *Goeben* made a bolt for freedom through the Dardanelles but ran aground at Nagara Burnu; while stuck fast, she was repeatedly bombed without effect by the R.N.A.S., and two 310-A4s, with torpedoes, were hastily embarked on *Manxman*, but arrived too late to join in the attack, for after a week the *Goeben*'s crew refloated her and she escaped to shelter in the Bosphorus.

To improve experience of torpedo launching, a series of trials were run at Calshot in February 1918, in which 40 torpedoes were launched by four 310-A4s; only three weapons were lost, and the lessons learned were put to use at the Torpedo School at Kalafrana, Malta. The majority of the 310-A4s

The first and only 310-B, S.311 (*8319*) at Rochester in September 1916.

in service were used in the long-range patrol role, when they had an endurance of six hours while carrying a crew of two and two 230-lb bombs. No submarine kill by a 310-A4 was ever confirmed, although a probable was scored by one from Kalafrana on a U-boat which attacked a French battleship off Malta on 8 February, 1918. The total number of 310-As built was 127, of which 50 remained in service with the R.A.F. at the Armistice; *N1404* and *N1409* were in use at Grain for experimental work in June 1918, and six, believed to be S.370–375 (*N1485–1490*), were supplied to the Imperial Japanese Navy for training and trials at the end of 1917.

The 310-B, completed in September 1916, was not adopted for production, being not a sufficient improvement on the 184. Possibly if all the torpedo-seaplanes had been needed in their original role there would have been some justification for a structurally similar long-range Scout, but, with no niche to fill, the prototype S.311 (*8319*) was used in April 1917 only for air-firing trials at Grain of a 6-pounder Davis recoilless gun, arranged to fire upwards and forwards as an anti-Zeppelin weapon. It was mounted on a trammel across the rear cockpit, which also had a Lewis gun for self-defence; the pilot was in front as in the 184, which the 310-B closely resembled in layout, although it was bigger all round and its deeper fuselage gave better protection to the crew. For some reason, no doubt to improve the pilot's view ahead as well as to

8319 about to take off for trials of 6-pounder Davis gun at Grain in April 1917.

133

avoid muzzle blast damage from the Davis gun, the top centre-section was left open and the radiator was separated laterally into two parallel blocks, with a clear space in the middle. The gun was a later model of that tested at Great Yarmouth in 1915 on Short pusher S.81 (*126*), but was still a single-shot type incapable of being reloaded in the air; in any case it could only be aimed at an angle to the flight path, so it was quite unsuitable for aerial use, even when directed downwards as an anti-submarine weapon.

Type 310-A4—Span 75 ft (22·85 m); length 45 ft 9 in (13·9 m); area 810 sq ft (75·3 m²); empty weight 4,900 lb (2,222 kg); all-up weight 7,020 lb (3,185 kg); max speed 79 mph (127 km/h); duration 6 hr.

Type 310-B—Span 68 ft 6 in (20·85 m); area 800 sq ft (74·4 m²); max speed 72 mph (116 km/h); all other data as for Type 310-A4.

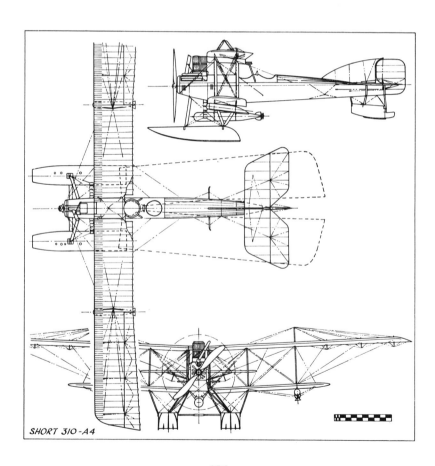

SHORT 310-A4

Scout No. 1, S.313, on the jetty outside No. 2 Shop at Rochester in January 1917.

Short Experimental Seaplanes N.2A and N.2B

The Royal Naval Air Service employed single-seat scout seaplanes from the earliest days of the war, and by 1916 had gained a comprehensive knowledge of their capabilities and limitations; they were almost exclusively derived from the Sopwith Tabloid, winner of the Schneider Trophy in 1914, and Sopwith Babies were built in large numbers by both the parent company and Blackburn; there was also an improved version redesigned by Fairey, called the Hamble Baby and built by both Fairey and Parnall. They were flown from many shore stations and formed part of the complement of most of the early seaplane carriers. As the U-boat menace increased, the diversity and quantity of gear required to be carried by anti-submarine scouts became too much for a solo pilot to cope with, and the need for a small fast two-seat seaplane became evident. During the latter part of 1916 Short Brothers put forward two designs for this role; the first was a 'pint-size' version of the 310-A seaplane, proposed by Horace Short, while the second represented a different approach by Oswald Short in collaboration with the Admiralty Board of Inventions and Research; both designs were intended to satisfy the Air Department's specification N.2A, which covered seaplanes and deck-landing landplanes. One prototype of each was ordered, the first from Rochester and the second from Eastchurch, both with the same engine, the 200 hp Sunbeam Afridi.

The Rochester machine, Experimental Scout No. 1, S.313 (serial *N36*), was ready first and was launched on 2 January, 1917; it was a stubby single-bay sesquiplane with the upper wing span much greater than the lower; the crew were placed close together behind the wings, which carried plywood wing-tip floats and were slightly staggered. The top centre section was open and incorporated a false spar aft of the true rear spar so as to provide vertical

135

hinges for wing folding. A refinement was the completely submerged radiator below the engine, for which cooling air was taken in through the open front cowling and discharged through side ducts above the lower wing roots. The engine was enclosed in a hinged, many-louvred bonnet, like a motor-car, and had bifurcated downswept exhaust pipes in front. Official insistence on compactness had resulted in the fuselage being shortened to the limit, and consequently Ronald Kemp found it nose-heavy and could not get it off the water, as it had insufficient elevator control; to put matters right an extra bay was inserted in the rear fuselage, increasing the tail arm by 2 ft; thus modified, it was redesignated Experimental Scout No. 2 and was flown rather precariously by Kemp on 23 January, but its handling and performance were disappointing, so it was abandoned. Experimental Scout No. 3, S.364, was entirely different in layout and indicated the divergence of young Oswald Short's ideas from those of his eldest brother. Although both were empiricists first and last, and Oswald had learned the art of design from Horace, he had taken notice of some wind-tunnel results obtained at the N.P.L. on various aerofoil sections and wing-plan shapes. While agreeing with Horace's preference for 'plenty of leading edge', i.e. a high aspect ratio, he wanted to try

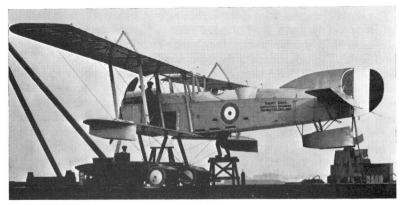

Two more views of S.313, showing the false rear spar for wing-folding and the air outlet from the buried radiator, also the boat-built wing-tip floats.

Scout No. 2 on the water at Rochester on 23 January, 1917; it was simply Scout No. 1 with an extra 2-ft bay inserted aft of the gunner's cockpit.

the effect of low-drag wings of B.I.R.31 section, combined with elliptical wing-tips, a large gap and a reduced fin area. So when S.364 appeared on Queenborough Pier on 9 March, 1917, its slender lines and generally 'tall' aspect were in marked contrast to the traditional Short layout. Another difference was the stiff straight trailing edge, which replaced the familiar cusped boundary formed by a hemp cord stretched between the tails of the ribs; cord had been used for some years to avoid the salt-water corrosion which attacked stranded wire trailing edges, causing the fabric to rot and split, however carefully protected. S.364 was first flown by John Parker on 27 March and found to be tail-heavy and seriously under-powered. Later a 260 hp Sunbeam Maori I engine replaced the Afridi and larger floats were fitted to carry the increased weight, but even then the military load was limited to two 65-lb bombs in addition to the observer's Scarff ring and Lewis gun. At the same time Admiralty policy veered in favour of deck-landing aeroplanes, following initial experiments on the aircraft-carrier *Furious*, so further development of small two-seater seaplanes ceased early in 1918.

Scout No. 3, S.364, was built at Eastchurch and is here seen after launching at Queenborough on 9 March, 1917.

137

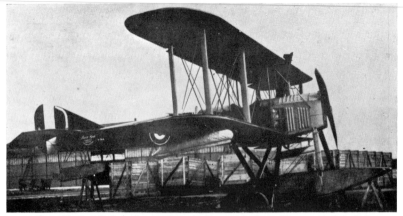

Scout No. 3 at Grain in August 1917, with larger main floats. (*Courtesy G. S. Leslie.*)

Horace Short died after a few days' illness on 6 April, 1917, and Oswald rose nobly to the occasion and took over the supervision of all design, in which he was assisted by Francis Webber at Rochester and C. P. T. Lipscomb at Cardington; Eustace Short reserved his interest, as hitherto, for the balloon and airship side of the business, which occupied the works at Battersea and Cardington. The first completely new design produced after Horace Short's death was a long-range two-seat patrol seaplane intended as a replacement for Type 184 as defined by Admiralty specification N.2B. Several prototypes were ordered, but only two (S.419–420, *N66–67*) were actually built, both having the 260 hp Sunbeam Maori I engine. Competitive designs were ordered from Fairey and J. Samuel White, and both these went into production with Rolls-Royce Eagle engines, but the Short N.2B was less favoured, and Oswald Short's request to be allowed to fit an Eagle was rejected by Alec Ogilvie, who in 1917 had become Controller of Technical Design at the Air Board.

The first prototype, *N66*, was launched at Rochester on 22 December, 1917; it had originally been designed with a radiator mounted on the upper centre-section, but was built with a frontal honeycomb radiator similar to that designed for Scout No. 3. The engine cowling panels were hinged and liberally provided with louvres, and the fuselage was a refined version of Type 184's, with a Scarff ring for the observer in the rear cockpit; the fin was smaller than the 184's and of higher aspect ratio, as in Scout No. 3. The wings were unstaggered and folded back, but the upper wing was flat and its extended tips were strut-braced; the lower wing had dihedral and carried plywood floats attached directly under each wing-tip, as in Scout No. 1. *N66* went to Grain for evaluation, and when tested there on 2 February, 1918, by Maurice Wright was found to have no better performance than Type 184 with the same engine, the climb to 10,000 ft taking 69 minutes. Oswald Short knew that with its original two-bladed airscrew its time to this height was less

138

than 45 minutes and found that the testing station had substituted a four-blader; he insisted on the original airscrew being refitted, and on 22 March, 1918, an official test figure of 10,000 ft in $40\frac{1}{2}$ minutes was confirmed, but by then the decision to adopt the rival Fairey IIIC for the R.A.F. had been taken. The N.2B was unofficially dubbed the *Camel Short* because of the absence of dihedral on the top wing, and it seems that this association of ideas created an entirely unfounded prejudice against it in the minds of those who had unhappy memories of the Sopwith Camel.

In the first prototype an attempt was made to improve performance by fairing the float to a point aft of the step and making the float bottom concave forward of the step; this was a compromise between the plain flat-bottomed pontoon and the long-heeled type developed for the German Hansa-Brandenburg monoplanes, which had operated so successfully from bases in the Heligoland Bight and the Friesian Islands. British attempts to emulate the Germans were unrewarding as a means of eliminating the parasitic tail and wing-tip floats, and after early trials of *N66* normal flat-bottomed pontoons were adopted for the second N.2B, *N67*, which consequently had a larger tail-float; it also had smoother engine cowlings with fewer louvres, and the

Two views of the first N.2B, *N66*, at Rochester in January 1918, showing main float-tail fairings and bomb racks.

139

central exhaust stack was inclined to starboard to keep fumes out of the cockpits. *N66* was allocated to Westgate for operational trials on 21 April, 1918, and on 16 May *N67* was delivered from Rochester to Grain for seaworthiness trials in comparison with the second Farnborough-designed C.E.1 flying-boat *N98*, which also had a Maori engine. On 17 August *N67* was damaged, new floats and new wings with reduced aileron area being fitted in September; it was serviceable again by 2 November and was sent to Westgate for operational trials from December 1918 to February 1919, after which it was loaned back to Short Brothers to be used as a basis for initial post-war civil projects. In February 1919 a mock-up was made of a modified N.2B fuselage with an enclosed cabin for six passengers between the wings and the pilot's cockpit aft, foreshadowing later de Havilland designs. A 375 hp Rolls-Royce Eagle VIII engine was proposed for this project, which was never built because no definite orders were promised. John Parker, who had not previously flown the N.2B,

John Parker and General Seely arriving at Westminster in *N67* on 9 April, 1919, having flown through Tower Bridge *en route*; soon after 1 May, when civil aviation legally began, flights through Tower Bridge were prohibited.

ferried *N67* back to Rochester from Westgate on 1 March, 1919, and on 9 April repeated Frank McClean's feat of flying through Tower Bridge on his way up the Thames to Westminster; this time he had as his passenger the Under-Secretary of State for War, General Seely, who had been summoned to reply to a Parliamentary Question while on a visit to Rochester and gladly accepted Oswald Short's offer of 'door-to-door' air transport; although the overall flight time of 43 minutes was unspectacular, the ease with which Parker alighted alongside the terrace of the House of Commons and took off again after transferring his passenger to a motor-launch attracted favourable notice and focused public attention on the impending legalisation of civil

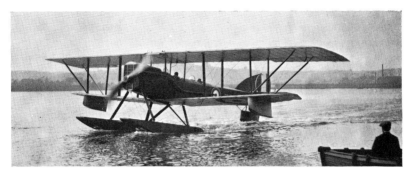

N67 with Rolls-Royce Eagle 'illegally' installed about to take off at Rochester on 24 May, 1919, with two-bladed airscrew.

aviation on 1 May, 1919, and the possibility of seaplane operation from sheltered water near a city centre.

With this in mind and in defiance of the Air Ministry's refusal to allow a Rolls-Royce Eagle to be officially tested in the N.2B, Oswald Short took the opportunity of extending the loan of the engine already borrowed for the *Shamrock* (as described later) from stocks reserved for the current F.3 flying-boat contract; this engine, a low-compression Eagle VIII (No. 5058), was installed in *N67*, using the radiator and cowling also salvaged from the *Shamrock*, and Parker flew it on 24 May with Oscar Gnosspelius as passenger; with the more powerful, but scarcely heavier, engine the N.2B's performance was completely transformed, and it was off the water in four seconds and 50 yards; a brief first handling test of three minutes at 800 ft was followed by an hour's flight, during which Parker climbed from 5,000 to 11,600 ft in 18

N67 flying with 'illegal Eagle' and four-blader on 1 June, 1919.

141

minutes. On 27 May Parker took Oswald Short for an 83-minute flight over London, climbing to 16,200 ft in 50 minutes and gliding back to the Medway with engine off in half an hour; but the top speed was increased by only 8 mph, and after one more flight over the marked speed course, with Gnosspelius as observer, the two-bladed airscrew was exchanged for a four-blader, which gave a speed of 90 mph at 2,000 ft when tested on 29 May. *N67* was demonstrated to Sir Frederick Sykes on 1 June, when Parker and Gnosspelius reached 3,000 ft in 4¼ minutes. On 10 July it was taxied around on land for seven minutes with wheels attached to the floats, possibly to assess its prospects in the amphibian class of the Air Ministry's proposed competition for civil aeroplanes, but no further work was done on these lines. On 26 July it was flown at a full load of 4,911 lb to 10,000 ft in 33 minutes and reached 93 mph at 2,000 ft, which put it ahead of the Fairey IIIC, but having illegally installed the forbidden Eagle, Oswald Short could hardly claim to have it retested at Grain. So, after one or two more flights, in which Parker took off straight across the Medway over Cuxton, the borrowed engine was returned to its crate and the Maori was reinstalled in *N67*, in which condition it was finally taken on charge by the R.A.F. at Grain on 2 January, 1920.

The second N.2B, *N67*, at Grain in 1920, showing plain floats and revised engine cowling.
(*Courtesy R. C. B. Ashworth.*)

Scout No. 1—Span 46 ft (14 m); length 31 ft 6 in (9·6 m); area 450 sq ft (41·8 m²). Scout No. 2—Length 33 ft 6 in (10·2 m); otherwise as for Scout No. 1. Scout No. 3—Span 39 ft (11·8 m); length 28 ft (8·53 m); area 375 sq ft (35·9 m²); weights and performance not recorded.

N.2B—Span 55 ft 2 in (16·8 m); length 40 ft 2 in (12·2 m); area 678 sq ft (63 m²); empty weight (Sunbeam) 3,120 lb (1,415 kg), (R-R) 3,200 lb (1,452 kg); all-up weight (Sunbeam) 4,741 lb (2,150 kg), (R-R) 4,912 lb (2,230 kg); max speed (Sunbeam) 92 mph (148 km/h), (R-R) 95 mph (152 km/h); duration 4·5 hr.

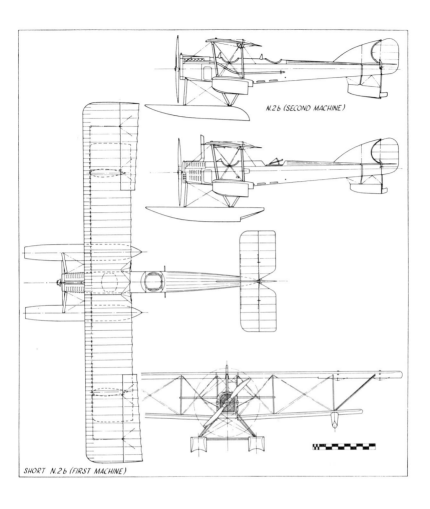

N.2b (SECOND MACHINE)

SHORT N.2b (FIRST MACHINE)

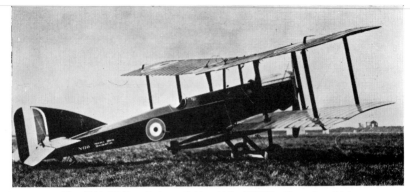

First Shirl, *N110*, at Grain on 27 May, 1918. (*I.W.M.—Crown Copyright.*)

The Short N.1B Shirl

The story of how the first carrier-borne torpedo-aeroplane, the Sopwith Cuckoo, came into existence has been well told elsewhere, and it is only necessary to recall here that the R.N.A.S. might never have had such a weapon after Commodore Murray Sueter's posting to the Mediterranean in January 1917, had not work on the prototype been revived six months later at the instigation of Wing Commander Arthur Longmore, who noticed it, set aside half-finished, during a visit to the Sopwith works. The Cuckoo proved to be an excellent aeroplane, its main drawback being that its 1,000-lb Mark IX torpedo was not powerful enough to be effective against large warships. The Admiralty therefore called, in the autumn of 1917, for a generally similar single-seat aeroplane to carry a Mark VIII torpedo weighing 1,423 lb, with a warhead 50 per cent larger than the Mark IX's; the requirements were embodied in specification N.1B (which was revised as RAF XXII after April 1918), and since deck-landing was not yet operationally practicable, because of delays in completing the new carriers *Argus* and *Eagle*, ditching gear and jettisonable wheels were specified, so that the returning aircraft could be salvaged if unable to reach a shore base after launching its missile. Tenders were submitted by two firms, Blackburn and Short Bros, and each received a contract for three prototypes to be powered by the Rolls-Royce Eagle VIII engine of 385 hp.

The Short proposal, later named Shirl, was a simple, solid, two-bay biplane; its fuselage was covered throughout with plywood to resist the effects of temporary immersion, and the wings and tail-unit were similar in construction to those of Oswald Short's previous design, the N.2B, with four ailerons, cord trailing edges and folding gear; the wings were of equal span, with square tips and neither stagger nor sweep-back. The engine was neatly cowled, with a frontal honeycomb radiator, and the landing chassis was arranged for release after take-off. At first this was a simple expendable two-wheeled

144

cross-axle arrangement, and in this form the first prototype Shirl (S.421, *N110*) was flown at Grain on 27 May, 1918, by John Parker, climbing to 10,000 ft with full load in 21 minutes; next day the test was repeated with a four-bladed airscrew but found inferior, so the original two-blader was refitted on 29 May. A few days later he delivered it by air to Martlesham Heath, carrying a dummy Mark VIII torpedo; five minutes after take-off the petrol-pump drive sheared and he had to make a hurried forced landing, but the trouble was quickly rectified and he was able to take off again; he then found that the throttle control adjustment had been displaced during the repair and that he was unable to close it. As he was determined not to abandon the delivery flight, he stayed on his course and prevented the engine from overspeeding by maintaining a steady climb; this resulted in his arrival over Martlesham at a height of 12,000 ft, from which he executed a masterly 'dead-stick' landing with the ignition switched off.

On completion of its official tests, with a temporary restriction of the engine to 345 hp, the first Shirl was returned to Rochester for modifications, including incorporation of a small amount of sweep-back to counteract tail heaviness when flotation bags were installed in the rear fuselage. At the same time a new landing chassis was fitted to permit either normal landing or ditching to be selected, irrespective of when the torpedo was launched. The revised chassis comprised two separate units, each with a tubular skid carrying a pair of wheels on a short cross-axle, a large flotation bag which could be inflated rapidly from a compressed-air bottle and a small hydrovane at the forward end of the skid. The axles were rubber-sprung and could be jettisoned for deck-landing or ditching, and the skids were carried by inclined struts from the bottom longerons and from the wing spars below the inner interplane struts. This arrangement allowed the torpedo to be launched without affecting the landing-gear configuration, although jury struts had to be rigged before the wings could be folded. *N110* was completed in this form on 1 July, 1918, and underwent satisfactory ditching trials at Grain. The second Shirl (S.422, *N111*), built to the same overall standard, but with larger ailerons and a fixed

Second Shirl, *N111*, at Grain in July 1918, before its flight to East Fortune.
(*I.W.M.—Crown Copyright.*)

145

tailplane, was dispatched to Grain from Rochester on 8 July; it was urgently needed for trials at the Torpedo Aeroplane School at East Fortune, near Dunbar, and Parker hoped to be able to fly it there immediately after a preliminary test flight at Grain. Unfortunately his first brief handling trial showed *N111* to be considerably more tail-heavy than expected, but a rapid consultation with Oswald Short indicated that an increase of tailplane incidence by 4 degrees would put matters right; the tailplane was removed at noon, new fittings were made in the Grain workshops and by four o'clock Parker was ready for a second flight, before which he took on a full load of fuel; he found longitudinal control satisfactory, so flew straight on to arrive at East Fortune $4\frac{1}{2}$ hours later. He cruised most of the 400 miles at 13,000 ft, his only instruments being radiator thermometer, engine tachometer, altimeter, cross-level, fore-and-aft level, an air-speed indicator that did not indicate and a small compass which had not been swung; but he found the Shirl a remarkably stable and untiring machine to fly and arrived with plenty of fuel in reserve, which proved the aerodynamic efficiency of the design.

At East Fortune the Shirl took part in operational torpedo trials along with the Blackburn Blackburd, but in spite of their higher power and weight-

N111 launching a torpedo off Dunbar in July 1918. (*Crown Copyright.*)

lifting ability, both lacked the agility of the Sopwith Cuckoo in taking evasive action after an attack. After these trials *N111* went to Martlesham for performance testing on 24 August, 1918, and was flown at a gross weight of over 6,000 lb; although its performance was excellent, it was criticised for not having a tailplane incidence adjuster like *N110*; consequently *N111* was found to be tail-heavy with the torpedo and nose-heavy without it. The third Shirl

Third Shirl, *N112*, at Eastchurch in April 1919, showing the final chassis design and the experimental half-ton mail container.

(S.423, *N112*) was not completed till 11 December and was delivered to Gosport early in 1919, being flown back to Eastchurch by Parker on 28 March in a hailstorm; thereafter it was flown at various weights to assess its potential as a civil mail-carrier; for this role a large plywood container of half a ton capacity was slung from the torpedo rack; on 1 April it failed to take-off at 7,400 lb, but three days later it climbed to 5,000 ft in 25 minutes at 6,762 lb. It had a revised tailplane adjuster and a new chassis which dispensed with the underwing struts, so that no jury struts were needed for wing folding. Shorts had been invited to quote for a batch of 20 Shirls in February 1919 and promised delivery in April, but the order was not confirmed, and a production contract already awarded to Blackburn for 100 Shirls was also cancelled in favour of more Cuckoos.

The Shirl's stability, fuel economy and weight-lifting ability made it an attractive proposition for an attempt to win the *Daily Mail*'s £10,000 prize for the first non-stop crossing of the North Atlantic, first offered in 1914 and revived in March 1919. It was proposed to convert *N112* into a two-seater for this purpose, and a few retouched photographs were issued by Short Brothers to show it as such, but the conversion was never made because the Air Ministry refused to lend it for this purpose, although they offered to make an engine available. Thereupon Short Brothers decided to sponsor the flight as a private venture and built a special variant of the Shirl, S.538, with increased wing area and an external fuel tank giving a still-air range of 3,200 miles, the total tankage being 435 gallons of petrol, 30 gallons of oil and 18 gallons of water. This was sufficient for an east–west flight against the prevailing summer headwinds, and it was planned to start from The Curragh, near Kildare in Ireland, where three square miles of level turf could provide a long unobstructed

147

The *Shamrock*, S.538, being prepared for flight at Grain on 8 April, 1919.

take-off path in any direction. S.538, nicknamed the *Shamrock*, was completed at Rochester at the end of March, with three-bay wings of 62 ft 2 in span and a large cylindrical fuel tank slung from the torpedo-rack attachment points; its low-compression Rolls-Royce Eagle VIII engine (No. 5058) was a short-term loan from Air Ministry stocks already held for the F.3 flying-boats being built at Rochester. The *Shamrock* was unregistered, but its fuselage and wing struts were painted white, with roundels on the khaki-doped wings, the Union Jack emblazoned on the fin and rudder and the maker's name and address prominently displayed on the fuselage sides; in addition to its crew of two, it carried their food, electrically heated clothing, lighting, maps, sextant, long-range W/T and direction-finding radio; to save weight it used a plain cross-axle chassis of the type initially fitted to the first Shirl; it also had a very large two-bladed airscrew whose pitch was coarse enough to prevent the engine exceeding its most economic cruising rpm; this limited it to 1,400 rpm on the ground, and was one of the reasons for choosing The Curragh as the starting-point. The pilot for the Atlantic flight was Major J. C. P. Wood and his navigator was Capt C. C. Wyllie; substantial support was given by C. C. Wakefield & Co, proprietors of Castrol engine oil. Parker made four preliminary test flights in the *Shamrock*, the first (of four minutes) on 8 April, when it was found to be tail-heavy, and the second next day, when he climbed to 9,000 ft in 28 minutes with 200 gallons of fuel and Major Wood as passenger.

On 18 April, 1919, at a gross weight of 8,400 lb, the *Shamrock* took off from Eastchurch at 3.15 pm to fly to The Curragh, and was accompanied by Parker flying *N112*. The two aircraft flew at 3,500 ft and passed over Holyhead at

7.20 pm, but 12 miles out to sea the *Shamrock*'s engine stopped and, finding that he could not restart it, Major Wood turned back in an attempt to reach land by gliding; he nearly succeeded, but had to ditch about a mile off Anglesey. Wood and Wyllie were both rescued by H.M.S. *Paisley*, and Parker managed to land his Shirl in a very small field, but broke the airscrew and some chassis struts against a stone boundary wall. The *Shamrock* floated well, and was in the water for 22 hours before it could be towed into Holyhead and beached; it was taken back to Rochester for inspection and repair, and the

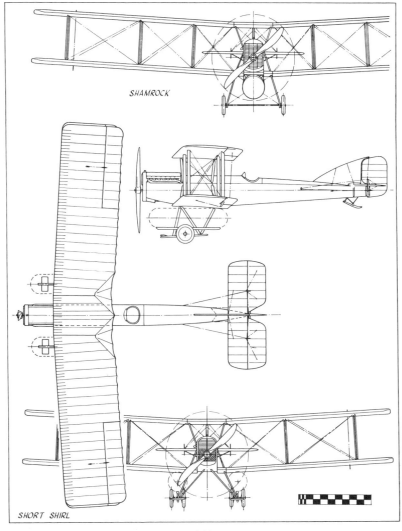

SHAMROCK

SHORT SHIRL

The *Shamrock* about to take off from Grain for Ireland on 18 April, 1919. (*I.W.M.—Crown Copyright.*)

cause of the engine stoppage was found to be an air-lock in the fuel transfer system. It was hoped to make a further attempt, but the effects of a whole day's immersion in sea-water were too serious for a quick overhaul, and in July the prize was won by Alcock and Brown in a Vickers Vimy, as everyone knows. Meanwhile, the *Shamrock*'s radiator and engine had been borrowed for temporary installation in the second N.2B seaplane *N67*, as already recorded. So the *Shamrock* was abandoned, but the Shirl *N112* was repaired and again test-flown by Parker at Eastchurch for 40 minutes on 28 July, 1919, before final delivery to the R.A.F. Twenty years later, when Short Brothers established their new factory at Belfast, Sqn Ldr J. C. P. Wood had become Officer Commanding R.A.F. Station Aldergrove; as the senior R.A.F. officer in Northern Ireland, it was his duty to attend official ceremonies, including the Opening of Parliament at Stormont, in full 'plumage', but he was known everywhere by his nickname 'Atlantic Jim'.

Shirl—Span 52 ft (15·85 m); length 35 ft (10·66 m); area 791 sq ft (73·5 m²); empty weight 3,300 lb (1,497 kg); normal all-up weight 5,950 lb (2,700 kg); max speed 92 mph (148 km/h); normal duration 6·5 hr; max overload weight 6,762 lb (3,065 kg) associated with 85 mph (137 km/h) and duration 10 hr.

Shamrock—Span 62 ft 2 in (18·95 m); length 35 ft (10·66 m); area 1,015 sq ft (94·3 m²); empty weight 3,962 lb (1,798 kg); max weight 8,400 lb (3,810 kg); duration 40 hr at 80 mph (129 km/h).

The Cromarty *N120* at Rochester before launching on 21 March, 1921, showing original airscrews without brass sheathing.

The Short N.3 Cromarty

Although Oswald Short had been a member of the firm from its very first venture into balloon manufacture, some nine years before Horace Short joined his brothers, he was always regarded by Horace as too young and inexperienced to be allowed a free hand in aeroplane design; even up to the time of Eustace Short's death in 1932, Oswald was always referred to by his elder brother as 'The Kid'. This did not prevent him from making his own very competent and continuous contribution to general progress, and in fact sprung floats and pneumatic flotation bags were both his invention, although nearly all patents for new inventions were taken out in the joint names of all three brothers. After war broke out in 1914 it seems that Oswald tried to gain a little more autonomy in design matters, rather against Horace's wishes, and on the famous occasion in 1916 when Horace at last acceded to John Parker's request to be allowed to fly, the conditions he stated were: 'You don't interfere with the design, and you don't take any notice of what the bloody Kid says.'

Oswald was evidently keen to build larger, more heavily armed seaplanes, as indicated by the twin-fuselage twin-engined design described in patent No. 3,203 of 1915, already mentioned as the possible basis of a twin-engined bomber. This patent was accepted in the name of H. O. Short alone, indicating that Horace either declined to support it or possibly was not even told of it at the time of application. It is nevertheless a fact that no interest in flying-boats or other large multi-engined seaplanes was ever shown by Horace, in spite of progress by John Porte at Felixstowe and Linton Hope at Southampton; this may have stemmed partly from Porte's well-known dislike of float seaplanes, which he would have liked to exclude from the Felixstowe establishment altogether. Had he lived longer, Horace might have acknowledged the

151

advantages of flying-boats; soon after his death Short Brothers removed from Eastchurch to concentrate their activities on the Medway, and about this time were asked to undertake production of standard designs, both aeroplanes and flying-boats, as part of the accelerated Ministry of Munitions programme. Early in 1918 they built 100 D.H.9 aeroplanes, some of which were adapted for carrier operation, and also began a batch of 50 Porte flying-boats, initially F.3s and later F.5s. These activities required extensions to the Rochester factory, and a large new erecting shop, No. 3, was built on the waterfront upstream of the existing works, involving very heavy excavations of chalk for the site at a cost of some £18,000. A boat-yard at Strood, on the opposite bank of the Medway, was also taken over for the manufacture of F.3 and F.5 hulls, which were towed across to No. 3 Shop for assembly of the wings, engines and tail unit.

The antepenultimate Rochester-built F.3, *N4033*, on the newly-built slipway at No. 3 Shop on 26 February, 1919, showing its horn-balanced ailerons.

The first Short-built F.3 boat, *N4000*, was ready for launching on 15 May, 1918, and since the slipway was not yet finished, the boat was hoisted out by the crane on the adjacent jetty. Thirty-five F.3s had been built by 8 May, 1919, by which time the remainder were nearing completion as improved F.5s of similar size and with the same Rolls-Royce Eagle VIIIs of 360 hp. Short-built Porte boats did well in R.A.F. service, although none arrived in time to see action before the Armistice; during July 1919 two of them (*N4041* and *N4044*, S.620 and S.623) from Felixstowe made a 2,450 miles tour of Scandinavian and Baltic ports; a further batch of 50 F.5s had already been ordered and were well under way by this time, but soon afterwards the last 40 were cancelled as a post-war economy measure; the last of the 10 built, *N4839*, was first flown by Parker on 23 March, 1920, while the previous one, *N4838*, delivered to Grain in February, remained there for tests under various loading conditions and was flown for a time with 'park-bench'

152

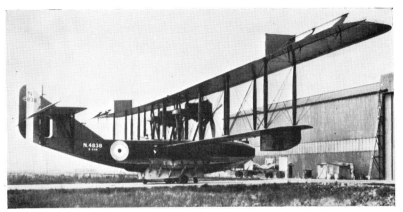

Short-built F.5 *N4838* at Grain in 1922 with experimental 'park-bench' aileron balances.
(*Crown Copyright.*)

aileron balances. In August 1922, *N4839* was temporarily fitted with Napier Lion engines and successfully completed an 18-day cruise from Grain to the Isles of Scilly and back. During 1920 a few F.3s were bought back from the Air Ministry to be reconditioned for export; one of these, Phoenix-built *N4400*, was sold to the Portuguese Government as *C-PAON* on 23 April, 1920; another, *N4019* (S.607), was fitted out as an air yacht, with a spacious luxury cabin amidships; registered *G-EAQT*, it was first flown at Rochester on 28 May, 1920, and was then shipped to Botany Bay for the private use of Lebbaeus Hordern, a wealthy resident of Sydney, N.S.W., but before it could be re-erected there his interest faded, and after the hull had been launched no further attempt was made to complete the assembly; the hull finished up as a

The F.3 air-yacht conversion *G-EAQT* at Rochester after launching on 12 May, 1920.

shelter for local fishermen. Nine of the cancelled new F.5s (S.546–554) were completed for the Imperial Japanese Navy in May 1920 and were shipped to Japan in advance of Colonel the Master of Sempill's British Naval Air Mission, which arrived in Tokyo in April 1921; the first to be re-erected, S.547,

153

S.547 being launched for its first flight at Yokosuka on 30 August, 1921. (*Copyright W. Pollard.*)

was launched and flown on 30 August, 1921, at Yokosuka by John Parker, who had gone out to Japan with Oswald Short to assist the Mission. The first of the batch, S.546, was reassembled later and reserved for training, together with one new F.5 (Taura No. 1) built entirely from local resources at the Hiro Naval Arsenal with assistance from a small team from Short Brothers; later the Aichi Tokei Denki Co of Nagoya built over 50 more F.5s, some of which were still in use at Yokosuka and Sasebo for training as late as 1929. Flying training of I.J.N. personnel was superintended by Major Herbert G. Brackley, who met Oswald Short and John Parker for the first time in Japan; the initial fleet of ten was augmented a year later by three Short-built F.5s with Napier Lion engines; one had a revised bow cockpit mounting a 1-pounder shell-firing gun; the first Lion-engined F.5 was flown at Rochester on 26 April, 1922, by Frank Courtney, deputising for Parker, who returned from Japan a

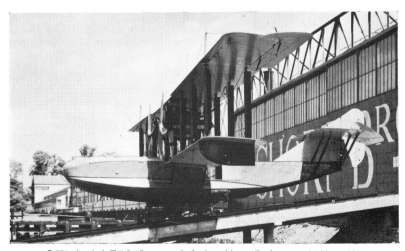

S.551, the sixth F.5 for Japan, ready for launching at Rochester on 10 May, 1920.

154

month later. F.5s remained the standard R.A.F. flying-boat, and although the 'Geddes Axe' precluded any new orders for them, 24 were returned to Rochester for major overhaul under contract No. 412569/23, and the first of these (*N4046*) was passed out by Parker on 10 January, 1924.

Short Brothers had been responsible for a number of detail improvements in the F.5, but the first flying-boat of their own design was a somewhat larger

Napier Lion engines were installed in the last three F.5s supplied to Japan from Rochester in April 1922, and another Lion-engined F.5 completed an 18-day cruise from Grain to the Scilly Isles and back in August 1922, an event in which the Cromarty came to grief at St Mary's.

aircraft, tendered in 1918 to the requirements of the Admiralty N.3 (later RAF XXX) specification for fleet co-operation duties. It was to be powered by two engines of 500–600 hp, either Siddeley Deasy Tigers or Rolls-Royce Condors, and to be capable of operating from deep water for long periods away from base. Just before the Armistice contracts for three prototypes each were awarded to Short Brothers and Vickers Ltd; the Vickers boat, the Valentia, had a Consuta sewn-plywood hull made by S. E. Saunders of Cowes, while the Short Cromarty was substantially an improved Porte design, using three-ply over a braced spruce frame. A feature contributing to clean running and good seaworthiness was the concave flare of the planing bottom each side of the keel, which kept down sideways spray and reduced interference with the airscrews and wing-tip floats, always troublesome on Porte boats. The hull had an open cockpit for two pilots side-by-side and a large bow cockpit with a gimbal for a 37 mm quick-firing anti-submarine gun; the rear top longerons sloped up towards the tail, with a curved fabric-covered decking; the design originally included two 'howdah'-type gunners' nacelles above the top wing, but this feature was deleted in favour of the heavy-calibre bow gun. The tail unit was an equal-span biplane with a large central fin and three balanced rudders. Work began on the first Cromarty hull at

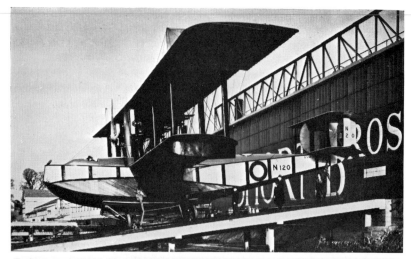

Engine runs on *N120* before launching; the anti-submarine gun mounting at the bow is clearly seen.

Strood in February 1919, but the flying-boat was not completed for nearly two years; only the first, S.539, *N120*, with Rolls-Royce Condors, was ever finished, the other two, *N121–122*, being cancelled when the second hull was half-built. *N120* was launched on 21 March, 1921, and first flown on 19 April by Parker; two days later he flew it to Grain, as it had been ruled that all performance and handling tests of prototype seaplanes must be done by the Marine Aircraft Experimental Establishment and not by the firms' own test pilots. During the next three months various modifications were made by a working party from Rochester, including metal sheathing for the airscrews, revised wing-tip floats, hull reinforcement at points of high stress, improved tail-unit bracing and additions to the wireless installation. Parker flew the Cromarty once more at Grain on 9 August, with a crew of four at an all-up weight of 19,800 lb, the design overload. He climbed to 3,000 ft in seven minutes and reached a top speed of 83 kt.

In September the rear cockpit coaming was raised to give the midships gunner better protection, and on 21 October the Cromarty commenced official type trials at the normal all-up weight of 18,000 lb; these were delayed by spray damage to the lower wings in December, but repairs were soon completed. After a period of mooring-out to establish the permanent water-soakage weight, type trials recommenced on 16 January, 1922, but, on the 23rd, excessive tail vibration developed in flight and further modifications had to be made to stiffen the tailplane attachments. These cured the trouble, and climbing trials were done on the 30th, as a result of which it was decided to fit the airscrews salvaged from the first Valentia *N124*, which had crashed at Grain on 15 June; these alone did not give the desired improvement in climb, so in May uprated Condors were installed, while the hull was under repair after repeated heavy landings. The new engines gave an acceptable performance, and after two months' further testing the Cromarty was handed over to the Seaplane Development Flight on 17 July, 1922. This unit was commanded by Sqn Ldr R. B. Maycock, O.B.E., who quickly gained a good opinion of the Cromarty; during August he took it, together with an F.3, a Kingston and the Lion-engined F.5 *N4839*, on a cruise along the south coast via Newhaven, Calshot, Torbay, Cattewater (Plymouth) and Newlyn to the Isles of Scilly, where it proved its ability to ride out a storm while at moorings in St Mary's Roads; soon afterwards it was unfortunately taxied on to a shallow reef and had to be beached hurriedly at St Mary's, where the hull damage was found to be beyond economical repair in view of the report of the Geddes Committee, so it was broken up, the remains being salvaged by *Ark Royal*, acting as depôt ship during the cruise.

N120 beached at St Mary's, Scilly Isles, after being holed in shallow water in August 1922; note the Vickers-designed airscrews taken from the wreck of Valentia *N124* at Grain.

Although proposals to build a civil version of the Cromarty came to nothing, Short Brothers had earlier put forward a scheme for a large 30-passenger twin-hulled triplane flying-boat with three Rolls-Royce Condors. The hulls had concave bottoms to reduce spray interference, and the accommodation was to include a dining-saloon and sleeping-berths; this was in 1919, 17 years before the Empire Boats entered service. Seaworthiness in a forced alighting was assured by a system of watertight bulkheads, and great stress was laid on the comfort and quietness to be derived from the remote location of the engines away from the cabins. Isolation of the crew from engine vibration had been one of the claims of patent No. 3,203/15 already mentioned, and the same aim underlay the design of Oswald Short's first twin-hull essay, described in patent No. 131,045, filed in November 1918 and accepted on 21 August, 1919. This illustrated a naval triplane from which the 30-passenger project was derived, but there was no commercial support for the latter, and no work was done on it apart from a model shown at Olympia in 1919. Shorts Model Aero Club sought to refurbish the model in 1938; sadly, it remained hanging in the old Fort next to No. 3 Shop until it was lost during construction of the nearby air-raid shelters. Like all wooden flying-boats of its day, the Cromarty suffered a severe weight penalty from water soakage after being moored out, and this was only one of the reasons which directed Oswald Short's attention to metal construction.

Span 113 ft 6 in (34·6 m); length 59 ft (17·9 m); area 2,243 sq ft (245 m²); empty weight 12,220 lb (5,545 kg); all-up weight (normal) 18,000 lb (9,080 kg), (overload) 19,800 lb (9,989 kg); max speed 95 mph (153 km/h); range 900 miles (1,450 km).

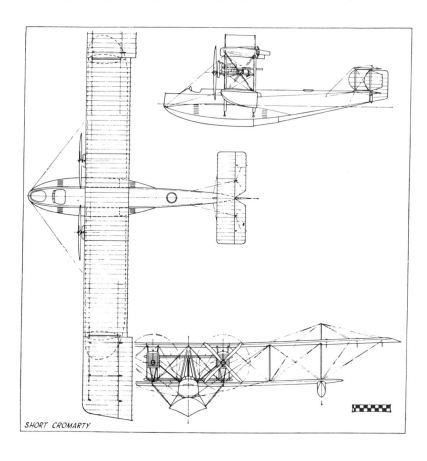

SHORT CROMARTY

158

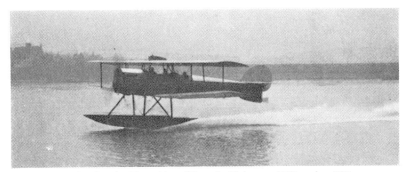

The first Sporting Type taking off from the Medway on 10 December, 1919.

The Short Sporting Type Seaplane

Short Brothers' first post-war product was a single-engined twin-float biplane called the Sporting Type Seaplane, which originated from a cancelled contract of early 1918 for two prototype training seaplanes to specification RAF XXXII. The Sporting Type had an overall resemblance to the N.2B, having a flat top wing and hollow-bottomed main floats with short faired tails aft of the steps, but the wings were of equal span and chord; the standard Short wing-folding gear was fitted. Nominally a four-seater, it had two cockpits, the front one seating two pilots in tandem with full dual controls, and the rear one seating two passengers side-by-side, or equivalent cargo; thus the seaplane could be used equally well as a trainer or a transport. The fuselage was a semi-monocoque structure with curved sides, flat top and bottom and several bulkheads, all in plywood; the fuselage top was faired by a light-weight fabric-covered decking. The wing structure was equally novel, with steel-tube spars and struts and fretted plywood ribs; it was the last Short design to employ the characteristic flexible cord trailing edge and represented Francis Webber's boldest essay in plywood at a time when Oswald Short was preparing to abandon wood altogether. The engine installed in the first machine was a 160 hp Beardmore of proven reliability and reasonable economy, with an oval frontal honeycomb radiator equipped with horizontal shutters. Fuel was carried in a 20-gallon main tank in the fuselage, whence it was pumped to a 12-gallon gravity tank on the centre-section. There were no wing-tip floats and the tail-float was directly attached to the underside of the fuselage and carried a hollow water rudder containing a spring-loaded drop-plate, which improved steering while taxying and hinged upwards on grounding in shallow water. Watertight transverse tubes were provided in the main floats forward of the steps, to accept an axle with two wheels for beaching, and the tail-float had a vertical socket into which a swivelling jockey wheel could be plugged. Three versions of the Sporting Type were offered: the original Beardmore model for touring, a primary trainer with a Siddeley Puma of 230 hp and an advanced trainer with a 300 hp Hispano-Suiza.

159

The first Sporting Type Seaplane on its beaching wheels at Rochester in December 1919.

Three seaplanes (S.540, 541 and 542) were built, and John Parker flew the first with the Beardmore on 10 December, 1919, and found it handled well; named *Shrimp* as an afterthought, it was registered *G-EAPZ*, and in February 1920 it was enamelled white and demonstrated to Lebbaeus Hordern of Sydney, who bought it and learned to fly on it, taught by Parker; on 22 March the registration was transferred to his name, and after substituting a Puma engine he shipped it to Australia in June 1921. It was entered on the Australian Civil Register in June 1922 as *G-AUPZ* and thereafter flown by Capt Frank Hurley, an explorer, who made two surveys of the coast of New Guinea recorded by ciné camera and gramophone, out of which was made a travel film entitled *Pearls and Savages*; this would have delighted Horace Short had he survived a few more years, in view of his adventures in those parts 30 years before. The film featured the *Shrimp* at Port Moresby and Elavala, and ran for three months at the Regent Street Polytechnic Cinema in London in 1924. The *Shrimp* created much interest among the Papuans, who recognised the twin floats as something akin to their own traditional catamarans, and called it 'the canoe that goes for up'. Capt Hurley found it excellently suited to this kind of exploration, with a good tropical performance, but the wooden floats gave constant trouble, as they dried out during flight and leaked on re-immersion; all-metal floats would have avoided

Four up in the *Shrimp G-EAPZ* in February, 1920.

160

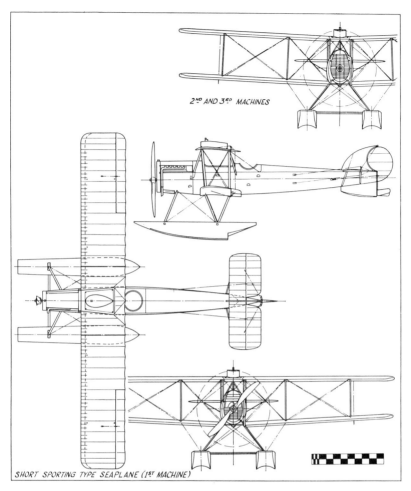

2ND AND 3RD MACHINES

SHORT SPORTING TYPE SEAPLANE (1ST MACHINE)

this defect. Finally, *G-AUPZ* was written off after crashing in Sydney Harbour on its return from New Guinea in January 1923.

The second Sporting Type was shown at Olympia in July 1920 and differed from the *Shrimp* in having equal dihedral on both wings; registered *G-EAUA*, it was flown by Parker with a Puma engine on 28 July and again on several days between 11 and 27 August. Ronald Kemp was interested in it as possible equipment for the Air Survey Company, but damaged it in a heavy landing at Rochester on 24 September; while under repair, the opportunity was taken to install a 300 hp Hispano-Suiza and full-span camber-changing flaps; thus modified, it was first flown by Reggie Kenworthy on 10 December, 1921, while Parker was in Japan. Parker himself flew it for the first time on 1 September, 1922, but found it a poor climber, at its best with normal camber; after a further flight on 16 September, he confirmed that variable camber was ineffective on this particular design, and the second aircraft, with dihedral on both wings, was more stable laterally than the first had been. *G-EAUA* was flown only twice more, on 7 and 28 March, 1923, when Parker gave dual instruction for 40 minutes on each day to four pilots converting to seaplanes. The third seaplane, *G-EAUB*, was identical to the second as originally built, and was first flown on 21 January, 1921, by Parker, who demonstrated it to various prospective buyers during February, but without effecting a sale; then it was stored during his absence in Japan and had still not found a buyer in 1923, in spite of being advertised at a bargain price; both the second and third airframes were scrapped in 1924, their engines and instruments having been borrowed for other purposes. The Beardmore originally fitted to the *Shrimp* was used in May 1921 in an experimental 'water glider', and the 300 hp Hispano-Suiza from the second machine was the basis of a larger twin-float high-speed 'skimmer' in which Parker reached 40 kt on the Medway on 17 May, 1924. These craft were intended for shallow waterways and lagoons and anticipated the later exploitation of hovercraft for the same purpose, although they were not, of course, amphibious like a ground-effect machine.

Span 44 ft 6 in (13·6 m); length 36 ft 9 in (11·2 m); area 510 sq ft (47·4 m²); all-up weight (Beardmore) 3,100 lb (1,407 kg), (Puma and H-S) 3,554 lb (1,613 kg); max speed (Beardmore) 83 mph (134 km/h), (Puma) 95 mph (153 km/h), (Hispano-Suiza) 100 mph (161 km/h); range (Puma) 270 miles (434 km).

The Short Silver Streak

During 1918, when the world's timber stocks were already seriously depleted after four years of war, it became very difficult for aircraft manufacturers to obtain adequate supplies of Grade A spruce, ash and mahogany, and attempts to use substitutes, such as Port Orford cedar, cypress and cottonwood, caused several failures in aircraft and had to be abandoned. Oswald Short already knew the qualities and limitations of plywood as a structural material from his experience of building the wooden rigid airships *R31* and *R32* at Cardington; to follow these vessels, the firm had taken over the assembly of the half-finished duralumin components of *R37* from Vickers Ltd and had also begun manufacture of the larger *R38* of similar design. Short Brothers thus began to learn the technique of using duralumin during 1916, and three years later Oswald Short had sufficient confidence in this alloy to propose its use as the principal material for an aeroplane, even for the covering of the wings and tail. He cited many advantages of all-metal construction, such as freedom from warping and deterioration under varying climatic conditions, absence of any water-soakage weight penalty (which could be as much as half a ton in a large flying-boat hull) and elimination of fire risk. But the official metallurgists (with the notable exception of Leslie Aitchison) were obsessed with various defects in aluminium-alloy structures which they had had to investigate and declined to accept Oswald Short's assurance that corrosion and fatigue failure stemmed from inefficient control of heat treatment and allied workshop procedures and not from some inexplicable tendency towards intercrystalline corrosion inseparable from aluminium itself. They ruled that duralumin was not permissible as a primary structural metal, and encouraged further research and development on the use of high-tensile steel, of which a great deal of experience had been accumulated by the makers of rims for wire-spoked motor-car and cycle wheels. Meanwhile Oswald Short carried out his own test programme on various components, including wing-ribs, and evolved a system of construction which exceeded all expectations both in strength and weight.

Silver Streak as built, at Rochester in July 1920 before being shown at Olympia.

In 1919, concurrently with the *Shrimp*, he designed a land biplane of similar size, using much of the same geometry except that the components were made from duralumin plate instead of plywood. He asked the Air Ministry to contribute to the cost of a prototype, and when this was refused, after several months waiting, he began in February 1920 to build it as a private venture. The result was the Swallow, soon renamed Silver Streak, which made its first public appearance at the Olympia Aero Show on 9 July, 1920. It was a two-bay unstaggered equal-span tractor biplane of conventional appearance, powered by a single 240 hp Siddeley Puma engine, with accommodation for a pilot and 400 lb of mail or cargo; alternatively, it could be modified to carry a pilot and two passengers. In construction it was completely unorthodox, having no fabric or wood anywhere. The wings had two spars, each of round 50-ton steel tube with collars sweated on for the attachment of duralumin-plate ribs pierced with lightening holes. The rib profile exceeded the basic aerofoil section by a small constant margin, and built-up

163

box-ribs served as compression struts between the spars. The rib margins were slotted at intervals, and short flanges were turned down at right angles in both directions to form ledges supporting the sheet aluminium covering, which was applied in chordwise strips rolled with upturned lateral flanges and two intermediate stiffening channels, each lateral flange butting against a rib and being secured by rivets applied externally through a capping channel enclosing the rib margin and its contiguous skin flanges.

The fuselage was a shell of duralumin plates riveted to L-section oval frames with longitudinal stiffeners between the frames; it was a constant feature of Short monocoque construction for many years that the frames were never cut or notched for continuous stringers and that the intercostals were interrupted at all the frames and were cleated to them; Oswald Short was very far-seeing and insisted on avoiding stress raisers, such as notches, in primary structure, from which cracks could originate. In the region of the cockpit and fuel tank cut-outs, thicker plates were used and stiffeners were dispensed with; the front end of the fuselage was closed by a solid plate frame forming a fireproof bulkhead, and the open-topped engine bay had built-up frames carrying the tubular-steel engine bearers, the outer skin plating being continuous with the rest of the fuselage; the lower wings were attached to root stubs built and faired into the bottom of the fuselage shell, and the upper wings were attached to a central box-rib, supported on oval-section steel tubes forming a cabane. The landing chassis comprised two steel-tube V-strut assemblies with a two-wheeled cross-axle supported on rubber-cord springs; an oil-filled dashpot was carried in the apex of each V to damp out the rebound of the axle; a rubber-sprung tailskid was provided, pivoted through a small cut-out, which, like the cockpit and engine-bay cut-outs, had its edge stiffened by a rolled duralumin bead. The tailplane was similar in construction to the wing, its attachment base being widened by two small struts outside the fuselage shell below the front spar. The nearly circular rudder was carried on a vertical tube pivoted at the top to a triangular fin, and all the rudder and elevator controls were enclosed within the fuselage shell. The ailerons and elevators were aerodynamically balanced with set-back hinges, and all control and bracing wires were of stranded cable, flying wires being duplicated and faired to an oval section, with patent low-drag end fittings replacing the normal A.G.S. turnbuckles.

The appearance of the Silver Streak (S.543) on Stand 44 at Olympia was without doubt the signal that a new era had begun in the aircraft industry, and observers agreed that it was the first time they had seen an aeroplane which could claim to be a true engineering job throughout. The pundits were worried about corrosion, to which Oswald Short replied: 'Why be so afraid of that? Corrosion has been with us ever since we started building structures, only we call it rust and are not afraid of it.' But the official experts remained unconvinced in spite of a series of tests made by Oswald Short with duralumin plates, both bare and painted, which he attached to the jetty at Rochester works so as to be immersed in the Medway at high tide and exposed to the air at low tide, thus simulating the most severe conditions to which any aircraft, even a seaplane, would be subjected. These tests went on for nine months, at the end of which the only signs of corrosion were small points of a white deposit, which left no pitting when scraped off; mild-steel plates exposed during the same period had almost rusted away. Before beginning manufacture of the Silver Streak, Oswald had made in September 1919 a partial fuselage shell, sealed by strong end bulkheads, into which he arranged to pump water under pressure; these tests proved that an internal hydraulic pressure of 7 lb/sq in could be sustained for half an hour without leakage or permanent distortion; he also applied shock loading to the riveted joints by plunging a 100-lb weight rapidly up and down in the water-filled shell, but still the rivets did not leak.

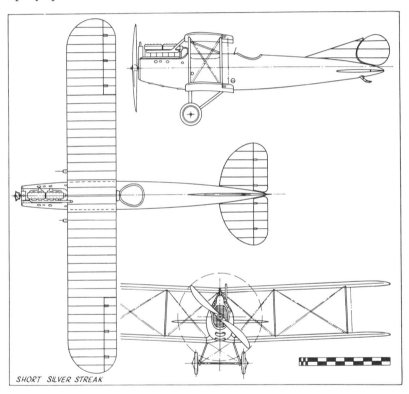

SHORT SILVER STREAK

Although the Silver Streak attracted a great deal of interest at the show, particularly from Americans, no firm enquiries were received, and it went back to Rochester to be prepared for flight tests. The civil registration *G-EARQ* had been reserved, but the issue of a Certificate of Airworthiness was refused on the ground that too little was known about the long-term behaviour of a duralumin primary structure; this was in spite of all the accumulated experience of the Zeppelin Co and Vickers Ltd on airship construction,

Two views of the Silver Streak after delivery to Farnborough in February 1921, showing the open front cockpit. (*I.W.M.—Crown Copyright.*)

which Short Brothers already shared. At length the Air Ministry decided to purchase the Silver Streak, modified into a two-seater, for evaluation at an agreed price of £4,500. John Parker first flew it at Grain on 20 August, 1920, for 12 minutes and to a height of 3,000 ft, but the original aluminium wing skin was found to buckle and dent too easily and had to be replaced by duralumin; flying recommenced on 27 January, 1921, at Grain, when Parker made a solo flight of 15 minutes, followed by an hour's flight with Oscar Gnosspelius as passenger, to a height of 7,300 ft; this had been intended as the delivery flight to Farnborough, but Parker had to turn back to Croydon because of fog; on 1 February the weather was clear, and Parker and Gnosspelius delivered it to Farnborough at a cruising speed of over 120 mph; on arrival the Silver Streak received the official serial *J6854*, but apparently never wore it. After a thorough but protracted survey by the R.A.E. specialists, reluctant permission was given for limited non-aerobatic flight tests, and after a 25 minute flight on 3 June, Flt Lieut Jack Noakes reported: 'Remarkably quick get-off; it lands without bumping owing to the dashpot arrangement on the chassis; the tailplane is the steadiest I have seen in the air; it has a remarkable climb and is very easy to control. . . .' In fact it climbed to 10,000 ft in 11

minutes and its top speed was better than 125 mph. Next day Sqn Ldr
Roderic Hill flew it for 15 minutes and on the 6th Flt Lieut E. R. C. Schole-
field did likewise, but in spite of its excellent performance, no further test
flights were permitted and thereafter the machine was reserved for structural
testing, so that it was not available for Short Brothers to show to any interested
enquirers. Oswald Short protested at being denied access or information, and
several Parliamentary Questions were asked, but the Air Ministry's replies
were evasive and its attitude inflexible. After some 18 months had gone by
since the Silver Streak's first appearance it was admitted, somewhat reluctantly, that corrosion was negligible, that in the wing-loading test, failure had
occurred at just above the calculated ultimate stress level by buckling of the
front spar outboard of the outer pair of struts and that the residual strength of
the buckled spar was still adequate for normal flying loads. The cantilever
tailplane, similarly tested, withstood an overall loading of 57 lb/sq ft and the
fin and rudder a lateral loading of 63 lb/sq ft, both figures being well in excess
of requirements for conventional wooden airframes; in a torsion test on the
fuselage shell a moment of 2,000 lb-ft produced no visible distortion or
permanent deflection. On completion of the static tests in September, the
airframe was subjected to 100 hours of vibration testing, at the end of which
in November no signs of cracking or loose rivets could be detected.

Convinced at last, the Air Ministry agreed to consider a design for a two-
seat fighter biplane, nominally as a Bristol Fighter replacement to D. of R.
specification 3A, and in January 1922 it was announced that two prototypes

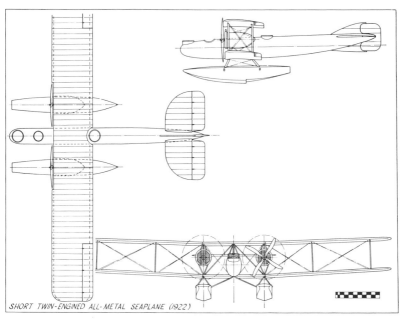

SHORT TWIN-ENGINED ALL-METAL SEAPLANE (1922)

167

with Armstrong Siddeley Jaguar engines were to be ordered; c/ns S.584–585 were allotted, but in July the order was cancelled as a result of economies enforced by the Geddes Committee. Despairing of ever getting an order at home, Oswald Short accepted Griffith Brewer's invitation to accompany him on a visit to the United States, and designed for the potential American and Canadian market an all-duralumin twin-engined twin-float seaplane, powered by either Jaguar or Napier Lion engines. He had obtained a master patent on monocoque metal construction (185,992) on 10 November, 1921, and for various types of rib construction (192,966 and 194,516) and metal wing covering (195,235) early in 1922; these were followed by a proposal for a true 'lobster-claw' monocoque wing without spars or ribs (206,998) which was far in advance of its time and of any other designs in Europe or America. Jerome Hunsaker recommended his methods to American aircraft manufacturers, but official apathy and economic difficulties after the war condemned these very sound and practical projects to a further period of stagnation. Perhaps the most successful outcome of this journey from Oswald Short's point of view was his visit to Orville and Katharine Wright in their family home at Hawthorn Hill, Dayton, Ohio.

Span 37 ft 6 in (11·4 m); length 26 ft 5 in (8 m); area 370 sq ft (34·4 m²); empty weight 1,865 lb (847 kg); all-up weight 2,870 lb (1,303 kg); max speed 125 mph (201 km/h); range 450 miles (723 km).

The Short Springbok

The two-seater D. of R. 3A project derived from the Silver Streak, provisionally ordered in January 1922, had been cancelled in June at the insistence of the Geddes Committee, but the decision taken soon afterwards to police Iraq and the North-West Frontier of India mainly with the R.A.F. instead of the Army had an important influence on re-equipment policy in the Air Council. The Geddes Committee's first Interim Report (Cmd 1581 of 14 December, 1921) noted, among other things, that the most numerous types of aircraft remaining in R.A.F. service were the Bristol Fighter (1,090), the Avro 504K (923) and the D.H.9A (663), out of a landplane total of 3,411 and a grand total (including naval aircraft and seaplanes) of 3,830. The Avro was used solely for training, and the other two types formed the backbone of the R.A.F. in the Middle East, where they were subjected to extremes of temperature and humidity, aggravated by termites and tropical fungi. There was thus the strongest possible case for early replacement of these ageing veterans by all-metal aircraft. By the end of 1922 the Geddes Committee's decision to axe the Bristol Fighter replacements (specification 19/21) had been reconsidered, and the order for two Short metal fighters was reinstated, with the difference that the engines were to be Bristol Jupiters instead of Armstrong Siddeley Jaguars. The resulting aeroplane, design index No. S.3, was named Springbok I and marked the beginning of more than 20 fruitful years' association between Short airframes and Bristol aero-engines.

The first two Springboks (S.586–587, serials *J6974–6975*) were straight military developments of the Silver Streak, with the same all-metal wings and tail surfaces, without any fabric covering. They had unstaggered wings of equal span and nearly equal chord, with the fuselage midway in the gap as in the Bristol Fighter and the root ends of the upper wings open, with the spars attached directly to fuselage main frames forward and aft of the pilot's cockpit; the rear gunner's cockpit, with a Scarff ring for twin Lewis guns, was just aft of the trailing edge, and the pilot had a forward-firing fixed Vickers gun on the port side, synchronised by a C.C. gear. On completion at Rochester, the first Springbok *J6974* was delivered by road to Martlesham Heath on 17 April, 1923; John Parker first flew it there on 19 April and again the following day, returning to make two more acceptance flights on 14 and 17 May; on

Springbok I *J6974* as built with duralumin wing skin and the exhaust manifold ring, which had to be removed because it scorched the back of the airscrew.

the last occasion he climbed with full load to 15,200 ft during an hour's flying. The second Springbok *J6975* was delivered to Martlesham by road on 18 July, 1923, and flown twice by Parker on the 24th and 26th; both Springboks were finished overall in glossy blue-grey enamel. From an engineering point of view, they required little maintenance, but they were too far ahead of their time; whereas there were plenty of skilled carpenter-riggers available to minister to orthodox wood-and-fabric aeroplanes, however fragile, trained sheet-metal tradesmen capable of repairing aluminium-alloy stressed-skin structures were as rare as icebergs in the Sahara. Furthermore, standard pieces of equipment, such as radio sets, were not designed to go through the limited apertures permissible in a monocoque fuselage, and daily inspections became a job for a boiler-maker rather than a self-respecting rigger, so Service opinion was heavily prejudiced against the Springbok from the start.

A defect which occurred in both aircraft was the splitting of the trailing edge skin through vibration in the slipstream. This showed first in *J6974*, which was returned to Rochester on 23 May, 1923, for its wings to be converted to doped-fabric covering; thus modified, it was test-flown at Detling

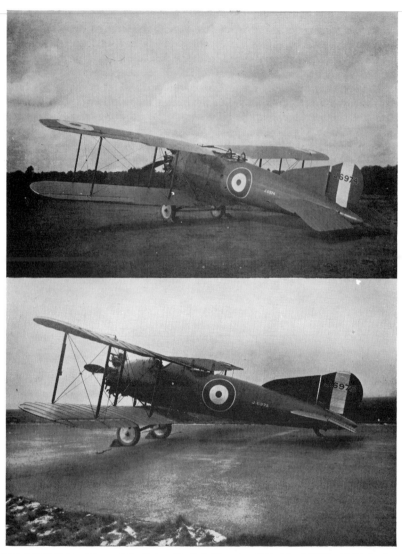

Both Springbok I prototypes at Martlesham Heath in November 1923: (*above*) *J6974* with fabric wing-covering; (*below*) *J6975* with thicker duralumin wing skin. (*Crown Copyright.*)

by Parker on 13 September, 1923, and returned to Martlesham, where it was finally accepted on 17 October. *J6975* retained its metal wing-skin, which was made thicker in its regions of weakness, and was flown again on 31 October at Martlesham; six more flights followed, and on 7 November, 1923, it was accepted after a climb to 16,000 ft in 38 minutes. Although its performance was up to specification, the Springbok I suffered from rudder-blanketing

170

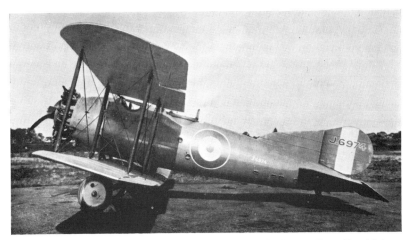

J6974 at Martlesham Heath with fabric wing-covering and stub exhausts. (*Crown Copyright.*)

during a spin, and *J6975* eventually spun into the ground, killing its pilot. After this accident had been investigated, including wind-tunnel tests at the R.A.E., a revised wing design, raised tailplane of increased area and larger fin and rudder were recommended, and in 1924 the Air Ministry ordered six more of a developed version, Springbok II, serials *J7295-7300*, with fabric-covered wings and tail surfaces, design index No. S.3a; later the contract was reduced to the first three aircraft only.

The Springbok II had the same Bristol Jupiter IV engine as the Springbok I, but the wings were mounted higher on the fuselage, which had raised frames to carry the upper wing roots, while the gunner's cockpit remained at a lower level; the lower wings were attached to stubs built into the bottom of the fuselage as in the Silver Streak. One rib-bay of the port lower wing,

The second Springbok II, *J7296*, at Grain on 3 April, 1925, before being flown; note the dished side panel to allow the pilot a clear view vertically downwards.

171

The third Springbok II, *J7297*, at Grain in May 1925.

adjacent to the root attachment, was left uncovered for camera and bomb-sighting purposes and, for the same reason, the port side of the fuselage had a dished panel alongside the pilot's cockpit to allow a clear view vertically. Fuel was carried in two 52-gallon external gravity tanks attached through and below the upper wings, where they were readily accessible for servicing or changing and not immediately exposed to risk from an engine fire; the ailerons had set-back hinges (the Frise patent had not then been published), and the elevators and rudder were horn-balanced. The fuselage was protected inside and out by Rylard high-gloss white seaplane enamel specially prepared for use on duralumin; it was based on tung oil, which had been found to give good adhesion and high resistance to salt-water corrosion, and was expected to be equally suitable for tropical conditions.

Before delivery, the three Springbok IIs were all flight-tested at Grain, where Parker flew *J7295* first on 25 March, 1925, showing off its paces over Rochester works during his second trip that day, but on 1 April he had to make a forced landing at Grain when the engine seized two minutes after take-off. After fitting a spare engine two half-hour acceptance tests were made on 3 April and three more on 6–8 April; after a final acceptance climb to 16,200 ft on 21 April, *J7295* was dispatched to Martlesham Heath, where it remained for over a year, appearing in the parade of new types at the R.A.F. Display at Hendon on 27 June, 1925; in 1926 it was returned to Short Brothers for conversion into an improved variant, the Chamois, which is separately described later. The second and third Springbok IIs did not go to Martlesham Heath;

172

J7296 was first flown at Grain on 6 May and *J7297* on 22 May, both being flown on delivery to Eastchurch on 25 June and 3 July respectively, after which no account of their movements has survived.

Springbok I—Span 42 ft (12·8 m); length 26 ft 11 in (8·7 m); area 463 sq ft (43 m²); all-up weight 4,080 lb (1,855 kg); max speed 121 mph (197 km/h).

Springbok II—Span 42 ft (12·8 m); length 29 ft 6 in (9 m); area 460 sq ft (42·7 m²); all-up weight 4,270 lb (1,940 kg); max speed 123 mph (198 km/h).

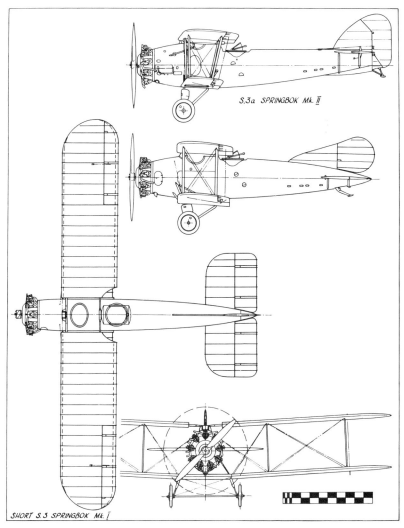

S.3a SPRINGBOK Mk. II

SHORT S.3 SPRINGBOK Mk. I

Oscar Gnosspelius with his man-powered ornithopter in No. 3 Shop in 1919.

The Gnosspelius Gull

Oscar Gnosspelius was one of the true pioneers of aviation, having begun to experiment with flying models in 1909 and a full-sized monoplane in 1910. Living at Hawkshead in the Lake District, where flat land was scarce, he decided to make a waterplane, for which purpose he investigated hydroplane design and came upon the stepped pontoon described in 1873 by the Rev Charles Ramus in his book *The Polysphenic Ship*. After many tests with towed models on Lake Windermere, he fitted a central pontoon to his monoplane, but with an Alvaston engine of only 20 hp could not get off the water. He then built a larger monoplane with a 40 hp Clerget inline engine and managed to take off on this in 1912; it flew quite well in the hands of Ronald Kemp and, variously modified, was still flying early in 1914. He also designed a large tractor biplane for Lieut Trotter and a pusher monoplane for Capt Wakefield of the Lakes Flying Co; this concern operated an entirely water-based school at Windermere, its chief instructor being Rowland Ding. When war broke out, Gnosspelius volunteered for the R.N.A.S., but the school continued as the Northern Aircraft Co and incidentally gave John Lankester Parker his first professional employment as a pilot. Gnosspelius was appointed to the inspection staff of the Admiralty Air Department and later to the Technical Department of the Air Board. He had thus acquired a great deal of experience of the design and construction of seaplanes when the war ended and, as an old friend of both Kemp and Parker, quite naturally gravitated to Short Brothers on demobilisation with the rank of Major. Oswald Short was delighted to gain his services and put him in charge of the embryo experimental department at Rochester, at the same time allowing him to undertake certain projects at his own expense. One of the first of these was an attempt to become airborne, even for a few yards, in a man-powered ornithopter, at

174

which he strove vigorously but unavailingly in the seclusion of the newly completed No. 3 Shop in March 1919.

From that time onwards he devised and built numerous test-rigs in No. 4 Shop for Oswald Short in connection with metal construction; his assistant was a fitter, Arthur Gouge, who had begun with the firm at Eastchurch in 1915 and shown a remarkable flair for experimental work, and was attending evening classes at Chatham Technical College to obtain an external degree in engineering. In addition to the structural test-rigs, Gnosspelius designed an ingenious pendulum testing-machine for measuring the lift and drag of model aerofoils; somewhat analogous to an Izod impact testing machine, the Gnosspelius Aerodynamic Pendulum was arranged to fall by gravity from a horizontal position, carrying a test aerofoil or other model mounted alongside the bob; drag was measured by comparing the up-swing heights reached with and without the test specimen, and lift was recorded by measuring the lateral deflection of the bob as it passed its lowest point, where a speed of 45–50 ft/sec could be attained. Smoke could be used for flow visualisation, and vortex formation could easily be observed; the method was free from the turbulence and wall interference inseparable from wind-tunnel working, and was a cheap and satisfactory substitute for even the simplest type of tunnel. Gnosspelius tested the air drag of floats, among other shapes, and noticed the apparent advantage conferred by a shallow step; he tried the effect of making a similar step in the upper surface of a lifting aerofoil, and in January 1922 a patent (No. 192,568) for this application was obtained in the joint names of Oswald Short, Oscar Gnosspelius and Arthur Gouge. He then began to design a small single-seat monoplane glider of maximum aerodynamic efficiency and, on the strength of his pendulum results, aimed at a very much higher L/D ratio than the best predicted by Professor Leonard Bairstow of Imperial College. The glider was still in the design stage when the *Daily Mail* gliding competitions were held at Itford Hill in 1922, but early in 1923 the Duke of Sutherland offered a prize of £500 for the longest distance flown on one gallon of petrol by an ultra-light single-seat aeroplane powered by an engine of not more than 750 cc capacity; the *Daily Mail* later added a prize of £1,000 for a similar competition to be held concurrently.

Gnosspelius promptly revised his glider to take a 697 cc Blackburne motorcycle engine and designed a chain transmission gear through which two 4-ft-diameter propellers could be driven at two-thirds engine speed in a low-drag installation. The resulting project was named the Gull, and a prototype was built by Short Brothers to Gnosspelius's private order; it did not rate as a Short design or receive a Short constructor's number, although it provided an interesting drawing-office exercise and occupied a few woodworkers at a time when official orders were scarce. The Gull was made entirely of wood, the circular-section body being boat-built of elm hoops planked with $\frac{1}{8}$-in spruce; extra longerons and struts reinforced the cockpit region, and the landing gear comprised two small wheels on a cross-axle slung on rubber cords in vertical slots above the two bottom longerons; the lower halves of the wheels protruded through cut-outs in the fuselage skin. The wing was made in three parts: a 6-ft wide centre-section was braced by struts to the bottom of the fuselage and carried the engine with its twin propeller transmission chains and extension shafts, also the fuel tank; the outer wings were cantilevered from the centre section and were of constant chord for about 40 per cent of their span and tapered thereafter to the tip, the leading edge sweepback being about 30 degrees; the ailerons, each of 12 ft 2 in span, were rectangular. The tailplane was almost an equilateral triangle in plan with a single-piece elevator hinged to it, and the fin also was triangular with a rectangular rudder. The front of the fuselage was swept down with a conical aluminium nose-cap like a seagull's beak, and the top of the fuselage between wing and tail was horizontal, giving a simple rigging datum. The novel feature of the whole design was the $\frac{3}{8}$-in step formed in the upper wing surface at 40 per cent chord, which improved efficiency quite noticeably in both model and full-scale tests; although at the time no scientific explanation could be given, it probably had the effect of stabilising the boundary layer, and so limited the aft movement of the centre of pressure. The wing section (RAF 19 modified) was very thin for a cantilever structure, and four box-spars with spruce flanges and three-ply webs were needed to obtain the requisite stiffness in bending and torsion; the ribs were braced lattice girders and the covering was lightweight doped fabric.

The first Gull at Lympne before its first flight on 26 May, 1923, showing the small wheels originally fitted. (*Central News*).

All controls were internal, with cables from the elevator and rudder running inside the fuselage and the ailerons actuated by torque tubes inside the wing, with coaxial dogs engaging at the wing joints. The centre-section lift struts were continuous oval-section tubes flattened and curved to lie flush round the underside of the fuselage. Although Professor Bairstow had stated that the best obtainable L/D ratio in a normal aeroplane was of the order of 9 : 1, Gnosspelius had recorded 16 : 1 in model tests on the Gull and confidently expected to attain 12 : 1 in the full-scale aircraft after allowing for the extra drag of the pilot's head and the power plant, which, being air-cooled, could not be buried.

On 26 May, 1923, the first completed Gull was taken by lorry to Lympne aerodrome, assembled by 3 pm, and with half a gallon of petrol in the tank

176

John Parker started the engine at the first attempt and took off in under 80 yards on a windless day; he climbed steadily to 200 ft, then to 1,000 ft and finally dived low and up again to 1,500 ft, all in the course of a 12-minute circuit; on landing he misjudged his height and stalled from about 18 in up, causing a bump which cracked a seat bearer. This was quickly repaired, and after a brief tea-break he took off again, climbing to 2,100 ft in 20 minutes, but found it too cold to remain at that height, so after another low pass he landed again. He recorded the maximum and minimum flying speeds as 65 mph and 30 mph, but found it necessary to make a fast flat approach because of the low tail clearance; this was improved by fitting larger wheels, and further satisfactory flights were made at Lympne on 3 June, by which time the registration *G-EBGN* had been allotted.

On 18 June Parker flew the Gull across country to Rochester, but had to land a few miles short, in a potato field, due to failure of the fuel-system air-pressure valve. No damage was done, and after replacing the valve Parker took off again and flew back to Lympne. After this promising start, Short Brothers laid down a second Gull and invited further orders, undertaking delivery within nine weeks for intending competitors for the Duke of Sutherland's Prize; the Gull was demonstrated at Lympne after the start of the Grosvenor Cup race on 23 June, when the engine refused at first to run, even when Col Moore-Brabazon tried his hand; eventually it fired and Parker took off, but then found that the fuel pressure-valve had failed again and had to resort to the hand-pump; the result of working this in so small a machine with marginal longitudinal stability was an exciting 'rocking-horse' fly-past which somewhat put off intending purchasers, but there was no doubt of the little monoplane's high performance on only 16 hp; this was attained at 2,500 rpm, the limit at which the engine could be usefully run (maximum propeller speed being 1,850 rpm), although it was capable of 24 hp at 4,500 rpm in a road vehicle. On this occasion the Gull was soared, with engine throttled back, at 800 ft over the ridge adjoining Romney Marsh, gaining height for some

Both Gulls at Lympne on 8 October, 1923.

177

The second Gull at Lympne in October 1923, with Oscar Gnosspelius at extreme right.

minutes in the hill-lift available that day; five days later Parker managed to fly the Gull to 3,400 ft in 20 minutes.

The second Gull, similar to the first except for a slightly larger fin, was completed at Rochester during August 1923 and first flown on 8 October by Parker at Lympne; both were entered in the light aeroplane competitions which had just begun there, the first being flown as No. 2 by Parker and the second as No. 19 by Rex Stocken. Both suffered from engine trouble in the

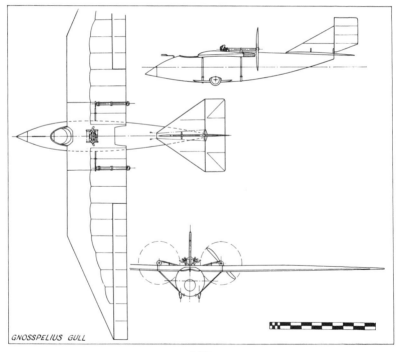

GNOSSPELIUS GULL

178

cold weather that prevailed; Stocken managed to complete three laps of the course and recorded an average speed of 55 mph, but neither covered the minimum aggregate distance of 400 miles required to qualify for an award. The second Gull was never registered, but was flown for 15 minutes at Martlesham by Parker during the service trials that were held after the Lympne competitions ended. Thereafter both Gulls were stored at Rochester, but late in 1925 the second was purchased by a syndicate of three members of the Newcastle-upon-Tyne Light Aeroplane Club; they were W. Baxter Ellis, P. Forsyth Heppell and R. N. Thompson, all of whom qualified for pilot's 'A' licences early in 1926.

By the end of February the Gull had been assembled but nobody could start the engine, so John Parker travelled up to Cramlington on 28 February and showed them how to do it; he then made a 10-minute circuit of the airfield and was followed by the club's flying instructor, Major Stanley Packman, who had to make a forced landing outside the boundary due to fuel shortage. Fourteen members man-handled the Gull over fields and hedges back on to the aerodrome, thereby gaining a healthy respect for the diminutive engine which made such light work of the same task. Further flights were made on 5 March by Packman and the owners, but soon afterwards the shock-absorber rubbers broke and various other repairs were found necessary; these were completed early in April, and Packman then set out to equal Parker's ceiling of 3,000 ft on this machine; on 24 April he reached 2,000 ft, which seemed to be the Gull's limit, since Packman weighed some 50 lb more than Parker. The Gull was thoroughly overhauled in June and flown again on the 24th by Heppell; then Packman took it up for a short flight, but undershot in landing and, in trying to clear a small obstacle, stalled and dived into the ground; he was thrown out and killed instantly, the Gull being a total wreck.

Long before this, Oscar Gnosspelius had become fully occupied with Arthur Gouge in designing and building the Rochester seaplane tank for Oswald Short; this was commissioned late in 1924, and Gnosspelius, Gouge and Jack Lower worked together in testing hull shapes from which hydrodynamic behaviour could be predicted. After five years on the experimental department staff, Gnosspelius voluntarily terminated his employment on the grounds that he already had adequate private means and did not wish to receive a salary while the firm was not making a profit. Oswald Short accepted this decision in the spirit in which it was offered, and thereafter Gnosspelius remained available as a consultant, but always declined to take any fee for his services; he flew from time to time with John Parker on test flights until after 1930 and was always welcome as an extra crew member in the larger flying-boats.

Span 36 ft 4 in (11·1 m); length 19 ft 6 in (5·9 m); area 142 sq ft (13·2 m²); empty weight 360 lb (163 kg); all-up weight 570 lb (258 kg); max speed 70 mph (112·7 km/h).

179

The Cockle, with original tail and added incidence, attempting to take off on 7 October, 1924.

The Short Stellite (Cockle) and Satellite

On completion of the design work on the rigid airship *R38* at Cardington, where he had remained with a small group of draughtsmen to assist Commander C. I. R. Campbell of the Royal Corps of Naval Constructors, C. P. T. Lipscomb returned to Rochester in 1921; he had joined Short Brothers as stressman to C. R. Fairey at Eastchurch in 1914, had moved to Rochester soon afterwards and then gone to Cardington in 1916. Having done all the detail strength calculations on the wooden airships *R31* and *R32*, he had progressed via the duralumin *R37* (taken over from Vickers Ltd) to the much improved and larger *R38*, which was being built for the United States Navy. He had acquired a thorough understanding of both Zeppelin and Vickers methods in using duralumin and was able to assure Oswald Short that this material was entirely reliable if uncontaminated by impurities such as zinc and not abused by cold-working or improper heat treatment. Oswald Short had begun to consider building all-metal seaplane floats and flying-boat hulls, to eliminate the water soakage and rapid deterioration in the tropics from which plywood suffered, and, as already mentioned, he and Francis Webber had drafted a design for a twin-engined float seaplane. As a second project, they schemed an all-metal version of the Cromarty, in which they proposed a fluted planing bottom to resist panting of the skin plating. This bottom was basically of the same concave V-shape as the Cromarty, with additional shallow chines parallel to the keel; in one version of this project it was intended to combine the wing-tip floats with outboard gunners' nacelles, as shown in patent No. 215,931 of April 1923; another scheme envisaged a three-engined layout with gunners' positions in the tails of the two outer engine nacelles. Although these designs came to nothing, they contained the seeds of the Singapore and Calcutta, which blossomed three years later.

Encouraged by the success of hydraulic pressure tests on the fuselage specimen for the Silver Streak, Oswald Short looked eagerly for an opportunity of building and testing an all-metal hull. Arthur Gouge made many mahogany model hulls which were sent for testing in the William Froude Ship Model Tank at Teddington, and gradually data on water resistance and spray

180

formation were amassed, for interpretation by Oscar Gnosspelius and J. H. Lower. Gouge had graduated to a B.Sc. (Eng.) degree through assiduous study at evening classes in Chatham Technical College, and Oswald Short had put him in charge of the experimental department, under the guidance of Gnosspelius and with Lower as technical assistant; their task was the study of the hydrodynamic behaviour and corrosion resistance of metal floats and hulls. Their chance came early in 1924; some time before Oswald Short had accompanied Griffith Brewer on one of the latter's regular visits to the United States, in the hope of interesting American manufacturers in a licence to build the twin-engined float seaplane; he had returned with plenty of goodwill but no firm orders, and then unexpectedly received a request from Lebbaeus Hordern to build a small sporting seaplane for cruising and fishing around Botany Bay. Oswald suggested a small single-seat flying-boat, to which Hordern agreed, so he and Webber designed the Stellite, the first to receive a design index number—S.1; this was the smallest flying-boat ever built at that time. The Stellite hull was launched in April 1924, and after being moored out for 24 hours the total leakage amounted to only an egg-cupful of water.

The Stellite (c/n S.638) had fabric covering for the wings and tail surfaces, but was otherwise entirely of metal; the wings had two spars made from corrugated high-tensile steel strip, with built-up duralumin ribs, and were mounted on top of the hull and braced from about half span to the chines by tubular struts. The hull was a duralumin monocoque with a flared V-bottom, a main step just aft of the c.g. and a second step halfway back to the tail. The steps were built on to the outside of the primary shell and their aft frames were open for free drainage after take-off, the intention being to avoid leakage into the hull through local damage to the steps; in fact, the separate steps did tend to trap sea-water and were the only locations where the skin later became perforated by corrosion. Originally it was intended to use two Bristol Cherub flat-twin engines of 32 hp each, but their vibration at full power was excessive, and less-powerful 697 cc Blackburne V-twins had to be substituted; these were directly coupled to extended airscrew shafts, without speed reduction, and only developed 16 hp each at their maximum usable speed of 2,400 rpm, although capable of nearly 30 hp at 4,500 rpm in a motorcycle. The wings had small floats under their tips and full-span ailerons which could be drooped symmetrically to increase camber and so reduce alighting speed. A horizontal tube through the hull just above the main step was arranged to receive large wheels on stub axles, which were plugged in for easy beaching and ground handling.

On completion the Stellite was registered *G-EBKA*, but the name was changed to Cockle at the request of the Air Ministry, who had already registered the Satellite and found the similarity of names confusing. It was launched on 18 September from No. 3 Shop slipway, but failed to take off during repeated attempts lasting 33 minutes; however, it survived this rough treatment with no sign of leakage. Taxying was resumed on 7 October, but it still showed no inclination to fly, even with increased incidence; at last, on

The Cockle with enlarged fin and rudder outside No. 3 Shop on 13 January, 1925.

7 November, after increasing wing incidence to 7 degrees, John Parker managed to coax it off the water; it then flew strongly for ten minutes, reaching a maximum speed of 57 mph, but it was too heavily loaded for its two tiny engines, and it was no great surprise when Hordern declined to take delivery. Parker, himself a lightweight, could fly it only in a minimum of clothing, and even wore plimsolls to save the weight of shoes, so it would have been of little use to a hefty Australian. Indeed, subsequent analysis of the first flight showed that the barometer was unusually high that day, the pressure altitude being 100 ft *below* sea level, which no doubt made all the difference in taking off. In January 1925 the Cockle's original low aspect ratio fin and rudder were replaced by a taller surface of more than twice the area, to take care of swing when one engine failed. Half-hour acceptance tests for a C. of A. were attempted on 16 and 18 March, but on the first occasion a fuel pipe broke after 12 minutes, and on the second the port engine faded after 27 minutes; in July 1925 it was loaned to the Air Ministry for evaluation at M.A.E.E., which had recently moved from Grain to Felixstowe, being given the serial *N193* for this purpose. Although only a few of the Felixstowe pilots succeeded in getting it off the water, Parker demonstrated it there on 5 September, and it

The Cockle at Rochester in July 1925 before delivery to Felixstowe as *N193*.

made a good impression, particularly on the score of resistance to salt-water corrosion; it was handed back to Short Brothers in August 1926. Back at Rochester, it was thoroughly overhauled and re-engined with two specially modified Bristol Cherub IIs with reduction gears; with these on 14 June, 1927, Parker only just managed to take off to a height of 10 ft, due to the starboard engine misfiring. He made a 12-minute flight at 600 ft on 27 June and a third flight of 35 minutes on 6 July, noting a vibration wave passing through the wing spars when both engines were synchronised. In a further acceptance test of 22 minutes on 13 July a top speed of 73 mph was recorded; the Cockle was then purchased by the Air Ministry and dispatched to Felixstowe, where, after a final test by Parker on 3 October, it was retained for exposure tests to obtain data on corrosion. It seems that the M.A.E.E.'s favourable experience with the Cockle led to the later order for the even smaller Parnall Prawn *S1576*, whose hull was in fact manufactured at Rochester by Short Brothers under sub-contract to Parnalls, to whom they had already supplied sets of metal floats for the Peto, Pike, Perch and Pipit prototypes; the Prawn never flew because its engine overheated and seized up while taxying, and no spares were available.

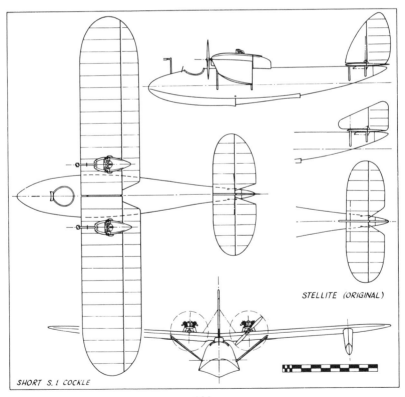

STELLITE (ORIGINAL)

SHORT S.1 COCKLE

183

Almost contemporary with the Cockle was a light monoplane built as an entry for the Air Ministry's competition for two-seaters to be held at Lympne in September 1924. In layout it was conventional, with a full cantilever mid-wing mounted on a duralumin monocoque fuselage of oval section and good streamline shape. As in the Cockle, the fuselage skin panels were developable surfaces applied to complete ring frames, with short longitudinals between and cleated to each frame. The design was started in July 1924, and in view of the imminence of the competition, it was decided not to risk delay by attempting to design a detachable cantilever root-end joint in a corrugated high-tensile steel spar, so the prototype had wooden box spars, with three-ply webs and laminated mahogany flanges; but the ribs were of duralumin, as were the tailplane, elevators, fin and rudder; full-span ailerons were fitted, and all the wing and tail surfaces were fabric-covered. The wing profile varied from a thin low-drag section outboard to a thicker section inboard, the depth being constant from tip to semi-span and tapering thence to the root; in plan the wing was parallel, with rounded tips. The fuselage shell was closed at the forward end by a fireproof bulkhead carrying a cast aluminium-alloy bracket for the flat-twin 32 hp Bristol Cherub air-cooled engine, which was faired by a neat conical cowling and spinner. The landing gear comprised two separate swing-axle units with rubber-in-compression shock absorbers and aluminium fairings, and the tailskid was a simple horizontal steel tube extending rearwards from a small under-fin, with a renewable shoe on the end. Gravity fuel and oil tanks were mounted aft of the firewall in front of the forward cockpit; full dual controls were installed, including a variable-camber gear for drooping both ailerons together, and the view from either of the tandem cockpits was excellent. Recorded in the design index as S.4, the little monoplane was named the Satellite, the constructor's number of the prototype being S.644.

John Parker flying the Satellite solo at Lympne in September 1924.

Flight testing of the Satellite began at Lympne on 10 September, 1924, but the engine was very rough-running at first, and Parker did not attempt the first straight flight till the 16th, without a passenger; two more solo flights were made on the 19th but it failed to take off with a passenger aboard with

184

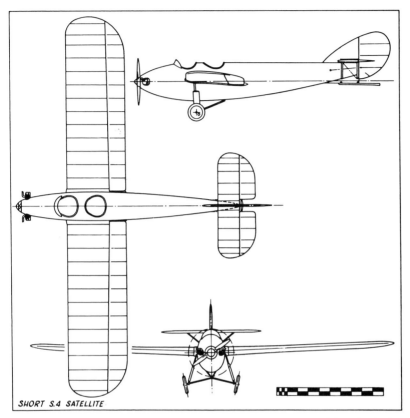

SHORT S.4 SATELLITE

the direct-drive Cherub I, in spite of changes of airscrew; with only Parker aboard, it flew fast and handled well, but the competition rules required two persons or equivalent ballast to be carried. No geared Cherub II was available, and in fact all the Cherub IIs in other machines had to be converted to direct drive during the course of the trials, because of the trouble experienced with them. Consequently, ten out of the 18 entrants on 27 September failed to pass the eliminating tests in the time allowed, and the Satellite (No. 8) was one of them. For the Grosvenor Cup race on 4 October a specially tuned Cherub I was available, and with this the Satellite had a much better performance and reached 72 mph; flying at a gross weight of 867 lb, Parker managed to complete the course and came in seventh. A geared Cherub II and a larger airscrew were installed later on, and with these Parker flew the Satellite to 1,000 ft in 7 minutes on both 30 March and 1 April, 1925, at Grain. During a test on 14 July at Grain, at an indicated speed of 90 mph, sudden violent wing flutter occurred; no damage resulted, so the span was reduced by 2 ft, and no further trouble was experienced even in dives up to 120 mph. The Satellite was next flown as a single-seater at the Lympne Bank Holiday

Meeting on 1 August, 1925, having meanwhile acquired the registration *G-EBJU*. During the first race the Cherub sustained internal damage, and although a replacement engine was fitted in time for the next event, this was a scratch race for two-seaters, and the Satellite barely managed to take off and did not complete the course; although its workmanship was greatly admired, the Satellite was obviously underpowered and soon became irreverently nicknamed *The Tin Kettle* or *Parker's Iron Balloon*.

In 1926 the Satellite was presented to a syndicate of R.A.F. officers at Eastchurch, called, from the number of its original members, the Seven Aero Club, who installed a 40 hp A.B.C. Scorpion II engine and Fairey-Reed duralumin airscrew. Parker tested it in this form at Northolt on 19 June, 1926, after which it was granted a C. of A. on 8 September before being flown as No. 15 in the 1926 Lympne trials by Flying Off G. E. F. Boyes. But in spite of its much enhanced performance with the new engine, the Satellite was still dogged by bad luck and damaged its landing gear; the judges refused to allow a repair, so it was out of the rest of the trials. This did not disqualify it from competing in the Grosvenor Cup race on 18 September, when it was matched against John Parker flying a new Short light monoplane, the Mussel. Although unplaced, Boyes finished the course, but Parker had to make a forced landing in open country. The Satellite was thereafter returned to Short Brothers and not flown again; for several years it was stored in the rafters of No. 1 Shop at Rochester, its C. of A. being cancelled in January 1928.

Two views of the Scorpion-engined Satellite as flown at Lympne in September 1926 by Flying Officer Boyes of the Seven Aero Club. (*Courtesy J. D. Oughton.*)

Cockle—Span 36 ft (10·95 m); length 24 ft 8 in (7·5 m); area 210 sq ft (19·5 m²); empty weight (Blackburne) 814 lb (370 kg), (Cherub) 880 lb (400 kg); all-up weight (Blackburne) 1,062 lb (482 kg), (Cherub) 1,205 lb (546 kg); max speed (Blackburne) 68 mph (110 km/h), (Cherub) 73 mph (118 km/h).

Satellite—Span 34 ft (10·3 m), later 32 ft (9·7 m); length 23 ft 9 in (7·2 m); area 168 sq ft (15·6 m²), later 160 sq ft (14·85 m²); empty weight 640 lb (290 kg); all-up weight 1,060 lb (481 kg); max speed 72 mph (116 km/h). With Scorpion for Grosvenor Cup: empty weight 666 lb (302 kg); all-up weight 867 lb (393 kg); speed 67 mph (108 km/h).

Eustace Short and John Parker with the Mussel II amphibian at Rochester on 8 March, 1930.

The Short Mussel

Towards the end of 1924, two important decisions, taken on their own initiative by two entirely independent aircraft manufacturers, were to lead to British pre-eminence in civil aviation during the decade that followed. One decision, taken by the de Havilland Aircraft Co in collaboration with Major Frank Halford, was to develop a cheap, rugged, four-cylinder aero-engine (the Cirrus I) and a simple, sturdy, light biplane to match it (the D.H. Moth). The other decision was by Short Brothers to build their own water channel in which to test model seaplane floats and hulls without having to wait their turn, often much delayed, to use the William Froude Ship Model Tank at the National Physical Laboratory, Teddington. Systematic testing in the 350-ft-long Rochester tank soon indicated the best line of development for metal floats, and those designed by Short Brothers for the Supermarine S.4 and Gloster III racing seaplanes entered in the 1925 Schneider Trophy contest at Baltimore were undoubtedly in advance of anything else in the world at that time. At last a clean-running narrow-heeled single-step float, long enough to eliminate the need for a tail float, yet free from any tendency to porpoise during the take-off run, could be built with a low drag in both air and water, and of such strength that, even when the Gloster III's chassis struts collapsed at Baltimore and allowed the airscrew to chop off the bows of both floats, the high impact pressure was contained by the front watertight bulkheads and the craft did not sink. These metal floats set a new standard and were quickly adopted wherever seaplane conversions of successful landplanes were contemplated; thus Short floats were invariably specified for the D.H.50, of which a Jaguar-engined version was flown to Australia and back in 1926 by Alan J.

187

Cobham, a few months after a similar Puma-engined seaplane had been supplied for the use of Lord Stonehaven, Governor-General of Australia. To correlate model and full-scale results, and so improve design still further, Short Brothers began in 1925 the design of a Cirrus-engined two-seat twin-float monoplane, using the familiar duralumin monocoque fuselage construction already proved on the Cockle, Satellite and Springbok. This design (index No. S.7) was named the Mussel, after the club-house near Short Brothers' first aeroplane factory on Sheppey in 1909.

Although primarily intended for experimental purposes, the Mussel conformed broadly to the established concept of a light (but not ultra-light) trainer and tourer for flying club use; indeed, it was originally proposed as a trainer for elevated aerodromes in South America, with a Bristol Lucifer radial engine, but revised to suit the smaller Cirrus engine when this came on to the market. It was built for hard work and to prove new aerodynamic and structural developments, but nevertheless was designed to fly as economically as possible, and its controls were beautifully harmonised. The fuselage was built up of single-curved skin panels riveted to complete ring frames with interrupted V-section stringers between frames, exactly as in the Cockle and Satellite. Forward of the fireproof bulkhead, the monocoque was extended into an open-topped channel similar to the engine bay of the Silver Streak.

John Parker taking a line from 'Sailor' Wadhams after the first flight of the Mussel I on 6 April, 1926; note the wooden airscrew and absence of wing-root fillets.

The Cirrus engine, an upright four-cylinder inline air-cooled type, was carried on special mounting brackets secured from outside the shell by horizontal shear bolts, whose accessibility made engine removal and replacement very simple, even while moored out. The wing section was RAF 33, a fairly thick cambered and reflexed aerofoil with a nearly stationary centre of pressure, hitherto untried at full scale. Structurally, the wings were semi-cantilevers, with pin-joints at the root and at mid-span, where each of the two parallel spars was braced by a streamlined compression strut from the top of the fuselage. The spars themselves were of box form, built up of corrugated duralumin strips, with local reinforcement by extra laminations where necessary. The ribs on the prototype were built up of spruce, but could equally well have

188

The Mussel I at Rochester in July 1926 soon after fitment of fabric root fillets and a prototype Short metal airscrew.

been of duralumin, as in the Satellite; the wings and tail surfaces were fabric-covered throughout. The duralumin floats, similar in design to those of the Gloster III, were protected with white Rylard seaplane enamel, but the fuselage was clear varnished apart from its registration mark, *G-EBMJ*.

When first flown by John Parker on 6 April, 1926, the Mussel (S.678) was unmarked and its performance was disappointing. The engine was bench-tested, but found to be giving full power, and changing the airscrew did not improve the reluctant take-off and sluggish climb. Then wing-root interference was suspected, and fabric root-fillets were applied; the effect of these was almost magical, and another lesson had been learned. An impressive demonstration was given to the Press on 28 June, and on 3 July an experimental metal airscrew was fitted with good results, being shown to R.A.E. specialists on the 28th, when Parker recorded a speed of 85 mph. On 15 September the Mussel was temporarily converted into a landplane, receiving a C. of A. the next day, in time to compete in the Grosvenor Challenge Cup race at Lympne two days later. Parker had bad luck on that occasion and had to make a forced landing, but did so without damage of any kind. Meanwhile,

The Mussel I as a landplane at Lympne in September 1926.

189

the float chassis had been loaned to a demonstration D.H. Moth, to be taken to the United States by Sir Alan Cobham (as he had become). The Moth seaplane was tested at Rochester by Hubert Broad in November 1926 and subsequently flown from alongside the *Homeric* at Sandy Hook into New York harbour. On 1 October the Mussel was fitted with a new set of improved floats, with downswept bows and carried on a stronger chassis with two extra struts above the step; it remained thus until 11 March, 1927, when it again became a landplane to be flown by Parker at the Bournemouth Easter race meeting; in the interim it had been used for testing a revised duralumin air-screw designed at Rochester, comprising two separate forged blades whose roots overlapped, so that both blades could be bolted up, together with wedge-shaped filler blocks, to form a solid boss on the engine shaft. In April an experimental land chassis was tested at Lympne, and on 20 July a further improved set of floats was installed, being demonstrated at Felixstowe a week

The Mussel I moored out on the Medway on 20 January, 1928, showing the fully cowled Cirrus II engine and the second set of floats.

later in spite of a rough sea which nearly caused disaster. In January 1928 a new Cirrus II engine of 85 hp was installed in an enclosed cowling, which reduced drag and improved performance to such an extent that on 10 July, piloted by Lady Heath with Miss Sicele O'Brien as passenger, the Mussel set up a new class record for seaplanes not exceeding 500 kg with a climb to 13,400 ft, but homologation by the F.A.I. was refused because the Mussel was found to have been 30 kg overweight at take-off. On 18 July *G-EBMJ* once more became a landplane and was flown by John Parker with Eustace Short on a circular tour from Gillingham via Mildenhall, Sherburn-in-Elmet, Cramlington, Brough, Hucknall, Hooton Park, Filton, Croydon, Lympne and East-church, returning to Gillingham on 25 July. On 1 August it resumed its floats for a flight over Dartford and remained a seaplane thereafter.

While the primary purpose of the Mussel was always to contribute to current research—for instance, the new floats were part of the Crusader pro-

190

The Mussel I landplane at Gillingham after returning from Eustace Short's tour of the flying clubs in July 1928.

gramme and were also put into production as standard for the Moth conversions exported to many countries—it owed its existence as a light touring seaplane to Eustace Short's latter-day enthusiasm for flying. Always a keen balloonist and devoted to the practical side of navigation both by air and by sea, he had been disappointed when there had been no post-war revival of interest in small airships and his plans for expanding the barge-yard had failed to pay their way. When the prospect arose of building a light seaplane in succession to the Cockle he had insisted that it should be a two-seater on which he might learn to fly, and no effort was spared to make the Mussel a really delightful machine to handle. John Parker gave him his first dual instruction in July 1926, soon after the interference trouble had been cured, and lessons continued concurrently with experimental flying until he went solo on 19 October, 1927. Thereafter he flew with great regularity, both with Parker and solo, quite regardless of rough weather, which he seemed to enjoy even more than fine. On one occasion, while exploring a coastal landmark, each pilot thought the other was flying the Mussel, and it was some 10 minutes before they both realised that it had been flying itself in a series of gentle dives and climbing turns round the object of their interest. On 24 August, 1928, Eustace was coming in after a solo flight when he touched one wing-tip on the mast of a barge in the Medway, and the Mussel cart-wheeled into the water. Short Brothers' boatman, George Wadhams, was quickly on the spot, and Eustace was rescued unhurt, but the seaplane had both wings torn off and the tail and chassis buckled. It was stripped for inspection in the works and condemned as uneconomical for repair, its C. of A. being cancelled in January 1929; later it was given to the R.A.F. Apprentices' School at Halton as a specimen of monocoque construction, and during 1930–1 the 23rd and 24th Boys' Entries were rebuilding it, but this exercise seems not to have been completed; Eustace Short's solo flying time on *G-EBMJ* totalled 23 hours 44 minutes.

It had been decided to build an improved Mussel because of its great experimental usefulness and to allow Eustace Short to continue flying, since he had little enthusiasm for landplanes but wanted to spend his time between wind and water. The Mussel II (S.750) was generally similar to the first in its final form, but it had an all-metal wing structure of NACA M.12 section

191

The Mussel II at Felixstowe for C. of A. trials in June 1929. (*I.W.M.—Crown Copyright.*)

and the fuselage was flat-sided at the wing-roots, so no fillets were needed; it had a 90 hp Cirrus III driving a Short patent metal airscrew, also water rudders to make taxying easier. It was launched for its first flight by Parker on 17 May, 1929, being flown to Felixstowe in June for airworthiness trials as *G-AAFZ*. On 28 June it was converted into a landplane for 10 days, then reverted to floats and was exhibited on Short Brothers' stand at the aero show at Olympia in July, together with a de Havilland Gipsy Moth equipped with a novel amphibian landing gear designed and made at Rochester. This consisted of a long central float carrying a cross-axle with a sprung wheel on each side; the axle could be rotated by the pilot so as to swing the wheels below keel level for land operation, or above the float for use from water. The heel carried a sprung water rudder which also served as a tailskid, and the conversion was completed by a pair of wing-tip floats carried on struts; all the floats were of Short Brothers' standard duralumin monocoque construction. The first of these amphibian gears was fitted to Gipsy Moth *G-AADV*, delivered to John Scott-Taggart in February 1929, shown at Olympia as stated and flown from the Solent during the period of the Schneider Trophy contest in August and September. Early in 1930 a similar gear was made for the Mussel II, being launched and flown under 'B' conditions with mark *M-1* on 8 March; it was very successful, and in due course its C. of A. was restored;

The Mussel II amphibian moored at Rochester in March 1930.

192

Eustace Short enjoyed flying it as an amphibian, and in fact John Parker at last persuaded him to apply for his 'A' licence (after accumulating more than 200 hours) which was granted on 22 February, 1931.

Meanwhile a second Moth had been converted to an amphibian, to the order of A. E. Guinness for private use on the Irish lakes; this was *G-AAVC*, delivered by de Havillands to Rochester with a Gipsy II engine in May 1930. Guinness was a big man, no longer as agile as in his youth, so a modified access door to the front cockpit had to be made; at the same time a more powerful Cirrus Hermes I engine was installed, and this major rebuild was allotted Shorts' c/n S.761. On 29 August the spare Gipsy II engine, complete with standard Moth cowling, was installed in the Mussel II, which Eustace Short continued to fly almost daily after its main development programme was finished; on 8 April, 1932, he returned from a brief flight and made a downwind but otherwise perfect landing on the Medway, but was seen to continue taxying until the seaplane grounded on the mud on the Cuxton side. George Wadhams went across at once, but Eustace was found to have died of a heart attack just after touching down, without time to cut the ignition. He evidently had some premonition of the event, for on his way out that day he had looked into Parker's office and said, 'One day I shan't switch off'; Parker called back, 'Are you all right?' but got no reply. Incidentally, Eustace Short never learned that ignition switches worked the opposite way to domestic ones, and Dick Rowett, who usually started his engine for him, always had to call 'Switch on' before sucking in and 'Switch off' instead of 'Contact' before starting.

The Mussel II in its final state with Gipsy II engine and without amphibian gear racing against Arthur Bray's speed-boat during the Rochester Regatta on 12 August, 1933. (*Courtesy A. J. Jackson.*)

After Eustace Short's death the Mussel II was again flown for experimental purposes, and on 29 June, 1932, was tested as a single-wheeled landplane, with skids under the tail and wing-tips, in the manner of the amphibian patented in America by Grover Loening in 1924. Parker made the first flight from a field near the Star Hotel at Gillingham, and on 5 July flew it across country to West Malling, but it was difficult to handle on the ground and was

193

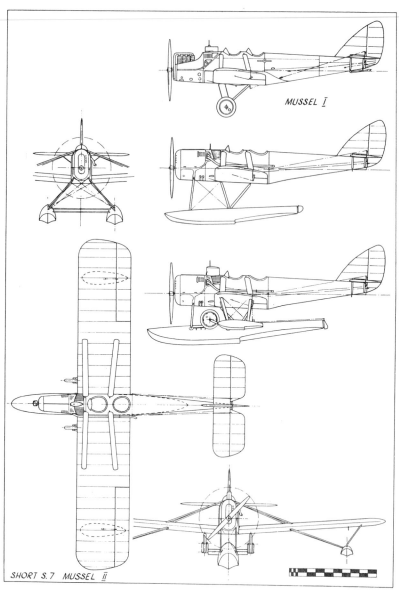

MUSSEL I

SHORT S.7 MUSSEL II

returned to the works. On 24 October it reappeared as a central-float sea-plane with the amphibian wheel gear removed and its cross-axle fairing de-leted; it remained in this state, and on 12 August, 1933, was raced by Parker against a Chriscraft speed-boat driven by Arthur Bray in the Rochester Regatta, repeating this performance at Sheerness on 6 September; *G-AAFZ*

194

appears to have flown for the last time on 15 September, 1933, with Dennis Kemp as passenger, and was scrapped in January 1934. Apart from being delightful and docile flying machines, and probably John Parker's favourite pleasure craft, the two Mussels accomplished an enormous amount of experimental work, of which the correlation of model and full-scale results was the most valuable; seldom has there been a more worthwhile private-venture investment.

Mussel I—Span 36 ft (10·95 m); length (s/p) 24 ft (7·3 m), (l/p) 23 ft 3 in (7·1 m); area 200 sq ft (18·6 m²); empty weight (s/p) 1,030 lb (467 kg), (l/p) 907 lb (411·7 kg); all-up weight (s/p) 1,576 lb (715 kg), (l/p) 1,430 lb (649 kg); max speed (s/p) 82 mph (132 km/h), (l/p) 87 mph (140 km/h).

Mussel II—Span 37 ft 3 in (11·36 m); length 25 ft (7·62 m); area 206 sq ft (19·15 m²); empty weight 1,061 lb (482 kg); all-up weight 1,640 lb (744 kg); max speed 102 mph (164 km/h); duration 4 hr.

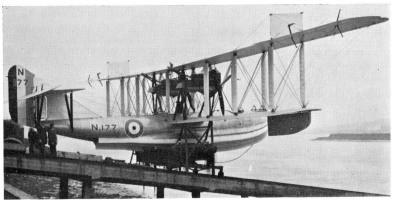

The metal-hulled F.5 *N177* before being launched on 31 December, 1924.

The Short Singapore I

Although Oswald Short had no luck in his efforts to interest the United States Navy in an all-metal version of the Cromarty in 1924, his return to England coincided with Lebbaeus Hordern's enquiry for a light seaplane, which led, as already recounted, to the building of the Cockle. Almost simultaneously the Air Ministry invited tenders for two hulls of modern design to suit the aerostructure of the standard F.5 flying-boat, emphasising the importance of durability and seaworthiness. Short Brothers tendered a duralumin hull derived from the projected metal Cromarty, designed by Francis Webber, who insisted on longitudinal flutes in the planing bottom (patent No. 244,898 of November 1924) to prevent panting of the plating under peak pressures; a rival tender was that of S. E. Saunders & Co of Cowes, who proposed a flat-sided hollow-bottomed hull (like an enlarged N.2B float) made from their patented Consuta wire-sewn plywood. At first the metal hull was rejected out of hand, but Oswald Short argued the case for duralumin, and finally won a contract after signing a guarantee accepting full financial responsibility if the metal hull was not watertight; he thus stood to lose the whole contract price of £10,000 if a single rivet leaked. The Short metal F.5 hull received the design index No. S.2 and serial *N177*, the Saunders hull being *N178*.

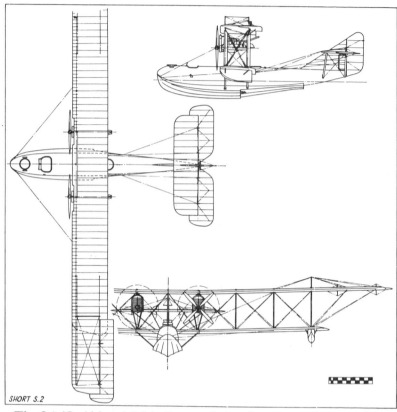

SHORT S.2

The S.1 (Cockle) and S.2 hulls were designed concurrently and construction began simultaneously, but naturally the small boat was finished first, and so acted as a pilot for the large one, any problems of leaking rivets or protective treatment being overcome on the Cockle before they arose on the F.5, where they might have been troublesome if encountered for the first time. The F.5 hull was built in vertical sections set upright on the bench, each frame being assembled to its adjacent band of skin plating; all the skin and frame segments were then joined up in a horizontal cradle, so that truing-up took place as the final operation, and no cumulative errors of alignment or twist could occur. The frames followed the flare of the chines, so the forebody was integral with the upper part of the hull, although the actual steps were separately built on to the outside of the shell, as in the Cockle; this ensured full ventilation and drainage of the whole interior surface of the skin, the only risk of trapping sea-water being at the steps, where detachable covers were provided in the inner skin for inspection. Apart from the extreme nose and tail caps, all the rings were plated without double curvature, so there was no need for panel beating, and consequently no risk of work-hardening the metal after ageing, which was by then recognised as a primary cause of fatigue cracks and corrosion. The hull below the waterline was protected with Rylard white seaplane enamel, and the remainder of the hull with Rylard clear varnish. The normal F.5 wings, tail unit, tanks, controls, engines and airscrews were assembled on to the new hull, the wooden wing-tip floats also being retained,

N177 about to take off from the Medway on 5 January, 1925.

and the complete flying-boat was launched from No. 3 Shop slipway on the last day of 1924, being flown by Parker on 5 January, 1925, when it was found to be slightly nose-heavy. After further handling trials at Rochester on 6 and 13 March, which showed it to have a cleaner water performance than the standard F.5, *N177* was delivered by Parker to the M.A.E.E. at Felixstowe on 14 March and began a series of strenuous and searching service trials over open sea, being continuously moored on the Orwell between flights and hauled ashore only when a gale was expected. Once, in a simulated heavy alighting test in a swell in the English Channel, it was deliberately stalled and dropped on to the water from a height of 30 ft, but even this violent treatment failed to spring any seams; in fact, the 16-gauge planing bottom was found to be amply strong and stiff enough to withstand all water loads even without the fluting, promising further reduction of skin friction and wave drag in future designs. Parker and Gouge went to Felixstowe to inspect the hull on 12 January, 1926, after one year's service, and found the underwater surfaces in excellent condition, with no serious corrosion outside and only a small amount inside; inevitably paint had been worn off by treadwear and abrasion, and in the closed space at the steps a skin of aluminium hydroxide jelly had formed, but this was negligible compared with the normal deterioration of a wooden hull during one year's exposure.

The excellent behaviour of the 'Tin Five', as the R.A.F. called it, at last

197

overcame the Air Ministry's opposition to duralumin, and late in 1924 Short Brothers were invited to tender for an improved all-metal version of the Cromarty; a prototype, named the Singapore, was ordered early in 1925 to specification 13/24, receiving design index No. S.5, constructor's No. S.677 and serial *N179*. This contract (519933/24) was not gained without a further fight by Oswald Short, who was disappointed, indeed aggrieved after all his pioneer effort, to find that the Supermarine Works had already received an order for six duralumin hulls for Southamptons at £10,000 each, while a duralumin hull had also been ordered from the English Electric Company for one of its Kingstons; moreover, the latter had a fluted bottom which actually infringed the Short patent, although Oswald could not afford to fight an action in the High Court. Some weeks after submitting the Singapore tender, having heard nothing more, Oswald Short rang up the Directorate of Technical Development; he was advised to enquire from the Director himself, who admitted that a metal-hulled prototype had been ordered from Blackburn but not from Short Brothers. Oswald instructed his works manager, W. P. Kemp, to order all materials for the Singapore at once and then telephoned Sir Geoffrey Salmond of the Air Council to say that in spite of having lost the order, he was going to build the Singapore for £20,000 as a private venture, even if the firm went bankrupt in the process. Sir Geoffrey replied, 'Good fellow, I will come down and see you tomorrow morning', and on being shown the Singapore drawings asked, 'Why have I not seen these before?' He would not hear of Short Brothers incurring a bigger overdraft and, although the Air Council's funds were all allocated for that year, was able to promise £10,000 in 1925 and the same amount in 1926.

Webber's original design for the Singapore hull included a fluted planing bottom, on which model tests were done in the William Froude tank in July 1924. A few months later the Rochester tank came into use and Gouge repeated the tests, but failed to get agreement with the N.P.L. results. The Froude tank was administered strictly under the rules of the Yarrow bequest, which made it difficult to get access to it at short notice; furthermore, it was intended only for measuring waterline drag of ship models, so Oswald Short made his own tank by excavating a shelf in the side of the chalk cliff behind No. 3 Shop. It was 250 ft long at first, but soon extended to 350 ft, with a width of 6 ft and a carriage speed of over 20 mph, and means for simulating wing-lift and recording spray patterns in addition to drag. Gouge's assistant in the seaplane tank was Jack Lower, trained at Chatham Dockyard, and for a time the junior in the team was Thurstan James, inevitably nicknamed 'Thirsty Jim'. Gouge puzzled over the discrepancy between the N.P.L. and Rochester tank results with the same model, eventually concluding that the higher drag found at Rochester was due to interference from the separate bow waves set up by each flute, which the N.P.L. apparatus was too insensitive to show. Information from a Göttingen research report supported this view and also showed how a flared metal bottom could be designed to dispense with flutes. Gouge and Lower spent a whole week-end, while the works were closed, comparing models with and without flutes and found that the

198

resistance of the latter agreed with the N.P.L. results. Further tests showed that a reduction in beam from 12 ft to 10 ft 4 in would ensure cleaner running and almost eliminate porpoising; Oswald Short was impressed with these results and told Webber to redesign the hull without flutes, but he resented being overruled and soon afterwards resigned to join Armstrong Whitworth at Coventry; on the Monday morning after Webber's departure Gouge was astonished to receive a letter from Oswald Short appointing him Chief Designer; for a few hours he seems to have doubted his competence for so responsible a post, but on being reassured by his colleagues he accepted his unexpected promotion with enthusiasm and energy.

Full advantage was taken in the Singapore of Oswald Short's patented method of deriving the hull shape from conical frusta of varying pitch, and the resulting lines were very pleasing, with an upswept stern reminiscent of a Venetian gondola and a flared forebody with a reduced beam and a deep keel. Plating of the frames began in October 1925, and by that time tests on corrugated duralumin box spars had established their suitability for larger wing

Singapore I *N179* at Felixstowe in November 1926, showing the original forebody, two-bladed airscrews and auxiliary rudders. (*I.W.M.—Crown Copyright.*)

structures. In general, the two-spar Göttingen 435 section wings followed, on a larger scale, the Mussel design, the Warren-girder ribs being of round duralumin tube and the Frise ailerons fitted on the upper wing only; the top centre-section carried the gravity fuel tanks within a slightly inflated profile and was attached to the hull and lower wing-root stubs by faired steel-tube struts which carried the two engine nacelles midway in the gap. The outer wings, unequal in span, had only a single bay of outward-splayed struts and neither stagger nor sweepback; their tips were elliptical, and they carried single-stepped duralumin wing-tip floats. The lower centre-section stubs were braced to the hull just above the chine, and the nacelles were monocoques, enabling the Rolls-Royce Condor III engines to be easily removed and reinstalled. The tailplane was set one-third of the way up the single fin, and the elevators and rudder were horn-balanced; like the wings, they were fabric-covered and aluminium-doped, while the hull, wing-tip floats and nacelles

199

were protected with white Rylard enamel inside and out. The engines had flat frontal radiators with horizontal shutters and drove two-bladed wooden airscrews. Accommodation was provided for two pilots side-by-side, with a bow gunner's cockpit forward and two waist gunners' cockpits aft, with a Scarff ring and Lewis gun apiece. The interior of the hull was unencumbered by structure and, in addition to the wireless operator's station, had cooking facilities and rest bunks installed, so that the Singapore could operate away from a shore base for lengthy periods. There had been some doubt about the ability of a central rudder to hold the machine straight with one engine dead, so auxiliary fins were fitted above the tailplane, one in each slipstream, carrying small rudders which could be biased as required.

The Singapore I was launched on 17 August, 1926, and flown by Parker the same day, with Eustace Short, George Cotton and A. E. Bibby as crew, but after two minutes a cowling panel on the port engine came adrift and fouled the airscrew, so the flight had to be quickly ended. It was flown again two days later for 20 minutes, but showed signs of a few isolated rivet leaks and was taken back into No. 3 Shop for rectification. It reappeared on 6 October, when Parker, with the same crew as before, flew it for half an hour and put it down at moorings off Upnor, downstream of Rochester bridge; next day he flew it for $1\frac{1}{2}$ hours at Upnor, climbing to 10,000 ft in 34 minutes and recording a speed of 103 kt. On 1 November he flew it from Rochester to Felixstowe in one hour, making a full-load test the same day and another on 3 November, after which it remained at the M.A.E.E. for service trials. Although it could fly well on one engine, the auxiliary rudders were insufficient to hold it on a straight course, and a more powerful servo-rudder was recommended. Parker had already sampled one of the Flettner type on a D.H.10 at Farnborough on 19 May, 1926, and favoured its adoption for the Singapore, so the latter was returned to Rochester and flown with a servo-rudder on 3 June, 1927, after which the auxiliary rudders were removed. Up-rated Condor IIIA engines were next installed and tested on 8 June, then the Singapore went back into No. 3 Shop to have the planing bottom stiffened and four-bladed airscrews fitted to take full advantage of the increased take-off power available. On 6 August it was flown back to Felixstowe, with Oswald Short aboard, in time to take part in the R.A.F. Scandinavian cruise which began on 12 August. This was a tour of Baltic seaports by four prototype flying-boats and was, in fact, intended to choose the type of boat to be standardised for the R.A.F. for many years to come. The Singapore was the only one of all-metal construction, the others being the Blackburn Iris II with a metal hull and wooden aerostructure and the Saunders Valkyrie and Supermarine Southampton I of all-wood construction. The flight was commanded by Sqn Ldr Scott, and the Singapore was flown by Flt Lieut B. C. H. Cross and Plt Off R. S. Darbishire, with a crew of four other ranks. The Valkyrie and Southampton took off first and the Iris soon afterwards with the Air Minister, Sir Samuel Hoare, aboard *en route* to the concurrent aero show at Copenhagen; the Singapore had to return to moorings with an engine fault, but next day flew non-stop to Oslo, the others having broken their journey at Esbjerg. The four boats were to fly on from Oslo to Copenhagen, thence via Gdynia, Danzig, Helsinki and Stockholm to Copenhagen and finally back to Felixstowe.

The first casualty was the Southampton, which broke down at Danzig on 30 August, then the Valkyrie came down with engine trouble and had to be towed into Königsberg. Eventually both arrived at Copenhagen, but crashed and sank while trying to take off in a rough sea for the return flight to Felixstowe; Scott in the Iris gave Cross in the Singapore an hour's start and bet him £5 that he would overtake him, but Cross got home 45 minutes ahead and collected his wager when the Iris arrived at the slipway. Both the Iris and the Singapore completed the tour of 5,000 miles without incident, proving the superiority of metal hulls in open sea conditions, but to Oswald Short's disappointment, the immediate order for three production aircraft went to Blackburns for the all-metal Iris III on account of its marginally higher performance with 50 per cent more power, and its claimed ability to take off with enough fuel to cross the Atlantic with only one stop in Greenland; but in fact it could only reach Iceland when put to the test. The Singapore, though smaller, had proved its ability to cruise for 11 hours on 600 gallons of petrol, equivalent to 900 miles, but was relegated to routine duties at Felixstowe, where it might have remained had it not been seen by Sir Alan Cobham at Rochester while being modified during July. He remarked, 'I could fly that round the world', and asked Oswald Short whether he thought the Air Ministry would lend it for that purpose; he made enquiries, but was told that a flying-boat which had cost the taxpayers £20,000 could not be lent to a civilian pilot for a stunt flight. Oswald referred the matter to Sir Geoffrey Salmond, who persuaded the Air Council to lend the Singapore back to Short Brothers for one year, provided they insured it in favour of the Air Council for £12,000. Cobham then went into the details of the proposed round-the-world flight and found that some sectors would be beyond even the Singapore's range against the worst head-winds, so he changed his plan to a 23,000 miles survey flight round Africa on behalf of Imperial Airways, who did not, however, have any funds available for sponsoring the flight; in the end the total cost of £20,000 was made up by Sir Charles Wakefield who gave £12,000, Short Brothers who put up £3,000, Rolls-Royce Ltd with £1,000, and the remainder in smaller subscriptions mainly from suppliers of materials and equipment.

The Singapore was ferried back from Felixstowe to Rochester in October 1927, to be prepared for the survey flight; new high-compression Condor IIIA engines were installed and all military equipment, including Scarff gun-mountings, was removed; the hull was cleaned and repainted with Rylard white enamel below the waterline and clear varnish above, as specified for the new Calcutta boats under construction for Imperial Airways. The Singapore received the civil registration mark *G-EBUP* and Parker flew it again for a 35-minute test on 3 November, accompanied by Eustace Short, George Cotton, Green and Conway of Rolls-Royce, and two others. On the next two days Cobham took the controls for two fuel consumption tests of $1\frac{1}{2}$ hours each; these were satisfactory, and on 7 November the C. of A. was issued and

Singapore I as *G-EBUP* at Rochester in November 1928 before starting the flight round Africa, showing four-bladed airscrews and enlarged oil-tanks under nacelles; the auxiliary rudders have been removed and a Flettner servo-rudder fitted.

the Singapore was flown for the benefit of the Press, though only for ten minutes, as the weather was very foggy. On the 15th Parker gave Cobham's co-pilot, H. V. Worrall, an hour's practice, but he landed rather far up-river at low tide and holed the bottom on a submerged snag; all on board baled vigorously, including apprentice Dick Rowett, who had stowed away in the stern, and Parker was able to taxi back to the slipway before the bilges filled; the damage was quickly repaired, and two days later the Singapore left the Medway on schedule, heading up the Thames over London and thence to Hamble, with Cobham and Worrall at the controls, Lady Cobham in charge of the commissariat, Conway and Green in charge of engine maintenance, and S. R. Bonnett of the Gaumont Co to make a complete film record of the tour. Take-off from Hamble was delayed by fog, but the next stop was made before nightfall on the 20th at Bordeaux, whence the route lay via Marseilles and Ajaccio to Malta; in the teeth of a sudden gale Cobham was unable to reach Kalafrana before dusk and put down in St Paul's Bay by the aid of a search-light on H.M.S. *Queen Elizabeth*, which sent a pinnace to assist. The flight to the R.A.F. base next day was uneventful until the Singapore was taken in tow across Marsa Scirocco Bay, where a heavy swell was running; just before reaching the anchorage, a roller lifted the port wing and the starboard wing float was torn off. Green, Conway and Bonnett immediately climbed out on to the port wing, and Cobham decided to turn back to shelter at Delimara, eventually gaining the lee of the cliffs, where he lay up until the storm abated.

On 30 November the boat was towed back to the seaplane base for repair on the slipway, but while waiting for the wind and swell to drop the port wing float became waterlogged and the boat had to be hurriedly beached, the trolley having been washed off the slipway by a wave. The Singapore was finally dragged up the slipway on its bare keel by the combined efforts of nearly 200 men, but was still in danger until hauled higher up on to the tarmac, and this could only be done by hacking off part of the damaged port lower wing in order to clear a wall. Rochester works built a complete new wing, two new elevators and two new wing floats within a fortnight and got them out to

202

Malta with great alacrity; the keel was undamaged by its drastic treatment, and the hull needed only minor repairs. After ten days the storm abated, and with unlimited help from the R.A.F. the aircraft was trestled for inspection; repairs were completed by 8 January, 1928, when Cobham checked the Singapore out in two test flights and found it completely satisfactory, but on the 10th it broke adrift in another gale and had to be repaired in Malta Dockyard after being held all night against a sandy beach by relays of R.A.F. personnel standing waist-deep in the sea. A fresh start was made on 21 January, when Cobham flew from Grand Harbour to Benghazi and Tobruk, reaching Aboukir Bay on the 22nd. Thereafter the flight went according to plan, up the Nile to Mongalla and thence to Entebbe and Mwanza on Lake Victoria, where a survey diversion of 2,700 miles to Khartoum and back was made at the request of the Colonial Office. The main flight was resumed via Lakes Tanganyika and Nyasa, thence 450 miles overland to Beira and round the coast to Lourenço Marques, arriving at Durban on 8 March; there the boat was lifted out of the water for inspection after 150 engine hours, and Cobham toured Rhodesia in a Moth lent by the Johannesburg Aero Club.

Three weeks later the survey flight was resumed via Knysna, and Cobham arrived at Cape Town on 30 March, the Singapore being the first flying-boat ever seen there. On 3 April the flight continued up the west coast, but five days later, at Banana Creek at the mouth of the Congo, Green had to be put on board a Belgian steamer whose doctor arranged to get him to hospital at Boma for urgent treatment. Next day the Singapore encountered a severe hailstorm and Cobham made a precautionary landing on a lagoon near Libreville; while waiting to take off again the tide ebbed and the keel just touched bottom, but cleared the sandbanks without apparent damage. At Lagos the boat was

G-EBUP in peril on the beach at Kalafrana on 1 December, 1928, with both wing-tip floats torn off and the port lower wing submerged. (*Courtesy J. D. Oughton.*)

203

lifted out to enable a small leak to be traced and repaired, but after an hour's flight *en route* to Abidjan on 17 April Cobham noticed an unusual vibration in one engine and put down at Fresco Bay; the crankcase was found to be fractured and the replacement engine took four weeks to arrive; during this time the hull became heavily encrusted with barnacles, which had to be cleaned off at Freetown after the flight was resumed on 15 May; thence the route lay via Bathurst, Port Etienne, La Luz (Grand Canary), Casablanca and Gibraltar. After returning to Plymouth via Barcelona and Bordeaux on 31 May, the crankshaft of the other Condor broke after take-off next day, but a new engine was installed at Calshot and the Singapore flew across London to Rochester on 4 June; then a tour of British seaports and coastal resorts was arranged in conjunction with the Air League, and the Singapore finally got back to its moorings on the Medway on 11 June, 1929, having flown over 23,000 miles and made some 90 take-offs and landings; the actual flying time up to 31 May was 330 hours, and more than 50 possible seaplane bases in and around the African continent were surveyed and reported on.

After the conclusion of the African flight the Singapore was returned to the Air Ministry and might well have sought honourable retirement, but such a glutton for punishment was too valuable to be laid aside, and already there were plans to rebuild the hull to conform with the improved planing bottom of the Calcutta and at the same time to test a pair of the new Rolls-Royce H.10 engines, later named Buzzard. These were rated at 850 hp each, and were installed in fully streamlined nacelles, with new radiators slung from the underside of the top centreplane; they drove 15-ft-diameter two-bladed airscrews and raised the Singapore's speed to 132 mph; the upper wing was fitted with Handley Page auto-slots, and the revised hull had a longer forebody. The structurally complete but unequipped aircraft was exhibited on Short Brothers' stand at Olympia in July; it was completed and relaunched at Rochester on 2 October, when Parker made a 12-minute handling flight with

Singapore I *N179* at Felixstowe in November 1929 after being rebuilt with a longer forebody, Rolls-Royce H.10 engines and Handley Page auto-slots; the four-bladed airscrews shown here replaced the very large two-bladers fitted earlier and shown at Olympia in July. (*I.W.M.—Crown Copyright.*)

the new engines. Adjustments were called for, and a satisfactory check flight was made on 1 November, followed next day by an hour's acceptance climb test; Parker flew it back to Felixstowe on 8 November, and it remained there as a Buzzard test-bed (with four-bladed airscrews for a time) and to check proposed features of the Singapore II, which was a larger four-engined development ordered as a prototype in 1928; this is described in a later chapter.

Span 93 ft (28·4 m); length 64 ft (19·5 m), later 65 ft 6 in (20 m); area 1,723 sq ft (160·5 m²); empty weight (Condors) 12,875 lb (5,840 kg), (H.10s) 12,955 lb (5,875 kg); all-up weight (Condors) 19,560 lb (8,700 kg), (H.10s) 20,000 lb (9,100 kg); max speed (Condors) 128 mph (206 km/h), (H.10s) 132 mph (212 km/h); ceiling 15,500 ft (4,730 m); range 900 miles (1,450 km).

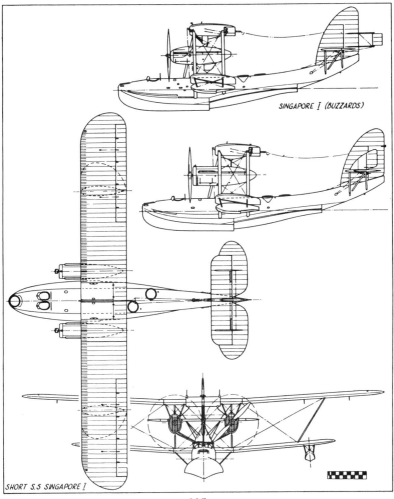

SINGAPORE I (BUZZARDS)

SHORT S.5 SINGAPORE I

205

The modified Chamois *J7295* at Lympne on 9 March, 1927, before its first flight.

The Short Chamois, Sturgeon and Gurnard

After the Marine Aircraft Experimental Establishment removed from the Isle of Grain to Felixstowe in 1924, the aerodrome at Grain was closed down, and a year later Short Brothers found themselves without a convenient site for flight-testing landplanes; hangarage reserved at Lympne was too far from Rochester for daily use, and this difficulty tended to discourage the firm from undertaking new land-based projects, although such opportunities were indeed few. Lympne was the venue for the annual Grosvenor Cup race and other light aeroplane competitions, and Short Brothers could do no better for a few years than to retain their foothold there, so as to be able to test landplanes when necessary.

In 1926, after spending nearly a year at Martlesham Heath, the first Springbok II, *J7295*, was brought back to Rochester for drastic modifications to suit it for the revised army co-operation role (specification 30/24) for a Bristol Fighter replacement, which had still not been decided. This involved considerable changes in the equipment schedule, but principally a better all-round performance at a higher all-up weight was demanded. Only its original Jupiter IV was available, but all possible steps were taken to suppress drag while increasing strength and stiffness. The wing layout was completely redesigned from two-bay to single-bay and the upper wing section was changed. The deeper profile enabled the fuel tanks to be completely submerged, and box-spars of corrugated high-tensile steel strip were substituted for the round tubes of the Springbok. The upper and lower wing-roots were carefully faired to reduce interference, and the open panels round the pilot's head were reduced to a circular opening. The Frise ailerons on the upper wing were inset from the tip and extended across four-fifths of the trailing edge, but the lower wing, smaller in span and chord, had no ailerons. The landing gear was strengthened, with tyres of larger section, and the fin area was slightly reduced; the fuselage retained its white Rylard finish, and all the fabric surfaces were aluminium doped, as in the Springbok II. The revised design, S.3b, was renamed Chamois, and the machine was completed in February 1927 and taken to Lympne for flight trials. Parker flew it on 14 and

29 March and climbed it to 15,500 ft in 38 minutes on 13 April. He ferried it on 27 April to Martlesham, where it remained for evaluation, appearing once more as a new type in the R.A.F. Display at Hendon in July. Again it was not adopted for squadron service, being underpowered with its Jupiter IV and in any case no match for the ingrained prejudice of R.A.F. tradesmen, who, reasonably enough, saw no need to forsake a well-understood tie-rod and fabric system of construction while this could still cope with the moderate performance of the aircraft of the day. Short Brothers had expected no more, and in truth had used the Chamois contract as a stalking-horse for experimental development of thick-wing construction, also adopted for a concurrent new project, the Sturgeon, index No. S.6, of which two prototypes were on order. The Chamois was immensely strong and could be thrown around like a fighter, but its monocoque fuselage was very noisy, and unfortunate occupants of the rear cockpit sometimes returned to the ground in a state of collapse, quite unappreciative of the pilot's *joie de vivre*.

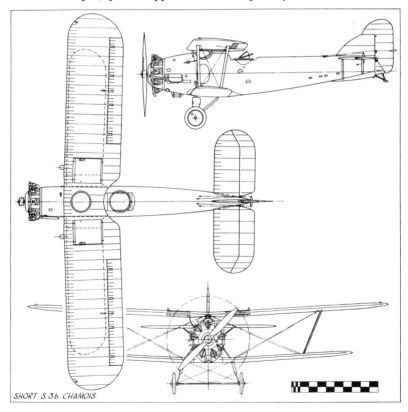

SHORT S.3b CHAMOIS

The two prototype Sturgeons, *N199* and *N200*, were ordered under contract No. 548673/25 to meet specification 1/24, for a three-seat fleet reconnaissance biplane (Fairey IIID replacement), capable of operating either as a seaplane or from the deck of an aircraft carrier. Short Brothers realised that they had little chance of winning a production order against the Fairey IIIF, with its Napier Lion engine, of which the Air Ministry had large stocks in store. Nevertheless, the two prototypes offered scope for proving the corrosion resistance of properly treated duralumin already demonstrated by the Mussel, which often remained moored out in the Medway for weeks on end. The Sturgeon had a Jupiter VI engine with a full exhaust manifold instead of open stubs, and so was expected to be less noisy than the Chamois; the fuselage shell comprised two monocoque portions with a bolted joint amidships. The wing construction was similar to that of the Chamois except that the spars were of duralumin strip instead of steel, and the wings were arranged to fold,

N199 flying at Rochester.

thus reviving a traditional feature of Short design. The single-bay wings were of equal span but unequal chord, with the aerofoil section being Göttingen 436; the four Frise ailerons were linked in pairs by round tubes with lightweight fairings; the interplane struts, like the chassis struts, were of oval steel tube. All the fuel was contained in the thickened top centre-section, and the lower wing-roots were attached to stubs braced to the fuselage by struts, being faired by fabric root-fillets laced to the outside of the shell. The Sturgeons were erected in No. 3 Shop on land undercarriages, but were never flown as landplanes, all their flying being done as twin-float seaplanes. The floats were similar in shape to the second set installed on the Mussel, but had no water rudders. The pilot occupied the front cockpit, which had a wide

208

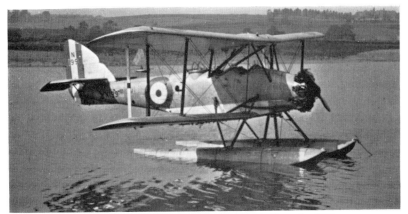

The first Sturgeon, *N199*, moored at Rochester in September 1927.

Triplex windscreen to keep out spray; the second cockpit had dual controls and accommodated the navigator/bomb-aimer, for whom a small sliding bomb-sight hatch was provided in the floor; the third cockpit was occupied by the wireless operator, who also manned a Lewis gun on a Scarff ring; the pilot had a fixed synchronised Vickers gun on the port side.

N199 (c/n S.710) was first flown by Parker at Rochester on 22 June, 1927; after three more flights the wing root-fillets were extended and found beneficial in two more flights on 27 September and 1 October; a three-hour flight with full load, to record climb and speed, was made on 4 October and a month later *N199* was ferried to Felixstowe by an R.A.F. pilot. The second Sturgeon, *N200* (c/n S.711), was first flown on 21 January, 1928, and again with a metal airscrew on 23 February, being dispatched to Felixstowe on the 27th; before delivery it remained moored out for over three weeks with its cockpits and engine protected by canvas covers; the latter have sometimes been mistaken for Townend or NACA cowlings, but in fact *N200* was identical to *N199* in all

The second Sturgeon, *N200*, moored out for weathering tests at Rochester in January 1928 before its metal airscrew was fitted, with engine and cockpit covers in use.

209

N199 taxying on the Medway, showing the gun blister on the port side.

respects but the metal airscrew. Due to the necessity for numerous fittings and cut-outs in the skin for such equipment as the windmill-driven generator on its swinging bracket, the fuselage shell had to be heavily reinforced in

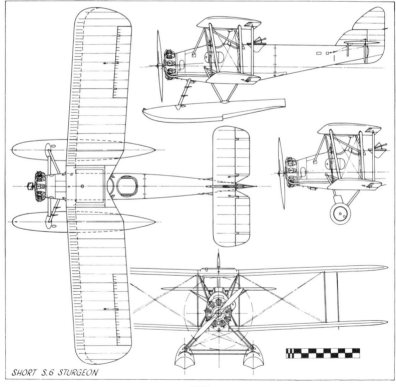

SHORT S.6 STURGEON

many places, resulting in an unfavourably high structure weight. Nevertheless, the flying qualities and water behaviour of the Sturgeon were excellent, and Short Brothers were invited to tender for two more prototypes to compete for a large production contract for two-seat deck-landing fleet fighters, as defined by specification O.22/26; but they were warned that monocoque construction of the whole fuselage would be unacceptable because of maintenance problems in the restricted hangar space of an aircraft carrier; in due course their tender was accepted against contract No. 772448/27.

Although primarily intended for fleet spotting and reconnaissance, the new fighter was required to have sufficient speed and climb to intercept enemy

Gurnard I *N228* lashed down on No. 3 Shop slipway for engine runs, 1 May, 1929.

bombers and was expected to replace the single-seat Fairey Flycatchers of H.M.S. *Eagle* and *Courageous*; although out-of-date, these were notably agile machines of great strength; in addition, the new fighter had to be strong enough to be catapulted in either deck-landing or seaplane condition, to resist ordinary wave damage and exposure while stowed on a cruiser's catapult and to occupy minimum space below deck on a carrier; moreover, all the duties formerly covered by a crew of three had now to be shared by two only, which posed difficult problems of equipment layout. So when it emerged, the S.10 design, later named Gurnard, was a complete breakaway from its Short forerunners, the only part remaining as a monocoque being the stern-cone assembly, which included the tailplane and fin attachment lugs, the whole unit being hinged horizontally for varying the tailplane incidence by means of a pilot's handwheel. The single-bay wings of nearly equal span but unequal chord were set at a pronounced stagger, with the upper dihedral greater than the lower. The two-spar wings were of constant chord without sweepback

211

Gurnard II *N229* at Rochester before launching on 16 April, 1929;
its first flight as a seaplane nearly ended in disaster.

and had blunt round tips, the centre-section trailing edge being deeply cut away above the pilot's cockpit; the wing structure was of duralumin throughout, with corrugated box-spars and tubular lattice ribs; wide-span Frise ailerons were fitted to the upper wing only, and all wing and tail surfaces were fabric covered. The fuselage structure, from the engine firewall to the stern-cone attachment frame, was a girder of welded steel tubing, faired by aluminium decking and cowling panels forward and large duralumin-framed fabric-covered panels elsewhere, all the side panels being readily detachable for easy access to equipment. The observer's cockpit, with its Scarff ring and Lewis gun, was close behind and below the pilot's, which was placed high to give a good view for deck landing; the pilot's seat could be raised and lowered by a lever during flight, being counterbalanced by rubber cords. The pilot's forward-firing Vickers gun was mounted in the top of the forward decking slightly to port, rather in the manner of the Sopwith Camel. It was probably this layout which evoked from Gouge, newly promoted to Chief Designer, the memorable protest which became a byword among juniors in the Rochester drawing office: 'Don't make it like the 'ump on the 'Awker 'Orsley!' The

Gurnard II *N229* at Lympne on 2 May, 1929, before its first flight as a landplane.

212

fuel tanks were installed in the fuselage ahead of the pilot, petrol being fed through an engine-driven pump. For comparison the Gurnard I, *N228* (c/n S.744), was fitted with a 525 hp Bristol Jupiter X supercharged air-cooled radial engine and the Gurnard II, *N229* (c/n S.745), with a Rolls-Royce Kestrel IIS water-cooled inline engine of equivalent output. The Jupiter was enclosed in a narrow-chord Townend ring, while the Kestrel was neatly installed in a smooth cowling behind a pointed spinner, its drum-type radiator, with conical front shutters, being slung under the fuselage between the undercarriage legs. The land chassis comprised two wheels on a faired cross-axle carried on a pair of Vs of which the front legs incorporated rubber-block compression springs with oleo damping; the tailskid was attached to the stern-cone. In the interchangeable seaplane gear the twin floats were of a low-drag shape derived from Schneider Trophy racing experience and were carried on a triangulated system of stainless-steel struts, faired to reduce drag to a minimum; in both versions the airscrew was a wooden two-blader.

Gurnard I *N228* flying at Lympne on 16 May, 1929.

The Gurnard II, *N229*, was ready first, and was launched on 16 April, 1929, but Parker's first flight in it nearly ended in disaster, for he found the ailerons hopelessly overbalanced, which had the effect of standing the machine first on one wing-tip and then on the other. Somehow he managed to nurse it back on to the Medway after a hair-raising five-minute circuit and the ailerons were modified to prevent a recurrence of this trouble. After that, the controls were found to be well harmonised, and the Gurnard could be looped, rolled and spun quite easily and safely, while retaining good lateral control down to the stall. The Gurnard I was not flown as a seaplane at Rochester; on 1 May it made a brief appearance as a landplane, lashed down on to No. 3 Shop slipway for engine running, then both were taken by road to Lympne, where *N229* made its first flight as a landplane on 2 May and *N228* followed up similarly on 8 May. Parker delivered *N229* to Martlesham Heath on 12 May in heavy rain and *N228* on 5 June; both were sent back for various modifications,

213

Gurnard I at Felixstowe in January 1930 after conversion to a seaplane, with its Townend-ring cowling removed.

N228 being finally redelivered on 25 July and *N229* on 13 August, both as landplanes; *N228* was first flown as a seaplane at Felixstowe on 29 January, 1930. The performance of both versions was well up to specification requirements, but they had to concede first place in the competition to the Hawker Osprey, which had the advantage of being derived directly from the Hart, already adopted as the R.A.F.'s standard day bomber; nevertheless, large numbers of Short floats were ordered for use with Ospreys.

Gurnard II taxying on the Medway as an amphibian on 15 June, 1931.

In 1931 *N229* was returned to Rochester for conversion into an amphibian by fitting a central float gear similar to, but scaled up from, that already tested on the Moth and the Mussel II. It was first flown with this gear by Parker on

214

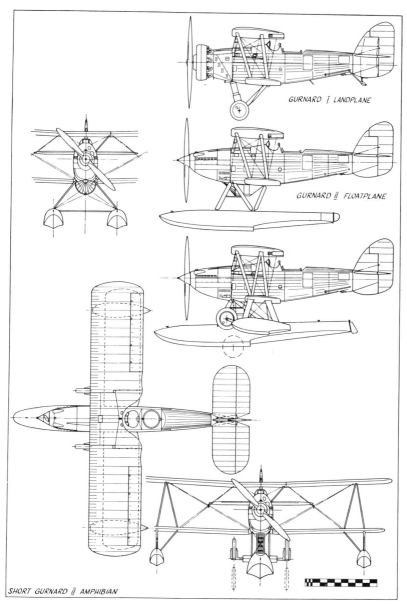

GURNARD I LANDPLANE

GURNARD II FLOATPLANE

SHORT GURNARD II AMPHIBIAN

15 June, 1931, when he made 11 landings at Eastchurch and nine on the Medway; he found it handled well, with little loss of performance compared with the twin-float version. It was delivered to Martlesham Heath on 24 June and appeared in the R.A.F. Display at Hendon, after which it was returned to

215

Gurnard II amphibian at Felixstowe with wheels lowered. (*I.W.M.—Crown Copyright.*)

Rochester on 6 July for a brief spell as a test-bed for Kestrel cooling development; the amphibian installation incorporated a vertical pillar form of radiator, which was eventually adopted for the Sarafand and Singapore III flying-boats. In October 1931 the main float was modified, and this was tested at Rochester on the 16th and 21st, when six landings were made on Lympne aerodrome and six on the Medway within the space of 1½ hours. It was then dispatched again to Felixstowe, where Parker flew it with centre of gravity aft on 11 December, 1931; thereafter it remained at Felixstowe as an engine and cooling-system test-bed.

Chamois—Span 45 ft 1 in (13·75 m); length 30 ft 1 in (9·16 m); area 440 sq ft (40·9 m²); all-up weight 4,210 lb (1,910 kg); max speed 120 mph (193 km/h).

Sturgeon—Span 45 ft 11 in (14 m); length (l/p) 30 ft (9·15 m), (s/p) 32 ft 6 in (9·75 m); area 650 sq ft (60·5 m²); all-up weight (l/p) 5,513 lb (2,500 kg), (s/p) 6,213 lb (2,820 kg); max speed (s/p) 115 mph (185 km/h).

Gurnard I—Span 37 ft (11·27 m); length (l/p) 28 ft 7 in (8·75 m), (s/p) 31 ft 6 in (9·6 m); area 429 sq ft (40 m²); empty weight (l/p) 3,086 lb (1,403 kg), (s/p) 3,486 lb (1,583 kg); all-up weight (l/p) 4,785 lb (2,176 kg), (s/p) 5,185 lb (2,356 kg); max speed (l/p) 160 mph (258 km/h), (s/p) 154 mph (248 km/h); duration 3·5 hr.

Gurnard II—Span 37 ft (11·27 m); length (l/p) 29 ft (8·85 m), (s/p) 31 ft 6 in (9·6 m), (amph) 32 ft 6 in (9·9 m); area 429 sq ft (40 m²); empty weight (l/p) 3,260 lb (1,482 kg), (s/p) 3,660 lb (1,662 kg), (amph) 3,966 lb (1,800 kg); all-up weight (l/p) 4,794 lb (2,180 kg), (s/p) 5,194 lb (2,360 kg), (amph) 5,500 lb (2,500 kg); max speed (l/p) 166 mph (268 km/h), (s/p) 160 mph (258 km/h), (amph) 132 mph (212 km/h); duration 3·5 hr.

Original strut-braced design of Crusader as a quarter-scale model for test in the N.P.L. Duplex wind-tunnel early in 1926.

The Short-Bristow Crusader

The Schneider Trophy contest, intended by its founder in 1913 to promote good design and operational reliability in seaplanes, had a dozen years later become a high-speed race of great international prestige, in which the preliminary seaworthiness tests were little more than perfunctory; the rules required the contestants to taxi round marks and remain at moorings for a specified period without sinking, but the real exercise of design ingenuity lay in combining maximum thrust with minimum drag in such a way that the resulting high-speed aircraft could be flown off sheltered water and back again with just enough fuel to complete the course. The key to low drag was mainly reduction of frontal area, and American successes in the 1924 and 1925 contests had shown the advantage held by twin-float seaplanes with carefully installed inline watercooled engines. In 1926 the venue was again Baltimore, where the previous year's British entries, the Supermarine S.4 monoplane and the Gloster III biplane, had failed to win back the Trophy; only the Italians challenged the American holders, who if they won a third time would be entitled to keep the Trophy permanently; both teams were backed with finance and technology by their governments, and the British Government had declined to follow suit. The Italians won with their Macchi monoplanes, and so brought the Trophy back to Europe. British manufacturers and taxpayers alike demanded Air Ministry backing for a British challenger at Venice in 1927, and the Treasury agreed to the formation of a Royal Air Force High Speed Flight as an operational research and training project, any attempt to win the Trophy or set up world speed records being, officially, purely incidental to the main programme. It was a foregone conclusion that the highest performance would be attained with an inline engine, but neither John Siddeley nor Roy Fedden wished to see the initiative in fighter engine design pass entirely to Napier and Rolls-Royce, and Fedden was sufficiently persuasive to obtain a development contract for a short-life up-rated version of his latest design, the Bristol Mercury nine-cylinder air-cooled radial, which

217

in service form was rated at 500 hp. For high-speed work this engine eventually produced no less than 960 bhp on the test bench in 1927, although limited for flight to 810 hp because of ignition difficulties.

The year 1926 saw the maximum mechanical development of the well-established Napier Lion engine; although it was shortly to be ousted from its leading position by Bristol and Rolls-Royce engines, the latter firm was not yet ready with a racing engine, so the Air Ministry backed the Lion to win in 1927, and ordered three Supermarine S.5 monoplanes and three Gloster IV biplanes of advanced design, all with Lions, for use by the High Speed Flight; they also commissioned for comparative trials a high-speed seaplane with a Bristol Mercury I engine, of which three examples had been ordered at a total cost of £13,000. The Mercury-engined project was supervised by Col W. A. Bristow, a well-known consulting aeronautical engineer latterly in partnership with Alec Ogilvie, and he secured as designer W. G. Carter, formerly of Hawkers and soon afterwards to progress, via de Havillands, to become chief designer of the Gloster company in succession to Harry Folland. Bristow and Carter tendered a twin-float monoplane design early in 1926, and specification 7/26 was drafted to define it, contract No. 67206/26 being awarded for one prototype, serial *N226*. A quarter-scale model was tested in the N.P.L. Duplex wind tunnel at Teddington, but its performance was not up to expectation, and the design had to be drastically revised to reduce drag to the absolute minimum; the original float-wing and inter-float bracing struts were replaced by streamline bracing wires of minimum cross-section, and the Mercury's cylinder heads, which at first had tail fairings only, were enclosed in slender individual helmets derived from the type proved successful in France on a Jupiter-engined Gourdou-Leseurre monoplane. The revised model was successfully tested and approved in November, but by then it was evident that only a well-equipped manufacturer could tackle the closely integrated problems of detail design and construction. Design and manufacture of the floats had already been assigned to Short Brothers, who had spent several years in developing low-drag duralumin floats for the Gloster I, Gloster III and Supermarine S.4 racers, and for seaplane conversions of many of the R.A.F.'s latest fighter prototypes. It was logical, therefore, to sub-contract the manufacture of the whole aircraft to the same firm and, named Crusader, it was allotted Short c/n S.736 early in 1927; having originated outside, it was not given a design index number, although all the detail design was undertaken by C. P. T. Lipscomb and a small team of draughtsmen, under the supervision of Arthur Gouge.

As finally built, the Crusader was a highly refined low-wing monoplane of composite construction in which wood predominated. The wings, originally 28 ft in span, were reduced to 26 ft 6 in and were of biconvex RAF 27 section and nearly elliptical plan, with maximum chord and thickness at half-span, where the bracing wires were anchored to the two spruce box-spars; the ribs were also of spruce, and the whole surface was skinned with thin mahogany sheet, covered overall with silk doped on and finished with high-gloss white

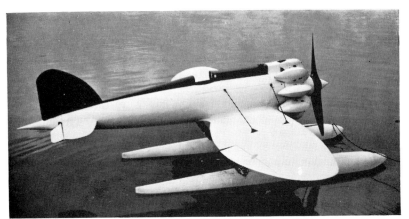
Crusader at Rochester after launching on 18 April, 1927,
showing the wooden airscrew fitted for taxying trials.

enamel. The fabric-covered ailerons had oblique hinges and were actuated by
cables running through common fairleads within the wing. The rear fuselage
was also all wood, being a monocoque of spruce ring frames and stringers
overlaid with two skins of mahogany veneer applied diagonally with grains
crossed; this also was covered with doped and enamelled silk; the cantilever
fin and tailplane were similarly constructed, with fabric-covered rudder and
elevators. From the bulkhead behind the pilot's seat to the engine mounting
plate the fuselage was a strut-braced frame of high-tensile steel tubes, sur-
rounding the main fuel and oil tanks and covered by detachable duralumin
panels. Each engine cylinder had an individual helmet cowl designed to admit
only as much air as was needed for cooling and to divert the remainder of the
slipstream with as little loss as possible. The top helmet merged into a long
parallel fairing which included the pilot's windshield and headrest and
tapered evenly to join the fin leading edge; this fairing, like the fin, rudder and
struts, was painted royal blue, the rest of the machine, including engine
cowling, tailplane and floats, being white like the wings. The twin duralumin
monocoque floats had been specially developed in the Rochester seaplane tank
and were similar in design to those supplied at the same time for the Gloster
IV racing biplanes; they were carried on two pairs of sharply raked tubular
struts faired to a low-drag section.

The Crusader was finished by 18 April, 1927, and launched the same afternoon; a Bristol gas-starter had been bolted to the floating stage of the jetty,
but darkness fell before the Mercury could be persuaded to start. Next morning the engine was carefully primed and, with the gas-starter running, it
fired and ran at the first pull on the wooden airscrew installed on the de-rated
engine allotted for early practice flying. The Air Ministry would not permit
the Crusader to be flown at Rochester, but after the engine had been warmed
up John Parker taxied it out into the Medway and tried its water behaviour at
speeds up to 55 kt, running cleanly on the step for half a mile and satisfying

himself that elevator and rudder power were adequate to control attitude and torque reaction during take-off. After a further period at moorings to establish water-tightness of the floats, the Crusader was dismantled and taken by road to Felixstowe, where the High Speed Flight had already begun practice on the Gloster I and Gloster III biplanes. After a thorough check-over by the M.A.E.E. engineering staff, engine running began in preparation for the first flight by the Australian test pilot H. J. L. Hinkler, who had flown the reserve Gloster III at Baltimore in the 1925 contest. Why Bert Hinkler was accorded this honour rather than Parker or an R.A.F. pilot is not clear, unless it was a question of insurance risk, which might have precluded a purely civilian pilot, at a period when none of the High Speed Flight pilots was sufficiently practised on seaplanes to cope with a monoplane having an unpredictable engine of untested design. Bert Hinkler, still holding a Reserve commission as a Squadron Leader, yet regularly employed as an expert free-lance test pilot, had a special dual qualification which allayed administrative doubts and obviated Parliamentary Questions.

Hinkler's first reaction to the Crusader before flying it was to ask for the rudder area to be increased by 70 per cent; apparently it was enlarged by a rather less amount, and as soon as the weather was right, on 4 May, the Crusader was towed out into the Orwell, the engine was started and Hinkler took-off easily and cleanly. Still with the de-rated engine of about 650 hp, he was clocked over the measured mile in both directions at a mean speed of 232 mph; at full throttle the Crusader seemed to snake a bit, but not seriously. Coming in to land ahead of the attendant motor-boat at quite a low speed, Hinkler touched down too soon with his port float, which was enough to snatch the aircraft violently to port less than 100 yards from the boat, which he only just avoided hitting; he brought off a very skilful cross-wind landing, but the float struts had been buckled and all the bracing wires were slack. Very carefully, wobbling like a jelly, the Crusader was towed back to the slipway and hauled up on to the hard; there Hinkler admitted that the original rudder was exactly right and when enlarged had caused severe hunting at top speed. The chief difficulty was with intake surging, aggravated by overheating of the sparking-plugs, which cut out intermittently. After these defects had been alleviated (though they were never cured) and the chassis struts replaced, Hinkler flew the Crusader once more with the normal rudder and was satisfied; the seaplane was then formally accepted for R.A.F. service and its rudder was painted with tricolour stripes and serial number; the chassis strut fairings, originally blue, were painted white after the repair.

The first R.A.F. pilot to fly the Crusader was Flt Lieut S. N. Webster, who eventually won the 1927 race on a Supermarine S.5. He made one or two flights in June and liked the feel of it, apart from the engine's disconcerting habit of cutting-out at short intervals and then cutting-in again at full power. Early in July Flying Off H. M. Schofield took over and he has left a vivid description of his experience in his autobiography *The High Speed and Other Flights*:

'I found little difficulty in getting off except that the view from the cockpit was unexpectedly bad. I could see very little ahead and my one hope was that if the engine was going to cut out, it would wait at least until I had a little height. . . . I had gained a bare 50 feet, heading straight for the harbour, when, with a whip that nearly took it right out of the machine, the engine packed up. I could do nothing but go ahead and kick the rudder a little to see . . . there were white horses where I knew I had to touch . . . after a heart-breaking banging and rattling we pulled up and waited, pitching and rolling to a sickening and really dangerous extent.'

Two days later Schofield took off again from Dovercourt towards Felixstowe, having been assured that the engine was now cured of its idiosyncrasies. He had just got clear of the water when the supercharger died, then cut in again with a bang; he was flying parallel to the seafront from Landguard Point towards the ¾-mile-long Town Pier with practically no room to manoeuvre and numerous groynes to avoid if he swung inshore by even a fraction, but somehow he came to rest without damage. The Crusader was then stripped for modifications, including an engine change, improved induction intake, special high-temperature sparking-plugs and an additional fuel tank in the starboard float to provide adequate range for the full Schneider Trophy course; Schofield was assured by the Bristol service engineer, Frank Abell, that there could be no further trouble with the boost control and took off for his third flight with hope restored. For five minutes his confidence remained unshaken, then suddenly the boost gauge showed a large minus reading and before he could close the throttle jumped again to +9 lb/sq in; this happened while he was flying at nearly 240 mph, and the sequence was repeated before he could recover; this time he managed to throttle back, and he cruised back to the Orwell and alighted without further trouble. In mid-July the High Speed Flight moved to Calshot, to fly their new S.5s and Gloster IVs, but the

Crusader at Felixstowe in July 1927, showing the coarse-pitch metal racing airscrew, modified air intake and repaired chassis struts. (*Courtesy Bristol Siddeley Engines Ltd.*)

Crusader remained at Felixstowe, and Schofield went back for a day to fly it for a Press demonstration; he was relieved to find the sea too rough for any kind of flying, so the journalists had to be content with an engine run on the tarmac with the helmets removed; by this time a forged duralumin racing airscrew of very coarse pitch had been fitted.

In mid-August the Crusader was shipped to Venice aboard the collier *Eworth*, arriving at San Andrea on 31 August, together with the Supermarine S.5 *N219* and the Gloster IVA *N222*. Within a week the Crusader was ready for flight with a new fully-rated engine and fuel in the starboard float as well as the main tanks; this reduced the buoyancy on that side and helped to offset the airscrew torque reaction, which was strong during the early stages of the take-off run and tended to swing the machine violently to port. The Crusader

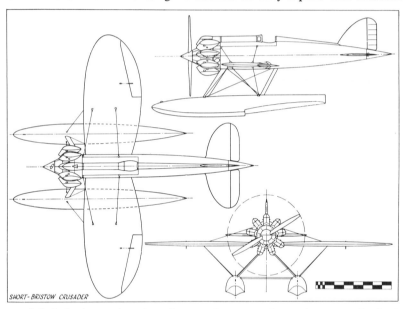

SHORT-BRISTOW CRUSADER

was definitely slower than the others, and so was to be used as a practice hack at Venice, to save wear and tear on the actual competitors. On 11 September Schofield climbed in, was 'battened down' and started the engine. He headed for the Lido and opened up; as expected with a full fuel load, the take-off was less brisk than before, and he held the machine down close to the water to gain speed before climbing. The weather was hot and bumpy, and the Crusader evidently hit a thermal which lifted the starboard wing suddenly to 60 degrees. Instinctively he moved the stick to the right, but the aileron cables had been inadvertently crossed, and instead of regaining an even keel the Crusader continued to roll to port, past the vertical, and plunged into the lagoon upside down at 150 mph. Schofield was thrown clear as the fuselage broke off across the cockpit, and when picked up was found swimming with

tremendous energy with all his clothing stripped off, although almost unconscious; indeed, the rescue party had quite a struggle to get him out of the
water, as his one idea was to go on swimming; his shoes were picked up, floating on bubbles trapped in the toes, and one float was retrieved several days
later from the Grand Canal. The rest of the Crusader, with engine and wings
nearly complete, was fished up from the bottom after a week, during which the
magnesium alloy crankcase had nearly all dissolved; but the aileron control
cables were intact, and clearly showed how the wrong halves of the turnbuckles had been connected together.

Although badly bruised all over, Schofield had broken no bones and made a
complete though painful recovery, later to become Test Pilot and General
Manager of General Aircraft Ltd; all concerned with the rigging error were
severely reprimanded, but none lost their jobs—in fact the A.I.D. inspector
attached to the High Speed Flight eventually became Director of Aeronautical
Inspection; although he personally learned his lesson, no official action was
taken to make wrong assembly physically impossible until after Roy Chadwick
and S. A. Thorn had been killed 20 years later by a precisely similar rigging
mistake in the prototype Avro Tudor II. The most important contribution of
the Crusader to future progress was its part in developing the Bristol Mercury
engine, whose progeny from Roy Fedden's drawing board—Pegasus, Perseus
and Hercules—were in later years to share with Short flying-boats and
bombers some of the most redoubtable operational feats of peace and war.

Span 26 ft 6 in (8·07 m); length 25 ft (7·62 m); area 120 sq ft (11·15 m²); empty weight
1,938 lb (878 kg); all-up weight 2,712 lb (1,227 kg); max speed 270 mph (435 km/h).

The Crusader at Felixstowe before being shipped to Venice.

223

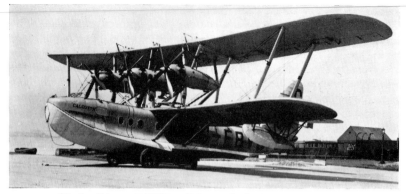

The first Calcutta, *G-EBVG*, at Felixstowe for C. of A. trials in July 1928.
(*I.W.M.—Crown Copyright.*)

The Short Calcutta

Whether or not McClean and Spottiswoode's Nile expedition in 1914 was really intended to survey a possible Cairo–Khartoum air route must remain conjectural, as any such enterprise was killed by the outbreak of war a few months later. By May 1917 Britain's faith in ultimate survival had increased sufficiently for the Air Board to set up a Civil Air Transport Committee to advise on post-war commercial aviation, some six months after George Holt Thomas, always forward-looking, had first registered his airline Aircraft Transport & Travel Ltd as a subsidiary of the Aircraft Manufacturing Company. The Committee reported to Parliament in February 1918, recommending the development, under Air Board sponsorship, of both ground facilities and aircraft suitable for operating routes to the French Riviera, Scandinavia, South Africa and ultimately across the Atlantic to Canada. They proposed a programme of government aid to the aircraft industry to encourage new civil aircraft, which in turn would help to maintain the security of distant parts of the Empire. But as early as 1920 all this quite sound though admittedly costly planning was demolished by Winston Churchill, who, doubling the offices of Ministers for War and Air, pronounced that 'civil aviation must fly by itself'. Three pioneer airlines, started by Handley Page, Holt Thomas and Instone, struggled on for five years in competition with subsidised French, Belgian and Dutch airlines and were eventually saved from extinction by meagre grants from a reluctant Treasury. In January 1923 a Civil Air Transport Subsidies Committee was set up under Sir Herbert Hambling 'to advise on the best method of subsidising air transport in the future' and to stop the waste inherent in supporting several airlines who were competing as much with each other as with foreign operators. Later that year a fourth airline was started by Hubert Scott-Paine to link Southampton and the Channel Islands by flying-boat, and soon afterwards the Hambling Committee reported in favour of a monopoly airline formed by the amalgamation of the four existing companies. So, on 31 March, 1924, Imperial Airways, 'the Chosen Instrument', came into being, and technical standards for its re-equipment and expansion were discussed at length and eventually agreed.

Among the first tenets of technical policy to be established was the rejection of single-engined aircraft for passenger-carrying; here the twin-engined Handley Page W.8 scored at first, but it soon became obvious that three engines were better than two in the interests not only of safety but also of regularity, since an airliner in reasonable weather might be expected to reach its destination with one-third of its power gone, whereas the loss of half its power only delayed the inevitable forced landing. The first three-engined airliners—Argosies and Hercules—entered Imperial Airways' fleet service in 1926, the former on the London–Paris route in July and the latter on the first stage of the Empire route, from Cairo to Basra, in December, a five-year agreement for a subsidised Egypt–India service having been signed on 28 October. Only four weeks earlier Alan Cobham had returned from his epic three-months' flying survey of the whole England–Australia civil air route, using a D.H.50J biplane equipped with Short metal floats for all but the Darwin–Sydney–Darwin overland stages. His successful use of a seaplane for so much of the route pointed the way for the future employment of flying-boats, and their value and potentialities were further emphasised by his African survey flight of 1927–8 in the Singapore I, already described.

In 1926 the Air Council decided to augment Imperial Airways' fleet with two three-engined flying-boats developed from the Singapore I and named Short Calcutta. The selection of this type for commercial development was strongly recommended by Imperial Airways' Air Superintendent, Major Herbert G. Brackley, whose pioneer work in training the Imperial Japanese Navy to use Short-built F.5 flying-boats had been terminated by the disastrous Tokyo earthquake of September 1923. Brackley had met Oswald Short and John Lankester Parker when they visited Japan in August 1921 to inspect the F.5 factory set up by Short Brothers in conjunction with Colonel Sempill's British Naval Air Mission; he approved of their methods and recognised their integrity, and he shared Alan Cobham's enthusiasm for the Singapore. Early in 1926 Oswald Short had taken the first Calcutta project drawings to Air Commodore J. G. Weir at the Air Ministry and pointed out how, with three engines, there was no yawing moment if the centre engine failed and that not much trim was needed with a dead outer engine. Some weeks later, he and Parker were summoned to see Sir Sefton Brancker, Director of Civil Aviation, who offered to order three Calcuttas for £42,000. Oswald Short replied that this would represent a loss of £6,000 per aircraft, but neverthe-less he would accept it; a few days later a contract was placed for two Calcuttas at £18,000 each. The Calcutta order was some compensation to Short Bro-thers for the fact that the Blackburn Iris and metal-hulled Supermarine Southampton had been adopted by the R.A.F. in preference to the Singapore. The first two Calcuttas, design index No. S.8, were allotted c/ns S.712–713, receiving civil registrations *G-EBVG* and *G-EBVH*.

In basic design, the Calcutta followed the Singapore very closely. Although the wing area was slightly greater, the overall span was the same, and the tail unit, with its horn-balanced elevators and rudder and Flettner rudder servo, was almost identical. The same wing construction, with corrugated duralumin box spars, tubular rib assemblies, fabric-covering and Frise ailerons, was adopted; the lower centre-section had walkways surfaced with duralumin sheet to provide generous working space round the three Bristol Jupiter IX radial engines, which were installed in monocoque nacelles supported by faired steel struts. The centre nacelle housed a Bristol gas-starter coupled to all three engines; this was also arranged to drive a bilge pump and generate electricity when the main engines were not running, power for electrical services being supplied during flight by a wind-driven generator in the slip-stream. All the petrol was carried in two gravity tanks of 240 gallons capacity each, submerged in the locally thickened upper wing profile above the out-board nacelles; there was no fuel in the hull, and consequently passengers were permitted to smoke during cruising flight. The hull was a deeper and wider version of the Singapore's, with a slightly longer forebody of improved lines to prevent wallowing due to the high thrust line of the engines; these lines were, in fact, retrospectively incorporated in the Singapore I during its major rebuild in 1929. Construction of the hull followed Short Brothers' standard practice, all duralumin parts being anodised before assembly and finally protected with Rylard clear varnish above the waterline and white enamel below. The two pilots sat side-by-side with full dual controls in an open cockpit ahead of the passenger cabin, with a radio compartment just aft and a mooring hatch in the bow; the co-pilot acted also as navigator and radio operator; the 500-watt radio transmitter had a range on either W/T or R/T of over 300 miles. The passenger cabin, 17 ft long, 6 ft 6 in wide and 6 ft 3 in high, had seven oval plate-glass windows in the starboard side and six in the port; it was luxuriously furnished for 15 passengers in four rows of three seats and one of two, with a single seat at the back. A gangway slightly to port of the centreline extended from a door opening into the pilots' cockpit at the forward end to the steward's seat, galley and toilet accommodation aft; the latter comprised a washroom and a separate water closet, both on the star-board side. The steward was provided with a buffet cabinet and a twin-burner oil cooker on the port side. The passengers' seats had tubular dural-umin frames and pneumatic cushions upholstered in royal blue leather, these being quickly detachable for use as life-jackets; the seat-backs had padded head rests and folding tables. The lower part of the wall trim was also blue leather, the roof being lined with buff felt and the remainder of the interior finished in white enamel. Four of the windows could be opened as emergency exits, and the cabin was ventilated through fresh-air louvres in the roof, supplied from a ram-air duct. Passengers entered through a hinged hatch on the port side at the forward end of the cabin, with space for coats opposite the hatch. Heavy baggage was carried, together with mails and freight, in a hold aft of the cabin, entered by a separate hatchway behind the wing large enough to accept a spare engine if necessary. Short Brothers' experience in building launches and cabin cruisers undoubtedly contributed greatly to the efficient planning and shipshape appearance of the passenger accommodation.

The first Calcutta, *G-EBVG*, was launched from No. 3 Shop slipway on 13 February, 1928, and moored out for 24 hours with no sign of leakage. The weather next day was rough, with a strong south-wester blowing, but this calmed down in the late afternoon, when John Parker, accompanied by Brackley as co-pilot and crewed by Eustace Short, Francis Short (Horace's son) and George Cotton, took off and flew straight for two minutes at 250 ft. Parker was not entirely happy about the trim at take-off and asked for the tailplane tips to be modified to give partial shielding to the elevator horn-balances; on the 20th he flew the Calcutta again, this time for 27 minutes. All was well, and next day he made three test flights totalling 98 minutes, followed two days later by two more, in which Sir John Higgins and Major Rupert Penny were passengers. On 25 February Parker flew *G-EBVG* with full load for the first time and Brackley made a full load climb to 12,000 ft two days later; Parker repeated this on the 28th with a flight of 56 minutes; after alighting he took off again, but after five minutes the middle engine failed, and he found that the Calcutta maintained height easily on the two outer engines, with no difference in handling. More full-load tests followed on 7 and 8 March, and on the 10th the Air Minister, Sir Samuel Hoare, was given a six-minute flight during a snow-laden north-east gale; on the 15th *G-EBVG* was delivered from Rochester to Felixstowe in 45 minutes by Parker with Brackley as co-pilot; there it underwent airworthiness and sea handling tests, being granted a full C. of A. on 27 July and returned to Rochester the same day, an attempted proving flight by Brackley from Southampton to Guernsey the previous day having to be abandoned because of fog in the Channel. On 30 July Parker made three specially slow and short landings on the Medway, with Eustace Short and George Cotton checking the alighting distances, and on 1 August, with Oswald Short on board as one of the crew, he flew the Calcutta from Rochester to Westminster, coming down on the Thames between Vauxhall and Lambeth Bridges; he taxied under Lambeth Bridge (then a suspension footbridge) before being taken in tow by a P.L.A. launch. The flying-boat lay at moorings off the Albert Embankment till the 5th, when Parker took off again from near Vauxhall Bridge, just clearing Lambeth Bridge and roaring low past the terrace of the House of Commons on his way back to Rochester. During the intervening three days *G-EBVG* was inspected by many members of both Houses, including Winston Churchill (then Chancellor of the Exchequer), being shown round by Oswald Short and Colonel the Master of Sempill, whose Blackburn Bluebird seaplane, *G-EBSW*, was moored near by. Writing many years later of their spectacular arrival, Oswald Short recalled, 'I don't know anyone else who could have put the Calcutta flying-boat down on the Thames as he did. . . . There was only just room and any miscalculation could have led to disaster. . . . We nearly entered the House of Lords by the back door.'

On 9 August Brackley took delivery of the Calcutta at Rochester on behalf of Imperial Airways and flew to Southampton, thence next day to Guernsey and back. On the 26th he began a proving flight to Queenstown (Cobh), returning next day to Southampton via Cherbourg; thereafter he gave dual instruction on *G-EBVG* to Captains Drew and Horsey and passed them as competent on the type. Meanwhile the second Calcutta, *G-EBVH*, which differed from the first in having Handley Page auto-slots on the upper wings, had been launched and flown by Parker on 3 May; he made seven more test flights between 5 and 17 May, and on the 22nd delivered it to Felixstowe, where it remained for R.A.F. evaluation until ferried back to Rochester early in September. It had been chartered by the Chairman of Imperial Airways, Sir Eric Geddes, for a cruise to Stranraer and Holy Loch, and on 12 September Brackley, with Parker as co-pilot, flew it to Southampton; two days later the party left at 9.40 am, passing Tenby at 12.10 and arriving alongside Lord Inchcape's yacht at Stranraer at 2.35 pm; the ailerons were slightly damaged

The second Calcutta, *G-EBVH*, taxying on the Medway on 3 May, 1928, showing the auto-slots open. (*Flight.*)

during mooring in a high wind, but were soon repaired, and on the 17th Brackley flew the party on via Ailsa Craig, Loch Striven and Loch Long, over Loch Lomond and back to Holy Loch to refuel; thence he returned to Stranraer the same evening and to Liverpool in a gale next day. On 21 September he flew *G-EBVH* to Belfast and back, repeating this trip the following day with Sir Sefton Brancker aboard and again on the 24th to take up the Lord Mayor of Belfast for a flight over the city from the Musgrave Channel; on the return flight to Liverpool he brought back the first consignment of Irish eggs ever to be sold in Liverpool on the same day as they were laid. Thereafter the Calcutta flew an experimental public service over the route till 4 October, when a wing strut was damaged, delaying the return to Southampton for two days while a new one was fitted. On 6 October Brackley flew the party back via Colwyn Bay, but had to land at Pembroke Dock with a broken valve in the middle engine; this was replaced overnight, and Southampton was reached the following afternoon.

Both Calcuttas then operated a service between Southampton and Guernsey until February 1929, when they were returned to Rochester for overhaul and minor modification; during this period Imperial Airways took over full ownership of them (up till then they had been on loan from the Air Council) and ordered a third Calcutta for concurrent delivery in March. *G-EBVG* was flown again by Parker on 27 February, but *G-EBVH* had been run aground during one of its Channel Islands trips and required more thorough treatment; very little new material was needed to complete the repair, and it flew again on 26 March. The new boat, *G-AADN* (c/n S.748) to design index No. S.8/1, was launched and first flown on 6 April; it differed from the earlier two in having a redesigned tailplane and elevators with set-back hinges but no horn-balance; this remained standard on all later Calcuttas and Rangoons and had been tested on the Singapore I *N179*. Parker flew *G-AADN* for 40 minutes on 9 April at the revised full load of 22,500 lb, and Brackley accepted and ferried it to Southampton on the 11th. During its trials at Felixstowe the Calcutta, originally designed for an all-up weight of 20,817 lb, had taken off with overloads of 23,500 lb in 29 seconds and 24,000 lb in 32 seconds; it also took off easily on the two outer engines alone with normal load, and could even do so at 21,117 lb (300 lb overload) in 42 seconds.

Imperial Airways began their new Mediterranean route from Genoa to Alexandria on 31 March. Through passengers for India flew from Croydon to Basle by Argosy, travelling thence by *wagon-lit* to Genoa and finally by another rail link from Alexandria to Cairo, whence they flew on to Karachi by Hercules. The three Calcuttas had been named respectively *City of Alexandria*, *City of Athens* and *City of Rome*, and their route lay via Ostia, Naples, Corfu, Athens, Suda Bay and Tobruk. Unfortunately Brackley was delayed at Southampton by bad weather, and when he tried to leave with *G-EBVG* on 16 April the gas-starter seized; however, he got away soon after midday and flew to St Nazaire via Alderney, Jersey and Dinard; next day he took off in fog and flew on to Marseilles via Bordeaux and Carcassonne, arriving at Genoa on the 18th; meanwhile the first service had left Genoa on schedule, flown probably by *G-EBVH*; unfortunately the log of this flight has not survived.

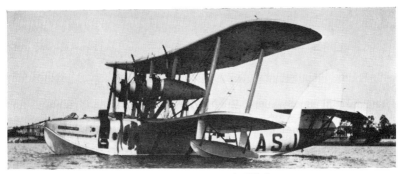

City of Khartoum, G-AASJ, on the Nile in 1932.

229

The service prospered in spite of difficulties in reserving adequate accommodation at the overnight stops, and a fourth Calcutta G-AASJ (c/n S.752) was ordered by Imperial Airways, being built concurrently with S.751 for the French Government. The latter (registered F-AJDB) was first flown by Parker on 1 September, 1929, and delivered by him to St Raphaël in two stages of 5½ hours on 9–10 September, with an overnight stop at l'Étang d'Hourtin (Dordogne); the French test pilots at St Raphaël were very much impressed by its performance and serviceability, and Oswald Short and Lipscomb discussed with Louis Breguet the possibility of Calcuttas being built in France under licence; in 1931 an agreement was concluded with the Société Anonyme des Ateliers d'Aviation Louis Breguet for five Calcuttas to be built for the French Navy, one at Rochester and four by Breguet in their new seaplane factory at Le Havre, where 29 of Short Brothers' personnel were sent to organise production; like F-AJDB, the Breguet boats were to have Gnome-Rhône Jupiter 9Akx engines, but were also to be modified for naval duties; thus they became Rangoons in all but name and are further described under that heading; F-AJDB was subsequently converted to a similar standard at Le Havre. It had been intended to build two Calcuttas for Air Union, but in 1932 the French Government decreed that no future contracts would be placed for aircraft of foreign design, even though manufactured in France; Breguet therefore designed the Saïgon (Br. 530) for Air Union, using Shorts' hull construction.

The French civil Calcutta F-AJDB alighting on the Medway on 1 September, 1929.

The delay in negotiating the Breguet licence was not due to technical difficulties. At the time of acquiring its first Calcutta the French Government was at loggerheads with the British and had refused to allow Imperial Airways to fly across France to Genoa, apparently because Imperial Airways, soon after its formation in 1924, had declined to share in a proposed Anglo-French flying-boat service from Marseilles to Alexandretta (Iskenderun); this was

230

why the overland route to Basle and the rail link thence to Genoa was necessary. Then in mid-1929 the Italian Government, having previously agreed to operate a parallel service between Genoa and Alexandria, using Dornier Super Wal flying-boats, suddenly demanded that the receipts over this sector from both their own airline and Imperial Airways should be pooled and shared equally; Imperial Airways refused, and so lost their rights to call at Italian ports as from 31 October; five days previously *G-AADN*, *en route* to Genoa from Naples, had left Ostia in a gale after refuelling; dusk was falling when the port engine developed trouble, necessitating a forced landing off Spezia; Captain Birt's SOS call was mutilated by coinciding with a test transmission from a ship in harbour, and it was only by chance that the flying-boat was seen and taken in tow some hours later by the tug *Famiglia*; in the dark and the gale the flying-boat was almost unmanageable in spite of the crew's efforts to maintain a heading with the two good engines; at last, all three towlines parted in quick succession, and the flying-boat capsized and sank without trace other than the bodies of the pilot and radio operator; the four passengers on board, as well as the crew of three, were all drowned, and none of the mails were recovered. Following on this disaster came the temporary disablement on 30 October of both the other Calcuttas in rough sea landings at Mersa Matruh, so, even if the route had not been closed by political action, there would have been no fleet to operate it. For a time, therefore, the route to India was switched to an overland one via Vienna, Budapest and Salonika to Athens; but this proved too hazardous during winter, so as soon as the Calcuttas had been repaired and returned to service, passengers travelled by rail from Paris to Athens and embarked in them. At the same time Imperial Airways moved their base in Crete from Suda Bay to Mirabella, where their depot ship *Imperia* was normally based, although she could move to Candia when required.

The two veteran Calcuttas were hard put to it until reinforced by the arrival of *G-AASJ*, *City of Khartoum*, first flown at Rochester on 10 January, 1930, and handed over next day after taking off at 22,500 lb in 19 seconds. A fifth Calcutta for Imperial Airways was already on order to replace *G-AADN*, and this, *G-AATZ*, differed from the others in having supercharged Jupiter XFBM engines; it was first flown on 28 May, 1930, and delivered on 3 June as *City of Salonika*; in April the rail journey had been shortened to terminate at Salonika, whence the Calcuttas flew an extra stage to Athens. Early in 1931 the Italian Government relented and agreed to a new Imperial Airways route from Brindisi to Corfu, Phaleron and Mirabella; for this operation the Calcuttas were replaced by larger Kent flying-boats and were themselves transferred to the Khartoum–Kisumu sector of the Cairo–Cape route. The Kents did not arrive till May, and for the first four months the four Calcuttas struggled alone to maintain both the Mediterranean and Nile services; by mid-1932 they had flown over 300,000 miles in the Mediterranean and 186,000 miles along the Nile. They also operated along the Indian route via Castelrosso and Cyprus to Haifa during 1931 and 1932. They continued for three more years with very little trouble, until on 31 December, 1935, *G-AASJ*, with 12 passengers aboard, ran out of fuel in darkness and crashed within sight of the flare-path at Alexandria, only the pilot being rescued alive; on the same night *G-EBVH* (by this time renamed *City of Stonehaven*) arrived with only 12 minutes' fuel left, and there was strong Parliamentary criticism of this marginal operation of the long stage from Mirabella to Alexandria without an intermediate refuelling stop. In preparation for the introduction of the Empire Boats (*q.v.*) it was decided to withdraw Calcuttas *G-EBVG* and *G-AATZ* for use as crew trainers, so in 1936 they were sold to Air Pilots Training Ltd, a new Imperial Airways subsidiary based at Hamble. *G-AATZ* (renamed *City of Swanage*) had been ferried home in September 1935 by Brackley, who also surveyed possible alighting places on rivers and lakes across France during this flight.

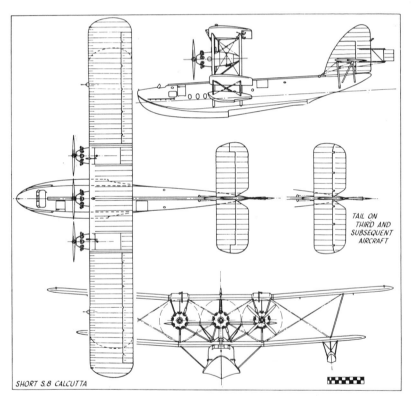

SHORT S.8 CALCUTTA

G-EBVG, which had flown over 200,000 miles in 2,250 flying hours, was returned to Rochester for a complete overhaul, and was found to be remarkably free from corrosion, so vindicating Oswald Short's contentions from the earliest days of his championship of duralumin. At the same time *G-EBVG*

G-EBVG at Rochester in September 1935, re-engined with Armstrong Siddeley Tigers as a trainer for Empire Boat pilots; note the landing light on the port bow.

was re-engined with three Armstrong Siddeley Tiger VI radials in long-chord NACA cowls; it was redelivered to Hamble in September 1935, but survived little more than a year, for in January 1937 it was capsized in a freak storm while alighting at Mirabella; it was salvaged and returned to Hamble, but scrapped because repairs would have been uneconomic. *G-EBVH,* also sold to Air Pilots Training in 1937, was scrapped soon afterwards, but *G-AATZ* survived at Hamble as a crew trainer till 1939.

Span 93 ft (28·4 m); length 66 ft (20·1 m); area 1,825 sq ft (169 m²); empty weight 13,845 lb (6,285 kg); all-up weight 22,500 lb (10,200 kg); max speed 118 mph (190 km/h); ceiling 13,500 ft (4,110 m); range 650 miles (1,046 km).

The first Rangoon, *S1433*, at Rochester before launching on 24 September, 1930.

The Short Rangoon

As early as 1927 Short Brothers proposed a naval reconnaissance version of the Calcutta to meet specification R.5/27, with a hull of Singapore shape but slightly larger all round; the pilots' cockpits were arranged separately in tandem, and the central Jupiter engine nacelle was raised slightly above the level of the two outboard nacelles to provide more airscrew clearance. Scarff gun-rings were installed in the nose and at each of the two waist positions, and an alternative version was proposed, to carry a torpedo under each side of the lower wing; in both versions wing area and tankage were increased to ensure long-range capability. Neither project was accepted by the Air Ministry, but two years later they formed the starting-point for an enlarged Calcutta development for the Imperial Japanese Navy, and for a more direct adaptation for the French Navy. Design work had already begun on the latter when the Air Ministry issued specification R.18/29 for a flying-boat to re-equip No. 203 Squadron, R.A.F., at Basra. This unit operated from the Shatt-al-Arab under exceptionally difficult conditions of extreme heat and humidity and had long since discarded their wooden-floated Fairey IIID seaplanes and wooden-hulled Southamptons; the latter had been replaced by Southampton IIs, but these still had wooden aerostructures, and their metal hulls, less sturdily built than by Short Brothers' methods, were nevertheless quite as heavy and, furthermore, were too cramped and ill-ventilated for regular tropical use. They had, however, successfully accomplished a magnificent formation flight to Australia and the Far East, and this had impressed the Air Staff with the continued usefulness of flying-boats as a long-term investment.

As always, the Air Staff were looking ahead to much more advanced equipment, but meanwhile they acceded to an urgent appeal from Basra for 'jam today' and agreed to order immediately three military Calcuttas for squadron trials. These were virtually the same, apart from details of armament and equipment, as the French naval Calcutta and had the same enlarged fuel tanks located in the upper wing between the outboard nacelles instead of above them; but they were also specially equipped for tropical use and had an enclosed pilots' cockpit with sun-blinds in the roof, also a large fresh-water tank and ice-box in addition to rest bunks and a small work-bench. Being directly derived from the Calcutta, the French naval version had design index No. S.8/2, while the R.A.F. version became S.8/8. Officially named Rangoon, the three R.A.F. boats were allotted c/ns S.755–757; they were laid down concurrently with the last civil Calcutta, having Jupiter IXF engines with exhaust ring manifolds, although the latter were discarded in service in favour of the short stubs preferred by Imperial Airways. The first Rangoon, *S1433*, was launched and flown by John Parker at Rochester on 24 September, 1930; for some reason, probably a higher modification standard, this was the third airframe, S.757; the other two were launched and flown in December, *S1434* on the 2nd and *S1435* on the 20th. All three were delivered for crew training to Felixstowe, whence they were flown in formation, commanded by Group Capt W. L. Welsh, to Basra during 1931, this being the first occasion on which any overseas R.A.F. station had been reinforced by a new squadron flown out as a complete unit. Rangoons were armed with a single Lewis gun at each of the Scarff rings and carried up to 1,000 lb of bombs on underwing racks. Their careers in the Persian Gulf and Iraq were unspectacular, and consisted mainly of surveying the Trucial Coast and suppressing smuggling along the trade routes, throughout which they remained quite trouble-free, while their enhanced comfort made them popular with their crews, so two more to an improved specification, R.19/31, were ordered. The first of these, S.764, had a stainless-steel planing bottom and was flown at Rochester by Parker on 9 March, 1932, being collected by the R.A.F. three days later as *K2134*, while the second, S.765, similarly plated, was flown on 1 November and handed over to the R.A.F. as *K2809* on the 4th. In October 1933 the squadron flew 4,000 miles from Basra to Aden and back to survey the Arabian coastline for Imperial Airways' revised land route.

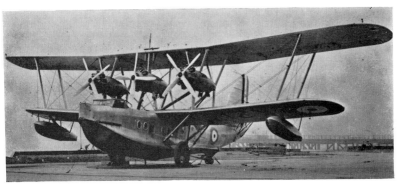

The fourth Rangoon, *K2134*, at Felixstowe in November 1932, showing the stainless-steel planing bottom. (*I.W.M.—Crown Copyright.*)

After this flight *S1433* was flown back to Rochester for major inspection and was found to be in excellent condition; after being brought up to R.19/31 equipment standard it was checked out by Parker on 9 February, 1934, and flown back to Basra for a further tour of tropical service. In September and October 1934 three of the squadron's Rangoons, under the command of Group Capt R. E. Saul, cruised from Basra to Melbourne to attend the centenary celebrations of the State of Victoria; they returned to Basra without trouble of any kind, having flown 19,000 miles, including two overland crossings of India and very severe monsoon conditions in Malaya. One final new Rangoon, S.780, with an Alclad bottom, was ordered at this time and was flown on 7 September, 1934, being delivered to Felixstowe two days later as *K3678*. The Rangoons' tropical service ended in August 1935, when No. 203 Squadron exchanged them for Singapore IIIs; all six were flown home without incident, five as temporary equipment for No. 210 Squadron at Pembroke Dock and the first one of all, *S1433*, to supplement the fleet of Air Pilots Training at Hamble. No. 210 Squadron was briefly deployed to Gibraltar in September 1935 during the Abyssinian crisis and returned to Pembroke Dock at the end of the year to re-equip with Singapore IIIs, its Rangoons being scrapped thereafter; the sole survivor, *S1433*, was stripped of all service equipment and completely overhauled at Rochester; Parker checked it out in an hour's flying on 1 February, 1936, after which it went to Hythe for conversion by Imperial Airways into a crew trainer, registered *G-AEIM* and granted a C. of A. on 26 September, 1936; it remained in use at Hamble for two years before being finally scrapped.

Rangoon *G-AEIM* (ex *S1433*) at Rochester after being modified as a trainer for Air Pilots Training Ltd in January 1936.

As mentioned earlier, the licence agreement with Breguet provided for one naval Calcutta (or Rangoon) to be built at Rochester as a pattern for the remainder being produced in a new seaplane factory at Le Havre. This boat, S.762, had been launched in June 1931 and was first flown by Boulton & Paul's test pilot, Cecil Rea; on his return from Japan, Parker flew it on 9 July

The first French naval Calcutta, S.762, built for Breguet, taking off at Rochester on 8 June, 1931, when it was flown by Sqn Ldr C. A. Rea of Boulton & Paul Ltd because of Parker's absence in Japan.

and 18 August; after four practice landings under Parker's supervision, Breguet's test pilot, Capt Costes of Air Union, ferried it to Le Havre on 30 August. Four more naval Calcuttas were built by Breguet during 1932, the last three having fully cowled Gnome-Rhône K.9 engines driving three-bladed adjustable-pitch metal airscrews. The Short manufacturing licence allowed Breguet to supply any Calcuttas or Rangoons ordered in Belgium, Spain, Turkey and Yugoslavia as well as in France, and also to adapt and exploit the basic hull design to suit their own future projects. There were, in fact, no orders from any of the specified territories, and in consequence of the

Three Breguet-built Calcuttas (Gnome-Rhône K.9 engines) of Aéronavale Escadrille 3-E-1 at Berre in 1934. (*Courtesy J. J. Noël.*)

237

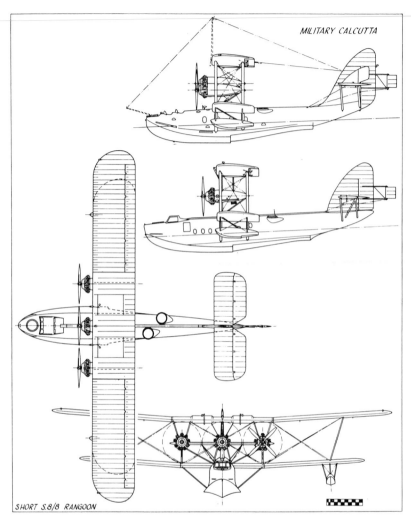

MILITARY CALCUTTA

SHORT S.8/8 RANGOON

French Government's decree of 1932 forbidding future contracts for aircraft and engines of foreign design, even though built in France, Breguet developed their own flying-boats using Short-patented construction. The prototype Breguet 521-01, named Bizerte, was first flown at Le Havre on 11 September, 1933, and underwent service trials for a year at St Raphaël, resulting in an order for three more, which were delivered in October 1935. The Bizerte had a completely different aerostructure from the Rangoon, being a strut-braced sesquiplane with three Gnome-Rhône K.14 engines; all the fuel was carried in the thick lower wing, giving 50 per cent more tankage than the Rangoon. Bizertes remained sporadically in production at Le

238

Havre until February 1940, when a total of 31 had been built; they equipped six squadrons of the French Navy and undertook long-range patrols from Biscay and Mediterranean bases after war broke out, but only two squadrons were retained by the Vichy Government. In November 1942 eight Bizertes still at l'Étang de Berre were seized by the Luftwaffe and employed on air-sea rescue duties from L'Orient and St Mandrier; one of these survived till August 1944, when it was recovered and flown by the Free French Air Force. Two prototypes of a 19-passenger civil transport variant, the Breguet 530 Saïgon, were ordered early in 1933 by Air Union, but did not go into production after this airline merged with others to form Air France in March 1933, and a projected all-cargo version, the Dakar, was never built. It is believed that at least one of the Breguet-built naval Calcuttas survived as a trainer at l'Étang de Berre until 1941.

Both the Bizerte and Saïgon, built by Breguet, employed Short-patented duralumin construction for their hulls, with stainless-steel planing bottoms. Here is seen Air France's second Saïgon, *F-AMSX Tunisie*. (*Air France.*)

Span 93 ft (28·4 m); length 66 ft 9 in (20·3 m); area 1,828 sq ft (170 m²); empty weight 14,000 lb (6,350 kg); all-up weight 24,000 lb (10,890 kg); max speed 115 mph (185 km/h); ceiling 12,000 ft (3,660 m); range 650 miles (1,046 km).

Valetta *G-AAJY* taking off for its first flight on 21 May, 1930.

The Short Valetta

Even before Sir Alan Cobham's flight round Africa in the Singapore I, Oswald Short recognised that the flying-boat had not entirely supplanted the float seaplane, in spite of its better seaworthiness in deep water. To reason that float seaplanes were useful only in small sizes and that all large seaplanes must be boats was, in his view, both facile and false; the criterion should be environment, not size. He noticed the advantage of twin-float seaplanes on sheltered lakes and rivers, because of their natural stability and easy handling in confined spaces. Short Brothers had already supplied many sets of dural-umin floats to convert landplanes for operators in Africa, Canada and India; Cobham's flight to Australia and back in a D.H.50 seaplane and Ronald Kemp's use of D.H.9 seaplanes for the Irrawaddy and Chittagong aerial surveys had proved the type's usefulness. In 1927 American designers had popularised a class of single-engined high-wing cabin monoplane, epitomised by Charles Lindbergh's famous *Spirit of St Louis*, which in seaplane form had quickly gained favour in Canada, since it could be brought alongside any ordinary landing-stage without outside help, and remained level and stable for loading and unloading; furthermore, light but bulky gear such as canoes and skis could be lashed to the floats without adverse effect on performance or balance.

Accordingly, Short Brothers began the design and construction of a twin-float cabin seaplane arranged as a high-wing semi-cantilever monoplane and powered by a single Bristol Jupiter IXF engine in the nose; it was readily convertible to a landplane and received design index No. S.9 and constructor's No. S.746. Oswald Short was prepared to finance it entirely as a private venture, but naturally showed the drawings to the Airworthiness Department of the Air Ministry to obtain their comments and advice at an early stage. It happened that a strong recommendation for a somewhat larger float seaplane for lake and river work had recently been submitted by Capt Frederick Tymms, Director of Civil Aviation for India, who had been impressed by Ronald Kemp's excellent work in Burma with only a pair of out-of-date D.H.9 seaplanes. There was also much official interest in the relative merits of flying-boats and float seaplanes of equal weight and power. The upshot of some months of discussion was a suggestion from the Air Ministry that a

240

three-engined float seaplane should be built for direct comparison with the Short Calcutta; Oswald Short agreed to suspend work on the S.9 in favour of a new project defined by specification 21/27, and a prototype was ordered under contract No. 799554/27, with design index No. S.11, and in due course the official name Valetta.

Although it appeared orthodox to later eyes, the Valetta was, at the time of its inception, a very real advance in British design practice. It was a logical extension of all Short Brothers' earlier work on metal construction and in effect a much enlarged high-wing version of the Mussel seaplane, with its power plant divided into three units. The floats, though perfectly standard examples of Shorts' latest design, were the largest ever built, each being nearly 40 ft long and having a displacement of 22,500 lb; as this was also the gross weight of the whole aircraft, the two floats together had 100 per cent reserve buoyancy. The fuselage, of basically good streamline form without excrescences, was a monocoque of round-cornered square section, parallel amidships and tapering towards the tail. It provided a constant-width, level-floored cabin for 17 passengers in six rows of Calcutta-type seats upholstered in grey Bedford cord; the pneumatic cushions could be used as life-jackets and were instantly detachable. There were six windows in the starboard side and five in the port side; the cabin was well sound-proofed with a felt-lined wall and roof trim, and a toilet compartment was installed aft. Forward of the passenger cabin was a fully enclosed cockpit for two pilots side-by-side, with a radio compartment adjacent; it had sliding side windows and roof hatch and was a true 'flight deck' in the modern sense, which would not have disgraced an airliner of 20 years later. Entrance to both the passengers' and crew's cabins was by a large door above a step-ladder cunningly concealed during flight within the hinged fairing of the forward diagonal strut of the port float. A similar ladder on the starboard side gave access, via the horizontal wing bracing, to a cargo door opening into a hold aft of the passenger cabin; this hold also had a large roof hatch for loading bulky items by crane, and a portable derrick was carried on board for this purpose; this hatch also served as an emergency exit via the toilet vestibule.

Fabric-covered Göttingen 436 section wings had constant chord and bluntly rounded tips. The duralumin box-spars and tubular-framed lattice ribs were simply scaled-up from those of the Calcutta, in turn derived from the Mussel. As in the Mussel, the spars were pin-jointed at the root ends to fuselage stubs and at mid-span to the lift struts, which were built-up box-girders tapering from maximum thickness in the middle to minimum at both ends, their fairings being correspondingly tapered in chord. The tailplane and fin were similar in construction to those of the Calcutta, with set-back hinges for the balanced elevators and a shielded horn-balanced rudder with a Flettner servo; the Frise ailerons were inset from the wing-tips. The wing lift-struts were connected at their lower ends to longitudinal tubes carried by pairs of struts from the upper and lower corners of the fuselage; to these tubes were attached the outboard float struts or, in the landplane version, the oleo-legs of the wheeled chassis. The three Bristol Jupiter XIF engines were rubber-mounted to suppress vibration and had exhaust ring manifolds; the two outboard engine nacelles were directly attached to the wing spars without any connection to the chassis struts, and all three engines were supplied with fuel by gravity from tanks in the wing roots; a Bristol gas-starter was installed above the cabin roof, and in addition to starting any of the engines could also drive a bilge pump for the floats and a generator for electrical and radio services while on the water.

The Valetta was begun early in 1929, and the wing spars were shown at Olympia in July, forming the balustrade of Short Brothers' stand; the main components were ready for final assembly in No. 3 Shop in October, and the seaplane was completed in May 1930, being launched on the 20th and first flown by John Parker next day, with the registration mark *G-AAJY*, its c/n being S.747. Its second flight followed on 27 May, with four more during August after sundry minor modifications; on 2 September Flt Lieut H. R. D. Waghorn, a Felixstowe test pilot and winner of the Schneider Trophy at Cowes in 1929, took the controls during a demonstration flight over Sheerness, making one take off and landing; there was a slight mist and the water was glassy, so that he misjudged the surface and stalled the Valetta from about 20 ft, alighting very heavily but without any resulting damage; on the previous flight Parker had taken off in 32 seconds at 19,000 lb with the centre engine throttled right back. On 24 September a Press show was laid on and ten air correspondents enjoyed a flight of 18 minutes; the Valetta went to Felixstowe on 27 October, and on the two following days Parker flew it through the full schedule of contractor's trials with full load of 22,400 lb, including a take-off in 19 seconds and a climb to 11,000 ft in 24 minutes. It remained to be flown by M.A.E.E. pilots until Parker flew it back to Rochester on 19 February, 1931. It was then modified in preparation for a survey of the Nile and Great Lakes of Central Africa to be undertaken by Sir Alan Cobham at the request of the Air Ministry and Imperial Airways, in readiness for the inauguration of a through passenger and mail air route from Cairo to the Cape. Parker flew the Valetta again on 1 July, 1931, after larger oil-coolers had been installed; the rear fuselage had been stiffened with external diagonal stringers, and an overload fuel tank had been fitted behind the gas-starter on the cabin roof. He tested it again after balanced water rudders had been fitted on 17 July, when a C. of A. was issued, and on the 19th and 20th Parker was co-pilot with Cobham, who then took delivery and made further crew-training flights after loading stores and other gear.

On 22 July, 1931, the survey flight began, when Cobham and his crew of five flew to l'Étang d'Hourtin, near Bordeaux; Cobham acted as pilot-navigator throughout the flight, with Howard ('Dinger') Bell of Shorts to maintain the airframe, Spencer of Bristols to look after the engines, Parish of Marconi as radio operator, Bonnett of Gaumont again filming the whole trip and Russell taking still photographs; the stores comprised various items of marine equipment for test, including a rubber dinghy, an anchor, drogues, a mooring

242

bridle and extra mooring lines; also 230 lb of engine spares, 100 lb of aircraft spares and tools, 40 lb of radio spares, 250 lb of photographic equipment and finally a complete engine-lifting gear. The seaplane base at Hourtin, 500 miles from Rochester, was reached in just over five hours; on the 23rd Cobham flew to Marignane on l'Étang de Berre, near Marseilles, and next day to Tunis, with a stop to refuel at Ajaccio. Thence he flew on the 25th to Kalafrana, the scene of his troubles with the Singapore four years earlier; this time the weather was fine and the successive stages to Corfu, Athens, Mirabella and Alexandria went according to schedule. On 29 July the Valetta retraced the route of McClean's S.80 up the Nile to Luxor, via Cairo and Assiut, the water rudders being found invaluable for manoeuvring on the river. Next day the seaplane reached Aswan in a shade temperature of 120 degrees, which taxed even the enlarged oil coolers to the limit between Aswan and Wadi Halfa. An attempt to cut across the Dongola Bend to Kareima was frustrated by a sandstorm, so Cobham had to find the Nile again and fly low where he could see the river banks, having no artificial horizon in those days. At Kareima the river was flowing at 12 kt, which made mooring very difficult, but all was well on 1 August for the take-off for Khartoum; then dust storms forced Cobham to turn back to Atbara, where in the absence of moorings reliance had to be placed overnight on the experimental anchor; this had been designed by Eustace Short, one of whose earlier anchors, made of cast aluminium alloy, had astonished him by floating in the Medway because of the porosity of the casting. The Valetta's new anchor was more practical and held through half a gale. Khartoum was reached without further trouble; a day

The Valetta moored on Lake Victoria at Entebbe in August 1931, showing long-range fuel tank.
(*Courtesy Bristol Siddeley Engines Ltd.*)

was spent there on maintenance and greasing the controls, and then the Valetta flew on to Malakal, refuelling *en route* at Kosti. From there the route rose to Butiaba on Lake Albert, altitude 2,037 ft, and thence to Port Bell and Entebbe on Lake Victoria at 3,726 ft. After a day's further maintenance, Cobham flew west to Katunguru, but bad weather prevented him from reaching Lake Kivu the same day, so he tried again on 8 August and after encountering violent up-currents in the mountains, causing the Valetta to rise rapidly from 8,000 to 11,000 ft, he reached the lake, but decided against

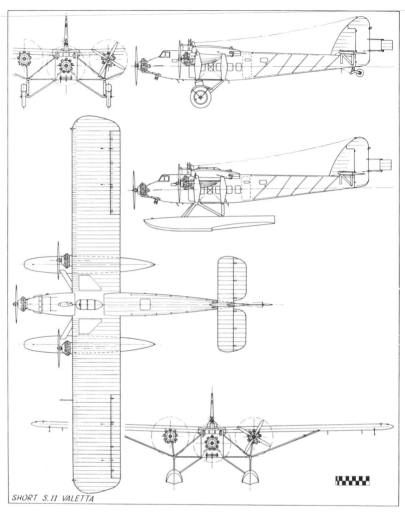

SHORT S.11 VALETTA

alighting and returned to Katunguru and Entebbe. The homeward flight
began on 14 August over the same route as far as Corfu; then Cobham flew
direct to Naples over the Apennines and on to Ajaccio. He tried to get through
to Hourtin with only a single refuelling stop at Marignane, but had to put
down for the night at Cette and finish the stage in rough weather next day;
the Valetta arrived on Southampton Water on 31 August and returned to
Rochester on 1 September, having completed 12,300 miles in a flying time of
128 hours.

After routine inspection and reconditioning, the Valetta was flown again by
Parker on 16 November, for the last time as a seaplane. During the winter

244

months the floats were replaced by a land chassis comprising two main wheel units with oleo-legs, Palmer pneumatic brakes and a castoring tailwheel; it was transported by road to Croydon, where it was reassembled and flown as a landplane by Parker on 13 May, 1932; after a further test flight on the 30th and several demonstration flights by Parker on 14 and 16 June, it was flown by Imperial Airways pilots during the next four weeks and appeared at the R.A.F. Display at Hendon on 25 June; on 26 July Parker delivered it to Martlesham Heath for airworthiness trials as a landplane, but it was not accepted for commercial service, being retained for radio testing and research by the Air Ministry. It was finally written-off at Martlesham late in 1933, becoming a radio-training airframe at Henlow. The Valetta was the largest float seaplane of its day and proved its claim to be easy to operate and handle in confined waterways, but the value of convertibility from seaplane to landplane, and vice versa, was not a sufficiently compelling advantage for it to compete successfully with flying-boats in view of their better overall seaworthiness; valuable experience gained with the Valetta was later used in the design of the upper component of the Mayo Composite. On balance, honours were even between the Valetta and Calcutta as representatives of two classes of seaplane; the Calcutta had a lower structure weight, and thus a higher payload and slightly longer range, but the Valetta had a better climb and was faster because its drag was lower; no doubt a monoplane flying-boat would have been as fast and as heavy as the Valetta, while a twin-float biplane might have carried an even bigger payload at the same speed as the Calcutta.

The Valetta as a landplane at Croydon on 13 May, 1932.

Span 107 ft (32·6 m); length 70 ft 5 in (21·45 m); area 1,382 sq ft (128·5 m²); empty weight (s/p) 14,535 lb (6,598 kg), (l/p) 13,935 lb (6,340 kg); all-up weight (s/p) 23,000 lb (10,420 kg), (l/p) 22,400 lb (10,170 kg); max speed (s/p) 135 mph (217 km/h), (l/p) 138 mph (222 km/h); normal range 525 miles (835 km).

Singapore II *N246* at Rochester after launching on 27 March, 1930.

The Short Singapore II and III

Although the Singapore I had performed very creditably on the R.A.F. Scandinavian Cruise in 1927, the Air Council, and in particular Sir Hugh Trenchard, Chief of the Air Staff, were dissatisfied with the results as a whole, and their policy was to make the best use of what they already had, by fitting metal hulls to Southamptons and ordering a minimum number of Blackburn Irises for extra-long-range work (and to use up available stocks of Rolls-Royce Condors), but not to spend any more money in developing larger and more advanced flying-boats. However, the later cruise of four metal-hulled Southamptons to Australia and the Far East, coupled with Cobham's flight round Africa in the Singapore I, helped to change this somewhat jaundiced view, and in 1928 proposals were invited for a long-range flying-boat smaller and faster than the Iris and more seaworthy than the Southampton, to be powered by three Bristol Jupiters or Rolls-Royce Kestrels. Such a type had been envisaged by specification R.5/27, which was shelved after the Copenhagen débâcle; a new specification, R.32/27, was then drafted, and it was this which was eventually issued to the manufacturers. Saunders-Roe and Supermarine came up with very similar three-Jupiter sesquiplane designs, while Blackburn tendered a monoplane with three Kestrels. Short Brothers first proposed a three-Jupiter biplane, the Naval Calcutta already described, but later put in an alternative design for an improved Singapore with four Kestrels arranged in tandem tractor-pusher pairs; the forward airscrews were to be larger in diameter than the aft, which were also to be of finer pitch; this design principle had first been stated by Horace Short in 1911 and confirmed by later experience. After careful consideration one prototype was ordered from each of Blackburn, Saunders-Roe and Supermarine, but Short Brothers' proposals were ignored. Oswald Short protested and pointed out that his firm had not had a failure with any of their flying-boat designs, whereas many hundreds of thousands of pounds had been spent on abandoned

246

metal prototypes ordered from other manufacturers, citing in particular the case of the Beardmore Inflexible; he made out a strong case for the four-engined Singapore, and in due course contract No. 836162/28 was awarded for one prototype, serial *N246*, to be called Singapore II.

Improvements in the Rochester testing tank and its measuring equipment, mainly to simulate wing-lift and wave effects more accurately, had provided Arthur Gouge with up-to-date and reasonably reliable data from which the hydrodynamic performance and behaviour of a new hull could be determined for weights as high as 70,000 lb. The Singapore II hull was designed for a maximum displacement of 36,000 lb and was generally similar in shape to the Calcutta, but with a more pronounced keel and deeper forebody. The maximum span permitted was 90 ft, 3 ft less than the Singapore I, but the disparity between the upper and lower spans was reduced so that the gross wing area was increased. The most important improvement in design was the substantial drag reduction gained by mounting each tandem nacelle on a single pair of very robust vertical struts, with only a single pair of horizontal struts between nacelles as additional support, with their mid-points anchored to the normal interplane bracing wires at their points of intersection. At the same time the vulnerable and drag-producing chine struts under the lower wing were suppressed altogether in favour of inflated lower wing-roots incorporating cantilever extensions from the hull main frames and containing ample space between the spars for the main fuel tanks, from which fuel was pumped up to smaller gravity service tanks within the normal upper-wing profile; the shape of the lower wing-roots allowed all the fuel to be used without having to provide special sumps. The monocoque nacelles were of excellent streamline shape, with fore-and-aft oil coolers in their sides adjacent to the oil tanks, which occupied the middle of the nacelle between the engine bulkheads; one nacelle also accommodated the R.A.E. gas-starter with its auxiliary generator and bilge pumps; the radiators were semi-cylindrical in tandem pairs, mounted on the underside of the upper wing above the nacelles, with conical radial shutters of the type initially installed on the Gurnard II. The tail unit comprised a large single fin and rudder with a shielded horn-balance, and a tail-plane with elevators on set-back hinges, the tailplane being braced as a semi-cantilever by struts which allowed the incidence to be varied by the pilot.

Structurally, the Singapore II followed established Short practice, with duralumin box-spars and tubular lattice ribs in the wings and tail, and duralumin plating and frames in the hull, where the main innovation was the substitution of stainless steel for duralumin for the underwater plating of the planing bottom and chines; the wing-tip floats also had stainless-steel planing surfaces and were carried on pairs of vertical struts with cable bracing laterally and fore-and-aft. The two pilots sat side-by-side in an open cockpit with a strongly framed wide windscreen; the radio cabin was just behind them, with a ward-room and chart board in the unobstructed hull space; here also were rest bunks, fresh-water tank, oil cooker, store cupboards and ice-box, together with a small but well-equipped work-bench—in fact, everything needed by a crew of six for extended operation away from base in any climate and all weathers. Armament comprised a Scarff ring and Lewis gun on a sliding hatch in the bow and two similar gun mountings amidships. The bow hatch was arranged to make mooring and towing as simple as possible through the hatchway exposed when the Scarff ring was slid back; the hull amidships and aft of the wing was flat-topped to provide ample deck working space, and could also carry a faired auxiliary fuel tank for extra-long range operation.

The Singapore II (design index No. S.12, c/n S.749) was launched at Rochester from No. 3 Shop slipway on 27 March, 1930, with pre-production Rolls-Royce F.XII engines installed, and flown later the same day for seven minutes by John Parker; he was not satisfied with the throttle controls, and when these had been modified spent some time taxying on 8 April, with only a brief flight of two minutes. Next day, after further adjustments, he flew *N246* for 20 minutes and on 22 April took it up for half an hour's full-speed trial; various other snags were corrected, and he flew again for an hour on 25 April and half an hour next day. On 5 May the maker's trials concluded with an entirely satisfactory climb to 13,000 ft (in excess of the specified ceiling), and on the 9th Parker delivered it from Rochester to Felixstowe in the record time of 32 minutes.

Singapore II alighting on the Medway after the full-speed trial on 22 April, 1930, showing the tendency to drop a wing at touch-down before ailerons were fitted to the lower wing.

The Felixstowe pilots liked it quite well, but found the single rudder inadequate for trimming out a dead engine in spite of the powerful Flettner servo; no doubt this would have been more effective had it been in a slipstream. They preferred the triple rudder arrangement, proved successful on the Southampton and adopted in an improved form, combined with a tail-gun position, on the Blackburn Sydney monoplane boat. So the Singapore II returned to Rochester later in the year to have a new tail unit fitted; this involved extensive alteration and replating of the hull to provide a tail-gunner's cockpit as well as a platform for the strengthened tailplane, which now had to carry three equal fins and rudders; the outer rudders carried 'park-bench' aerofoil balances, and the middle fin was adjustable to counteract yaw with a dead engine. At the same time the Frise ailerons on the upper wing

248

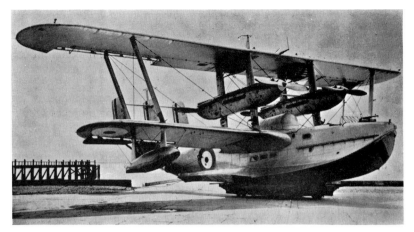

Singapore II at Felixstowe in August 1931 ready for tropical trials at Aden; note lower ailerons, triple rudders, enlarged radiators and long-range fuel tank. (*I.W.M.—Crown Copyright.*)

were reduced in area and supplemented by similar ailerons on the lower wing; the new aileron control circuit was contained entirely within the lower wing, which reduced friction and backlash, the upper ailerons being linked to the lower by parallel pairs of cables; up-rated production Kestrel engines were installed, the tractors being Mk II and the pushers Mk III. Parker tested the modified Singapore II on 17 and 19 February, 1931, after which it was collected by a Felixstowe crew and later accepted for tropical trials, in preparation for which it returned in July for the long-range fuel tank to be installed on deck. In this form Parker checked it out on 29 July, and on 15 August it left Felixstowe for Aden in company with the Saunders-Roe Severn, the Sydney and Southampton X not having completed their home trials by that time. The Singapore II's tropical trials at Aden, under the command of Flt Lieut H. Davies, with a crew of seven, were very successful, except that a small amount of electrolytic corrosion occurred at the seams along the boundary of the duralumin and stainless-steel plating, particularly at the wing-tip

Singapore II at Rochester in May 1932 with evaporative cooling system, enclosed pilots' cockpit and Alclad planing bottom.

floats; also the larger rectangular radiators already fitted proved inadequate for full-load take-off and climb on very hot days.

After its return to Felixstowe on 16 September, having cruised over 6,500 miles, *N246* was brought back to Rochester for a duralumin planing bottom of new design to be fitted, together with new wing floats; new evaporative-cooling radiators were installed, of a 'gothic' shape evolved by Rolls-Royce, together with larger oil coolers, and a pilots' cockpit enclosure was added at the same time. Parker flew *N246* again on 6 May, 1932, and found the new planing bottom a great improvement; he made four more flights during the ensuing two weeks while the radiator performance was being checked, and finally climbed to 14,000 ft on the 26th, after which *N246* was returned to the R.A.F. In July 1932 it came back to Rochester once more to have the original evaporative-cooling system replaced by low-drag vertical radiators of a type developed on the Gurnard amphibian; these were installed below the nacelles in line with the struts and greatly reduced interference drag, which had been giving trouble. This type of installation was adopted for the Sarafand, which had begun flying in June, and was found equally satisfactory on *N246* when flown at 28,000 lb on 11 August and redispatched to Felixstowe for further trials. This time there was no more hull corrosion, and since the Severn prototype had sunk after a forced landing off the Antrim coast on 13 July, the Singapore II was a clear favourite to replace the Southampton and Rangoon overseas.

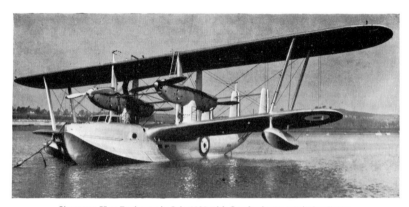

Singapore II at Rochester in July 1932 with Sarafand-type vertical radiators.

N246 was overhauled again at Rochester during the spring of 1933, and Parker checked it out on 31 May with a climb to 13,000 ft. Still the cooling was not entirely adequate, and in November larger radiators were installed above the port nacelle and below the starboard nacelle for comparison; these were developed from those fitted to the Japanese K.F.1 boat and designed originally for the Buzzard engine. On 23 November Parker flew *N246* with this asymmetric arrangement and reported in favour of the high position, fully

Two views of Singapore II flying near Felixstowe in 1935, showing its final state with revised planing bottom with pointed step and the asymmetric radiator layout. (*Charles E. Brown.*)

recorded suitability trials of both installations being flown on the 29th, after which the Singapore II remained at Felixstowe for trial installations of design features specified for the production version (R.3/33), of which four were ordered as Singapore III in August 1933 under contract No. 244794/33. In 1936, its useful flying life having ended, *N246* was lifted by the M.A.E.E.'s 50-ton hammerhead crane at Felixstowe and dropped on to the water 16 times from heights increasing progressively from 2 to 14 ft; in the last drop impacts of 9 *g* in the hull and 11 *g* in the wing structure were recorded, resulting in local failures by buckling in the wing spars and hull bulkheads, but no sign of damage to the planing bottom.

The final planing bottom fitted to *N246* had a pointed main step, raked back from the chines to the keel, which was found to be effective in preventing porpoising at maximum weight. It had been developed by collaboration between Harry Garner, Principal Scientific Officer at the M.A.E.E., and Arthur Gouge, who was finding the Rochester seaplane tank inadequate for accurate results at increased take-off speeds. In 1928 the R.A.E. had designed and ordered from G. Parnall & Co two monoplanes in which the parasol wing was mounted on a drag-measuring dynamometer linkage. This had proved to be a useful research tool for correlating wind-tunnel and full-scale results, and had been adapted for the measurement of the float water-drag of a Fairey IIIF seaplane; in 1930 Garner and Gouge applied the same principle to the measurement of forces on the Singapore II hull. A 25-ft long model hull to the scale of 1 : 2·4 was made at Rochester in the form of a central float to be attached, through a dynamometer linkage, to a Gipsy Moth biplane, together with wing-tip floats of suitable size. A metal Gipsy Moth airframe, *K2235*, was assembled at Farnborough from standard spares for use at Felixstowe, and the combination was found to yield sensitive and reliable results, particularly at hump speed, which could not be accurately simulated in tank tests. It was relatively easy to modify the shape and position of the main step, and even the dead-rise angle on the model hull, which evolved progressively from Singapore IIA to IIB and finally IIC, the improved design fitted to *N246* in 1931; a slightly deeper hull with these refined underwater lines was adopted for the Singapore III, design index No. S.19.

First Singapore III, *K3592*, at Felixstowe in July 1934. (*I.W.M.—Crown Copyright.*)

Construction of the four Singapore III hulls began in August 1933, and the first completed boat, S.770, serial *K3592*, was launched from No. 3 Shop and flown by Parker on 15 June, 1934. About this time it appeared from the latest stress calculations that the horizontal struts between the nacelles were carrying virtually no load because of the reserve of stiffness in the vertical struts, so during *K3592*'s initial engine runs Gouge had the horizontal struts removed; he then took up a position where he could see the slightest deflection of the nacelles and agreed a signal with Dick Rowett, who was to start the engines and be ready to cut them instantly in the event of trouble; in fact, some flexibility was visible during slow running, but this disappeared when the engines were opened up, and the contention that the horizontal struts did practically no work was justified; but they were retained because the performance gained by leaving them out was too small to be worth the trouble of convincing the Air Ministry that it was safe to do so. Acceptance trials of the first Singapore III were completed by 16 July, and the second, S.771, *K3593*, was first flown on the 24th. After its second flight on the 30th it was slightly damaged while being moored, and its final acceptance was delayed by repairs till 22 November; meanwhile the other two boats, S.772–773, *K3594–3595*, had first flown on 3 and 11 November respectively. These four were regarded as pre-production aircraft, and a new specification, R.14/34, was issued for a fully developed production version with further up-rated Kestrels (Mk VIII and IX), a batch of nine, S.781–784 and S.798–802, *K4577–4585*, being ordered under contract No. 330930/34; *K4577* was first flown on 8 March, 1934, and the last of the batch on 29 August, 1935; by this time a new contract (No. 396872/35) had been awarded for 16 more (S.805–809 and S.823–833, *K6907–6922*), increased again by four (S.852–855, *K8565–8568*) in 1936. These were all flown and delivered between December 1935 and February 1937; a final batch of four (S.856–859, *K8856–8859*) ordered under contract No. 511905/36 brought Singapore III production to an end in June 1937. The Singapore III differed from the final version of *N246* mainly in having blunter wing-tips and a deeper hull of revised internal layout, having numerous openable port-holes and a large crew entry door on the starboard side aft of the pilots' cockpit; the wing-tip floats were larger and closer to the wing, and the waist cockpit was wide enough to span the hull. The characteristic sweepback was retained, and the main fuel tanks occupied the full span of the upper centre-section, overload fuel only being carried in the lower wing-roots; all the tanks were of stainless steel, and the overload fuel could be jettisoned; the Handley Page auto-slots initially fitted to *N246* had been deleted at an early stage and did not reappear in the Singapore III.

The four development aircraft, *K3592–3595*, were issued singly to squadrons for operational training, and *K4577* remained for a time at Felixstowe for armament and equipment trials. In September the Singapore III attached to No. 210 Squadron flew Sir Philip Sassoon to Cairo on the first stage of his 20,000 miles tour of R.A.F. units and civil air routes as far east as Singapore; after leaving him at Cairo, the flying-boat cruised round the Mediterranean on a goodwill tour, returning to Pembroke Dock on 9 October. The first Singapore IIIs to re-equip a full squadron went to No. 203, who exchanged their Rangoons for them at Pembroke Dock in August 1935 and flew them back to Basra. Concurrently, No. 230 Squadron had been reformed at Pembroke Dock and, in fact, received their first Singapore III in April 1935, but did not go overseas to Alexandria till later in the year and took up their permanent station at Seletar, Singapore, in March 1936. No. 210 Squadron received Singapore IIIs at Pembroke Dock after returning with their temporary Rangoons from detachment at Gibraltar in September 1935, and flew them out to No. 205 at Seletar to replace that unit's ageing Southamptons, which they ferried back to Pembroke Dock; No. 230 arrived at Seletar soon afterwards to reinforce No. 205; between 7 and 25 May, 1936, one of No. 205's Singapores surveyed the Empire Air Mail route from Singapore to Sydney

Two Singapore IIIs of No. 209 Squadron, seen from a third in echelon formation over Felixstowe in May 1938. (*Flight.*)

with Brackley and Hudson Fysh as passengers, returning to Singapore with Brackley on 16 June. In 1936 the R.A.F.'s original Perth squadron, No. 209, exchanged these for Singapores, but gave them up in November 1938 on moving to Invergordon, where they flew Stranraers; their Singapores were reissued to No. 240 Squadron at Calshot, who had previously flown Scapas since being reformed in March 1937; four Singapores, *K4578–4580* and *K4584*, the earliest in service, were returned to Rochester for reconditioning between May and September 1938.

Apart from a few early failures in the tailplane incidence gear, one causing some uncomfortable minutes to a crew over Iraq and another enforcing a heart-stopping descent on to the 700-yard-long ornamental lake at Hever Castle, near Edenbridge, Singapore IIIs gave unfailing service for thousands of hours without trouble and with very few accidents, particularly those of No. 203 Squadron in the Persian Gulf and at Aden. This unit held the remarkable record of having carried coal from H.M.S. *Fowey* at Muscat to H.M.S. *Deptford* in the Persian Gulf after the latter had run out. This sounds incredible until it is explained that both ships were oil-burners and the coal was one day's supply for *Deptford*'s galley! No. 203 Squadron re-equipped with landplanes in 1940, but left their Singapores, now camouflaged in 'sand and spinach', at moorings at Aden as a deterrent to raiders from Somaliland; No. 210's were based in Algeria during September 1937, and No. 205 sent their last four, *K6912* and *K6916–6918*, as far east as Fiji, where they remained from August 1941 as the nucleus of No. 5 Squadron, R.N.Z.A.F., until replaced in 1945 by Catalinas. The only other squadron to use Singapores was No. 228, who flew them briefly at Pembroke Dock immediately after being reformed there in 1936, but were soon afterwards allotted Stranraers.

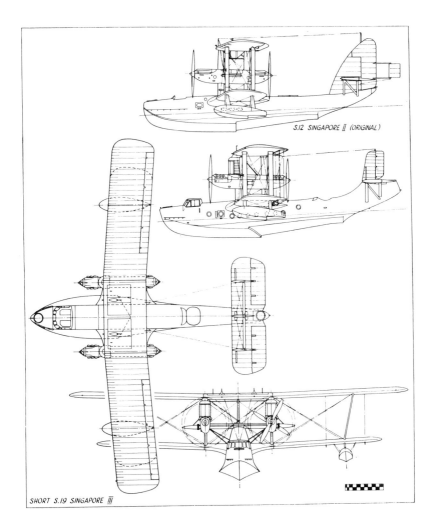

S.12 SINGAPORE II (ORIGINAL)

SHORT S.19 SINGAPORE III

Singapore II—Span 90 ft (27·4 m); length 63 ft 9 in (19·4 m); area 1,750 sq ft (163 m²); empty weight 17,940 lb (8,140 kg); all-up weight 31,500 lb (14,300 kg); max speed 140 mph (226 km/h); ceiling 14,000 ft (4,270 m); range 1,000 miles (1,610 km).

Singapore III—Span 90 ft (27·4 m); length 64 ft 2 in (19·5 m); area 1,834 sq ft (170·5 m²); empty weight 18,420 lb (8,360 kg); all-up weight 31,500 lb (14,300 kg); max speed 145 mph (233 km/h); ceiling 15,000 ft (4,570 m); range 1,000 miles (1,610 km).

255

The Sarafand at Felixstowe in August 1932, showing the original stainless-steel planing bottom.
(*I.W.M.—Crown Copyright.*)

The Short Sarafand

Almost as soon as he had obtained the contract for the prototype Singapore II, Oswald Short began to investigate the possibility of building a really big flying-boat with transatlantic range capability and a far better performance than the 12-engined 50-ton Dornier Do X, then the world's largest aircraft. The sheer size of the Do X made it impressive, but its performance was poor because of its crude aerodynamic and hydrodynamic design; it needed a desperately long run to take-off and, when fully loaded with fuel for the quite moderate range of 1,000 miles, had no margin for payload. Oswald Short knew, from the success of the Singapore and Calcutta, that a well-streamlined flying-boat of the same power and two-thirds the weight would be fast enough and economical enough to carry a useful load over the longest stages anywhere in the world, and he believed the development of such an aircraft to be essential in the interests of Empire security and prosperity. At first he was alone, for even Arthur Gouge doubted whether so large a boat was technically feasible, but Oswald Short convinced him that it could be done by an extension of the integral nacelle-and-strut principle already applied in the Singapore II. So the outline drawings of a large biplane flying-boat, with six Rolls-Royce Buzzards in three tandem pairs, were prepared and indexed S.14, the index No. 13 being discarded by tradition.

On completion of these drawings, Oswald Short took them to the newly appointed Director of Technical Development, Air Commodore Adrian Chamier, who expressed more enthusiasm than any of his predecessors had ever done, but there the matter appeared to end. After waiting some weeks for a reply, Oswald Short decided to make a direct approach to the Chief of the Air Staff, Sir Hugh Trenchard, to whom he had already successfully appealed about the Singapore II contract. Sir Hugh was not at all encouraging at first; he considered that flying-boats were not really necessary to the Royal Air

Force and that later variants of the Southampton would meet all foreseeable service requirements in that direction. He also spoke about all the money that had been wasted in trying to build very large aeroplanes, and in particular one which had cost the Air Ministry £100,000 for cancellation of the contract. Oswald replied that Short Brothers, at any rate, had had no failures and decided not to pursue the argument, but asked to be allowed to submit proposals in writing. Trenchard assented, but as Oswald rose to go said, 'Sit down, Short, I like talking to you', and made him stay for a further hour's discussion. At the end of that time Trenchard had agreed to support the project to the tune of £60,000, exclusive of engines and armament to be supplied on embodiment loan. On returning to Rochester, Oswald Short put the proposition to his design team, who found it technically feasible provided the upper wing had steel spars instead of duralumin, because of the very large end loads. Gouge designed the spars of both upper and lower wings in corrugated stainless steel, but was unable to obtain the optimum gauge of strip, and a weight penalty of about 300 lb had to be accepted on this account; apart from this the design went ahead as planned without a hitch. An 8 ft span $\frac{1}{14}$ scale model was tested in the R.A.E. wind tunnel and found satisfactory, and in due course the contract was signed, after a suitable specification, R.6/28, had been drafted to define the project; this necessarily had to be issued to other manufacturers with an invitation to tender, and resulted in a comparable design for a 40-passenger civil monoplane being ordered from Supermarine, but although the keel of this boat was laid in 1931, it ran into difficulties and was abandoned soon afterwards; this civil application had been supported by Lord Thomson, who became Air Minister after the General Election of 1929 and was killed in the *R101* airship disaster in October 1930. Meanwhile Sir Hugh Trenchard had resigned from the Royal Air Force to become Chief Commissioner of the Metropolitan Police, so the Short R.6/28 was almost the last new project he sponsored as Chief of the Air Staff. Although no civil variant of the Short boat was contemplated, a further specification, R.10/30, was issued for its adaptation as a 'depôt ship' for possible use as a mobile headquarters in the Far East, but this was dropped in favour of a floating dock which could accommodate two Singapores simultaneously for major overhauls.

Design of the six-engined boat was nearly complete by the summer of 1931, when construction of the single prototype, S.763, serial *S1589*, began in No. 3 Shop. By November the hull had begun to take shape and the wing structure, with its integral monocoque nacelles, was erected early in the spring of 1932; but No. 3 Shop was not high enough for the upper wing to be permanently assembled, so, after a trial fit, it was taken down and a substantial jury rig was built to support the nacelles and lower wings, with the floats in position and wing-tips removed to clear the doorway. In this state, the giant boat was launched on 15 June and floated down the river to a new slipway at the former barge-yard, where it was hauled up for final erection. The upper wings were then raised on tall scaffold-lifts and the final assembly

Preparing to launch the Sarafand from No. 3 Shop on 15 June, 1932, showing jury struts supporting the lower wings and nacelles before the upper wing was assembled.

The Sarafand being towed from No. 3 Shop to the barge-yard on 15 June, 1932.

Erecting the upper wings of the Sarafand at the barge-yard.

went through without a hitch. At first there was a certain amount of vibration in the nacelles, due to resonance at critical engine speeds, but this was soon corrected by modifications to the structural bracing. On 30 June the completed boat, later to be named Sarafand, was launched, and after waiting all day for the gusty wind to abate, John Parker flew it in the evening for ten minutes, with Oswald Short as co-pilot to help to hold the controls if for any unforeseen reason the stick forces became excessive; but the controls were beautifully light and well balanced, and practically no adjustments were needed before the second flight, of 25 minutes on 3 July.

Air Commodore Chamier visited Rochester on 9 July and, after being re-assured that no undue risk had been taken in making the first flight so late in the evening, was given a ten-minute flight; next day Parker flew the Sarafand down river to Kingsnorth, where it was moored until the following morning when, with superbly planned showmanship, several hundred Press representatives were embarked at Strood Pier on the specially chartered paddle-steamer *Essex Queen*. As the steamer approached, the Sarafand's engines were started and Parker, with Brackley as co-pilot and a crew of eight, taxied in tight circles to demonstrate the flying-boat's easy handling on the water while warming up the engines; then he turned into wind astern of the steamer, opened up the six throttles and was airborne in 19 seconds as he passed alongside at a gross weight of 55,000 lb; he flew slowly past the ship once more, then turned and came back at full speed of about 150 mph, leaving the various photographic light aeroplanes apparently standing still; finally, he made a beautifully judged touch-down alongside the steamer, having been in the air for 40 minutes. As an example of airmanship, Parker's performance that day was unequalled, and that he should have done it with the world's second largest aircraft, which he had flown only four times previously in less than a fortnight, was almost incredible; even more important was the triumphant vindication of Oswald Short's design philosophy, so disdained ten years earlier.

The Sarafand was, in the main, a straightforward development and enlargement of the Singapore II. The hull had a stainless-steel planing bottom, with a straight main step and wide-flared chines, although the upper part and waist were kept relatively narrow to reduce frontal area. The three nacelles, each with a pair of Rolls-Royce Buzzard engines, were built integrally with the two vertical girders which passed through and supported them; the central nacelle had two additional pairs of splayed struts to the lower wing-roots, and the three nacelles were further braced by pairs of intermediate horizontal struts. The wings were of equal span and chord, with detachable tips, constant di-hedral from the centre-line and slight local thickening of the profile to contain four fuel tanks in the upper wing (2,110 gallons total) and two lower wing-root tanks (1,272 gallons total); the six oil tanks held a total of 96 gallons, and the six cooling systems contained 171 gallons of water. The central nacelle radiator fairing also housed the R.A.E. gas-starter and an A.B.C. auxiliary power unit driving a 1-kW generator, bilge pumps, refuelling pump and air compressor; in flight the 12-volt d.c. electrical system was fed by a 1-kW wind-driven generator on the starboard front strut of the central nacelle; the bilging system comprised pipes from all watertight compartments in the hull and from seven points in each wing-tip float; the latter had stainless-steel bottoms and incorporated means for bolting on small renewable plates of pure zinc, which acted as sacrificial anodes and effectively prevented electrolytic corrosion elsewhere; this cure was suggested by Oswald Short, who recalled the results of early immersion tests on specimens of dissimilar metals in contact. The hull structure made extensive use of Alclad, which had just become available, and was anodised throughout. The tail unit comprised a rectangular tailplane and single main fin, with the elevators and rudder carried on set-back hinges; the rudder carried a Flettner servo, and the elevators had 'park-bench' type balancing aerofoils on both sides; the tailplane also carried auxiliary tracking fins for trimming out any yaw resulting from a dead engine, and its incidence was adjustable by the pilot.

The Sarafand at Kingsnorth on 10 July, 1932.

The Sarafand was designed for a normal crew of ten; the two pilots occupied tandem seats in an enclosed cockpit, with a sliding roof and side windows, and an automatic pilot was installed. Forward of the pilots' station was the bow compartment, with a Scarff ring which could be slid aft to expose a mooring hatch; provision was also made for a 37-mm 1½-pounder shell-firing gun instead of the usual Lewis gun. Below the pilots' station was a passageway from the bow compartment to the ward-room, which contained a chart board and table, together with the engineer's control panels and the crew's entry hatch on the starboard side. Aft of the ward-room, between the main spars, was a cabin for senior officers or passengers, containing a folding table and four folding bunks, and next to it the galley, a drying cupboard and the hatchway on to the centre plane; aft again was a crew cabin with four folding bunks, and between this and the two waist gunners' cockpits were two more bunks and a stretcher stowage, also a work-bench with a vice and comprehensive tool kit; the flat roof of this compartment had a large bolted-on detachable cover, through which a complete spare engine could be loaded; it was normal to carry two spare airscrews, which, being two-bladers, were easily stowed. At first the radio-operator was located near the waist gun-rings, but later this station was moved forward to the ward-room to be near the pilots and navigator. The waist Scarff rings were staggered and recessed into the top camber of the hull, and aft of them were a toilet and a folding wash-basin, with various other stowages; finally, a catwalk led to the tail-gunner's Scarff ring behind the rudder. Intercom telephones linked nine crew stations, and most of the floor panels were quickly detachable for inspection of the bilges and hull plating; there were partial watertight bulkheads at intervals below floor level, and several of the compartments above floor level could be sealed off by sliding watertight shutters. A portable jib was carried for changing engines while afloat, also special mounting gear for the airscrews.

Following the Press demonstration at Kingsnorth, the Sarafand was flown back to Rochester the same day and prepared for service trials. Parker flew it to Felixstowe on 2 August, 1932, and next day completed handling tests at its full load of 70,000 lb with c.g. normal, c.g. forward and c.g. aft. On the 5th he flew it for 1 hour 40 minutes to check oil-system suitability, and next day climbed to its service ceiling of 12,000 ft. The Sarafand was then taken on charge by the R.A.F. and was flown by M.A.E.E. crews until June 1933, when

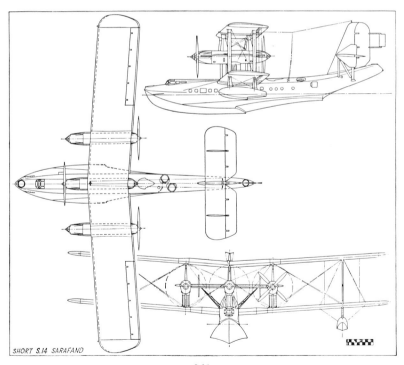

SHORT S.14 SARAFAND

it came back to Rochester for overhaul; after minor modifications it was test flown by Parker on 13, 15 and 16 June and redispatched to Felixstowe, whence it returned after six months for a Singapore IIC-type pointed main step to be fitted; at the same time the planing bottom was replated with Alclad in place of stainless steel. It was relaunched and flown on 29 April and twice more to check radiator and oil temperatures on 1 and 12 May, before redelivery to Felixstowe. In June 1935 it was flown at the head of a formation of prototype flying-boats to the R.A.F. Display at Hendon; thereafter it was used for a wide range of experimental flight tests, notably on ground effect, for comparison with wind-tunnel results. Finally, it was scrapped at Felixstowe in 1936, having been overtaken and outmoded by the new generation of monoplanes, which could not, however, have been built with such confidence in large sizes without the experience gained from the Sarafand; in all, it was a remarkable tribute to Oswald Short's leadership, and to the skill and team-spirit of all his staff and work-people at Rochester, that so large an aircraft

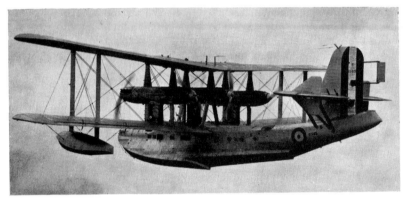

The Sarafand over Felixstowe in 1935, showing the revised Alclad planing bottom with pointed main step.
(*Aeroplane.*)

should have proved so trouble-free and viceless from its very first flight and, withal, have had the best all-round performance of any large biplane flying-boat ever built.

Span 120 ft (36·6 m); length 89 ft 6 in (27·3 m); area 3,460 sq ft (214 m²); empty weight 44,750 lb (20,300 kg); all-up weight 70,000 lb (31,700 kg); max speed 153 mph (246 km/h); ceiling 12,000 ft (3,660 m); range 1,450 miles (2,337 km).

262

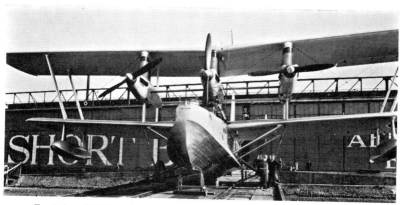

Front view of K.F.1 outside No. 3 Shop on 3 October, 1930, a week before launching.

The Short-Kawanishi K.F.1

Under the guidance of the British Naval Air Mission of 1921, led by Colonel the Master of Sempill, the Imperial Japanese Navy had made a good beginning in all branches of aviation, including manufacture of F.5 flying-boats in a factory planned and organised by Short Brothers. Major H. G. Brackley had been appointed Air Adviser to the Navy and had completed all but seven months of his three-year appointment on 1 September, 1923, when Tokyo and Yokohama were devastated by one of the worst earthquakes in modern history. The British Mission could do little to help the Japanese in their plight and were called home, Brackley himself helping to raise funds for the relief of many thousands of victims; but with characteristic energy and courage, the hardy Japanese set to work at once to rebuild their civilisation and had established a thriving aircraft industry by 1925, when air transport services began between Tokyo and Osaka. Civil war in China, and the Japanese intervention in Manchuria to prevent its extension, brought further expansion of the Army and Naval air services, with corresponding prosperity in the aircraft industry, whose ranks were joined by well-established engineering and shipbuilding firms. Among the newcomers in 1924 were the Kawanishi Machinery Works, of Hyogo, Kobe, who began making single-engined mail and passenger carrying biplanes for the Japan Aviation Co, followed in 1927 by a successful single-seat fighter for the Navy. They built an up-to-date wind-tunnel and other experimental facilities, and in November 1928 formed a separate company to take over all their aviation activities, known as the Kawanishi Aircraft Co, Ltd (Kawanishi Kokuki Kabushiki Kaisha). In 1929, with the agreement of the British Government, Kawanishi's chief engineer, Yoshio Hashiguchi, visited Rochester to inspect Short Brothers' flying-boat designs and manufacturing methods and hoped also to negotiate a licence to build Rolls-Royce engines, in view of the excellent service given by the Eagles in F.5s.

263

Three-quarter rear view of K.F.1, showing the flat deck amidships and tail-gunner's cockpit.

The Imperial Japanese Navy wanted Kawanishi to build them a fast long-range flying-boat of the best available design, and Short Brothers were permitted to demonstrate the Calcutta and Singapore I, but not to show them any later designs, such as the Singapore II and Sarafand. Kawanishi liked the Calcutta, but did not want to use Bristol Jupiter engines, for which their rival Nakajima already held the Japanese manufacturing and selling rights; however, Rolls-Royce were willing to sell them the rights for the Buzzard, as already installed in the Singapore I exhibited that year at Olympia. So finally Short Brothers undertook to design an enlarged naval version of the Calcutta with three Buzzard engines, and a licensing agreement for its production in Japan was concluded. Kawanishi built a large modern factory for the specific manufacture of Rolls-Royce Buzzards and large flying-boats, on a new waterfront site at Naruo, between Kobe and Osaka. Meanwhile Short Brothers detailed the design (index No. S.15) and began construction of one prototype, c/n S.753, designated simply K.F.1.

Assembly of the K.F.1 began in No. 3 Shop soon after the dispatch of the Singapore II and completion of the Valetta, and continued alongside the first three Rangoons. Apart from its size and power plant, it differed from the Rangoon only in minor respects, being generally similar in wing design, with duralumin box-spars and tubular lattice ribs; the hull was wide-flared at the chines, to keep the waterline beam proportional to the cube-root of the all-up weight, but the waist was not widened in the same ratio, and the top of the hull aft of the wing was flat, as in the Singapore II, which it also resembled in having a stainless-steel planing bottom. The tail unit comprised a central fin with a balanced rudder on set-back hinges and a rectangular tailplane with similarly hinged elevators; the tailplane had variable-incidence gear and also carried small auxiliary fins with rudders which could be used to trim out yaw with a dead engine. The two pilots sat side-by-side in separate open cockpits, with a Scarff gun-ring ahead on a sliding panel covering the mooring hatch in the extreme bow; the hull contained stations for an engineer and a radio operator, a ward-room, a galley and living accommodation for a crew of eight while on long-range reconnaissance. There were two more Scarff gun-rings on the flat deck amidships and a fourth in the extreme tail aft of the rudder, reached via a catwalk through the stern. The Buzzard engines drove two-bladed wooden airscrews and were mounted in line midway in the gap, with low-drag vertical radiators above them. All the nacelles were of the standard monocoque design, the centre one being carried on two pairs of splayed tubular struts from the lower wing-root attachments, with a single pair of struts above to the junction of the upper wings on the centre-line. There was no centre-section, and the dihedral of both upper and lower wings was constant from root to tip; the roots of both upper and lower wings were thickened to accommodate the considerable tankage required for the specified range of 2,000 miles. The outboard nacelles were similar to the centre one, but each was carried on a single pair of vertical struts which passed through from wing to wing, the only additional support being horizontal struts between the nacelles and pairs of chine struts below the outboard nacelle struts. Both upper and lower wings had Frise-type ailerons and the wing-tip floats were carried on vertical struts with lateral wire bracing. Erection of the wings began in August 1930, and the K.F.1 was completed by 3 October, except for the addition of the Flettner rudder servo; it was launched and flown for 17 minutes on 10 October by John Parker, who found nothing amiss during the first flight; he flew it again next day and on the 20th and 21st, when he spent some time taxying in order to check maximum oil temperatures and manoeuvrability on the water. On the 22nd it was flown to Felixstowe by Flt Lieut Weblin of M.A.E.E. for brief handling tests before being brought back to Rochester, to be crated and dispatched as deck cargo to Japan; a British C. of

Three-quarter front view of K.F.1 at Rochester on 3 October, 1930.

265

A. (No. 2899) was granted for it to Kawanishi on 2 December, 1930. A party of Short Brothers' specialists in design, stressing, construction and inspection under C. P. T. Lipscomb, eight in all, went to Japan to superintend its re-assembly and trials at Naruo, whither Parker also travelled via Canada at the end of February 1931.

K.F.1 being flown by John Parker at Naruo, Japan, in April 1931.

The K.F.1, still with the British 'B conditions' mark *M-2* and the Japanese red markings on the wings and hull as its only decoration, was completed and launched at Naruo at the end of March, and Parker flew it at light load for over an hour on 8 April; next day he flew it at full normal load of 35,000 lb for $1\frac{1}{2}$ hours, and on the 13th he did a speed trial at this weight, reaching 122 mph. Later the same day he flew for half an hour with overload of 37,000 lb, and finally on the 14th for half an hour at the maximum permitted overload of 39,000 lb. The directors of Kawanishi and the Japanese naval pilots were delighted with its performance, and it was accepted for immediate production,

The third H3K2 at Tateyama in 1933. (*Courtesy Vice-Admiral Kuwabara.*)

266

using local materials as far as possible, with Lipscomb and his team (including Bob Boorman) staying on for over a year to instruct the Japanese and supervise construction. The second K.F.1, officially designated Kawanishi Navy Type 90-2 (later H3K2), flew in March 1932 with imported Buzzard engines, and three more were built, one in November 1932 and two in 1933, entirely of Japanese materials; all four were similar to the first in most respects, but had modified bow cockpits and enclosed pilots' cockpits, which were very necessary to reduce the noise from the three big engines so close overhead; for this reason also all were later fitted with long exhaust pipes. They were flown on training and reconnaissance missions until the end of 1936, and in July 1932 one flew non-stop from Tateyama to Saipan Island in the Marianas, a

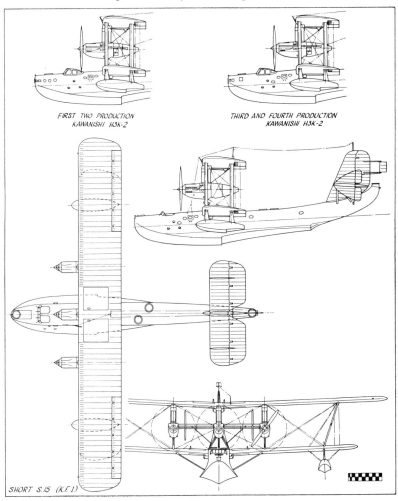

FIRST TWO PRODUCTION
KAWANISHI H3K-2

THIRD AND FOURTH PRODUCTION
KAWANISHI H3K-2

SHORT S.15 (K.F.1)

distance of over 1,400 miles, under the command of Admiral Sukemitsu Ito. On 8 January, 1933, however, this machine (*Ta-1*), while being used for night flying training, stalled on to the sea off Tateyama, due to an altimeter lag error, and broke up on impact, three of its crew of nine, including the pilot, being killed. Short Brothers' methods of hull construction were used in later Kawanishi flying-boat designs, of which the H8K1 of 1938, known to the Allies as 'Emily', proved to be a formidable adversary in the Pacific War. It is of interest to note that one of the present directors of the Shin Meiwa Industry Co Ltd, successors to Kawanishi, is Vice-Admiral Torao Kuwabara, who took command of flying-boat training on F.5s at both Yokosuka and Sasebo Naval Air Training Centre.

Span 101 ft 10 in (31·05 m); length 74 ft 5 in (22·55 m); area 2,300 sq ft (214 m²); empty weight 22,100 lb (10,030 kg); all-up weight 39,000 lb (17,700 kg); max speed 124 mph (200 km/h); range 2,000 miles (3,220 km).

The Short Kent and Scylla

The closing of Italian seaports to Imperial Airways in October 1929 deprived the Cairo route of the air stages from Genoa to Corfu, which was circumvented by using rail transit from Paris to Salonika, as already stated; this was serious enough, but more inimical to safe operation was the loss of the refuelling stop at Tobruk in Italian colonial territory. A substitute was found at Mersa Matruh, the railhead on the Egyptian side of the border, but this harbour lacked shelter and could be dangerous in stormy weather. Imperial Airways decided that the Mirabella–Alexandria stage must be flown without refuelling and obtained Government backing to order three new flying-boats with sufficient range for this operation. They did not need to carry a greater number of passengers, but required much more capacity for the mails, which, at the current surcharge, brought in a far bigger revenue; at the same time they wanted better seaworthiness, minimum maintenance costs, four-engine reliability and maximum comfort for both passengers and crew. The result was an enlarged development of the Calcutta, design index No. S.17, known as the Short Kent and allotted c/ns S.758–760; they were registered *G-ABFA* to '*C* and individually named *Scipio*, *Sylvanus* and *Satyrus* respectively.

Imperial Airways specified Bristol Jupiter XFBM engines, which were moderately supercharged to give maximum power at 5,000 ft, but interchangeable in most respects with the Jupiter IX and IXF already standardised in their fleet; since the cooling of the aft engines in tandem pairs of Jupiters had already proved marginal in some other installations (e.g. the Do X), all four engines were arranged as tractors, the monocoque nacelles being supported by single pairs of struts, with horizontal stretchers, as in the Singapore II, Sarafand and K.F.1. Using 11-ft-diameter four-bladed airscrews all in one line, the lateral pitch of the nacelle centres could not be less than 11 ft 6 in,

268

The second Kent, *G-ABFB*, (later *Sylvanus*) taking off from the Medway on 31 March, 1931, flown by Major H. G. Brackley.

and this defined the span of the centre-section, the maximum hull width inside the lower-wing roots being slightly less. The beam needed to be no more than 11 ft at the chines, so the hull cross-section amidships above deck level was almost square, giving an internal cabin width, after allowing for structure and wall trim, of 8 ft 9 in and a ceiling height of 6 ft 6 in. This spacious saloon, located directly below the wings, was 14 ft long and furnished in the best *Train Bleu* tradition; the 15 luxurious high-backed lounge seats were ranged in four rows of facing pairs with tables between them, with a wide central gangway. The square saloon windows were large and had curtains; aft of the saloon was a steward's station and galley on the port side, with a toilet compartment and wash-room on the opposite side. Forward of the saloon on the port side was a mail compartment and the main passenger entry hatch; forward again was a wide enclosed pilots' cockpit with a radio station behind on the starboard side; the pilots sat side-by-side and had full dual controls, with easy access to the mooring hatch in the extreme bow, where a stout towing bollard was provided. Aft of the passenger accommodation, the hull contained a large freight and mail hold, with a separate entry hatch on the starboard side and a capacity of two tons; the tail unit was similar to the Calcutta's, except that the rudder horn-balance was partly shielded as in the Valetta. A hatch in the freight-hold roof gave easy access to the centre-section and engine nacelles, one of which contained a gas-starter coupled to all four engines. Three fuel tanks, each of 240 gallons capacity, were installed within the thickened profile of the top centre-section, and any of the four engines could be fed by gravity from any of the tanks, which could also be refilled from a central point with a pump. The wings were similar to the Calcutta's, but 20 ft greater in span and with somewhat blunter tips; they had four inset Frise-type ailerons and the wing-tip floats were carried on pairs of vertical struts as in the Singapore II. The passenger saloon and crew's stations were exceptionally well sound-proofed, and full exhaust collector rings and long tail-pipes helped to reduce engine noise, with the result that the Kent provided more comfort and quietness than many other forms of transport.

Structurally, the Kent was similar to the Calcutta, except that the planing bottom and chine plating below waterline was of stainless steel, for long life and minimum maintenance at moorings, without the necessity for frequent beaching for inspection; a simple but valuable operational refinement was the quick-release mooring hook aft of the rear step, enabling the pilot to start and warm up all four engines before leaving the buoy.

Manufacture began in October 1930, and the first hull was floated to No. 3 Shop on 14 January, 1931; *G-ABFA* was completed and launched on 24 February, when John Parker flew it for half an hour and found it in perfect trim; he did not fly it again, as he was on the point of leaving for Japan, and Brackley had agreed to undertake all the acceptance testing, including the first flights of the other two Kents. Brackley visited Rochester on the 26th with Col Francis Shelmerdine, the new Director of Civil Aviation in succession to Sir Sefton Brancker (who had been killed in the *R101* wreck), but arrived too late to fly before dusk; he returned on 2 March, but found the engine controls being modified; finally, he flew it at 28,000 lb on 12 March, and next day, at full load of 32,000 lb, took-off in 21 seconds and climbed to 5,000 ft in seven minutes. On the 18th he made two flights to check handling at extreme c.g. limits, and on the 25th delivered it to Felixstowe for official airworthiness trials. The second Kent, *G-ABFB*, was launched on 31 March, and Brackley flew it with Captains Walters and Wilcockson as co-pilots alternately. On 20 April a large official party arrived for a demonstration, but the starboard outer engine refused to start, and Brackley could make only a brief flight in the evening with Major Mayo and Captain Bailey, after the others had gone home. *G-ABFA Scipio* was due to leave Southampton on 27 April to start the new Mediterranean service from Genoa to Alexandria, but was delayed while Brackley returned to Rochester for the first flight of *G-ABFC Satyrus*, the third Kent, which was launched on 30 April and flown on 2 May with Sir Samuel Instone aboard. After taxying back to the buoy, the starboard outer engine backfired and burned a hole in the fabric of the lower wing; this was repaired next day, but the engine could not be changed in time for a further flight that day, and next morning Brackley left Hythe in *Scipio*, reaching Marignane in 6 hours 50 minutes after fighting a headwind all the way. There Bailey took it on to Genoa, while Brackley returned to Rochester to check out more pilots in *Satyrus*. On 15 May Brackley flew this boat to Bordeaux and on to Marignane in a gale, thence next day to Genoa at a height of only 300 ft in blinding rain for $3\frac{1}{2}$ hours; returning to Rochester for the final acceptance flight of *Sylvanus* on 26 May, he delivered it to Hythe on the following day, which saw also the departure on her maiden voyage of the new Canadian Pacific liner *Empress of Britain*, which the Prince of Wales had gone to inspect before she sailed; as she cast off, the Prince went aboard *Sylvanus* (not *Satyrus* as reported in the daily Press) and took the controls beside Brackley for a fly-past salute to the new liner as she steamed into the Solent. After further pilot-training flights at Hythe, *Sylvanus* returned to Rochester for a special flight for Imperial Airways' directors and the Press. Sir Eric Geddes attended, and Oswald Short escorted him to the flying-boat at moorings, but refused point-blank to show him round the works; he had not forgotten nor forgiven the Admiralty's high-handed sequestration of his Cardington airship factory in 1919, when Sir Vincent Raven had done the talking and Sir Eric had been present to add silent authority. Oswald Short was within his rights in refusing entry, and Sir Eric had to admit defeat, although he was unaccustomed to being denied anything. By contrast, Oswald Short made a special point of writing to thank Brackley, saying, 'The whole firm feels indebted to you for the prompt and safe manner in which you put the three Kents through their final tests.'

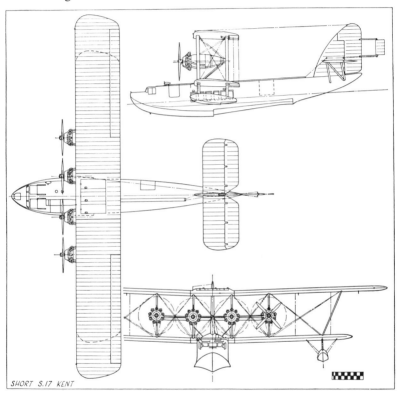

SHORT S.17 KENT

Meanwhile on 16 May *Satyrus* had inaugurated the new Mediterranean route from Genoa at the same time as *Scipio* left Alexandria in the opposite direction with the mail from India. Unfortunately *Scipio* arrived at Candia during a storm and lost a wing-tip float in the heavy seas that were running across the wind direction; Captain Horsey saved the boat by accelerating and taking off again, landing successfully in the more sheltered bay of Mirabella. Repairs kept *Scipio* out of service for a month, and hardly had they been completed when *Sylvanus* collided with a Dornier Wal in Genoa harbour

271

while under tow and had two engines damaged. These accidents put a very heavy strain on the veteran Calcuttas, which tried to cope with Kent schedules but had insufficient tankage for the non-stop Mirabella–Alexandria stage, as has already been noted. However, the Kents were all back in service by August, and in October began operating from Brindisi in accordance with the new Italian agreement. From this time on, the Indian and African routes diverged at Athens, with the latter keeping to the Mirabella–Alexandria stage, while the former was flown by Kents via Castelrosso to Haifa; between April and October 1932 the Kents also operated an air mail service from Alexandria to Cyprus via Haifa. Each of the three Kents had to fly more than 4,000 miles a week to maintain this double schedule and turn-round, and inspection times had to be cut to a minimum; nevertheless, they never failed with any mechanical or structural defect, although on 4 March, 1933, the captain of *Satyrus* attempted unwisely to fly direct from Alexandria to Athens and ran out of fuel 20 miles short of Piraeus; he was later to be the sole survivor when the Calcutta *City of Khartoum* crashed at Alexandria on New Year's Eve 1935 from the same cause. The first Kent to be lost, from arson rather than accident, was *Sylvanus*, set on fire by a disgruntled Italian and burnt out at Brindisi on 9 November, 1935; then on 22 August, 1936, just before the first Empire Boats came into scheduled service, *Scipio* landed heavily at Mirabella and sank in deep water. Only *Satyrus*, having got away with near-murder in 1933, survived to be scrapped at Hythe in June 1938 after seven years' hard labour; in April 1937 it surveyed the proposed Empire Boat route to the Cape as far as Lindi, Tanganyika, then, in June and July, the Australian route as far as Singapore via Rangoon and Victoria Point, followed in October and November by a third survey flight, to Singapore via Bangkok.

In the spring of 1933, caught between accidents and heavier traffic demands, Imperial Airways found themselves suddenly and seriously short of landplanes on the busy continental routes from Croydon and tried without success to order two more Handley Page 42s. So they asked Short Brothers to build a landplane version of the Kent, using the same wings, tail unit and power plant, to save spares or even use up those in stock. Brackley inspected and approved a mock-up of the proposed 38-passenger fuselage at Rochester in April 1933, and two 'Scipio landplanes' were ordered as a matter of urgency; from the design angle they were more of a modification than a new type and took the index No. S.17/L, later simplified to L.17; they had no type name, but were allotted c/ns S.768–769 and registrations *G-ACJJ* and *G-ACJK*, later being individually named *Scylla* and *Syrinx*. Their wings and tail units were completely interchangeable with those of the Kent, except that the nacelles were designed to take Pegasus or Perseus engines as alternatives to the standard Jupiters, without further structural modifications; also the Bristol gas-starter was moved down to a compartment in the fuselage, so that all engines could be started from ground level. The landing-gear comprised two separate Dunlop main-wheel units with rubber-in-compression oleo-legs and pneumatic brakes, and a fully castoring tailwheel unit.

Because of the short time available, no attempt was made to design an optimum monocoque fuselage like the Valetta's, and a semi-monocoque, with braced floor and side frames, was adopted, with an unstressed longitudinally corrugated Alclad skin; consequently the structure weight was higher than it would have been in a fully stressed shell. However, this penalty was accepted by Imperial Airways as part of the price for quick delivery, and it was hoped to have both biplanes in service early in 1934. The fuselages were well forward by September 1933, but there was nowhere to fly them on Short Brothers' own premises, so it was decided to erect them at the newly acquired Rochester Airport. Here there was a further snag, because, although the airfield was in use, only the concrete base of the large hangar had been finished. So Short Brothers decided to repeat the open-air assembly which had been successful in the case of the Sarafand, and the components of the two biplanes were taken by road to the airport, together with the jacks and high trestles used at the barge-yard for the Sarafand.

Scylla being erected at Rochester Airport in February 1934.

All through January and February the work was hampered by bitter cold and high winds, and often one day's progress had to be undone next day in expectation of a gale. A. E. Bibby, the works manager, needed all his great gifts of leadership to keep his loyal band of riggers up to schedule, but by 24 February the upper wings were permanently in place and Brackley and Parker held a pre-flight conference; various minor changes to the pilots' station, fuel system and cabin furnishings were agreed, and a schedule of acceptance flights was drawn up. On this occasion one of the riggers, who for weeks had been working precariously on narrow planks high above the ground, was heard to say of Parker, 'That's the test pilot—I wouldn't care for a dangerous job like his!'

Scylla's first flight was made on 26 March, 1934, with Parker at the controls, accompanied by Gouge, Bibby and the Bristol engine representative Spencer. After a first 15-minute trial at 25,300 lb, Parker took off again with Brackley beside him and six passengers in the cabin. Next day Parker and Brackley flew to Martlesham for a check on weight and c.g., returning the same day; five more flights followed at progressively higher weights, till on the 31st the full-load schedule had been completed with c.g. forward and aft at 33,500 lb, including climbs with one outer engine idling; a rudder bias gear and the Marconi AD41A/42A radio sets were installed, and on 20 April Parker flew *Scylla* to Martlesham for official C. of A. trials, with Oswald Short, Walter Browning, Jack Manson (R.T.O.), Spencer of Bristols and Valette of Marconi aboard. A week later Parker and Brackley delivered *Scylla* from Martlesham to Croydon, where Capt A. B. Youell and other Imperial Airways pilots began training under Brackley, finally giving a special demonstration on 13 May, attended by Major Mayo, Oswald Short and Parker.

Syrinx landing at Filton on 23 July, 1934, bringing the Parliamentary Air Committee on a visit to the Bristol Aeroplane Company's aero-engine factory.

Meanwhile *Syrinx* had been finished at Rochester Airport, where Parker flew it on 17 May, but had to collect *Scylla* from Croydon on the 22nd to have a tailwheel defect rectified. The opportunity was taken to modify *Scylla*'s rudder servo to the same leverage as on *Syrinx*, which handled particularly well. Parker redelivered *Scylla* to Croydon on 2 June, and *Syrinx* followed on the 7th; both then went into service on the Croydon–Paris run, setting a new standard of comfort and spaciousness. The passenger accommodation was in three cabins with seating mainly five abreast; the forward cabin, where smoking was permitted, had four seats with their backs to the front bulkhead, faced by five seats, with tables between, all furnishings being similar to the Kent's. Aft of this cabin and in line with the airscrews, where the noise was loudest, were a buffet unit on the port side and a 75 cu ft baggage compartment and two toilets on the starboard side; aft again, between the wing-spar main frames, was a cabin with two facing rows of five seats each, communicating

274

Scylla at Rochester Airport in February 1935 after modification of rudder for trials of inset trim tab.

through a wide arched bulkhead with a rear cabin having 19 seats in four rows similarly arranged and upholstered; farther aft was the rear entrance door and vestibule, and there was a similar front entrance door between the smoking cabin and the flight-deck, both doors being on the port side. The flight-deck for two pilots with radio and Sperry auto-pilot was completely enclosed, with two sliding roof hatches and upper quarter lights added at Brackley's request. Aft of the rear cabin, with a large double loading-door on the starboard side, was the main baggage-hold of 215 cu ft. With a mean cabin width of nearly 11 ft, *Scylla* and *Syrinx* offered a new dimension in comfortable travel, enhanced by an efficient fresh-air trunking system with temperature controls and punkah louvres for uniform distribution, stale air being extracted by venturis. At first the noise and vibration level in the plane of the airscrews was unacceptable to Imperial Airways and, after attempts to cure the trouble by cropping the inner airscrews, the cabin and buffet sections were given extra

Scylla in service at Croydon in 1936. (*K. A. Winkley.*)

275

lagging and double-glazed windows, which made a big improvement, though at the expense of payload; after entering service two seats were removed from the rear cabin, giving a wider gangway and easier meals service.

Both *Scylla* and *Syrinx* were flown on the summer schedules from Croydon to Paris, Brussels, Basle and Zürich, to supplement the Handley Page 42s, but on 3 August *Scylla* landed at Le Bourget with one wheel-brake locked and tipped up on its nose. The damage, though not serious, was fairly extensive and kept the machine out of use for some days, while a combined repair party of Short Brothers and Imperial Airways personnel made and fitted replacement parts at Croydon, whither it had been flown back light. As a result of this mishap the c.g. limits were extended 3-in aft to counteract any tendency to nose heaviness. There had been complaints from pilots of yawing and wallowing in rough weather, to cure which an improved aileron control circuit was fitted to *Syrinx*, while on *Scylla* a new rudder was tried out, having a narrow-chord trim-tab in place of the Flettner servo; after four flights with this modification in February 1935, Parker considered the trouble cured, but a week later he flew *Syrinx* with the c.g. aft limit extended 3-in more and remarked that in this condition it handled even better than *Scylla* with the new rudder.

In June *Scylla* was fitted with rubber-bushed engine mountings and with experimental auxiliary fins on the tailplane because there had been a tendency

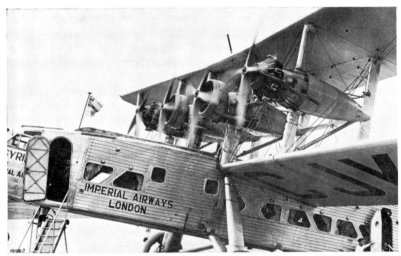

Syrinx at Croydon in July 1935, with Perseus sleeve-valve engines replacing the two inboard Jupiters.

to turn to starboard when the engines were synchronised to minimise vibration. About the same time *Syrinx* had its two middle engines replaced by Perseus IIL sleeve-valve engines, of which four had been loaned by the Air Ministry for endurance testing in airline service; the first pair began flying on 29 June and had run 300 hours by 4 August, when they were replaced by the

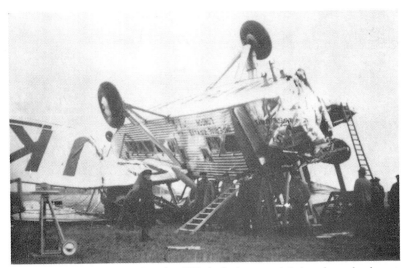

Syrinx overturned at Brussels in November 1935; the fuselage was relatively undamaged and no passengers were injured. (*Courtesy S. Swayland.*)

second pair. The tests continued, using each pair of Perseus in turn, until, after four months, *Syrinx* was blown over by a gale at Brussels and had to be returned by barge to Rochester for repairs. While these were in progress, Imperial Airways decided to fit a set of four Pegasus XC engines at the ratings approved for the Empire Boat under normal operating conditions. Parker flew *Syrinx* again with these engines at Rochester on 12 September, 1936, and they were permanently retained, but *Scylla* was never re-engined in the same way; with Pegasus XC, *Syrinx* at 32,000 lb could climb to 10,000 ft in 13 minutes. The opportunity was also taken of trimming *Syrinx*'s cabin in the colours and materials proposed for the Empire Boats, to test passenger reaction; for this reason all the windows were made rectangular.

Syrinx at Croydon in 1938 after being rebuilt with Pegasus XC engines, rectangular windows and Empire Boat interior trim. (*Courtesy A. J. Jackson.*)

277

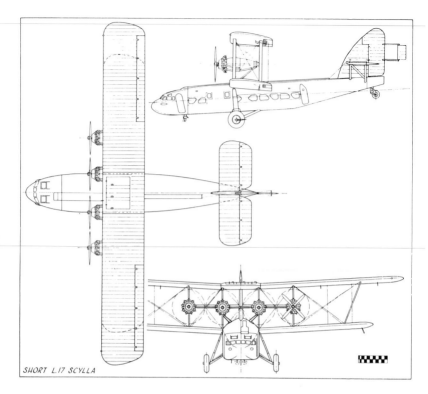

SHORT L.17 SCYLLA

Kent—Span 113 ft (34·4 m); length 78 ft 5 in (23·9 m); area 2,640 sq ft (245 m²); empty weight 20,460 lb (9,290 kg); all-up weight 32,000 lb (14,510 kg); max speed 137 mph (220 km/h); ceiling 19,500 ft (5,950 m); range 450 miles (760 km).

Scylla/Syrinx—Span 113 ft (34·4 m); length 83 ft 10 in (25·5 m); area 2,615 sq ft (243 m²); empty weight 22,650 lb (10,290 kg); all-up weight 33,500 lb (15,200 kg); max speed 137 mph (220 km/h).

When war began in August 1939, *Scylla* and *Syrinx* led the exodus from Croydon, with the rest of Imperial Airways' big landplanes, to their emergency base at Whitchurch, Bristol, whence they flew under the auspices of National Air Communications. After taking the advance parties to Bristol, they were dispersed to Exeter to reduce congestion at Whitchurch and shared with the Ensigns and Handley Page 42s the task of transporting military stores and R.A.F. ground personnel to A.A.S.F. bases in France. In November they were camouflaged and, when most of the airlift to France had been completed, they were used to maintain essential internal flights to Scotland and Ireland. *Syrinx*'s C. of A. expired just before Christmas 1939, and it was stripped for major inspection. Both aircraft were requisitioned by the R.A.F. in March 1940, but there was delay in putting the order into effect, and it was cancelled after *Scylla*, calling at Drem on 14 April, 1940, to pick up Imperial Airways ground crews, had been detained there by an approaching gale, only to be torn from its pickets by severe squalls during the night and overturned; *Syrinx* had already been condemned at Exeter, where its fuselage became a useful addition to the office accommodation.

On one of *Syrinx*'s last flights it had called at the Westland aircraft works at Yeovil, where the airfield had just been elaborately camouflaged with dummy 'hedges and ditches' sprayed on to the grass with a mixture of paint and saw-dust. This looked very realistic on a dull November afternoon, and Capt O. P. Jones, with very little load on board, managed to land across the airfield from north to south in about 50 yards, coming to rest without actually over-running any of the painted stripes, to the delight of several Westland

Scylla, view looking forward from the rear of the aft cabin. (*Imperial Airways.*)

employees and the gratification of the works defence officer. Next morning Westland's chief test pilot, Harald Penrose, had to deliver a Lysander to Boscombe Down; he made a typical 'three-point take-off' in his best Lysander demonstration manner and continued climbing at more than 45 degrees. *Syrinx* then took off, unsticking in about twice its own length, and climbed equally steeply, though in a level attitude. This spectacle seriously misled another visiting pilot, following in a Miles Whitney Straight light monoplane, into thinking there was a strong westerly wind shear, but in fact there was very little wind, and his determined leap off the ground was followed by a stall, from which he only just managed to recover without damage.

So *Scylla* and *Syrinx* passed from the wartime scene with all the stateliness of full-rigged ships, sharing with the Singapores the distinction of being the last Short biplanes to be designed and remain in service.

The Knuckleduster outside No. 3 Shop in November 1933, showing the original tie-rod bracing of the wing-tip floats, and the open tail-gunner's cockpit.

The Short R.24/31 (Knuckleduster)

Soon after ordering the last three Rangoons specifically for tropical operation in the Persian Gulf in 1931, the Air Staff drafted a more advanced specification, R.24/31, for a twin-engined general-purpose flying-boat of similar size, capable of flying on one engine and suitable for long-range patrols with a crew of five. Ease of maintenance was emphasised, and construction in Alclad with longitudinal corrugations instead of riveted-on stringers was recommended; the A.14 hull built on this principle by Saunders-Roe to match the aerostructure of Southampton *N251* had proved successful. Three prototypes to R.24/31 were eventually ordered, the Saro and Supermarine designs being biplanes with Pegasus engines, while Short Brothers received a contract for a more ambitious monoplane with experimental Rolls-Royce Goshawk steam-cooled engines.

Short Brothers had not built a monoplane flying-boat since the little Cockle ten years earlier and, although a much enhanced performance was promised through drag reduction, the structural problems were formidable. Gouge designed a trussed box-spar with four stainless-steel tubular booms as a means of obtaining high torsional stiffness in a cantilever wing with conventional fabric-covering, so as to avoid twisting of the wings from root to tip which could cancel out or even reverse the desired effect of aileron deflection, and at higher speeds and altitudes could lead to flutter, with ensuing catastrophic failure. In addition, it was necessary to mount the engines high enough for their large-diameter geared-down airscrews to be well clear of spray at take-off; water-tank and wind-tunnel tests showed that the best compromise was likely to be a gull-wing geometry, with the high-lift Göttingen 436 outer wings carried on stiff inner wings growing out of the hull at a dihedral angle of 30 degrees, the engine nacelles being faired into the leading edge at the wing joint or 'knuckle'; from this feature the flying-boat, which never had any official name, was nicknamed the Knuckleduster. Design index

No. S.18 and c/n S.767 were allotted, and construction began early in 1933 under contract No. 226328/33, when serial *K3574* was reserved for it.

By May 1933 the wings had been completed in skeleton and the hull was well advanced in No. 3 Shop. Although the planing bottom followed the lines developed for the Sarafand and Singapore III, with a pointed main step, its chines were modified to give clean running without flaring the sides, which were nearly flat and plated with long planks stiffened by rolled longitudinal channels. The straight-sided frames were built up from single and back-to-back channels and were strongly boxed and braced by diagonal frames at the wing-root attachments; these, with eight continuous box-section longerons, formed a complete girder from the bow to the rear step, aft of which the hull reverted to standard monocoque design similar to the Singapore's; both frames and plating were of Alclad, with stainless-steel fittings at highly stressed points. The primary structure of the wings was a deep rectangular girder formed by four high-tensile stainless-steel tubular booms with screwed end sockets, to which tubular lift and drag struts were also attached; the tube diameters and wall thicknesses reduced progressively from root to tip to match the loads, and the booms were braced by tie-rods, the space within the truss containing the two 178-gallon semi-cylindrical main fuel tanks feeding 46-gallon gravity service tanks; at the extreme tip the spar terminated in a pyramidal frame tapering to a tubular boundary member; the ribs were built up of duralumin tubes as in normal biplane practice, with continuous plating of the leading edge and the walk-ways above the spar; Frise ailerons were fitted, and the wing-tip floats were carried on pairs of vertical struts. At the root ends the four spar booms were attached to the hull main frames by large-diameter expanding shear bolts; structural wing-loading tests proved that all design conditions were met, particularly those for torsional stiffness. The tail-plane was adjustable and braced by struts in the usual way, with twin fins and rudders above at two-thirds span and braced by single diagonal struts to the top of the hull. The engine nacelles each had an 11-gallon oil tank and cooler outboard in the leading edge, and gothic-shaped steam condensers and hot-wells above. These were contained in long-chord low-drag ducted fairings, each with a short vertical radio mast at its apex. The crew stations comprised a gunner's cockpit in the bow, with a bomb sight and mooring gear; an en-closed cockpit for pilot and navigator side-by-side, with removable dual controls for the latter; a navigator's station with chart table and sighting ports, also two folding bunks; then the engineer's and radio stations between the spar frames; next the crew's living-quarters with one folding and two fixed bunks and a galley with an ice-chest and wash-bowl. In the waist forward of the rear step was the midships gun mounting, with an engineer's bench, drogue stowages and toilet adjacent, and finally, along a catwalk, the stern gunner's cockpit. Each gunner's position mounted a Lewis gun on a Scarff ring, and the mid-gun mounting could be slid athwartships on rails. Strong points were installed for underwing bomb racks and a torpedo could be transported, but not launched, under the starboard wing-root close to the hull; a portable winch was provided for hoisting bombs, also a light-weight derrick for changing engines. The beaching chassis comprised two separate tubular units carrying single heavy-duty pneumatic-tyred wheels, and a steerable tail trolley to fit under the rear step.

The Knuckleduster was launched from No. 3 Shop slipway on 29 November, 1933, and John Parker, with George Cotton and 'Dinger' Bell as crew, made the first flight the following afternoon. It took off extremely quickly, without porpoising, at a weight of 13,560 lb, but almost at once Parker noticed the fins flexing and landed after a circuit of 2 minutes at 100 ft; the rudder control was not affected by this fin movement, and the boat taxied cleanly and turned easily on the water. Modifications were made to stiffen the fin and tailplane attachments before the next flights of 20 minutes on 15 December and 25 minutes on 8 January, 1934, when the boat was found stable at all speeds up to 137 kt and touched down smoothly at 57 kt, although it could not be trimmed to fly straight and level against a dead engine. Before the fourth flight on 31 January the rudder area was increased by 18 per cent and the wing floats were remounted on triangulated oval tube struts with a diagonal oleo-damper as a drag-bracing to isolate the wings from shock loads and vibration originating in the floats. The rudder was now effective against a dead engine, but too heavy to hold over continuously. While a cure for this was being found, trials continued, and the first full-load test at 17,760 lb on 2 February showed a rate of climb of 830 ft/min at 85 kt. On the 9th Parker attempted to reach service ceiling, but had to abandon the climb when the port engine overheated at 7,000 ft; during an earlier flight the same day with Major Rupert Penny of M.A.E.E. and Jack Manson (R.T.O.) on board, the boat suddenly went into a climb, which Parker could control only by closing the throttles; after landing he found the cause to be the distortion and subsequent collapse of the fairing of the tail-gunner's cockpit. After these two flights both engines were changed, the rudder balance was increased, and both fin leading edges

The Knuckleduster on the Medway in May 1934, showing the sprung wing-tip floats and the revised tail unit with tail-gunner's cupola closed.

282

The Knuckleduster at Felixstowe in its final form, with improved sprung wing-tip float struts.
(*I.W.M.—Crown Copyright.*)

were further toed-in by 1 degree. Parker complained strongly about the tail design, even requiring a complete redesign and causing one hearer to exclaim, 'It's not possible!' Gouge replied, 'Only one man can say what's possible and that's John', and put in train major structural modifications to the tail unit reputed to have cost nearly £10,000. Before starting these, seven flights to check stability at full load with various c.g. positions were made on 19 March, and on the 23rd Parker and a crew of three climbed to 15,000 ft in 35 minutes with full load. Three days later, with Jack Manson, George Cotton and Bob Boorman as observers, Parker completed satisfactory diving tests from 6,000 ft at speeds over 200 mph; parachutes were being worn for the first time, and Boorman, in the co-pilot's seat, concentrated strictly on reading his instruments; his natural apprehension as a 'stress-merchant' had not been allayed by Parker's final briefing before take-off: 'Bob—if I say jump now, you bloody well jump!' This was the first time full diving trials in a military flying-boat had been done by a contractor's test pilot before delivery to Felixstowe. After this the boat went back into No. 3 Shop for the agreed tail and sternframe revisions; these included deepening the hull frames to incorporate a fixed forward fairing for the tail-gunner's position, which now had a quarter-spherical tilting cupola over the gun-ring. After relaunching, an entirely satisfactory 45-minute flight was made on 26 May in very rough weather. New airscrews were installed, and on 7 June a true speed of 152 mph was recorded at 5,000 ft; later that day a demonstration was arranged for the design staff, who had worked so hard to push the job through. Oswald Short and Gouge were on board, but after four minutes the starboard engine back-fired and stopped, and Parker had to alight immediately at quite a high speed downwind; even so, there was hardly any porpoising. It was found that many valve springs had failed in both engines, probably through overspeeding in a dive earlier in the day; these were replaced, and on 11 June the demonstration flight was repeated at a lower weight, when the Knuckleduster was manoeuvred easily with each engine throttled in turn. A few days later a crew from M.A.E.E. flew it to Felixstowe for official trials, from which it returned to Rochester on 1 October for repairs to damage to the bows and wing-floats

283

The Knuckleduster flying over Felixstowe Town Pier in April 1935. (*Aeroplane.*)

after a taxying collision. This work, to contract No. 373495/34, included also revised low-drag struts, still with oleo-dampers, for the floats and was completed in February 1935. On 4 March Parker made two half-hour flights over the marked course on the Maplin Sands, reaching 150 mph at 4,500 ft; then the Knuckleduster went to Calshot for service assessment, till April when, with the prototypes London *K3560* and Stranraer *K3973*, it deputised at Mount Batten for No. 209 Squadron's Perths, all of which were out of commission till September; the three R.24/31 prototypes returned to Felixstowe in October, having taken part in the fly-past at the R.A.F. Display at Hendon in June, when the formation of experimental flying-boats was led by the Sarafand. Thereafter it remained on routine duties at Felixstowe and was on view to the public on Empire Air Day, 1938; a few weeks later it was honourably retired to become an instructional airframe (*1154M*) at No. 2 School of Technical Training, Cosford. During one period of its service at Felixstowe, it became afflicted by repeated engine failures during take-off, which baffled all attempts at rectification until the gravity fuel tanks were examined internally; then detached pieces of solder were found which could obstruct the tank outlets in a nose-up attitude, though not while level.

The Knuckleduster was not expected to win a production order in the R.24/31 competition, for which the role was eventually filled by both the Saro London and Supermarine Stranraer biplanes, the latter being equipped mainly for northern latitudes and the former for the Mediterranean, while Short Brothers received a substantial contract for Singapore IIIs for tropical service. It did, however, provide valuable data on the steam-cooling of engines and the handling of monoplane flying-boats. It is interesting to speculate what its performance might have been, for instance, with close-cowled Bristol Perseus engines; in particular, it showed that a clean-running straight-sided hull could be designed with a narrower beam than that derived from the classic $\sqrt[3]{W}$ rule, and thus contributed to the design of the Empire Boat and Sunderland.

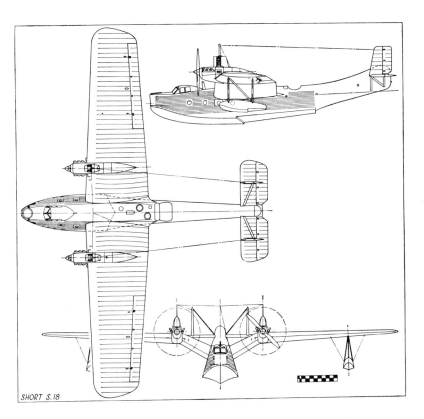

SHORT S.18

Span 90 ft (27·4 m); length 63 ft 3 in (19·3 m); area 1,147 sq ft (106·5 m²); empty weight 11,720 lb (5,320 kg); all-up weight 18,500 lb (8,395 kg); max speed 150 mph (240 km/h); ceiling 15,500 ft (5,030 m); range 1,040 miles (1,675 km).

285

Prototype Scion at Gravesend (*above*) as first flown with flat-topped rear fuselage, and (*below*) with decking added.

The Short Scion

In 1927 Douglas R. Pobjoy, Bristol-born lecturer in aero-engine design and construction at the R.A.F. Cadet College, Cranwell, undertook the design of a small and efficient seven-cylinder radial engine of 67 hp, to match a sporting single-seat monoplane, the C.L.A.7, being designed by his colleague Nicholas Comper for the Cranwell Light Aeroplane Club. Before this was finished Comper resigned from the R.A.F. and began manufacture of the C.L.A.7 as the Comper Swift. Meanwhile Pobjoy had built a prototype engine from sub-contracted components, and after running it first at Cranwell and later in his home workshop at Minster-on-Sea, Sheppey, for 120 hours, submitted it for a 50-hour civil-type test by the Air Ministry, which it passed in 1928 with notable economy and absence of wear; flight trials in the Parnall Imp were equally successful, and enough enquiries came in for him to begin manufacture in a small factory adjoining Comper's at Hooton Park, Cheshire, in 1930. The production engine, known as the Pobjoy 'R' to distinguish it from the prototype 'P', was slightly increased in bore and developed 80 hp, which made it an attractive alternative to heavier inline engines of similar power. Either by chance or design, the diameter of the Pobjoy R was almost exactly half that of the Bristol Pegasus; this was to be a significant factor in the history of Short Brothers.

The Pobjoy R was standardised for the Comper Swift and several other light aeroplanes; it did well in the 1931 King's Cup race and was selected for the production version of the Monospar ST-4 twin-engined four-seat cabin monoplane, which became popular when introduced in 1932; Oswald Short agreed with Arthur Gouge that the time was ripe for a five-passenger light transport, and after an intensive survey of the potential market a twin-Pobjoy high-wing cabin monoplane was put in hand. The design, S.16, aimed at a low selling price (around £2,500), easy maintenance and robust construction for use in undeveloped territories, and economy in flying costs. To keep the price low enough, monocoque construction had to be rejected in favour of a welded steel-tube girder fuselage with fabric-covering; the cantilever wing, of Göttingen 436 section, was similar to the outer wings of the Knuckleduster, except that cruciform-section extruded duralumin booms were used instead of steel tubes, with duralumin tubes for compression and drag struts. The pilot sat well forward of the wing in an enclosed cockpit, with a sliding roof hatch and excellent vision through the deep windscreen and opening side windows; the passenger cabin was entered by a door on the port side below the wing spar and accommodated two rearward-facing passengers in front and two forward-facing passengers at the back, with a single seat amidships opposite the door, against which a sixth folding seat could be installed if required. All the control surfaces were balanced and the tail unit was of orthodox Short design in duralumin with fabric-covering. In the prototype the Pobjoy R engines were uncowled and mounted on nacelles slung below the wing spar; the landing-gear comprised two vertical coil-spring-and-oleo shock-struts, under the spar inboard of each nacelle, carrying low-pressure wheels with differential pneumatic brakes, and a fully castoring tailwheel; 31 gallons of fuel were contained in two aluminium tanks in the leading-edge between the nacelles and the fuselage. In the prototype the nose was a fabric-covered duralumin framework, and the rear fuselage aft of the wing was flat-topped. The prototype took c/n S.766 and was registered *G-ACJI* concurrently with *Scylla* and *Syrinx*.

On completion at the Rochester seaplane works it was taken by road to Gravesend Airport and re-erected there, being tentatively named Alpha. John Parker made two short flights in it on 18 August, 1933, at a light weight, unfurnished, of 1,700 lb; he called for various alterations and flew it again solo at 2,000 lb on 4 September for 12 minutes, then for 10 minutes with Gouge and Francis Short at 2,400 lb and finally at full load of 3,000 lb for half an hour with a climb to 3,000 ft; next day he climbed with full load to 6,000 ft and asked for the aileron leverage to be altered. On the 7th, after a brief solo check of the ailerons, he flew with Gouge and Jackson to Ipswich Airport in 51 minutes against a brisk headwind, returning to Gravesend the same afternoon in 32 minutes. Six more flights followed at intervals while the furnishings were being completed, and on the 30th he flew it to Croydon for demonstration to Brackley and Hudson Fysh, managing director of Qantas, who was on a brief visit to England; on returning to Gravesend that afternoon he took Douglas Pobjoy up for 12 minutes. After this a deep curved decking was added to the rear fuselage, fairing into the wing and greatly improving handling

287

and performance. Oswald Short had his first trip in it on 3 October, and two days later, probably at the suggestion of Thurstan James, the new name Scion was agreed on. Numerous flights followed till 1 November, and on 16 December Parker flew it to the embryo Rochester Airport, remaining there till the 29th to put in three hours' flying time on fuel consumption checks over the Christmas holiday. All through January 1934 the Scion was flown almost daily, until on the 23rd Parker flew it to Martlesham for C. of A. trials, returning next day to Gravesend, where on 7 February he took up the Gouge family and five days later introduced Harold Piper to it. A full C. of A. was granted on 14 February subject to further tests at Martlesham which were cleared on 20, 21 and 29 April. On 2 May Parker took up Douglas Pobjoy and W. P. Kemp (Shorts' general works manager), and on 2 June Piper flew the Scion to Croydon in formation with *Scylla* in order to ferry Parker back to Rochester; Piper just managed to keep station at nearly full throttle on the outward journey.

Scion I *G-ACUX* (*above*) as a seaplane at Rochester in October 1934, and (*below*) as a landplane at Bankstown, Sydney, in 1965. (*Courtesy A. J. Jackson.*)

288

Pobjoy Niagara IIIs of 90 hp had been chosen for the first batch of five production Scions, c/ns S.774–778, registered *G-ACUV* to '*Z*, which had been put in hand at Rochester. The first of these was urgently completed in time to appear at the S.B.A.C. trade show at Hendon on 1 July, when Parker flew it with his usual grace enhanced by the fully-cowled Niagara's gentle purr. Thereafter Parker and Piper between them flew *G-ACƷI* and *G-ACUW* on a series of over 1,000 scheduled 15-minute flights between Rochester and Southend Airports to demonstrate the potential of the Scion as a shuttle ferry on a short but awkward river crossing; these flights extended from 28 June till 26 October. In August *G-ACUV* was sold to Aberdeen Airways for their service to Orkney, and on 5 October *G-ACUX* was launched on the Medway as a twin-float seaplane, having been ordered in that form by Major H. Hemming's company, Papuan Concessions Ltd, for operation from Port Moresby, scene of Frank Hurley's pioneer use of the *Shrimp* in 1923; before delivery it had to go to Felixstowe for C. of A. trials as a seaplane. Parker flew it there on 26 November, but on the return trip on 21 December, with Walter Browning and Jack Manson as passengers, he flew into dense fog and had to land off Sheerness while he could still see open water; after taxying for an hour they arrived at an old naval sloop in Stangate Creek and tied up to it for two more hours, finally rowing in a borrowed dinghy to Iwade, near Sittingbourne, where they spent the night, collecting the Scion next day. As *VH-UUP*, *G-ACUX* gave long and valuable service in New Guinea and Australia, ending up as a landplane at Sydney in 1954, owned by Marshall Airways. *G-ACUY* was first flown on 10 December, and after completing its trials in January was retained by Short Brothers as a demonstrator and company transport, to replace *G-ACUW*, which was sold in April 1935 to Lundy and Atlantic Coast Air Lines at Barnstaple, Devon.

Meanwhile *G-ACUZ* had been completed as the first revised model for 1935, designated Scion II; the chief differences were the raising of the engine thrust line to the level of the wing datum, an improved windscreen with upper quarter-lights in the roof, better cabin windows in line with the cockpit side-windows, six passenger seats as standard and a new hinged moulded nose giving easy access to the controls and back of the instrument panel; streamline spats were also fitted to the main wheels, but were removed later because they collected mud, which often froze during flight. Its first flight at Rochester Airport, on 13 February, 1935, had to be curtailed after 8 minutes when an engine stopped with fuel starvation, and electric fuel booster-pumps were then introduced to supplement the limited head provided by the A-C mechanical pumps fitted as standard on Pobjoy engines. The remaining trials went without a hitch, and '*UZ* was flown by Parker to Martlesham for C. of A. approval on 7 March. Piper collected it on 13 March, and it received its certificate on the 21st; it was then sold to Airwork Ltd for use at Tollerton Airport, Nottingham, and was the first to be impressed, as *W7419*, in March 1940. A further batch of 10 Scion IIs, c/ns S.785–794, were by this time in production in a new factory at Rochester Airport, with registrations *G-ADDN*

Scion II *VH-UTV* at Rochester Airport before dispatch to Adelaide in 1936.

to *G-ADDR, VH-UUT, G-ADDT, VH-UVQ, G-ADDV, VH-UTV* and *G-ADDX* respectively, the three for Australia having been ordered by Robert Bryce for Adelaide Airways. Of these *G-ADDN* flew on 9 June and was delivered on the 14th to Southend Flying Services Ltd, to share the Thames Ferry duty with *G-ACUY*; this recommenced on 20 May and included a call at All Hallows-on-Sea. *G-ADDO* was first flown by Parker on 10 July and went to Olley Air Service at Shoreham next day, but returned to Rochester for repair six weeks later and was redelivered on 14 September. *G-ADDP* was also flown on 10 July, by Piper, and delivered two days later to West of Scotland Air Services for their Renfrew–Mull service. *VH-UUT* was flown by Parker on 23 August and shipped to Adelaide, where it crashed in January 1936 and was returned to Rochester, to be rebuilt as *G-AEOY* and sold to Arabian Airways at Aden, where it was finally written off in April 1938.

Scion II *G-ADDR* as *M-3* with experimental wing and Gouge patent flap, at Rochester Airport on 6 August, 1935.

The next Scion, *G-ADDR*, was retained for experimental work by Short Brothers, and in August 1935 emerged for its first flight with a tapered, highly polished plywood-covered wing fitted with high-lift trailing-edge flaps; this wing was a scale model of the design proposed by Gouge for the Empire Boat, and Parker flew it from 6 August till 7 October, with the 'B conditions' mark *M-3*, on a schedule of tests for Gouge; on 24 October Parker delivered it to Farnborough for assessment by three R.A.E. pilots, who agreed that the flap reduced both take-off run and landing speed. On 27 November he collected it, after which it remained at Rochester for further test work till 20 February, 1936, when the experimental wing was removed. *G-ADDR* flew for the first time with a standard wing on 1 April, 1936, thereafter being used for night-flying practice and anti-aircraft co-operation with searchlight posts around Chatham and Erith till 18 June, when the starboard engine failed and Parker returned quite happily on the port one alone. Then the experimental wooden wing was reinstalled, the flaps having been extended to the full span and fitted with retractable spoilers in lieu of ailerons. With these Parker took off on 22 July on a flight that nearly ended in disaster, for as soon as he was airborne he realised that the lateral control was totally ineffective; by juggling with the rudder and differential use of the throttles he completed a precarious circuit and landed safely, apparently less worried than any of those watching from the ground. This device of Gouge's was quickly forgotten, and the standard wing was reassembled; *G-ADDR* re-emerged fully furnished on 24 September, 1936, and remained as a company hack until impressed in March 1940 as *X9366*; at the same time *G-ADDN*, *G-ADDP* and *G-ACJI* were also commandeered as *X9364*, *X9374* and *X9375* respectively; *G-ADDP* had been resold in 1938 to Williams & Co of Squire's Gate, Blackpool, for joy-riding, and *G-ADDV* and *G-ADDX* were bought for the same purpose in May 1936 by the airport authorities of Ramsgate and Plymouth respectively; *G-ADDV* was resold to Southern Airways in 1938 to fly a summer service between Ipswich and Clacton, and *'DO*, *'DV* and *'DX* were impressed in 1940 as *AX864*, *X9456* and *X9430* respectively. More adventurous was *G-ADDT*, belonging to Pobjoy Airmotors Ltd, which C. E. Gardner flew to India, leaving Rochester on 21 January, 1936, and returning on 13 March, having covered nearly 16,000 miles in the interval, including 1,500 miles flat-out on 14 February in the race for the Viceroy's Cup at Delhi; its short but merry life ended the same year in a crash at Porthcawl on 26 July.

By early 1936 the rising tempo of the Empire Boat programme had begun to conflict with continued production of Scions, but the latter represented valuable business to Douglas Pobjoy, who went to dinner one night with Oswald Short to discuss the possibility of Short Brothers investing some badly needed capital in the Pobjoy firm. It appears that Pobjoy mentioned a five-figure sum, to which Oswald assented before the party ended; next morning Pobjoy reminded him of it, and Oswald did not deny the possibility, but said he must first refer the matter for legal advice. Some days later Pobjoy was summoned to Oswald's office, where his solicitor produced a licence agreement giving Pobjoy the sole manufacturing rights for the Scion II, together with the lease of a suitable production line, the fee named as consideration being the same amount as Pobjoy had asked Oswald Short to invest. Pobjoy knew when he had met his match and at once re-registered the name of his firm as Pobjoy Airmotors & Aircraft Ltd of Rochester Airport, with Short Brothers listed as a substantial shareholder. Douglas Pobjoy was a clever engineer and an ambitious businessman, but was inclined to underrate his customers' perspicacity and stick out for too high a price. One enquiry he received was from two Naval staff officers who were interested in the possibility of adapting the Scion as a slow-flying fleet spotter for convoy protection, based on an escorting aircraft carrier; for this role folding wings were essential, and in a few days the Scion design office at Rochester worked out a scheme for folding the wing back about a normal rear spar-hinge and then rotating it on a turn-table built into the hinge-mounting to lie flat against the fuselage; this project also featured extra tankage, a camera, light-bomb racks and a downward-firing Lewis gun. Pobjoy knew there was a possibility of getting an order for as many as 50 aircraft if the scheme were approved, but quoted such a high price that the officers walked out without further discussion.

Before taking on the Scion concession, Pobjoy had commissioned Harold Boultbee to design a two-seat light monoplane suitable for a single Niagara. Having gained early aircraft experience as a draughtsman under Henri Coanda at the Bristol works at Filton in 1913, Boultbee had gone on to Handley Page Ltd, from which he resigned in 1928 to form the Civilian Aircraft Co at Burton-on-Trent; there he designed and built a series of five Civilian Coupés, neat and original two-seat cabin monoplanes which were raced in 1930 and 1931 with some success, but in the 1933 depression the firm closed down. In 1934 Boultbee designed the Pobjoy Pirate, derived from the Civilian Coupé but having tapered wings like the D.H. Leopard Moth. This was registered *G-ADEY* and built at Rochester in the early months of 1935; Parker agreed to test it, and in fact flew it three times, first for half an hour on 25 June, 1935, again for 25 minutes on the 29th and finally on 10 July for 15 minutes, but it was not good enough to compete with others in the same class and was abandoned forthwith. As its name suggests, it was not a Short Brothers product, and is mentioned here only as an interloper of transient interest.

The first two Pobjoy-Scions were sold in 1937 to Palestine Air Transport

Second Pobjoy-built Scion II, *VQ-PAB*, in service at Haifa in 1938.

Ltd as *VQ-PAA* and *'B*, to operate a thrice-weekly service between Haifa and Lydda; a year later, with the acquisition of Scion Senior *G-AECU* as *VQ-PAD*, the service was extended to Beirut until stopped by the war in June 1941, the two Scions being impressed for the Lydda Communications Flight, R.A.F., as *Z7189–7190* and scrapped early in 1943. Of the remaining four Scions completed by the Pobjoy company, *G-AEIL* went to Arabian Airways at Aden in July 1936 and was impressed there four years later as *Z7187*, being scrapped in April 1941; *G-AEJN* was bought by C. G. M. Alington in September 1936 and resold in 1939 to E. D. Spratt, and *G-AETT* went to Lundy & Atlantic Coast Air Lines in April 1937 to assist *G-ACUW* in operating the daily service between Barnstaple and Lundy Island; *'TT* crashed at Barnstaple in February 1940 and *'UW* was impressed as *AV981* three months later, along with Short Brothers' *'UY* as *AV974* and Spratt's *'JN* as *AV990*. The sixth and seventh places on the Pobjoy production line were reserved for the abortive naval spotter project, on which no work was done. The final Pobjoy-Scion, *G-AEZF*, was first flown in seaplane form by Parker at Rochester on 9 December, 1937, and was then shipped to Sierra Leone to share Elders Colonial Airways' Bathurst–Freetown service with Scion Senior *G-AENX*. When this service was abandoned in September 1939, *'ZF* was shipped back to England and converted by Pobjoys into a landplane in November 1941, being then used by Short Brothers as *M-5* at No. 24 E.F.T.S., which they were then operating at Barton-in-the-Clay, Beds. In September 1942 it gained its first British C. of A. as a landplane and resumed its normal registration, remaining as a hack until 24 E.F.T.S. closed down in 1945; during this period it was damaged by a gale in December 1942 and taken to Shorts' flying-boat factory at Windermere for repair, returning to service in April 1943 at Sealand, whither 24 E.F.T.S. had moved meanwhile. In August 1946 it came on to the books of Short & Harland Ltd, who sold it to Air Couriers in March 1947; in August it was resold to a private operator at Woolsington, and finally was auctioned for £450 to a Birmingham purchaser, migrating via Elmdon to subsequent owners at Exeter in 1950 and Croydon in 1953; there it remained after its C. of A. expired in May 1954 until taken to Redhill four years later; after a further year's storage it was retrieved by a party from Tradair and transported to Southend, where in 1966 its remains were derelict and any hopes of restoring it to a presentable state for preservation and display were diminishing rapidly.

None of the impressed Scions returned to civil use, although all gave useful wartime service either as ferry pilots' hacks or on anti-aircraft co-operation and radar calibration duties, mainly with No. 6 A.A.C.U. at Ringway and No. 116 Squadron. *W7419* had the distinction of being stabled during 1940 at Waddington as the personal transport of Sir Arthur Harris, A.O.C. 5 Group, and after being damaged was repaired by 54 M.U., Cambridge, and reflown in April 1941 at 51 O.T.U., Cranfield, being then reissued to No. 116 Squadron and later, after overhaul at Gatwick in 1942, to Standard Motors; it was finally scrapped at Kemble in April 1944, together with *AV974* and

AX864; earlier casualties were *AV981*, which stalled and spun in on an approach to Ringway on 1 November, 1940; *X9374*, which was condemned at Gatwick in April 1941; and *X9430*, also condemned at Gatwick in February 1941, but subsequently rebuilt and flown by Air Service Training until written off in April 1942. Five others grounded during 1941 were *AV990*, *X9364*, *X9366*, *X9375* and *X9456*, which became instructional airframes *2722M–2726M* respectively, and were finally scrapped after the end of the war.

Scion II *VH-UTV* re-engined with Gipsy Minors, at Alice Springs in 1965.
(Copyright A. E. Flanders.)

In Australia two Scions were still in airworthy condition in 1966, *VH-UUP* (ex *G-ACUX*) at Bankstown, Sydney, and *VH-UTV* of Connellan Airways at Alice Springs, N.T., which was unique in having been re-engined in 1946 with Gipsy Minors; in February 1965 it was proposed to convert *VH-UTV* into an air ambulance carrying a team of four medical parachutists, but this was frustrated by the Australian Department of Civil Aviation's insistence on being supplied with a full Type Record before renewing the C. of A.; unfortunately the only documents from which this could have been compiled had been destroyed at Rochester during the war.

Although usually remembered as a fairly sedate small feeder-line transport, the Scion had a lively performance and beautifully harmonised controls, as demonstrated by Harold Piper when he looped *G-ACUY* at the Rochester Hospital Carnival Fête at the Airport on 12 September, 1936; on another occasion, with Jack Lower as his only passenger, 'Pip' cruised for a time quite happily with arms folded and feet on top of the scuttle, surely the ultimate in 'hands and feet off' demonstration!

Span 42 ft (12·8 m); length (I) 31 ft 6 in (9·6 m), (II) 31 ft 4 in (9·56 m); area 256 sq ft (23·8 m²); empty weight (l/p) 1,875 lb (850 kg), (s/p) 2,125 lb (963 kg); all-up weight 3,200 lb (1,452 kg); max speed (l/p) 126 mph (203 km/h), (s/p) 122 mph (196 km/h); ceiling (l/p) 13,000 ft (3,960 m), (s/p) 11,500 ft (3,506 m); range (l/p) 390 miles (624 km), (s/p) 370 miles (595 km).

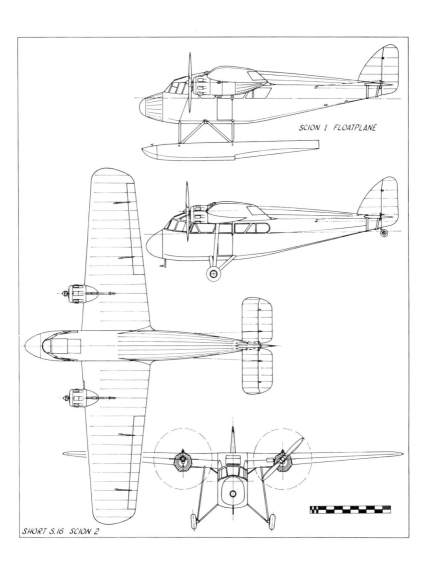

SCION 1 FLOATPLANE

SHORT S.16 SCION 2

295

The second Scion Senior seaplane, *VT-AHI*, for the Irrawaddy Flotilla Co in August 1936, showing the small lower fin extension.

The Short Scion Senior

The twin-engined Scion had been conceived as a small cheaply operated feeder transport for internal services, and in fact it admirably fulfilled this role on the short over-water ferry routes on which it was introduced; but the sad fact was that if a service proved popular the traffic demanded a larger aircraft, and if it did not, even small aircraft could not pay their way. Short Brothers decided in 1935 to offer a larger ten-passenger version of the Scion with four Pobjoy engines; where there was sufficient regular traffic, such an aeroplane with one pilot could do the same amount of work as two Scions requiring two pilots, the fuel and maintenance costs being slightly less because the larger aircraft was likely to be aerodynamically more efficient. However, the Scion Senior, as it was named, failed to win orders from internal airline operators, who had already adopted the de Havilland Dragon and Dragon Rapide; instead it proved attractive as a seaplane for survey and river transport purposes overseas, and the first order came from the Irrawaddy Flotilla Company in Burma, with a promise of further orders if the first seaplane proved satisfactory. So the Scion Senior, index No. S.22, was designed basically as a seaplane with an alternative land chassis, as the Valetta had been.

The design followed that of the Scion very closely, and in fact the fuselage was hardly any deeper and was widened only by 15 in to accommodate three-abreast seating, but the length was increased by one-third and the wing area by 56 per cent; at the same time a more efficient wing plan similar to that of *M-3* was chosen, with more taper and elliptical tips but without flaps. The cabin, increased in length from 10 to 17 ft, had all its seats facing forward, in three rows ahead of the entrance door (on the port side) and two rows aft; in the standard layout the third row had only a single seat on the starboard side, and the back row had three seats in line; this allowed a toilet to be installed amidships on the starboard side opposite the door. The pilot's cockpit had its own emergency exit door on the starboard side of the nose, as well as a sliding roof hatch and opening direct-vision windows in the windscreen.

296

Structurally, the Scion Senior was similar to the smaller Scion, having a fuse-lage of welded steel tubing with light wood fairings and fabric-covering; the wings had the same kind of braced box-spar with extruded duralumin booms and tubular bracing struts; the duralumin ribs were fabric-covered except for the leading edge, which was skinned with Alclad back to the front booms, the fabric being attached to the leading edge spanwise boundary member by an ingenious clamping strip and to the ribs by skewers, both being Short Brothers' patents. As in the Scion, the boom extrusions were basically cruciform in section, being progressively reduced in area by milling off to T-section and L-section from root to tip. All the control surfaces were fully balanced, but no flaps were fitted. The two fuel tanks, each of 30 gallons capacity, were cylindrical of oval section, made of duralumin with the ends flanged and riveted by the de Bergue process, which employed large-headed flush rivets and a sealing membrane between the joint surfaces; this process superseded Shorts' crude but time-honoured and effective method of sealing fuel tanks with freshly masticated chewing-gum, which for many years was a free issue in the tinsmiths' shop, but had to be prepared with more expendi-ture of mandibular energy than mere enjoyment would have required. The floats were carried on a triangulated welded chassis of streamline steel tubes, forming a rigid and robust structure needing no truing-up in service; the four Pobjoy Niagara III engines were close-cowled and faired into the leading-edge as in the Scion II.

The first Scion Senior, S.779, was originally registered *G-ACZG* but first flown as *VT-AGU* by John Parker on 22 October, 1935, having been launched earlier that day. Parker completed the full schedule of handling trials in six hours' flying before 14 November, when he flew it to Felixstowe for C. of A. approval, collecting it on 4 December; then it was shipped to Rangoon, its C. of A. being issued on 11 January, 1936. After satisfactory initial operations by *VT-AGU* a second Scion Senior was ordered in June; this, S.810, first registered *G-ADIP*, was launched and flown as *VT-AHI* on 10 August and cleared for dispatch to Rangoon three days later; it differed from the first only in having a small under-fin to increase the vertical tail area. Meanwhile a batch of four more Scion Seniors had been laid down, and the first of these, S.834, had been completed as a landplane demonstrator, *G-AECU*, and flown on 15 June; after 4 hours 40 minutes testing, Parker flew it to Hatfield on the 29th and gave a brief demonstration, but had to return forthwith to Rochester and could not appear at the S.B.A.C. trade show at Hendon on 1 July, as intended. He took it to Martlesham for C. of A. trials on 17 July and flew back the same day, its C. of A. being issued on the 28th. Next day Parker flew Oswald Short as the only passenger to Speke and thence to Newtownards for a conference with the Northern Ireland Government, Belfast Harbour Commissioners and the directors of Harland & Wolff Ltd on the possibilities of building an additional aircraft factory at Belfast; they returned the follow-ing afternoon via Speke to Hatfield, where Oswald Short caught a train to London, leaving Parker to fly the Scion Senior back to Rochester alone; on 13

Scion Senior landplane *G-AECU* as flown in the King's Cup race on 11 September, 1937.

August Brackley flew it while on a visit to Rochester to inspect the first Empire Boat. For a time it was discussed as the basis for a low-cost coastal reconnaissance aircraft, for which design index No. S.24 was reserved, but this project came to nothing. Thereafter *G-AECU* was flown mainly as a company transport and demonstrator by Harold Piper, who flew it as Oswald Short's entry in the King's Cup race on 11 September, 1937. It was leased to Jersey Airways for the 1938 summer season and sold in December that year to Palestine Air Transport as *VQ-PAD*, being based at Haifa and eventually impressed there in February 1942 as *HK868*.

The remaining Scion Seniors were all seaplanes; S.835, registered *G-AENX*, was actually first flown as a landplane by Parker on 22 June, 1937, but converted forthwith and made its first flight on floats on 24 August, completing full-load trials on the 27th and 31st and being dispatched on 16 September to West of Scotland Air Services for their route between Greenock Harbour and Stornoway, its C. of A. being issued on 11 September, 1937. In February 1938 it was resold to Elders Colonial Airways Ltd, to operate the western sector from Freetown to Bathurst of the extension air mail route from Kano via Lagos, Accra and Takoradi; in fact, the Takoradi to Freetown link was never opened as planned, but *G-AENX* arrived by sea at Freetown in April and was flown on 6 May, operating a regular weekly service to and from Bathurst thereafter. During its annual C. of A. renewal inspection in December the steel lower longerons near the tail were found to be seriously rusted, and a repair party flew out from Rochester to weld in new tubes. In January 1939 the service was restarted from Freetown to Bathurst and Dakar via Conakry and Boulama, so as to connect with the Deutsche Lufthansa air mail service to South America; operations ended in August when *G-AENX* was sunk at moorings at Bathurst, repairs to the salvaged seaplane being abandoned after war began.

The last of the batch, S.837, was built as a seaplane with extra fin area as in *VT-AHI*; it was flown as *VT-AIJ* on 12 December, 1936, and shipped to Rangoon to join the two earlier Scion Seniors of the Irrawaddy Flotilla Co; but the last to be delivered was S.836, provisionally registered *G-AETH* for a projected ferry service between Sydney Harbour and Newcastle, N.S.W., but bought by the Air Ministry for experimental work on flying-boat hull design; Short Brothers built a flush-riveted central float as a half-scale model of a Sunderland hull, and this was attached to the Scion Senior by means of a dynamometer linkage similar to that employed on Gipsy Moth *K2235* in developing the Singapore IIC planing bottom. The Scion Senior 'flying-boat' had wing-tip floats of suitable size carried by long struts, and was first flown as *L9786* by Parker at Rochester on 18 October, 1939, for a short straight of one minute only, followed two days later by a successful half-hour handling test and a final pre-delivery flight of 25 minutes on 20 December; it then went to M.A.E.E., which when war broke out had removed from Felixstowe to Helensburgh in Scotland. There it was employed to measure hull resistance during fast taxying and provided data which enabled a faired main step to be

Scion Senior 'flying-boat' *L9786* being launched by crane at Rochester in October 1939.

designed for the Sunderland III. In August 1942 it was equipped with a forced-ventilation system wherein compressed air was ejected from holes distributed along the planing bottom, but this attempt at 'air lubrication' failed to give any reduction in water drag—later full-scale experiments with a Sunderland, however, showed that the main step could be virtually suppressed by careful siting of naturally ventilated slots close behind the step position. In November the same year *L9786*, with the dynamometer linkage locked, was flown to measure attitudes, stability and accelerations during take-off and landing at 5,900 lb, with steps of various depths and with various fairings; it gave much better correlation with full-scale Sunderland behaviour than the small tank models previously used, particularly after finer-pitch airscrews had been fitted to improve low-speed acceleration; finally, it was sunk at sea in 1944.

Scion Senior *L9786* on the Medway in October 1939.

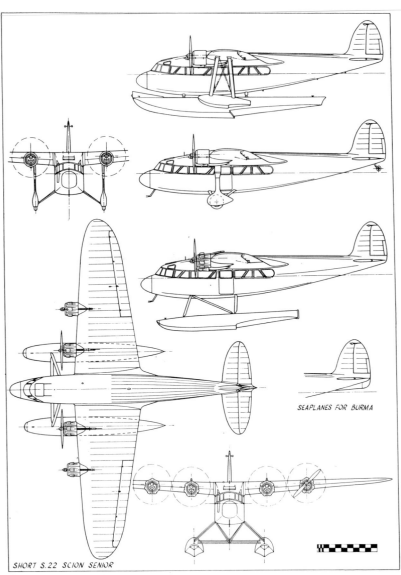

SEAPLANES FOR BURMA

SHORT S.22 SCION SENIOR

The Scion Senior's most important assets were its excellent performance and handling qualities and the fact that its Pobjoy engines were half the diameter of the Bristol Pegasus; these two features added up to a strong recommendation for its overall configuration to be adopted, with linear dimensions doubled, as the best layout for the Empire Boat. Although Pobjoy Airmotors & Aircraft Ltd acquired the manufacturing rights for the Scion Senior in

1937, no more were laid down to follow S.837, as the Pobjoy Company was by then fully extended on sub-contract work for Short Brothers, who acquired most of its share capital in 1938.

Span 55 ft (16·75 m); length 42 ft (12·8 m); area 400 sq ft (37·2 m²); empty weight (l/p) 3,315 lb (1,500 kg), (s/p) 3,650 lb (1,637 kg); all-up weight 5,750 lb (2,607 kg); max speed (l/p) 140 mph (226 km/h), (s/p) 134 mph (216 km/h); ceiling (l/p) 12,000 ft (3,660 m), (s/p) 10,000 ft (3,050 m); range (l/p) 420 miles (675 km), (s/p) 400 miles (645 km).

The Mayo Composite complete on its beaching cradle at Felixstowe in May 1938.
(I.W.M.—Crown Copyright.)

The Short-Mayo Composite

Nearly a century elapsed between Sir Rowland Hill's inception of the Penny Post and the introduction of a flat-rate Empire Air Mail Service in 1937. Air mails themselves originated in 1870 during the siege of Paris, using pigeons for inward and balloons for outward traffic, but there the inward destination was fixed and the outward one immaterial, so long as the enemy lines were bridged without interception; balloons were no more predictable for carrying messages between two points than bottles in the ocean, nor could aeroplanes at first compete with more reliable and cheaper surface vehicles. When civil aviation began in 1919 the Post Office reluctantly granted contracts for carriage of air mail at substantial surcharges, but offered no subsidy for rapid transit such as Rowland Hill had given to Samuel Cunard. As traffic increased, the surcharges came down, and by 1930 had become standardised for all European destinations; meanwhile, for diplomatic and strategic reasons, the R.A.F. had pioneered the Cairo–Baghdad desert air mail in 1921 and had allowed public participation once the service was established; in 1927 it was taken over as a going concern by Imperial Airways as part of their route to India, the mail being carried as a profitable adjunct to passengers.

With the continued combination of mail and passengers in view, Imperial Airways proposed a scheme in 1933 whereby they could carry by air at a flat rate all first-class mail throughout the British Empire, except to Canada and the West Indies. Parliament approved it on 20 December, 1934, and it was scheduled to begin in June 1937. Prior to this, Imperial Airways and Qantas, who were to share the service to Australia, had demonstrated its feasibility with a limited series of experimental flights, gallantly and precariously pioneered in the Wells Fargo manner, from which they concluded that they must have a new standard type of aircraft, available on all sectors of the trunk routes, and that flying-boats were more economical and reliable than land-planes. So, for their main African, Indian and Australian routes, Imperial Airways, on the advice of Major Robert Mayo, their General Manager (Technical) and a pioneer Martlesham test pilot, issued a specification for a large four-engined flying-boat, and in due course Short Brothers' tender was accepted, with the unprecedented result that 28 aircraft were ordered straight off the drawing-board; thus was born the magnificent Empire Boat, whose epic career is described later. Meanwhile the problem of extending the air mail service to North America had still to be solved, since the Empire Boat unaided could only just cover the distance if all the disposable load were devoted to fuel.

There were, at first sight, two natural staging posts in the Atlantic—the Azores and Bermuda; on closer examination these proved unacceptable except on a reserve route, for both strategic and geographical reasons. Bermuda offered an excellent seaplane base, but the only harbour in the Azores, Horta, was too restricted and busy for regular use by heavily laden flying-boats and the open sea was too dangerous. On the most direct Great Circle route from Ireland to Newfoundland the strength of the prevailing westerly winds made very large fuel reserves imperative, while a sub-arctic route via Iceland and Greenland was only practicable under ideal summer conditions, and not always then. Two possible solutions to the problems of taking off at Horta were advanced; in the first, Major Rupert Penny of the Air Ministry proposed using catapult launching from barges specially fitted-out as depot ships, in the manner of the *Imperia* at Crete, with refuelling and repair facilities. Both the French Aéropostale and Deutsche Lufthansa airlines had begun air mail services to South America via Dakar, the Germans using an intermediate catapult ship, but they carried no passengers and even their hand-picked crews found the launching accelerations (up to $4\frac{1}{2}\,g$) barely tolerable; a more cogent condemnation of catapult launching lay in the fact that it had to be done at sea-level, from which the heavily laden mailplane had to climb un-aided to its operating altitude, at great cost in both fuel and time. The second solution, proposed by Sir Alan Cobham, was for an Empire Boat to take off at normal weight with a moderate fuel load and then take on more fuel from a tanker aircraft at a suitable altitude, since the Azores could provide the necessary airfield length for a landplane tanker, and a flying-boat starting from Lisbon could be refuelled over Horta if a reliable method of ensuring a rendezvous could be worked out. This scheme seemed feasible if experience confirmed that the difficulties of adverse weather and limited winter daylight were surmountable, and it was later adopted for the direct Ireland–Newfoundland route, after the techniques of coupling hoses and transferring fuel had been improved.

Meanwhile, Major Mayo had been working since 1932 on a third solution, which was to carry a heavily loaded mailplane to operational height on the back of a larger, more lightly loaded aeroplane; there the upper component of this Composite Aircraft would separate from the lower and fly to its destination, burning enough fuel *en route* to be below its maximum permitted landing weight on arrival; the lower component would return at once to base in readiness for the next launch, or to be operated independently as a short-haul transport until needed again for launching. At an estimated £60,000 for both components, this project would be much cheaper and more versatile than installing a catapult on a barge, and could be ready for operation several years sooner than flight refuelling. The Air Ministry and Imperial Airways both supported Mayo's scheme and agreed that both components should, for the prototype, be seaplanes; in 1935 a contract based on specification 13/33 was placed with Short Brothers, with the cost shared equally by the Treasury and the airline. Design index numbers for the upper and lower components were S.20 and S.21 respectively, and their c/ns were S.796 and S.797.

The idea of a 'pick-a-back' composite aircraft was not novel, for it had been the subject of a bold experiment by Cmdr John Porte at Felixstowe on 17 May, 1916, when he took off in a Porte Baby flying-boat carrying on its upper centre-section a Bristol Scout C held in place by crutches and a quick-release toggle; when this combination reached 1,000 ft, the Scout pilot, Flt Lieut M. J. Day, whose engine was already running, opened up to full bore, rose from the flying-boat, it was said, 'like a dove from a roof' and landed safely at Martlesham. The purpose of this experiment was to test the feasibility of carrying a fast-climbing Scout within striking range of a Zeppelin, but it was not repeated. Twelve years later Norman Macmillan, while Fairey's test pilot, obtained a patent (No. 317,774) for 'aircraft coupled in pairs or trains', in which an aeroplane carried above itself a gliding 'bomb' whose wing area was just enough to support its own weight; the patent specified that, 'the bomb . . . may also be provided with propelling means . . . may be used for attack, or for the supply of ammunition, stores or mails.' In fact, it appears to have been applied only as a means of launching target-gliders for anti-aircraft gunnery practice, and Macmillan did not oppose Mayo's first patent (No. 400,292), granted in April 1932, for 'aircraft carrying other aircraft'. Originally separation was to have been induced by means of the upper component's elevator control, but this was soon discarded as too risky, and in successive patents (402,895; 402,951 and 402,997) use was made of the differential lift-coefficients of suitably chosen aerofoils for the two components, so arranged that as speed increased the upper component took a greater share of the total lift than the lower, thus producing a positive separating force sufficient to overcome spring detents holding the components together; release could be prevented until a safe minimum airspeed had been reached and the upper component's flying controls could be locked until the instant of release to prevent relative yawing forces being applied before separation. In a further patent (445,829) a barometric control prevented separation at too low an altitude, and finally, in January 1936, the fully developed design, including a weigh-beam registering the separating force, with indications to both pilots, was described in patent No. 469,557, granted jointly to Mayo and Short Brothers; as a final embellishment three months later, patent No. 472,546 covered the possibility of refuelling the upper component from the lower after separation, thus taking a leaf out of Cobham's book.

In deciding the aerodynamic and structural design of the two components, Short Brothers concentrated on making the upper component as efficient as possible, while the lower component was adapted from the concurrent design of the Empire Boat. Gouge's first thoughts on the latter inclined towards a biplane, which would have been a four-engined derivative of the Sarafand; but when Oswald Short and he went with Parker to see the start of the MacRobertson race from Mildenhall to Melbourne in October 1934, they were all so impressed by the clean design of the Douglas DC-2 entered by K.L.M. (which almost stole the race from the winning D.H.88 Comet, in spite of being fully furnished and carrying a payload) that they decided forthwith that the Empire Boat must be a cantilever monoplane; had a biplane been chosen for the Empire Boat, a different monoplane boat similar to the Knuckleduster would have been necessary to serve as the lower component. When coupled, the two components of the Mayo Composite behaved in all respects as a single aeroplane, because the upper pilot could not move his controls, and his only responsibility before release was to contribute thrust and lift to 'the edifice' (as C. G. Grey called it). The higher centre of gravity of the Composite necessitated more positive lateral stability on the water, and this was attained by increasing the beam of the planing bottom and the displacement of the wing floats, which were also lowered so that with full load both were awash simultaneously. In addition to having a slightly wider

Maia at the barge-yard before first flight, with wooden fixed-pitch airscrews.

304

beam than the Empire Boat, the lower component had flared chines and a distinct tumble-home in hull cross-section, bringing the wing-roots closer together; at the same time the engine nacelles were mounted farther out along the span to give adequate clearance for the floats of the upper component. The wing of the lower component had the same overall span as the Empire Boat, but was 250 sq ft greater in area, and there were corresponding increases in the chord and area of the tail surfaces; moreover, the hull was upswept towards the stern so as to raise the tailplane in relation to the wing, thus obtaining the best compromise location to suit both the Composite 'biplane' and the solo lower component. It had a cabin which could be furnished for 18 passengers, with rectangular windows like the Kent's, but in all other respects and in detail the design was similar to the Empire Boat.

The upper component (S.20) was a very clean twin-float mid-wing seaplane of minimum fuselage cross-section and low overall drag, with four air-cooled Napier–Halford Rapier engines disposed across the span in nacelles carefully faired into the cantilever wing. The floats were carried by only two pairs of struts each, with wire drag bracing. The wing had a single main box-spar formed by two Warren girder beams and intermediate parallel stringers enclosing a spanwise elliptical-section tank designed as a stress-bearing tube and providing torsional and flexural stiffness. The tank was divided by chordwise baffles which extended outside the shell to form plate ribs; these baffles had hinged flaps in them to allow fuel to flow only inwards from tip to root and so prevent surging; the total fuel capacity was 1,200 Imperial gallons, giving a still-air cruise range of 3,800 miles; most of this fuel could be jettisoned to reduce weight if a forced landing were necessary early in the flight, since the maximum permissible solo weight was 16,000 lb. The oval-section fuselage, carefully blended into the wing by integral root fillets, was of standard Short Brothers monocoque construction, but had in addition a strong longitudinal box-beam to distribute the load of over 5,000 lb carried by the single attachment hook under the centre of gravity; apart from this central tensile connection, the two components were located only by six spherical knobs carried on pylons on the lower component and nesting in corresponding cups in the upper component, one forward and one aft on the centre-line of the fuselage and similarly under each float. The whole seaplane was skinned with Alclad sheet except for the control surfaces, which were fabric-covered; the rudder and elevators had inset trim tabs. The pilot and navigator sat in tandem in an enclosed cabin forward of the wing, where also the radio was installed; a hold for 1,000 lb of mail was located under and aft of the wing, with a door in the port side for loading and crew entry. The flying controls of the upper component, except the trim tabs, were all locked in the neutral position until the instant of release; this was achieved by the insertion in the S.20's controls of a quadrant normally free to rotate, containing a tapered cut-out; a vertical sliding rod with a wedge-shaped end fitted into this slot, thereby locking the S.20's controls until the two aircraft parted. To ensure that the S.20 was correctly trimmed fore and aft on becoming free and also to give the upper pilot some initial control feel, the S.21 pilot could, by separate control, withdraw the wedge by an amount sufficient to permit a small degree of movement in pitch, and nose- or tail-heaviness was indicated by lights to the lower pilot, together with the build-up of separating force to both pilots. The lower pilot waited for all four lights (forward trim, aft trim, 3,000 lb tension, 5,000 lb tension) to appear simultaneously; he then pulled his release lever; the upper pilot's lights would already be indicating both 3,000 lb and 5,000 lb tension on his hook, and he would pull his release lever on hearing by telephone that the lower pilot's hook was free; a third hook would then be automatically released as soon as the tension exceeded 5,000 lb by a pre-set spring-controlled load. It was arranged that on release the upper component would rise in a level attitude and accelerate, while the lower component fell away, so that the risk of collision immediately after separation was ruled out, although for a brief interval neither pilot could see the other aircraft.

Maia taxying on the Medway, showing the flared chines and large wing floats.

The lower component, registered *G-ADHK* and named *Maia*, was launched first and flown for 20 minutes on 27 July, 1937, by John Parker, before its pylon structure was attached and with temporary four-bladed wooden airscrews. Two more flights followed, then three-bladed metal variable-pitch airscrews were installed for a level speed test at 6,000 ft on 9 August, and next day the pylon was assembled for a check flight prior to a Press demonstration on the 12th. The upper component, registered *G-ADHJ* and named *Mercury*, was launched and flown by Parker for 15 minutes on 5 September, and after a 40-minute handling flight next day was shown to the Press on the 8th. Both aircraft continued flying separately, to determine stability margins and position errors, until on 1 January, 1938, Parker began the initial taxying trials of the complete Composite assembly, with Harold Piper aloft in *Mercury*; he taxied for an hour that day, followed by 45 minutes on the 3rd, and 40 minutes, after the Composite had ridden out a gale at moorings, on the 19th. During these taxying trials Bill Hambrook, whom Gouge had put in charge of the project, stood on top of the lower component, hanging on to the pylon, to observe the release gear. While he was up there Parker accelerated to hump speed and inadvertently became momentarily airborne, due to the increase in position error, as yet undetermined, with both aircraft coupled. On the 20th Parker made the first combined flight of 20 minutes at the controls of *Maia*, with Piper at *Mercury*'s throttles. The Composite handled well with the upper component's controls locked, but the load indicators were incorrectly set, and no separation was attempted. On 5 February, after adjustments to put matters right, the Composite flew a second time, but the weather was too rough for the attempt, and it landed again as one unit. Next day, in the course of half an hour's flying, the first separation was decided more or less on the spur of the moment, since conditions were excellent and *Mercury* was flying within its permitted landing weight. The parting was uneventful and went unrecorded by any camera, being witnessed only by casual spectators in Rochester and Strood. The second separation, fully ciné-recorded by British Movietone News, was made according to plan at only 700 ft on 23 February in a public demonstration to the Press; Parker had Capt A. S. Wilcockson of Imperial Airways as co-pilot and, on being asked to comment after the flight, said, 'I think the chief thing we discovered was that it wasn't a fluke the first time.'

Mercury being lowered on to *Maia* by the M.A.E.E.'s 50-ton crane, during official trials in May 1938.
(*Flight.*)

The way was now clear for official trials to begin at Felixstowe, and after full-load tests at forward and aft c.g. limits on 4 March, Parker delivered *Maia* to M.A.E.E. on the 17th, with Piper following close behind in *Mercury*. Both pilots returned to Felixstowe on 6 May to make a full-load Composite take-off and landing, and on the 9th they made the first full-load separation, after which Sqn Ldrs Martin and Pickles of M.A.E.E. took over and Parker and Piper watched their separation from Scion Senior *G-AECU*. *Mercury* and *Maia* were flown back separately from Felixstowe on the 19th, the former having successfully demonstrated the jettisoning of 1,000 gallons of fuel, which called forth the usual protest from a few purse-conscious taxpayers, who demanded to know why water could not have been used instead of wasting expensive petrol! In June, *Mercury*'s original Rapier V engines were replaced by moderately supercharged Rapier VIs, and the Composite was handed over to Imperial Airways for fuel consumption tests by Captains Wilcockson (*Maia*) and D. C. T. Bennett (*Mercury*).

Mercury leaving *Maia* over Foynes on 21 July, 1938, at the start of its non-stop flight to Montreal.
(*Charles E. Brown.*)

On 14 July *Mercury*, piloted by Bennett with A. J. Coster as radio operator and an Air Ministry observer, was launched over Southampton and flew 2,040 miles to Foynes on the Shannon and out over the Atlantic, returning to Southampton after nearly 12 hours, having made short-wave radio contact with both Foynes and Botwood, Newfoundland. A week later, just before 8 pm on 21 July, *Mercury* was launched over Foynes at a gross weight of 20,800 lb, including 600 lb of newspapers, press photographs and newsreels as payload, and arrived at Boucherville, Montreal, after having been flown by Bennett and Coster 2,930 miles in 20 hours 20 minutes; the average headwind encountered was 25 mph, with long periods much stronger, and the cruising height varied from 5,000 to 11,000 ft. On arrival at Montreal 80 gallons of fuel remained, so that consumption was less than 54 gal/hr, substantially better than that specified and very much better than the Air Ministry's somewhat pessimistic calculations. After refuelling and flying on to Port Washington, Long Island, *Mercury* was flown back via Boucherville to Botwood on 25 July, thence to Horta next day, arriving at Hythe via Lisbon on the 27th; the average speed for the entire round trip was over 160 mph.

After this outstanding success, Bennett suggested to Sir Kingsley Wood, the Air Minister, that *Mercury* should be used for an attempt on the world's seaplane distance record, and eventually this was agreed, mainly because on 10 August a Deutsche Lufthansa Focke-Wulf Condor landplane had flown 3,970 miles non-stop from Berlin to New York, returning non-stop two days later in under 20 hours. So *Mercury* went back to Rochester to have its floats sealed for use as transfer tanks, thereby increasing its fuel capacity to 2,130 gallons. By this time the official performance estimators had revised their basic assumptions and considered that the absolute distance record was within *Mercury*'s reach, so on 21 September the starting-point was moved north from Southampton to Dundee, and Ian Harvey (who held both pilot's and radio operator's licences) replaced Coster, because it was felt that two pilots were desirable on a flight lasting two days. *Mercury* and *Maia* had just been loaded and fuelled at Dundee when the Munich crisis halted preparations for a time, but after a further wait for better weather *Mercury* was launched on 6 October at a gross weight of 27,500 lb (a wing loading of 45 lb/sq ft), and course was set due south in hope of reaching Cape Town non-stop.

Having been launched at 4,700 ft, Bennett had intended to cruise most of the way at 10,000 ft, but was forced down by icing to 3,000 ft over southern England; also one of the engine cowling panels came adrift soon after separation and was torn off, causing an increase in drag which would reduce the ultimate range by 3 per cent. Over the Channel the ice disappeared and he began a steady climb back to 10,000 ft to gain terrain clearance over the Atlas Mountains, crossing the Algerian coast after ten hours flying. Severe headwinds over the Sahara and tropical thunderstorms over Equatorial Africa diminished the chances of reaching the Cape on the available fuel and to add to their adversities Bennett and Harvey had to take turns at the stand-by hand pump to transfer fuel from the floats, because the electric pumps refused to lift it; at 12,000 ft without oxygen this soon became an exhausting exercise, and for several periods during the night, having obtained a star-fix, Bennett relied entirely on the auto-pilot while Harvey was getting his breath back; by judicious throttling the flight was prolonged beyond Luderitz into daylight, and eventually *Mercury* alighted on the Orange River off the Alexander Bay diamond-mine settlement, having flown 6,045 miles in just over 42 hours. After refuelling from five 40-gallon drums floated out to the seaplane, they flew on to Cape Town and thence to Durban for inspection; the flight was duly homologated by the F.A.I. as an international seaplane record for distance in a straight line at 5,997·5 miles; even had they reached their objective

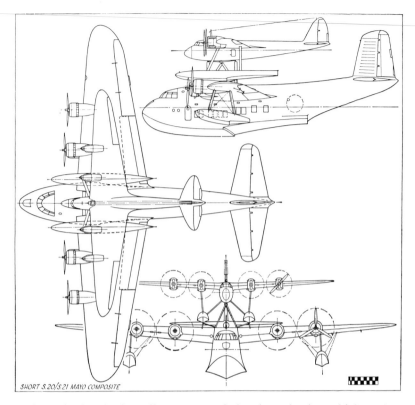

SHORT S.20/S.21 MAYO COMPOSITE

as planned, the absolute distance record thereby gained would have been surpassed by the R.A.F.'s Wellesleys which flew from Ismailia to Darwin a month later.

After flying back from Durban to Southampton in seven stages, *Mercury* was experimentally equipped with Dunlop de-icing boots along the wing, fin and tailplane leading edges, also modified engine intakes, to prevent a recurrence of icing trouble at altitude. Trials of this equipment were interrupted in November, when the unprecedented build-up of Christmas air mail taxed the resources of Imperial Airways' fleet to the limit, and on the 29th *Mercury*, loaded to capacity, including mail-bags in the floats, was launched from *Maia* over Southampton, and Bennett and Coster flew 2,200 miles non-stop to Alexandria at 152 mph, carrying more than a ton of payload; this flight was repeated on 12 December, adding a modest quota to the staggering total of 350 tons of air mail carried to and from Empire destinations before Christmas, in spite of a heavy surcharge on air mail originating in Australia. These achievements in actual traffic by the Mayo Composite encouraged Imperial Airways to propose ordering a small fleet of a landplane version, comprising four upper components to be launched from two suitably adapted Armstrong

310

Whitworth Ensigns, for a total cost of £200,000; but these plans were turned down flat by the Air Ministry in March 1939, on the grounds that segregation of mails and passengers was unacceptable as a long-term policy; the most they would offer was to give *Maia* and *Mercury* to the airline free of charge. Imperial Airways were disappointed at the Air Ministry's ruling, as they had hoped to condense the bulk of the mail into microfilm for transmission as 'airgraphs', to promote which a company had been formed jointly by Imperial Airways, Pan American Airways and Eastman-Kodak.

Meanwhile *Mercury* could not be flown into Botwood while the harbour was still icebound, and the resumption of summer services in 1939 was frustrated by the imminence of war and preoccupation with flight refuelling trials, so *Mercury* remained out of use for over a year, although *Maia* was furnished to carry ten passengers for flights between Southampton and Foynes during the transatlantic trials of *Caribou* and *Cabot* (*q.v.*). On 5 August, 1939, at Foynes, it carried a distinguished complement of passengers, including Mr Eamon de Valera, Sir Francis Shelmerdine and Sir John Salmond, to witness *Caribou*'s first scheduled refuelling before flying to Botwood; thereafter it was employed for navigational training, but remained available for launching. On 18 June, 1940, *Mercury* was flown by Bennett to Felixstowe to be handed over to No. 320 (Netherlands) Squadron, whose personnel had escaped from the German invasion of Holland, bringing their Fokker T-8-W seaplanes with them; this unit moved to Pembroke Dock for coastal reconnaissance duties, taking *Mercury* with them as a trainer, but a year later they re-equipped with Hudsons and *Mercury* was then returned to Felixstowe for disposal; the R.A.F. flew it back to Rochester on 9 August, 1941, and it was broken up soon afterwards. After *Mercury*'s requisitioning the launching pylons were removed from *Maia*, which was retained by B.O.A.C., being finally destroyed by enemy bombing on the night of 11 May, 1941, while moored in Poole Harbour.

So ended an experiment which must be accounted a considerable technical success for its day, for its performance exceeded the agreed specification by a handsome margin and repeatedly confuted the more pessimistic pundits; had war not intervened, and had the principle of segregation of mails from passengers been officially accepted in conjunction with active exploitation of airgraphs, air mail history could have been made on a vast scale. In 1939 French preparations to try out the 'pick-a-back' principle were frustrated by the war also, but in 1940–1, when heavy Allied shipping losses were being incurred by attacks from long-range Focke-Wulf 200s, Shorts collaborated with Hawkers in a scheme to mount a Hurricane on a Liberator bomber, but this had to be abandoned because no Liberators were available for this purpose when needed. Later in the war the Luftwaffe actually applied the principle to a combination of fighter and bomber, but in this case the Composite was flown entirely by the upper (fighter) pilot, the lower (bomber) component being unmanned and loaded with high explosive so as to form a 'stand-off' bomb; it seems that this may have been derived from early pre-war discussions between Major

Mayo and General Milch, who at that time showed interest but did not initiate any development.

In recent years the 'pick-a-back' principle was applied by Shorts to a series of proposals in which high-speed jet fighters, normally requiring long runways, could be air-lifted vertically by VTOL launching platforms derived from the S.C.1; the operation of this Composite was not confined to launching but provided also for retrieval and descent of the fighter at the end of its sortie. The Mayo Composite can justly claim to have been a small step in the direction of satellite launching, just as the skills acquired in flight refuelling contributed to the more recondite techniques of orbital rendezvous and docking.

Maia—Span 114 ft (34·7 m); length 84 ft 11 in (25·9 m); area 1,750 sq ft (162·5 m²); empty weight 24,745 lb (11,234 kg); all-up weight 38,000 lb (17,252 kg); max speed 200 mph (322 km/h); ceiling 20,000 ft (6,100 m); range 850 miles (1,360 km); for Composite launching the max weight of *Maia* was limited to 27,700 lb (12,580 kg).

Mercury—Span 73 ft (22·2 m); length 51 ft (15·5 m); area 611 sq ft (56·8 m²); empty weight 10,163 lb (4,614 kg); all-up weight (solo) 15,500 lb (7,030 kg), (for normal Composite launching) 20,800 lb (9,443 kg), (for Cape flight) 26,800 lb (12,160 kg); max speed (solo) 212 mph (339 km/h), (at max weight) 195 mph (314 km/h); range (normal Composite) 3,900 miles (6,240 km), (Cape flight) 6,100 miles (9,820 km).

The Short Empire Flying-Boats

In the annals of the British aircraft industry 1932 and 1933 marked the beginning of the end of the lean years stemming from the 'Geddes Axe' of 1922; not that there were as yet any obvious signs of prosperity or increased hope of employment for the majority of those seeking an aeronautical career, but technical advances in engine performance, aerodynamic design and structural materials all converged to produce a significant forward movement in the state of the art. There were new political pressures, too, which were to affect civil aviation as profoundly as military requirements during the next few years. For 10 years the British imperial air routes had been laboriously extended without serious competition from other national airlines; except on the high-prestige routes, between London and Paris, Brussels and Cologne, direct rivalry was a question of political negotiation rather than technical superiority. So Imperial Airways concentrated on developing larger aircraft suitable for the limited existing airfields along the routes to India and the Cape, making the most of comfort and safety rather than speed.

Three factors combined to disturb this environment; first, American transport operators, having built up a sound ground organisation with the backing of Post Office mail subsidies, had progressed to the point where they could already compete with surface transport for overland passengers and were extending their services to overseas operations between offshore islands round the coast and in the Caribbean; this enabled them to offer fully developed high-performance aeroplanes and seaplanes to customers in Canada, South America and even Europe; secondly, the resurgence of German nationalism

Corinna alighting with flaps fully extended. (*Charles E. Brown.*)

and emergence of Adolf Hitler had strengthened German links with South America and South Africa, the latter becoming increasingly critical of British influence on the Cairo–Cape air mail route; thirdly, progress with R.A.F. flying-boat operations had shown the value of deploying these aircraft at important Empire outposts such as Gibraltar, Aden, Basra, Colombo and Singapore; in the latter direction also, air mail competition from K.L.M. along their Amsterdam–Batavia route had begun to deprive Imperial Airways of traffic. Imperial Airways had countered the Netherlands threat by ordering Armstrong Whitworth Atalanta monoplanes of similar performance to the Dutch Fokkers, but their rivals soon retaliated by re-equipping with Douglas DC-2s, of which Fokker acquired the European manufacturing rights. The Atalantas had necessarily to be capable of operating on the African as well as the Asian routes and were designed to take off safely from the small, hot, humid, high-level airfields of the Cape route, most of which had not been much enlarged since the early Cobham–Blackburn days and all of which were frequently unfit for traffic; indeed, it was said that in the rainy season the airfield at Juba was more suitable for flying-boats than landplanes and what the Atalanta really needed was a planing bottom. With these problems in mind, coupled with the proof already given by Cobham and the R.A.F. that flying-boats could operate without difficulty through Central Africa to Durban and across India to Singapore and Australia, George Woods Humphery and S. A. Dismore recommended that Imperial Airways should re-equip with flying-boats for all their trunk routes and that this would save the transfer of mails and passengers between seaplanes and landplanes, which was really no more tolerable than break of gauge on a railway. Dismore, the Secretary of Imperial Airways, had estimated that his proposed Empire Air Mail Scheme could handle 2,000 tons of mail a year, for which the Post Office would pay

313

nearly £1,000,000, including additional grants for Christmas traffic. Woods Humphery and his Chairman, Sir Eric Geddes, worked out detailed requirements and, having obtained Parliamentary approval of the Scheme in December 1934, invited Short Brothers to submit proposals for a much improved Kent flying-boat to carry 24 passengers and $1\frac{1}{2}$ tons of mail at an economical cruising speed of 150 mph over a range of 800 miles; these figures were chosen after consultation with operating staff and analyses of traffic and weather data collected from every point on the Imperial Airways route map.

A few months earlier the Air Ministry also had invited Short Brothers, among others, to tender a design to specification R.2/33 for a long-range four-engined flying-boat having the same overall performance, but not so much bulk, as the Sarafand; Imperial Airways expected to order two prototypes and the Air Ministry one. Arthur Gouge recognised the general similarity of the two sets of requirements and had begun to examine layouts for suitable bi-planes when he went with Oswald Short and John Parker to see the aircraft competing in the MacRobertson race to Melbourne, due to start in October from near Parker's home at Mildenhall. All three of them admired the DC-2, to be flown in the race by Parmentier and Moll of K.L.M., and decided that the day of the biplane was definitely over. They mulled over various mono-plane layouts, based on their experience with the Scion and the Knuckle-duster, and decided that there were no real snags in the structural design, provided a better wing-to-hull junction could be devised; discussing stability and performance, Parker pointed out that the Scion handled excellently and there was every reason to expect the forthcoming Scion Senior, with four Pobjoy engines, to have a performance similar to that required by both specifications; since the Pobjoy was half the linear size of the Bristol Pegasus engine preferred by both customers, what would be better than a monoplane flying-boat with twice the linear dimensions of the Scion Senior? The only snag was that the wing loading would be much higher than that of a biplane, but Gouge found an acceptable solution to this by devising a retractable trailing-edge flap which increased the lift coefficient by 30 per cent without any significant penalty in trim or drag. A series of careful tank tests enabled the beam of the planing bottom to be made 18-in narrower than the 11 ft 6 in dictated by the $\sqrt[3]{W}$ law, so that the hull sides were vertical without flares from chine to wing-root, giving minimum frontal area and maximum usable space inside. The hull was made taller than strictly necessary in order to obtain a simpler wing attachment, and this resulted in a two-deck layout which compensated to some extent for the narrowness of the cabin compared with the Kent. Short Brothers had some misgivings on this score, but Imperial Airways were delighted with the design, increasing their proposed order first to 14 and soon afterwards to 28; their need was urgent and their faith in Short Brothers well founded, so they were prepared to share the technical risk of dispensing with prototype trials in advance of signing the contract, whose total value was £1,750,000. The Air Ministry ordered a single prototype R.2/33, for competition with one from Saunders-Roe (also a monoplane), and in due course this emerged as the Sunderland; meanwhile the civil design was

314

indexed as S.23 and, in the absence of any official type-name other than Imperial Airways' designation of 'C-class', became universally famous by its popular name Empire Boat; later Imperial Airways adopted the official class-name Imperial Flying Boat, but the popular name continued to stick.

It was a prerequisite of the project that the Empire Boat should have as low a drag as possible for the agreed layout, so all joints in the Alclad skin were joggled, and all rivets were flush countersunk; the wing spar was a braced structure of four T-section L.40 extrusions, trussed vertically by tubular struts in N-girder formation and horizontally by lattice compression beams, which took the place of the booms of conventional ribs, the whole box being cross-braced against torsional loads by swaged tie-rods; separate nose and tail ribs of flanged plate were assembled to the front and rear faces of the spar box to complete the wing profile, which was based on Göttingen 436. Circular arc tracks carried the roller-mounted flaps, which nested flush when retracted and were actuated by screw-jacks geared to a cross-shaft driven by an electric motor in the hull, where it was easily accessible; the Frise-type ailerons were fabric-covered, as were the mass-balanced rudder and elevators, carried on set-back hinges; the tailplane and fin were cantilevers similar to the wing on a smaller scale, but fabric-covered between the spar booms; they were bolted to root-stubs built into the stern section of the hull, and longitudinal trim and rudder bias were obtained by means of trim tabs set into the trailing edges of the elevators and rudder. The hull was of classic Short Brothers design, with two massive built-up box frames in line with the spar booms, forming double-skinned bulkheads with doorways. The main deck extended from the bow to the rear entrance door on the port side midway between the two steps, with a higher-level floor back to the aft step; the deck was braced to the planing bottom frames, to which were cleated close-pitched interrupted keelsons of Z-section folded plate having numerous flanged lightening-holes; the upper frames and intercostals were of similar design and the main keel was a built-up I-beam, extrusions being avoided wherever possible because of the delay in obtaining delivery in the lengths and quantities required. However, one very important extruded section was an I with the flanges curved into circular arcs; from this stock were made numerous plug-ends for tubular struts, thus saving an enormous amount of weight and cost compared with forged and machined end-fittings. Double curvature in the skin plating was almost totally eliminated, which was essential in view of the magnitude of the contract and the shortage of skilled panel beaters beyond normal requirements. By the time the drawings were ready for issue to the shops, the entire aircraft industry had become involved in the 1935 R.A.F. re-equipment programme, and it was impossible to attract skilled workers from other districts where formerly there had been unemployment; consequently, Short Brothers' aircraft works manager, A. E. Bibby, had no choice but to take on unskilled local labour and train them by working alongside his older hands. It was greatly to the credit of all concerned, and a splendid example of the *esprit de corps* engendered over the years by Oswald Short's strict but paternal management, that no difficulties or complaints of 'dilution' arose to impede production; everyone knew the penalties for late delivery or inferior performance and workmanship that would be exacted by the customer, and the men and women at the bench shared the responsibility for success or failure equally with the management.

There were many ingenious design features in the Empire Boat, most of which were patented by Short Brothers. The engine nacelles were of monocoque construction and built into the leading edge, but adjacent sections of the latter were arranged to hinge down to serve as maintenance platforms for the engineers. The Bristol Pegasus XC engines were installed in long-chord NACA cowls with exit gills adjustable in flight; these were actuated by a quick-thread which derived linear motion from the rotation of transverse shafts which entered the hull from the wing roots and were manually operated by the engineer, whose station was adjacent. The wing-tip floats were of standard design, with watertight partitions and bilge-pump connections, and their struts were wire-braced to a shock-absorbing centre link of ingenious design and very low weight and drag; the advantage of springing the floats fore-and-aft to isolate the wing spar from water-excited shock-loads and vibrations had been proved on the Knuckleduster; for the first time, too, it became necessary to put automatic tensioners in the control cables to compensate for differential thermal expansion. The two 326-gallon fuel tanks were located within the wing-spar truss between the nacelles and rested on built-up plywood floor panels to prevent chafing; they were approximately cylindrical, with cruciform internal baffles and flanged top and bottom ends secured by de Bergue rivets and numerous vertical stay rods; they were made of light alloy and fixed in the wing through large cut-outs in the top skin closed by stress-bearing covers attached by numerous set-screws. All unclad aluminium-alloy parts throughout the aircraft were anodised before assembly. Cabin furnishings and sound-proofing, together with all wiring, control runs, ventilation ducts and piping, were completely installed in the hull before final assembly of the stern section and flight-deck canopy; then each wing, complete with engine nacelles, fuel system and control runs, was bolted to the root spar joints each side of the hull, having been pre-assembled to make the best use of the available floor space and allow nine aircraft to proceed at one time.

The interior layout provided an upper deck forward of the wing spar containing a spacious flight-deck with stations for captain and first officer at side-by-side dual controls and a radio operator, together with a sealed auxiliary power unit driving a generator for electrical services when the main engines were not running. A flight engineer was added to the crew for long-range operation, but not normally carried on the Empire routes. This deck also provided stowage for mail-bags, and a purser's desk and cupboard for ship's papers, reached by a ladder from the steward's pantry below; aft of the wing spar, and accessible through it, was a hold for stowage of bedding. The upper mail compartment was loaded through a hatch on the starboard side just forward of the wing root. Below the flight-deck, in the extreme bow, was a mooring compartment containing anchors, drogues and a folding towing bollard which could be erected when the bow hatch was opened; a retractable landing lamp was recessed into the port side and a ladder gave access from the flight-deck. Immediately aft of the bow compartment and still below the flight-deck was the smoking lounge with seats for five passengers facing inwards and two facing forward, all of whom had lightweight tables for meals service. Aft of this cabin on the port side was the forward entrance door and lobby, with two toilet compartments adjoining; on the starboard side opposite was a completely equipped steward's pantry or galley, with a central corridor leading to the midships cabin, between the main spar bulkheads, accommodating three passengers in seats by day, convertible into bunks by night, with an additional upper bunk folding into the ceiling. Through the aft bulkhead was the promenade cabin with eight seats in four rows and a wide 'promenade' with elbow rail along the windows on the port side; this terminated aft with one step up to the rear entry door and a second step through a partition into the after cabin with six seats. The rear wall of this cabin was built above the rear step of the planing bottom and formed the aft limit of the passenger accommodation; behind this was the main freight hold, with a large loading hatch on the starboard side. The general cabin trim was in green leathercloth with a paler ceiling and fitted carpet; the seats were of Imperial Airways' own design, quickly removable and adjustable to five angles of recline; they had headrests with side-wings and were upholstered by Rumbolds on a Moseley pneumatic cushion base; the seat frames were of welded magnesium-alloy tubing, and it had been intended that Rumbolds should manufacture them after prototypes made by Imperial Airways had been tested and approved. A seat development unit was formed for this purpose, and by a strange coincidence its workshop was set up in the same Southern Railway arches that Short Brothers had originally occupied as their Battersea balloon factory. The technique of welding magnesium proved more difficult than expected, and eventually all the thousand or so seat frames for the entire fleet of Empire Boats were produced by Imperial Airways at Battersea and sent to Rumbolds for trimming.

The first two Empire Boats, S.795 and S.804, were registered *G-ADHL* and *'M*, concurrently with the Mayo Composite, and received individual names *Canopus* and *Caledonia* respectively. The latter was one of two boats ordered for the specific purpose of surveying the North Atlantic route; it therefore remained unfurnished and had its fuel capacity increased from 650 to 2,320 gallons by installation of six extra tanks within the wing truss, inboard of the inner and outer nacelles and across the top of the hull aft of the flight-deck; the second Empire Boat to the same long-range standard was S.813, *G-ADUV Cambria*, third of the first production batch of 12, S.811– 822, *G-ADUT* to *'VE*; all the rest of these were standard, as were the 14 in the second batch, ordered immediately after the first, S.838–851, *G-AETV* to *'UI*. Not long after production of the 28 for Imperial Airways had begun, three more, S.876–878, were ordered direct by Qantas and were allotted initial British registrations *G-AFBJ* to *'L*, changed before delivery to *VH-ABA*, *'B* and *'F*. Even these did not end the Empire Boat line, for, as will be seen, ten more of modified versions were to follow before the exigencies and priorities of wartime put a stop to civil aircraft production.

Canopus was completed without upholstery in June 1936 and launched on 2 July, 1936. Next day was the company's Sports Day at Gillingham, and all but those directly concerned with the prototype's first flight left promptly at midday. John Parker had *Canopus* cleared for flight and intended only to do some fast taxying on so new a type, but it handled so well during the first run that he changed his mind and made a flight of 14 minutes, at the end of which he reported that all was well apart from some reluctance on the part of the flap mechanism; this was soon rectified, and on the 6th he flew for an hour. Further adjustments followed, and on the 10th one engine failed at take-off, but he completed the circuit on the other three without trouble. Position error checks were made on the 13th, and three days later Parker flew for an hour to determine full speed at various altitudes. On 9 September he made the first full-load trial, and then *Canopus* went back into the works for fitting-out and furnishing. Meanwhile *Caledonia* had been launched and Parker made an initial flight of 20 minutes on the 11th, followed next day by one of 80 minutes at medium load and the day after by two flights totalling 1 hour 40 minutes at full load. He delivered it to Felixstowe for C. of A. trials on the 15th, by which time *Canopus* had re-emerged fully furnished for demonstration to Brackley on the 18th and 19th. On the 26th and 30th Parker and Sqn Ldr Martin of M.A.E.E. shared *Caledonia*'s C. of A. tests at Felixstowe, including 40 minutes, with two take-offs and landings, at an overload of 45,000 lb. Finally, Martin gave the O.K. and Parker flew *Caledonia* back to Rochester in 25 minutes on 1 October; then started a week of demonstration flights in *Canopus*; on the 5th the passengers included Lord Swinton, the Air Minister, and Sir Edward Ellington, Chief of the Air Staff, with their entourage; next day it was the turn of the directors of Imperial Airways, including Sir Eric Geddes and Sir John Reith; on the 6th Sir Samuel Hoare (First Lord) and the Board of Admiralty enjoyed a trip while the Sperry auto-pilot was being tested and demonstrated; on the 7th Brackley flew *Canopus* for an hour to practise take-offs and landings with various flap settings, and on the 9th Parker did a fuel consumption test. Various small snags were attended to, and on the 20th, after a final 20-minute check by Parker, *Canopus* was handed over to Imperial Airways with a brand new C. of A. Brackley made two more checks, and on the 22nd flew it away from Rochester on its first route-proving flight to Rome via Caudebec, Bordeaux and Marseilles. At Lake Bracciano it was taken over by Capt F. J. Bailey, who made a proving flight to Alexandria, whence he returned on the first scheduled C-class flight, via Athens and Mirabella to Brindisi, in under $7\frac{1}{2}$ hours on the 30th; he made the first outward-bound scheduled flight on 2 November.

Attention at Rochester was then focused again on *Caledonia* for most of November, alternating fuel consumption tests by Parker with check-outs of Imperial Airways captains by Brackley, culminating in *Caledonia*'s delivery to Hythe for long-range training flights in preparation for the North Atlantic survey programme, due to begin as soon as the ice was clear at Botwood. At once it was pressed into service to carry Christmas mail, and on 13 December Capt Cumming flew it with $5\frac{1}{2}$ tons of letters for India on a proving flight, returning with a similar load; on the inward journey he left Alexandria on 21 December and flew 1,700 miles non-stop to Marseilles in 11¼ hours, then direct across France to Southampton next day in 4¼ hours. *Cambria* was launched and flown by Parker on 11 January, 1937, and accepted by Brackley on the 20th for a proving flight to Marseilles, whence it returned to join *Caledonia* at Hythe on the 30th. Meanwhile production of Empire Boats at Rochester was in full swing; *G-ADUT Centaurus* emerged on 29 October, 1936, and was shown to the Press on 11 November; *G-ADUU Cavalier* followed on the 21st, *G-ADUW Castor* on 15 December, *G-ADUX Cassiopeia* on 23 January, *G-ADUY Capella* on 11 February and *G-ADUZ Cygnus* on 2 March. Then *Canopus*, which had returned for a refit on 30 January after a strenuous two months of scheduled flying by Capt Bailey between Brindisi and Alexandria, was redelivered from Rochester on 12 March. Regular service flights from Marseilles to Alexandria via Rome, Brindisi and Athens had begun on 4 January with *Castor*, flown by Capts G. J. Powell and A. G. Store, and on the 12th *Centaurus* began the service from Alexandria through to Southampton, with a night-stop at Brindisi, flown by Capt L. A. Egglesfield; he made the first outbound flight on the same schedule on the 16th and 17th, being followed by Capt Powell on *Cassiopeia* on the 26th to connect with the African mail at Alexandria. *Castor*, with Capt Alger in command, went into service between Southampton and Alexandria on 8 February, and ten days later *Caledonia* flew the whole distance of 2,222 miles non-stop in just over 13 hours; finally, on 5 March Imperial Airways' new flying-boat base at Hythe was formally opened, and from that date no more Empire services were flown by landplanes from Croydon, whence only European routes were served up to the outbreak of war in 1939.

At Rochester the tempo of production quickened as Bibby's new recruits found their feet on high scaffolds, hardened their knuckles and got their eyes in at the split-second trick of closing a flush rivet in a dimpled hole with a single hammer-blow. Newly finished hulls and wings jostled for floor space in No. 3 Shop with the last eight Singapores, which in turn were succeeded by the Mayo Composite and prototype Sunderland. By the end of 1937 a total of 22 Empire Boats had been delivered to Imperial Airways, and two more, *VH-ABA Carpentaria* and *VH-ABB Coolangatta* were ready for collection by Qantas, to whom also the next Imperial Airways delivery S.849 *G-AEUG* had been transferred as *VH-ABC Coogee*, which made its first flight of 40 minutes on New Year's Eve, to round off the busiest twelve months in the Seaplane Works' history. But for Imperial Airways 1937 had brought losses among its new fleet. The first casualty was *G-ADVA Capricornus*, which with only ten hours in its log and carrying the first through air mail for Australia, crashed on 24 March near Lyons, Capt Paterson having lost his bearings and turned back in a snow-storm over the French Alps. Next was *G-ADVC Courtier* in Phaleron Bay on 1 October when Capt Poole misjudged his height on final approach, flew into a glassy sea and burst open the hull, three passengers (including Wing Commander W. R. D. Acland, a pioneer of R.N.A.S. deck-flying) being drowned. Only two months later

319

G-ADUZ Cygnus was lost at Brindisi on 5 December when the captain attempted to take-off with flaps fully down and the aircraft porpoised out of control and sank, two passengers being drowned, and seven, including Air Marshal Sir John Salmond (a director of Imperial Airways), injured.

In the official enquiries into these last two accidents Imperial Airways were censured for having specified inadequate means of escape from the cabins, and all Empire Boats were forthwith given larger roof emergency exit hatches and additional push-out windows; but the direct cause of the Brindisi accident remained something of a mystery, since *Cygnus* was not fully loaded and should have been controllable even with flaps fully extended. In the last S.23 Empire

Cooee, the last S.23 built, in which John Parker demonstrated the danger of take-off from glassy water with flaps fully extended; here it is seen in service with Q.E.A. (*Qantas photo.*)

Boat, still undelivered, S.878 *G-AFBL* (later *VH-ABF Cooee*), Parker demonstrated at Rochester, with three Shorts' people aboard, that a take-off could be quite safely carried through under these conditions, and in fact he did it twice on the same day; he was then asked to repeat the test with representatives of the Air Ministry, Imperial Airways and the insurers as passengers. This time the Medway was dead calm and porpoising developed 'frighteningly fast', but, though nearly thrown out of his seat, Parker retained control and brought the boat safely to rest; he then realised that the first day's tests had been made on choppy water and quite cheerfully agreed to repeat the experiment while the river was still glassy, although the danger was fully realised, and some of the official observers flatly refused to sign 'blood-chits'; on the second run the same porpoising developed, and Parker again barely kept control, thus proving that the combination of flaps fully down and glassy water was potentially lethal at take-off, even at reduced weight. There were other minor mishaps, as when *Corsair* was rammed by a launch at Hythe and *Castor* broke away from moorings and collided with a yacht, but the crews always made herculean efforts to regain lost time; on 23 June, when one of *Canopus*'s engines faded out and forced the boat to come down in the Mediterranean, the crew taxied to Mirabella, removed the faulty engine, blanked off the open front of the nacelle and flew back to Hythe on three engines; *Canopus* lived on to complete 15,026 hours before being retired in 1946. In October 1937 *G-AEUA Calypso* began the regular service from Alexandria to Karachi

Canopus at the barge-yard in July 1937 after flying home from Mirabella with one engine removed and its nacelle blanked off.

via Habbaniyah and Sharjah, which had been surveyed a month earlier, via the Dead Sea, by *G-AETX Ceres*; the mail had been flown from Southampton to Alexandria by *G-AETY Clio,* and the return service from Karachi to Southampton was flown throughout by *G-AEUB Camilla* between 7 and 10 October. On 15 November *G-AEUD Cordelia* left Karachi to survey the route to Singapore, arriving on the 21st; Capt J. W. Burgess in *Centaurus* then left Hythe on 3 December for the first civil flying-boat survey of the whole route to Australia and New Zealand, flying from Sydney to Auckland on 27 December. But these flights were insignificant compared with the transatlantic survey flights of *Caledonia* and *Cambria* during the summer of 1937.

Following *Caledonia*'s long-range flights to and from Alexandria, *Cambria* in May flew up the Nile to Khartoum at the beginning of a 20,000-mile survey of African routes by Capt Egglesfield ending on 4 June, the air mail service to Durban having meanwhile been initiated by *Capella* and *Courtier*. *Caledonia* and *Cambria* were then flown to Foynes at the mouth of the Shannon for proving flights to and from New York, via Botwood and Montreal, in co-operation with the Sikorsky S-42 Clippers of Pan American Airways. On 5 July *Caledonia*, commanded by Capt Wilcockson, left Foynes at 1800 hr GMT, three hours before the departure of *Clipper III* from Botwood, both arriving at their destinations without incident. Next day *Cambria* flew from Hythe to Lisbon to survey the first leg of the southerly route via the Azores, returning for further flights to Botwood on 29 July and 27 August, with corresponding returns on 8 August and 27 September; this last flight was the fastest of the series, in 10 hours 36 minutes. *Caledonia* had returned on 15–16 July in $12\frac{1}{4}$ hours, and on 15 August flew from Foynes to Botwood to

Cambria in its original long-range condition, after arrival at Botwood from Foynes in July 1937. (*Courtesy A. J. Jackson.*)

321

check radio performance in daylight, returning overnight on 20th–21st; *Caledonia* crossed to Botwood again on 13 September and back on the 23rd. After the completion of these five round trips between Foynes and Botwood, *Caledonia* moved to the Lisbon–Azores route, ice at Botwood having put an end to the northern survey programme for the winter. At the other end of the southerly route the demand for a New York–Bermuda service had long been heard, and under pressure from Juan Trippe, president of Pan American, Imperial Airways recalled *Cavalier* from the Mediterranean; its tankage was doubled at Rochester, and it was then dismantled and shipped in 21 crates (the one containing the hull being 90 ft long) to Bermuda as deck cargo on S.S. *Loch Katrine*. Arriving on 30 December, 1936, the largest crate was off-loaded by the only available heavy crane, at Somerset, lowered into the dock and knocked down, leaving the hull afloat so that it could be towed five miles to the flying-boat base at Darrell's Island for reassembly. *Cavalier* was test-flown on 19 February, 1937, and began proving flights to New York on 21 May, concurrently with the Pan American *Bermuda Clipper*. Scheduled ser-vices began on 16 June, and 405 passengers had been carried at a single fare of £20 for the 6-hour trip by the end of November, when the American terminal was temporarily changed to Baltimore to avoid ice. *Cavalier* main-tained the service alone throughout 1938, but on 21 January, 1939, on its 290th scheduled flight, was forced down while outward bound from Port Washington, L.I., commanded by Capt M. J. R. Alderson, who found it impossible to avoid icing-up of the two inner engines. Unable to restart them after descending to a lower altitude, he made a comparatively good landing in the heavy swell, but the impact tore a hole in the hull, and the boat sank in a few minutes. After ten hours in the water the ten survivors were rescued by the tanker *Esso Baytown*, three others, including the Belfast-born junior steward Robert Spence, having died earlier. *Cavalier* had not originally been intended for the Bermuda service, and in 1939 could not be replaced in the changed circumstances arising from the Munich crisis. The first half of 1938 had seen the delivery of the final six S.23 Empire Boats to Qantas, and the only casualty that year was *G-AETW Calpurnia*, which crashed in Lake Habbani-yah at night during a sandstorm on 27 November, Capt Attwood, F/O Spottis-wood and two passengers being killed and the other two crew members injured; the R.A.F. did gallant rescue work and salvaged the Christmas mail comprising most of the payload.

The Empire Boat designated for the Bermuda run was the first of an im-proved model, design index No. S.30, powered by Bristol Perseus XIIC sleeve-valve engines and strengthened to permit a gross weight of 46,000 lb for take-off, with tankage for 1,500 miles as finally installed in *Cavalier*. This boat, S.879 *G-AFCT Champion*, was first flown by Parker at Rochester on 28 September, 1938, trials continuing till the end of October, when its type C. of A. was granted; from 17 to 21 October it was flown with wooden air-screws, but these were replaced by standard D.H. metal ones on the 26th. It was then caught up in the Christmas air mail rush and had still not been released from the eastern routes when *Cavalier* was lost; then a 400-hour

Cabot taking off at Rochester on 27 November, 1938.

flight development programme to improve the de-icing of Perseus engines kept *Champion* at Hythe until the imminence of war and availability of new Boeing 314s for Pan American caused Imperial Airways to withdraw entirely from the Bermuda route; *Champion* was re-engined with Pegasus early in the war. The next four S.30s, S.880–883 *G-AFCU* to '*X*, named *Cabot*, *Caribou*, *Connemara* and *Clyde*, had 2,500 gallons tankage with flight-refuelling gear and were cleared for a refuelled gross weight of 53,000 lb, after take-off at 46,000 lb. *Cabot* was first flown by Parker at Rochester on 27 November, 1938, followed by *Caribou* on 6 December and *Clyde* on 24 January, 1939, this last having D.H. constant-speed airscrews. Piper was the first to fly *G-AFCW Connemara*, in December, and in March it went to Hythe to be flown upwards of 12 hours a day by Capts Kelly Rogers and Bennett in order to complete 400 hours before entering regular transatlantic passenger service; but on 19 June it was burned out when fire broke out on the refuelling barge alongside.

The last three S.30s of the main batch, S.884–886 *G-AFCY* to '*DA*, originally ordered by Qantas as *Captain Cook*, *Canterbury* and *Cumberland* for the Sydney–Auckland route, were transferred to Tasman Empire Airways Ltd, jointly formed by the United Kingdom, Australian and New Zealand Governments to extend the Empire Air Mail Service to New Zealand. The standard S.30 tankage of 1,500 gallons was adequate for the 1,348 miles between Sydney and Auckland, so flight refuelling was not required, but the take-off weight was raised to 48,000 lb after satisfactory trials of *Cabot*'s jettison system at Felixstowe in March, the maximum landing weight remaining at 46,000 lb. First to be flown, on 4 April, was *G-AFCZ Australia* (fitted with a Smiths auto-pilot), followed by *G-AFCY Aotearoa* on the 18th and *G-AFDA Awarua* on 9 May; the latter two registrations were changed to *ZK-AMA* and *ZK-AMC* respectively in 1940 before delivery to New Zealand. In 1939 negotiations with the Australian and New Zealand Governments had still not been completed, so Imperial Airways retained the three TEAL S.30s to assist *Champion* and *Clyde* on the rescheduled Southampton–Karachi service which began on 3 July, the intention being to work them through to Sydney by September and inaugurate the Tasman Sea route on 1 October;

323

Australia at Hythe before leaving on its ill-fated first service to Karachi on 6 July, 1939. *(B.O.A.C.)*

meanwhile a ninth S.30, S.1003, had been ordered as a replacement for *Connemara*, and this was eventually launched and flown at Rochester as *G-AFKZ Cathay* on 21 February, 1940, and delivered to Hythe early in March. *Australia* left Hythe on its first trip to Karachi on 6 July, 1939, but ran aground on a mud-bank while taking off from Basra on 9 August and had to be stripped for major repairs on site, before being returned to Hythe for modification to the same standard as *Clyde*; it re-entered service with Imperial Airways in October 1939, renamed *Clare*.

Meanwhile plans for a flight-refuelled passenger service between Foynes and Botwood had gone ahead. The first experiments in flight refuelling had been made in 1923 in America by the U.S. Army Air Corps and were taken up by aspirants to endurance records, such as Jackson and O'Brine, who stayed up in a Curtiss Robin light monoplane for over 420 hours between 6 and 24 July, 1929, over St Louis, Mo. In Britain, a method was developed by the R.A.F. and patents were granted to Flt Lieut R. L. R. Atcherley in 1935; concurrently Sir Alan Cobham had made early experiments with D.H.9 and Handley Page W.10 biplanes in 1932–3, and on 24 September, 1934, he and Sqn Ldr Helmore took off from Portsmouth in an Airspeed Courier, which then took on 275 gallons into overload cabin tanks before attempting to fly non-stop to India, with further refuelling from R.A.F. aircraft *en route*; this flight ended with a forced landing at Malta after the throttle control broke, but would almost certainly have been successful. Imperial Airways and the Air Ministry encouraged further experiments by Sir Alan's company, Flight Refuelling Ltd, to whom Atcherley's patents were assigned, and in the following year the airline's directors witnessed a demonstration by two Virginias of the R.A.F. In 1937 faster tankers, in the shape of the prototype A.W.23 and H.P.51 transports, were made available, and on 20 January, 1938, the A.W.23 refuelled *Cambria* for the first time in a series of all-weather trials, during which successful contacts and transfers were made in storm, rain, low cloud and even fog. In the spring of 1939 three Handley Page Harrow bombers were equipped as tankers carrying 900 gallons of fuel as transferable cargo; two (*G-AFRG* and *'H*) were shipped in April to Hattie's Camp, Newfoundland (later known as Gander), and the third, *G-AFRL*, went to Rineanna (now

Shannon Airport) to be flown by G. A. V. Tyson, after preliminary training flights over Hamble, where *Cabot*, flown by Parker, was successfully refuelled on 24 May and *Caribou* on 3 July; on the 12th *Caribou* was cleared for take-off at 50,500 lb and landing at 48,000 lb, and on 5 August Capt Kelly Rogers began the first weekly scheduled transatlantic service from Southampton, calling at Foynes and being refuelled after take-off *en route* for Botwood, Montreal and New York. A total of eight crossings were made each way until the service ended with *Cabot*'s eastbound flight on 30 September; refuelling was accomplished without a hitch on 15 occasions and was not needed on the remaining flight, because Kelly Rogers had a westerly tailwind of gale force, which brought *Cabot* across to Foynes in under ten hours with enough fuel left to reach Southampton. The actual refuelling process took only eight minutes to pass 800 gallons after three to seven minutes spent in making contact and linking hoses. *Cabot*'s westbound flight on 23–24 September was made from Foynes to Botwood in the record time of 13 hours.

In 1939 Imperial Airways had only one fatal accident with an Empire Boat, when *Challenger* crashed in Mozambique harbour on 1 May as a result of the captain's grave error of judgment, but lost two other boats without loss of life; on 12 March *Capella* was wrecked at Batavia and three months later *Centurion* was capsized by a violent gust while landing on the Hooghly at Calcutta; this was always a restricted fairway for both landing and take-off, and on one occasion Capt D. C. T. Bennett flew *under* the Willingdon Bridge after unsticking too near to climb over it. On 12 December, 1938, one of Qantas's six Empire Boats, *VH-ABE Coorong*, had been driven ashore by a gale at Darwin, and only the engines and Christmas mails could be salvaged at the time, although the whole boat was later retrieved and repaired, being exchanged for *Centaurus* in September 1939 and reverting to U.K. registration as *G-AEUI*; at the same time *Corio* was exchanged for *Calypso* and became *G-AEUH* again; this exchange was made to enable the R.A.A.F. to impress *Centaurus* and *Calypso* as *A18-10* and *A18-11* on the outbreak of war.

In 1938 *Ceres* had caused many headaches by running aground and getting inaccessibly bogged at Lake Dingari in India, but this was nothing to the problem presented on 14 March, 1939, when *Corsair*, driven off course by adverse weather, ran short of fuel and made a forced landing on the River Dangu in the Belgian Congo, 150 miles south-west of Juba; nobody was hurt and the mail was retrieved, but the hull was stove-in and the boat sank in shallow water. A repair party composed of both Short Brothers and Imperial Airways engineers was flown to Juba and got as near as they could by road, to Faraje, but the last few miles had to be covered on foot. With the help of many local tribesmen the boat was successfully beached and repaired; Brackley visited the site on 22 May and wrote: 'Shorts' men are doing magnificent repair work under trying conditions of heat, humidity, flies, mosquitos and hornets. I've had my full share of bites from a small black beetle-shaped fly with a sting like a hornet. I've never met this type before and I don't want to again!' By the end of June the boat was complete and the rainy season was at its height, with the river in spate; Capt Kelly Rogers decided to risk a take-off although there was a dangerous bend halfway along the narrow fairway, from both sides of which trees and undergrowth had been cleared. With the tail mooring rope lashed to a stout stake, Kelly Rogers opened the throttles fully before pulling the release, but having to swerve at the bend prevented the boat from unsticking in a safe distance, so he abandoned the take-off and began to taxi back for another try, but then *Corsair* was holed for the second time, on a submerged rock; this time the engines had to be taken out to lighten the boat, which was raised by lashing petrol drums together, half filling them with water, tying them under the hull and then pumping the water out. Jock Halliday of Imperial Airways, in charge of the operation, realised that the dry season would arrive before the second repair job was finished and decided to dam the river so as to make a big enough lake for take-off; many more tribesmen were recruited to fell and haul timber, build a village for all the workers and make a road for transport of spares flown into Juba from Alexandria. Eventually repairs were complete and the engines and instruments reinstalled, but not until the rains began again could the boat be launched on a waterway that would still be only 50 yards wide—12 yards more than *Corsair*'s own wing span. This time, with all-up weight reduced to 20,000 lb, Kelly Rogers managed to take off soon after dawn on 6 January, 1940, and refuelled at Juba before flying to Alexandria for a complete overhaul; this episode, lasting ten months, left as its memorial the new village of Corsairville, with its adjoining lake and road.

Three more Empire Boats were ordered in 1938 to make good Imperial Airways' earlier losses and were of another variant, S.33; these had strengthened hulls, but were at first limited for take-off at 40,500 lb while fitted with Pegasus XI engines; in later service they were up-rated to 53,000 lb after Pegasus XXIIs had been installed; the first two, S.1025 and S.1026, were launched at the end of April 1940 as *G-AFPZ Clifton* and *G-AFRA Cleopatra*, but work on the third, S.1027 *G-AFRB*, was stopped in May on the instructions of Lord Beaverbrook soon after his appointment as the first Minister of Aircraft Production.

Only a month before war began, the British Overseas Airways Corporation Bill had received the Royal Assent, its purpose being to combine and expand the resources and operations of both Imperial Airways and its independent rival British Airways, so as to qualify for Treasury subsidies in much the same way as had been arranged at the formation of Imperial Airways itself in 1924. The official commencing date for the new Corporation was 1 April, 1940, but the war emergency brought forward the actual operational merger very quickly; many European landplane services ceased perforce, but *Cabot* and *Caribou* completed their transatlantic refuelling schedule according to plan, before being requisitioned by the R.A.F.; Pan American Airways continued the New York–Foynes service with their newly acquired Boeing 314 Clippers, and a Poole–Foynes link was maintained, together with twice-weekly services to Sydney and later, via Malta, to Egypt and India, and once-weekly services to Kisumu and Durban; all these were flown by the Empire Boats, including *Aotearoa* and *Awarua*, which were finally worked out to Sydney in March

1940; the former commenced the weekly service to Auckland on 30 April, commanded by Capt J. W. Burgess. Early in August, after Pan American had opened the Auckland–San Francisco route, the Tasman frequency was increased to three return flights a fortnight, and this schedule was maintained unbroken by *Aotearoa* and *Awarua* alone until July 1946.

In October 1939, after completing their transatlantic flights, *Cabot* and *Caribou* were impressed for R.A.F. use together with their crews, being assigned to the Special Duty Flight at Invergordon for trials with A.S.V. radar; they were allotted serials *V3137* and *V3138*. While their crews were being trained in their new duties, the two boats were fitted with makeshift defensive armament consisting only of seven free K-guns, the formidable-looking 'machine-guns' sticking out of the tail cone being in fact dummies made from broomsticks. The radar gear was experimental and unreliable, but during the next five months they amassed between them about 400 flying hours on long-range patrols off the north of Scotland, and once *Caribou* detected an enemy ship and reported its presence to the Navy.

In April 1940, when Germany invaded Denmark and Norway, *Cabot* and *Caribou* were stripped of their radar and urgently converted at Hythe into transports for special missions to Norway, taking ground radar and specialist personnel to Harstad, the main base for Allied operations against the Germans at Narvik. On 4 May they arrived at Harstad and flew next day to Bodø, where they were to unload their stores and remain for ten days to assist the R.A.F. in searching for suitable airfield sites. Almost as soon as they moored they were seen by four Heinkel 115s, which passed over but returned to attack them an hour later. Capt Gordon Store got *Cabot*'s engines started and was taxying out of the harbour when a Heinkel attacked eight times, putting the starboard outer engine out of action and making several holes in the hull, so he ran the boat aground in soft mud. Meanwhile *Caribou*'s engines had been reluctant to start, its fuel tanks had been ripped open by bullets and four of Capt Long's crew had been wounded. As soon as the Heinkels flew away the two crews waded ashore and got their wounded into hospital, then came back and salvaged armament and equipment from both boats as the tide went out. Soon afterwards *Caribou* was bombed and burnt out, but both crews, with the help of two motor-boats from the town, managed to tow *Cabot* several miles to shelter under steep cliffs, where it was invisible except from directly above; but on 6 May their hiding-place was detected, and a Dornier flying-boat went straight to *Cabot* and set it on fire with incendiaries. The crews were brought safely home, including the wounded, who had had to stay in Bodø hospital for three weeks.

To replace *Cabot* and *Caribou*, two earlier Empire Boats, *Clio* and *Cordelia*, were impressed in July 1940 as *AX659–660* and flown to Belfast to be modified for coastal reconnaissance under the designation S.23/M. In addition to A.S.V. radar, each was equipped with armour plates at vital points around the flight-deck and inner fuel tanks, together with two Boulton-Paul A-type four-gun turrets, one amidships and offset to starboard, the other in a new tail fairing built into the stern, the rudder being cropped at its lower end to match;

Clio coming ashore at Queen's Island in September 1940, before the slipway was built.

Clio being relaunched as *AX659* on 12 March, 1941, the first flying-boat to use the Queen's Island slipway.

Clio taxying in Belfast Lough before dispatch to the R.A.F. in April 1941.

they also had provision for carrying internally six 430-lb depth charges, to be released through sliding hatches on both sides of the hull; these modifications were completed between September 1940 and March 1941 by Short & Harland Ltd at Queen's Island, *Clio* being relaunched on 12 March and *Cordelia* on 16 April. Both were at first attached to No. 119 Squadron and patrolled between Islay and Iceland; they also carried stores to R.A.F. units there and in the Shetlands, Orkneys and Hebrides; but their Service lives were short, for *Clio* crashed into high ground during an attempt to land on Loch Indaal after an engine failure on 22 August, 1941, and *Cordelia* was returned to B.O.A.C. after six weeks' service at Stranraer attached to No. 413 Squadron, R.C.A.F., in December 1941.

All the Empire Boats operating from the wartime base at Poole, including *Caledonia* and *Cambria*, were converted to 'austerity' furnishing for 29 passengers and maximum cargo capacity; as their Pegasus XC engines became time-expired, they were replaced by more powerful Pegasus XXIIs, which were readily available, since they were in production for the Sunderland; with these engines the normal take-off weight was raised to 52,500 lb. The

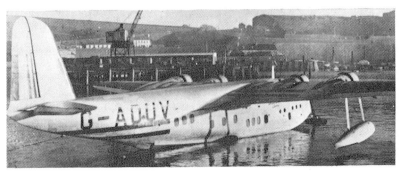

Cambria converted to austerity standard for 29 passengers, in service on the Horseshoe Route in 1940.
(Courtesy A. J. Jackson.)

entry of Italy into the war on 10 June, 1940, had been foreseen, and the closing of the Mediterranean ports found *Clyde* at Malta and *Cathay* at Ajaccio, both homeward-bound, while *Caledonia* was at Corfu *en route* for Alexandria via Athens and Navarino. *Clyde* had on board Sir Robert Brooke-Popham and his staff, whose return to England was most urgent, but had also lost power on one engine; Capt Kelly Rogers nevertheless risked a daring take-off run from the stormy open sea into the calmer water of Kalafrana Bay and cleared the shore by 200 ft. On arrival at Alexandria, *Caledonia* went straight into service on the Horseshoe Route, already planned with its maintenance base at Durban to link the African and Eastern routes via Cairo. There were 16 other Empire Boats south and east of Cairo on 11 June, and a weekly service was started from both Durban and Sydney on the 19th.

By contrast, the collapse of France had not been expected, and a trans-Sahara landplane route had been planned to link England with Cairo; when this was cut on 28 June *Cathay* and *Champion* came to the rescue with a twice-

329

weekly long-range service between Poole and Lisbon. A week earlier Capt D. C. T. Bennett had flown *Cathay* to Biscarosse with General Sikorski to contact Polish Army units still in France; all that day and night the flying-boat lay hidden on a sandy beach, ready for a quick escape, and at dawn took off with the General and his daughter, together with Polish staff officers; Bennett flew through the thick smoke from burning oil tanks to avoid enemy fighters and got his party back to Poole without trouble.

On 5 August Capt A. C. Loraine was preparing to take *Clyde* from Poole to Foynes in readiness to share a flight-refuelled transatlantic service for priority passengers and propaganda purposes, already started two days earlier by *Clare*; at a moment's notice he was told to fly to Lagos instead of New York, with eight of General de Gaulle's Free French staff officers headed by Col de Larminet. *Clyde* reached Lisbon next day, and since no flight-refuelling was available there, Loraine risked taking off at 53,000 lb after dark, almost hitting a small ship in the fairway; a fatal collision was averted by violent evasive action by the co-pilot (Capt May), and part of the port aileron was torn off by the ship's mast; on arrival at Bathurst, after flying all night and next morning, the crew managed to find a piece of duralumin sheet left behind by Deutsche Lufthansa and the aileron was patched up. Next day Loraine flew *Clyde* on to Freetown, narrowly avoided being run down after mooring by the massive refuelling barge and was finally ducked when the launch in which he had embarked to supervise refuelling was rammed and sunk by another launch! On the 9th *Clyde* arrived at Lagos, only to be sent up the Congo to Leopoldville on the 19th because of the French political situation; by this time *Clyde*, used as a conference room, was overdue for overhaul, but in spite of various minor mechanical failures, Loraine flew it home from Leopoldville in seven days, being by that time very ill himself with malaria.

Clyde's daring mission to Leopoldville won over Col Carretier at Brazzaville to the Free French cause and was followed a month later by a survey flight up the Congo to Stanleyville and Lake Victoria to join the Horseshoe Route. This was undertaken by Capt Harrington in *Corinthian*, Capt Davys in *Cassiopeia* and Capt Bailey in *Cooee*, all arriving safely at Durban to reinforce the fleet and allow the Horseshoe schedule to be doubled. Meanwhile Capt Kelly Rogers had maintained the Foynes–Botwood schedule single-handed with *Clare* from 3 August till 23 September, making four round trips; *Clyde* arrived at Foynes in time to make one trip on 4 October, returning on the 11th as the ice began to close over Botwood harbour. From mid-October 1940 to February 1941 *Clyde* flew the Poole–Lisbon–Lagos route, but on 15 February was sunk at moorings in the Tagus by a devastating hurricane; it was salvaged later, but was beyond repair.

Clyde's hairsbreadth take-off from Malta on 11 June, 1940, was not the end of B.O.A.C.'s operations to the island, and a regular service from Alexandria was maintained by Empire Boats arriving and taking off under cover of darkness. After Germany invaded Greece, *Coorong* and *Cambria*, on arrival at Cairo, were diverted to Alexandria, camouflaged to look like Sunderlands and flown to Suda Bay to pick up Allied troops evacuated from Greece. Between

22 April and 5 May, 1941, they made 13 round trips and brought out 469 troops, averaging 36 passengers per flight with a maximum of 47, the procedure being to stop emplaning only when the freeboard at the forward door-sill disappeared. In July Empire Boats began operating between Lagos and Cairo via Libreville, Pointe Noire, Leopoldville, Cocquilhatville, Stanleyville and Port Bell, after the Lisbon–Lagos route had been reinforced by B.O.A.C.'s Boeing 314s working south from Foynes; on 12 October a weekly service from Lisbon to Cairo via Gibraltar and Malta was begun by *Clare* and continued by *Champion* and *Cathay*; it was interrupted in February 1942 during the German retreat from Libya and resumed by the landplanes of the Tedder Plan.

On 8 December, 1941, Japan entered the war and threatened the Horseshoe Route itself; on the 22nd, *Cassiopeia*, with a cargo of ammunition for Singapore, surveyed a reserve route via the Andaman Islands, but on the return flight on the 29th was wrecked on take-off from Sabang, Sumatra, four passengers being drowned in spite of heroic rescue attempts by F/O Blunt. By then, Penang was already occupied by the Japanese, and the bombardment of Singapore began a week later; so the Horseshoe Route was cut and B.O.A.C. had to stop at Rangoon, while a Qantas shuttle service was maintained, at great peril, from Batavia into Singapore, the last flight out with 40 passengers being made by Capt Crowther on 3 February, 1942. Ten days later the rapid Japanese advance forced the B.O.A.C. terminal back to Calcutta, while Qantas abandoned the Sourabaya–Darwin sector after Capt Koch in *Corio* had been shot down on 30 January near Koepang by seven Zero fighters. Most of his passengers were killed by the first bursts of fire, and he himself was wounded; in spite of evasive action just above wave level, he was forced down five miles from land with two engines on fire; he and five others were thrown clear, and all managed to swim ashore after several hours in the sea.

Thereafter *Circe*, *Coriolanus* and *Corinthian* operated a shuttle service from Broome to Tjilatjap in Java, but *Circe* was shot down on an inbound flight on 28 February, and Broome itself was heavily bombed on 3 March, *Corinna* and *A18-10* (alias *Centaurus*) being destroyed along with a dozen other flying-boats of various types; *Coogee*, impressed in July 1940 as *A18-12*, crashed at Townsville on 28 February and *Corinthian* at Darwin a few days later; *Coolangatta*, impressed as *A18-13*, survived to be returned to Qantas on 13 July, 1943, but *A18-11* (ex *Calypso*) was destroyed at Daru, New Guinea, on 8 August, 1942. During the year *Coriolanus*, *Camilla* and *Clifton*, marooned in Australia by the Japanese invasion, were transferred to Qantas by B.O.A.C. in exchange for *Carpentaria*, *Coorong* and *Cooee*, which were in India when the route was cut. In December the first two began a daily service from Townsville via Cairns to Port Moresby and later Milne Bay, achieving an annual utilisation of 4,900 hours each and making 564 flights in the first year, in which some 12,750 passengers were carried; *Camilla* had barely escaped destruction in the bombardment of Darwin on 19 February, 1942, and was doomed to be lost off Port Moresby on 22 April, 1943; again Capt Koch, recovered at length from his escape from *Corio*, was in command, but this time the enemy was not Japanese fighters but a tropical storm. After seven hours of attempting to penetrate the weather blanket, he decided finally to land blind off Port Moresby, but *Camilla* stalled and sank, 18 survivors, including Capt Koch, being rescued after 20 hours in the sea. *Coolangatta*, later released by the R.A.A.F. to replace *Camilla*, itself crashed on 11 October, 1944, in Sydney Harbour, where *Clifton* had suffered the same fate nine months earlier on 18 January, but *Coriolanus* survived the war, having transported more than 10,000 troops and evacuated many hundreds of casualties, to become the first Qantas aircraft to re-enter liberated Singapore on 8 October, 1945, returning to Sydney on the 17th with 34 released prisoners of war; thereafter *Coriolanus* inaugurated the Fiji–Sydney service, via Noumea and Brisbane, on 19 November, 1945, and maintained it till December 1947.

At their end of the broken Horseshoe, B.O.A.C.'s Empire Boats had also suffered losses; *Clare* failed to reach Bathurst after leaving Lagos on 14 September, 1942, and *Ceres* was destroyed by an explosion at moorings at Durban on 1 December the same year. Empire Boats were being supplemented by longer-range demilitarised Sunderlands, but were still chosen to pioneer new routes; in April 1942 *Cooee* had made use of Kallia on the Dead Sea (nearly 1,300 ft *below* sea-level), which thereafter became a regular port of call; later in the year *Champion* surveyed the route from Kisumu to Madagascar, via Dar-es-Salaam and Lindi, on which a regular weekly service began on 25 January, 1943. For the remainder of the war the Empire Boats served unfailingly on the Durban–Calcutta sectors and resumed through-working to Sydney as soon as the Japanese surrendered Burma and Malaya; when the Horseshoe Route finally closed in 1947 *Castor* flew the last service from India, arriving at Cairo on 15 January, and *Caledonia* was the last Empire Boat in Africa and in B.O.A.C.'s fleet when it left Durban for Southampton on 12 March.

Of the 13 B.O.A.C. survivors, *Canopus* the first-built with over two million miles logged in 15,026 hours, and *Cleopatra* the last-built with 10,513 hours, led the melancholy procession to the breaker's yard in November 1946; the

Cleopatra, the second S.33 and last Empire Boat to be built, arriving at Durban on the Horseshoe Route in 1944. (*I.W.M.—Crown Copyright.*)

332

others—*Caledonia* (15,143), *Cambria* (13,892), *Castor* (15,789), *Corsair* (13,262), *Cordelia* (11,665), *Cameronian* (15,652), *Coorong* (12,472), *Carpentaria* (14,989), *Cooee* (14,307), *Champion* (12,013) and *Cathay* (6,683)—all followed during 1947; only *Coriolanus* of the original Imperial Airways fleet saw longer service with Qantas, and was in fact the last Empire Boat still flying when it flew in from Noumea to Rose Bay on 20 December, 1947, with a total of 2,523,641 miles in some 18,500 hours to its credit. Tasman's *Awarua* had been withdrawn in June 1947 after 8,740 hours flown mainly between Sydney and Auckland, and *Aotearoa* had retired on 29 October, 1947, after its 442nd crossing of the Tasman Sea, having logged 1,230,000 miles in 8,500 hours, to become the only one of its class to be preserved, at least for a time, at Meçhanic's Bay, Auckland, where it was earning its humble keep as a coffee-bar in 1957.

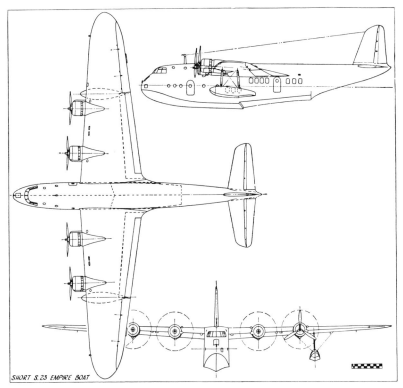

SHORT S.23 EMPIRE BOAT

Span 114 ft (34·7 m); length 88 ft (26·8 m); area 1,500 sq ft (139·5 m²); empty weight (S.23) 23,500 lb (10,670 kg), (S.30 & S.33) 27,180 lb (12,320 kg); all-up weight (S.23) 40,500 lb (18,380 kg), later 52,500 lb (23,810 kg); (S.30) 48,000 lb (21,780 kg), later 53,000 lb (24,200 kg); (S.33) 40,500 lb (18,380 kg), later 53,000 lb (24,200 kg); max speed 200 mph (322 km/h); ceiling 20,000 ft (6,100 m); ranges—S.23/33: 760 miles (1,245 km); S.30: 1,300 miles (2,090 km); *Cavalier*: 1,500 miles (2,415 km); *Cabot/Caribou*: 2,500 miles (4,030 km); *Caledonia/Cambria*: 3,300 miles (5,300 km).

333

Golden Hind on the Medway after being launched on 17 June, 1939.

The Short Golden Hind

By the beginning of 1936 the Short Sarafand had been thoroughly investi-gated by M.A.E.E. during its active four years' career spent entirely on experimental work at Felixstowe. It had, indeed, done all that Oswald Short claimed for it, and had shown that the limit of structural design of large flying-boats had not yet been reached, but it seemed to the Air Ministry's scientists that a limit to size would be imposed, not by structural considera-tions, but by ability to take off. The M.A.E.E. criterion of suitability for service operation was a time-limit of 60 seconds for take-off in still air from smooth water; the Sarafand could just achieve this at a gross weight of 72,000 lb, corresponding to a wing-loading of 21 lb/sq ft, many earlier proto-types having failed to unstick at all when loaded to their permitted structural design weights. The Short Empire Boat's proposed normal wing-loading of 27 lb/sq ft was therefore viewed with considerable scepticism and doubts were expressed on the ability of the generally similar R.2/33 prototype to meet its specified performance without some form of take-off assistance. Proposals had already been made for a small fleet of naval auxiliary refuelling barges or tankers with strengthened hulls to mount catapults capable of launching air-craft of 80,000 lb or more; a flying-boat of this size would have obvious applications for long-range maritime reconnaissance and as a trans-oceanic mail-carrier; if the cost of providing enough catapult vessels could be justified on strategic grounds some of these could be made available for civil operations in peacetime; both weight and drag could be reduced in a catapult-launched flying-boat, whose planing bottom could be simplified by dispensing with steps and hard chines to cater only for alighting and taxying, with the ability in reserve to take off from sheltered water at light weight. In due course, Short Brothers were invited to tender to specification 35/36 for a catapulted flying-boat. Meanwhile Imperial Airways, aware of American progress with large flying-boats, particularly Boeing's Type 314, requested a design study for a straightforward enlargement of the Empire Boat, to carry mails or passengers across the Atlantic without refuelling between Ireland and Newfoundland.

Short Brothers began work on both designs concurrently, the enlarged

334

Empire Boat being indexed as S.26 and the Catapult Boat as S.27, both being powered by four Bristol Hercules engines of 1,400 hp each. Confidence in the basic Empire Boat concept was fully justified by the first few flights of *Canopus*, and when *Caledonia* went to Felixstowe for C. of A. tests on 15 September, 1936, the M.A.E.E. pundits were considerably astonished to find that it could take off at 45,000 lb (30 lb/sq ft) in little more than 30 seconds 'easily and gracefully' as E. T. Jones put it in a report in which he estimated that it would also be able to take off in 60 seconds at an overload of 54,000 lb (36 lb/sq ft). He attributed this unexpected take-off efficiency to the combination of high slipstream lift at hump speed, clean hydrodynamic design with low spray interference, smooth hull finish without highly flared chines and the effect of the Gouge flap in reducing take-off speed, time and distance. He noted that at the achieved top speed of nearly 200 mph there was a strong case for reducing parasitic air drag caused by wing-tip floats, steps and hard chines, and urged a research programme to determine the magnitude of the separate drag contributions of these features, whose cumulative effect was to add some 40 per cent to the drag of a basic streamline body; he concluded: 'The ability of the heavily loaded seaplane to take off unassisted is assured, and there are strong indications that its top speed and range can be made comparable with the landplane, though for a given wing loading the seaplane will always have a slightly lower top speed. By virtue of several small practical advantages that the seaplane has at high wing loadings, it is probable that this loss of speed will be turned into a gain by operating seaplanes at much higher wing loadings than landplanes.' These findings were endorsed by Harry M. Garner, Chief Technical Officer at Felixstowe, who suggested not only retracting the wing-tip floats but (*a*) hinging the main step so that it could be retracted after take-off, (*b*) fairing the rear step and (*c*) rounding off the chines, retractable hinged strakes or spray-dams being fitted along the chine lines to throw down spray during take-off; as an alternative, he suggested blowing air from slots across the planing bottom instead of having physical steps, thus getting rid of after-body suction during take-off but retaining it for touch-down so as to shorten the landing run.

Following up these suggestions, Arthur Gouge made numerous tests in the Rochester tank with variously faired main and rear steps, for comparison with others made in the R.A.E. tank. He obtained patents for two designs of main step fairing and for wing-tip floats having flush-fitting extensible hydrofoils instead of steps. No results were available soon enough for incorporation in the Empire Boats, whose main development was limited to structural strengthening and power increases to permit take-off in 60 seconds at 52,500 lb for the S.23 and 53,000 lb for the S.30 and S.33; in the case of the less-urgent R.2/33 and S.26 boats it was possible to introduce a pointed rear step giving a 9 per cent reduction in air drag, although this had to be deepened to a vertical knife-edge to avoid porpoising. Concurrently with their increased order for 28 Empire Boats, Imperial Airways ordered three of the S.26 type, to be known as their 'G-class', for which c/ns S.871–873 were allotted; the Air

Ministry at first intended to order two prototypes of the S.27, for which c/ns S.874–875 were reserved, but soon afterwards the Air Staff rejected the whole catapult project, having been satisfied that the R.2/33 could perform all that the R.A.F. asked of it, ordering the latter into production as the Sunderland and cancelling the S.27 at the same time. At £87,325 the price of the S.26 was more than double that of the Empire Boat (£41,000), and the Air Ministry subsidised the purchase in consideration of the three G-Boats being immediately available to the R.A.F. in time of war; consequently, the S.26 had many detail features in common with the Sunderland, such as extrusions in place of folded plate members, and Rafwire tie-rods with A.G.S. end fittings for the internal bracing of the wing truss; the tailplane and fin were Alclad-covered between the spar booms, as in the Sunderland, and the S.26 also had an enlarged flight-deck with an independent flight engineer's station. In their original specification, Imperial Airways required the G-Boat to be suitable for carrying passengers on the existing Empire routes, although the primary role was to carry a crew of up to five and two tons of mails for 2,500 miles against a 40-mph headwind; it was intended to put them into service first as mail-carriers between Foynes and Botwood, so the hulls were left unfurnished; the resulting vast hold for mail-bags was partitioned by waist-high watertight bulkheads with doors which were to be locked during take-off and landing. Six drum-type tanks containing 3,600 gallons of fuel were located within the wing truss exactly as in the Empire Boat, but the increased depth of the wing allowed easier access to the interior of the wing for inspection and maintenance.

X8274 after launching at Rochester on 8 July, 1940.

The three G-Boats were originally registered and named as *G-AFCI Golden Hind*, *G-AFCJ Grenadier* and *G-AFCK Grenville*, but before completion the last two names were changed to *Golden Fleece* and *Golden Horn* respectively. With a hull depth of 19 ft and span of 134 ft 4 in, the *Golden Hind* was the largest flying-boat ever to have emerged from No. 3 Shop when it was launched on 17 June, 1939, and towed round to the barge-yard for final inspection and engine runs, being first flown by John Parker on 21 July for 33 minutes; he found nothing wrong, and his second flight on the 25th lasted 72 minutes while the remainder of the handling schedule was completed; after two further half-hour tests on 29 August and 5 September, *Golden Hind* was handed over to Imperial Airways for crew training at Hythe on 24 September. Within a few days all three G-Boats were commandeered for R.A.F. service, together with their crews, who were rapidly gazetted in appropriate ranks, kitted out and posted to Stranraer for a training course in long-range maritime reconnaissance.

X8274 Golden Fleece at Rochester in June 1940 before launching, showing the tail turret without fairing.

Meanwhile design work was begun on the major alterations needed to convert the G-Boats to a military role; these included the installation of three dorsal gun turrets, armour plates for the protection of crew stations and inner fuel tanks, underwing racks for eight 500-lb bombs, stowages in the hull for 8 smoke floats, 20 reconnaissance flares and 28 flame floats, and a flare-launching chute above a hatch behind the aft step. The turrets were Boulton-Paul BPA Mk II, electrically powered with four Browning guns and 600 rounds per gun; one was located amidships between the spar frames, one half-way back to the tail and offset to starboard, and the third in the stern aft of the rudder, which entailed a major rebuild of the stern-cone. *Golden Horn* was flown as *G-AFCK* by Parker on 24 February and 9 March, 1940, before conversion, and again on 13 May to check the effect on stability of the tail turret; in July it became *X8273* and was followed by *Golden Fleece*, launched as *X8274*, having carried its civil marking only during assembly in No. 3 Shop; this was first flown by Parker on 8 July with all three turrets installed, but turbulence round the tail turret caused directional instability and a forward fairing had to be added, the bottom of the rudder being cropped to make

X8273 Golden Horn with faired tail-turret and A.S.V. radar in March 1941.

337

room for it; after its second flight on 13 August it was cleared for delivery, with *X8273*, to Blackburn Aircraft Ltd at Dumbarton, where further equipment, including radar, was to be installed to complete the conversion in accordance with contract No. 105174/40, on which Blackburn also undertook the full conversion of *Golden Hind*, which had been flown to M.A.E.E. at Helensburgh for evaluation in July and joined the others at Dumbarton on 17 September as *X8275*. Blackburns completed *Golden Fleece* on 19 November, *Golden Hind* on 13 December and *Golden Horn* on 22 February, 1941.

The first two were delivered to Stranraer to be equipped with A.S.V. radar, and their crews began operational training as convoy escorts; on Christmas Eve *X8274* became the first aircraft of 'G' Flight at Bowmore on Loch Indaal, Islay, and was joined by *X8275* on 5 February, 1941; five weeks later 'G' Flight became No. 119 Squadron and was joined on 10 April by *X8273* on completion of its A.S.V. and armament trials at Helensburgh; during these tests, involving many rough-water take-offs and landings, *X8273* had sprung a leak and on 26 April it had to be flown to Rochester for repairs; these were completed by 10 May, when it rejoined the other two G-Boats at Mount Batten, on attachment to No. 10 Squadron, R.A.A.F., for special flights to Gibraltar and the Middle East, mainly with ammunition and spares for No. 272 Squadron's Beaufighters based on Malta and Egypt. These long-range operations began on 11 June, but on the 20th *X8274*, outward bound for Gibraltar, developed trouble in two engines simultaneously and made a forced alighting in heavy swell off Cape Finisterre; the hull caved in, and eight of the crew and one passenger were drowned, the only other passenger and remaining four crew being rescued and taken prisoners by a U-boat called to the scene by an enemy seaplane. Three days later *X8275* was found to be leaking at the main step, which had previously been damaged and patched, and both it and *X8273* were then flown to Hythe for repair and overhaul by B.O.A.C. *X8273* was redelivered to the R.A.F. at Calshot on 30 August and flown back to Bowmore on 13 September, going on immediately to further trials by M.A.E.E. at Oban during October, only to be damaged at moorings on the 29th, when it had to be hauled ashore for repairs to the hull and port wing-tip float. Meanwhile No. 119 Squadron had moved to Pembroke Dock, where it was disbanded on 6 December, after which both G-Boats were returned to B.O.A.C. and restored to the civil register.

After removal of the turrets and other military equipment, they were converted to carry 40 passengers in 'austerity' seating and received their first C.s of A., but had to retain their tail-turret fairings because the original tail-cones had been lost. In standard wartime camouflage, with prominent flashes on the fin and the civil marks underlined with red, white and blue stripes to reassure over-zealous Free French gunners, in spite of the Union Jacks on both sides of the nose, *Golden Hind* and *Golden Horn* began a service for priority passengers and diplomatic mail on 18 July, 1942, from Poole to Foynes, thence to Lisbon, Bathurst, Freetown, Accra and Lagos, flying from Lisbon to Bathurst in 13 hours without refuelling; on the return stage from

338

Lisbon to Foynes they carried very many European refugees on their way to a new life in America. After the loss of *Clare* in September 1942, the S.30 Empire Boats were withdrawn from the West African route and were not replaced by demilitarised Sunderlands till March 1943, so the two G-Boats became much harder worked.

On 9 January, 1943, *Golden Horn* crashed at Lisbon during a test flight after engine overhaul; following a piston seizure, a severe engine fire broke out and involved the tail unit before Capt Lock, blinded by smoke in the flight-deck, could check the boat's steep descent on to the Tagus; the hull split open and 12 B.O.A.C. personnel on board were killed, only the radio officer surviving. On 27 May *Golden Hind* resumed the Poole–Foynes shuttle service for a year and then went to Hythe for overhaul and to be fully furnished for the first time, to carry 38 passengers and a crew of seven. It was then flown to Durban under the command of Capt Mollard and on 24 September, 1944, began a fortnightly service between Kisumu and Seychelles, via Mombasa, Pamanzi and Madagascar. This service was extended to Ceylon via the Maldive Islands on 28 November after a survey by *Golden Hind* from Mombasa during the week 10–17 November; the Kisumu–Madagascar service ended on 30 August, 1945, after Qantas resumed their direct route from Australia to Ceylon after VJ-Day, so *Golden Hind* returned once more to Poole, being then sent to Short & Harland at Belfast for a major refit and installation of Hercules

Golden Hind in its final state in 1953, showing the longer tail cone. (*A. J. Jackson.*)

XIV engines; at the same time the turret fairing was removed from the tail and the original rudder area was restored, the new tail cone being adapted from the underside of the turret fairing and remaining noticeably longer than the original.

Equipped for 24 passengers in first-class furnishings, *Golden Hind* began its first truly commercial peacetime operation on the once-weekly Poole–Augusta–Cairo route, which it took over from Empire Boats on 30 September, 1946, flown by Capt Dudley Travers. When this service ended on 21 September, 1947, *Golden Hind* remained at Poole for six months until sold to Buchan Marine Services, who planned to use it for charter flights to South America and Australia; on 17 April, 1948, it made what proved to be its last flight, to the Medway at Rochester, where it remained at moorings, with a watchman to maintain it in good order, for five years after the Seaplane Works closed; then in October 1953 it was sold again to an Australian pilot, F. C. Bettison, who had it towed to moorings at Sheerness, but there gravel damaged the planing bottom at low tide, so it was moved to the Swale at Harty Ferry, the intention being to take it later to Hamble for overhaul; but it never left Harty Ferry and was scrapped after being damaged in a gale, when it foundered in May 1954.

The S.26 was only the first step in Gouge's plans for progressive increases in the size and performance of flying-boats, as outlined in a paper he would have read, but for the war, to the International Congress of Mechanical Engineers in America in 1939. Experimental progress with faired main steps

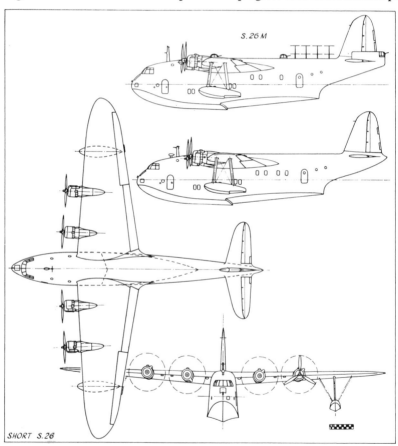

Span 134 ft 4 in (40·9 m); length 101 ft 4 in (30·9 m), later 103 ft 2 in (31·4 m); area 2,160 sq ft (201 m²); empty weight 37,705 lb (17,100 kg); all-up weight 74,500 lb (33,800 kg); max speed 209 mph (336 km/h); range 3,200 miles (5,120 km).

had already led to the design adopted for the Sunderland III, and Gouge confidently predicted a much larger six-engined flying-boat capable of carrying five tons of payload across the Atlantic on a regular schedule, the all-up weight being 163,000 lb and cruising speed 237 mph; this assumed the availability of Centaurus or similar engines giving 2,000 hp each and that the cruising height would be limited to 12,000 ft to avoid the need for a pressure cabin; Gouge was strongly in favour of having a compression-ignition engine developed for this application, but at that date nobody could have foreseen the impact of the gas turbine on high-altitude performance or the world-wide post-war availability of paved runways which could rob flying-boats for ever of the hidden advantage hitherto held by them, as Harry Garner had pointed out.

The Short S.32 Airliner

The survey flights of *Caledonia* and *Cambria* in 1937, followed by the Mayo Composite's air mail flight in 1938 and *Cabot* and *Caribou*'s refuelled operations on a regular schedule in 1939, were a rational sequence of development leading up to the intended first regular transatlantic air mail and passenger service, to be shared by Imperial Airways' G-Boats and Pan American's Boeing Clippers. Before war intervened to frustrate this plan, one further step had been taken by the Air Ministry as a consequence of the Cadman Committee's report in February 1938, recommending the merger of Imperial Airways and British Airways into a single nationalised airline as a prerequisite of increased Treasury support for civil aviation. In preparation for the next generation of long-range airliners, the Air Ministry issued two specifications, 14/38 and 15/38, for the Empire and European routes respectively. Some months before, the aircraft industry had put forward various proposals for a four-engined monoplane successor to the Ensign, which had become outdated almost before entering service because of its delayed delivery; among these had been one by Short Brothers with four Armstrong Siddeley Terrier three-row radial engines, but this project (design index No. S.28) had lagged because the engines never emerged from the design stage and was dropped altogether when the Stirling prototypes were ordered. With so much emphasis on R.A.F. re-equipment, and particularly on bombers, Short Brothers were deeply involved in preparing for Stirling production on a massive scale, but nevertheless submitted a tender to specification 14/38, more or less as a landplane derivative of the G-Boat. Somewhat to their surprise, they were awarded contract No. 762587/38 for three prototypes, one of which was to be pressurised for high-altitude operation; c/ns S.1022–1024 were allotted and registration marks *G-AFMK* to '*M* were reserved for them, together with design index No. S.32.

The Air Ministry required provision for a crew of seven and a payload of 7,500 lb to be carried 3,000 miles against a 30-mph headwind, and Imperial Airways asked for both night and day accommodation for 12 first-class

S.32 in model form.

passengers, convertible to day seats only for 24. These requirements were found
to be compatible with a mid-wing monoplane of excellent streamline shape,
having a wing of 127 ft 6 in span, similar to the Stirling's but with extended
tips, and a circular-section fuselage suitable for pressurising, laid out very
much like an Empire Boat; it incorporated a flight-deck for a crew of five, with
a crew rest-station. Comfort and spaciousness were particularly important to
both passengers and crew on the northern transatlantic route, on which it was
expected that a 12-passenger layout would be adequate for traffic demands
when the S.32 entered experimental service in 1940. This low density of payload simplified the problem of carrying the wing loads across the fuselage, as
space could be found for massive box-frames at the spar roots, with a strong
floor connecting the lower booms and arched doorways in line with the central
gangway; the compartment between the spar-frames was a convenient size for
a lounge on the starboard side facing a buffet-bar on the port side, but could
be converted into a cabin with four seats for shorter Empire route stages. In
the provisional layout the section forward of the wing was shown as a smoking
cabin for four passengers, and the toilet compartments were at either end of
the main aft cabin, which had two groups each of four seats facing on to
tables and a promenade on the port side; but it is probable that actual experience would have recommended that some of the baggage accommodation
should be moved forward, together with the toilets, to keep passengers out of
line with the airscrews, which were much nearer the cabin walls than in a
double-deck flying-boat. The bulk of the mail was to be stowed in the under-
floor holds, with passengers' baggage aft of the main cabin; the well-tried
Modified Göttingen 436 wing section, with large-area Gouge flaps, permitted
a c.g. range of 0·29–0·33 of the mean aerodynamic chord, giving ample scope
for all normal combinations of loading. Although only one of the three prototypes was required to be pressurised at a differential of 6 lb/sq in, the design
of all three was geometrically the same, with heavier skin-plating in the pressurised one. It was hoped that the existing design of spherical Perspex flight-
deck glazing could be made pressure-tight after minor modification and proof-
testing, but in the prototypes a nose-wheel landing gear was considered too
formidable a problem, so the undercarriage comprised twin-wheel main

units and a single tailwheel. As in the Stirling, the inboard engine nacelles were below the wing datum, and the wheels, though not totally enclosed, were retracted into a low-drag position behind the engines. The eight fuel tanks were of Short Brothers' standard cylindrical design in duralumin with de Bergue-riveted ends, and had a total capacity of 3,200 gallons. The tailplane had 5 degrees dihedral and carried two end-plate fins and rudders, thereby increasing the effective aspect ratio and improving longitudinal stability without incurring too great a weight penalty. All the control surfaces were fabric-covered and had set-back hinges and controllable trim-tabs.

At a take-off weight of 71,000 lb (34·5 lb/sq ft) the S.32 was expected to need a somewhat longer run than was generally available in 1938, but this was a reasonable development for transatlantic landplane operation in 1940, and provision was already being made for it when war broke out. The high-altitude version had turbo-supercharged Hercules VIC engines with a slightly higher specific fuel consumption than Hercules IV, but this was compensated by a higher cruising speed and shorter journey time; in both versions fully feathering airscrews were proposed. Whether the unpressurised operation at 10,000 ft or the pressurised at 25,000 ft would prove the more economic was still an unknown factor, because there was very little information about head-winds at high levels, and one of the objects of the S.32 contract was to obtain such operational data in statistical quantities. Short Brothers made a quick start with building a pressure-cabin for proof-test, and the three fuselages were shown to the King and Queen during their visit to Rochester on 14 March, 1939, but completion of the first aircraft within the ensuing year became an

Fuselage of S.32 under construction at Rochester in March 1940.

343

impossible target under wartime conditions, and the project was abandoned finally in May 1940, along with the last S.33 Empire Boat. It was intended, in any production version of the S.32, to introduce a nose-wheel landing gear and to provide sufficient tankage for non-stop flights from Shannon to Montreal and New York; alternatively, the prototypes could have used flight refuelling to achieve this with their existing tankage and with a reduced take-off run. It was very disappointing that so advanced a design should have been frustrated by the war.

When, three years later, Short Brothers were able to turn their attention to the Brabazon Committee's recommendations, they did not revive the S.32 concept, but investigated several much larger layouts, one of them a conventional monoplane with six Griffon engines and another an equivalent tailless monoplane with five Griffons, based on G. T. R. Hill's Pterodactyl VIII design; these were private-venture proposals to meet the Brabazon Committee's Type I requirement, but Short Brothers were neither invited to tender nor allowed access to details of specification 2/44. At the 1949 International Aeronautical Conference in New York, David Keith-Lucas of Shorts referred to a design study for a 'double-bubble' pressurised four-engined airliner suitable for the London–Sydney route, but this was only for comparison with an equivalent flying-boat design.

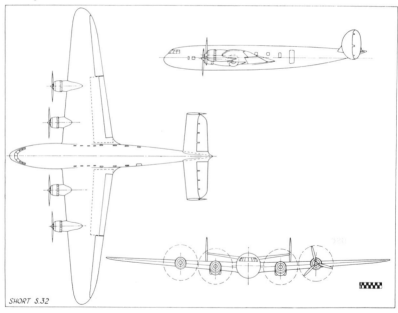

SHORT S.32

Span 127 ft 6 in (38·8 m); length 90 ft 9 in (27·7 m); area 2,020 sq ft (189 m²); empty weight 39,050 lb (17,710 kg); all-up weight 71,000 lb (32,210 kg); max speed 275 mph (443 km/h) or 330 mph (530 km/h) if pressurised at 25,000 ft (7,620 m); range 3,400 miles (5,470 km).

A rare photo of the prototype Sunderland *K4774* in October 1937, showing the original unswept wing with all airscrews parallel.

The Short Sunderland and Seaford

In November 1933, after taking delivery of the Sarafand, the Air Ministry invited tenders to specification R.2/33 for a long-range general-purpose flying-boat with an equal or better performance but more compact in size, and with four engines giving the same power-loading as the six Buzzards in the Sarafand; this was thought to be the best all-round compromise attainable in a large flying-boat, and no firm preference between biplane and monoplane was indicated. Imperial Airways' request for an Empire Boat proposal arrived during Short Brothers' early discussions on the R.2/33 tender, but contained nothing to influence the choice, except to show that the military and civil designs could be made approximately the same. Then, in October 1934, as already recounted, Oswald Short, Arthur Gouge and John Parker all went to Mildenhall to see the MacRobertson race competitors and decided firmly in favour of a monoplane after seeing the Douglas DC-2. The geometry of the new flying-boat was finally settled by their conclusion that it would be difficult to improve on that of the Scion Senior. The Empire Boat was urgently needed and had to be designed on the basis of existing knowledge, with minimum technical risk and maximum use of available materials, but the Air Ministry were looking farther ahead and were prepared to wait a few months longer than Imperial Airways in order to gain a more sophisticated product. So although the Short S.25 design, as tendered, closely resembled the Empire Boat, it fully complied with the Ministry's strict rules on protective treatment, interchangeability and maintainability in R.A.F. service; it made extensive use of extrusions, some of which were not available in time for the Empire Boat, and the opportunity was taken to improve the shape of the planing bottom to reduce aerodynamic drag, mainly by tapering the rear step to a vertical knife-edge. The Air Ministry had received a competitive R.2/33 tender from Saunders-Roe Ltd also, and ordered one prototype from each firm, allotting serials *K4773* to the Saro A.33 and *K4774* to the Short S.25; the latter's c/n was S.803 and its contract No. 351564/34.

By March 1936 the Air Ministry were satisfied with design progress and placed development contracts for 11 more boats with each firm, the Saunders-

345

Roe batch being *L2147–2157* to specification 21/36 and the Short batch *L2158–2168* to specification 22/36; three months later the first flight of *Canopus* confirmed the reliability of Short Brothers' basic assumptions and the final design conference was held, at which specialists from the Air Ministry and R.A.F. brought forward their criticisms and suggested changes in the design; only one of these was really serious, entailing the deletion of a Vickers 37-mm shell-firing gun and its mounting in the bow and substitution of a new F.N.13 four-gun turret in the tail for the single Lewis gun previously required there, the new bow armament being a single Lewis or Vickers K-gun in an F.N.11 turret; a substantial rearward shift of the centre of gravity resulted, and could be compensated only by sweeping the wings back through $4\frac{1}{4}$ degrees and moving back the main step a corresponding distance; this in turn changed the depth of the step and necessitated further modification to regain the designed hydrodynamic performance. This change was agreed for incorporation in the development batch, and the production jigs were revised accordingly; *K4774* was to be flown as already built and modified as soon as possible, before starting flight-tests at full load. The S.25 was given the official name Sunderland, and construction of the first 11, S.860–870, went ahead under contract No. 533317/36. On 14 October, 1937, *K4774*, retaining its unswept wing and temporarily powered by 950 hp Bristol Pegasus X engines, emerged from No. 3 Shop for taxying trials, which were found quite satisfactory with sufficient forward ballast; on the 16th John Parker, with Harold Piper as co-pilot and George Cotton as engineer, made two flights totalling 45 minutes. After routine adjustments they made a third flight of 55 minutes on the 21st, and a week later the fourth flight of $1\frac{1}{4}$ hours satisfied Parker that all was well with the basic design apart from the known excessive tail-heaviness. Then *K4774* went back into No. 3 Shop to have its rear spar root-ends cut back to the new sweep-angle and its planing bottom opened up for the main step to be repositioned; at the same time Pegasus XXII engines of 1,010 hp were installed. *K4774* was ready to resume flight-trials on 7 March, 1938, when Parker began a series of light-load tests, followed by full-load tests with c.g. aft on the 15th and 17th; handling and fuel consumption trials were completed between 29 March and 8 April, after which Piper flew it to Felixstowe for M.A.E.E. appraisal.

Meanwhile, the first batch of 11 Sunderlands had progressed rapidly through the shops, and Parker flew the first, *L2158*, for 40 minutes on 21 April and again on the 27th and 28th; on 9 May Parker climbed it to 13,000 ft at a weight of 44,600 lb, and later the same day delivered *L2159* to Felixstowe to share official trials with *K4774*, having made its maiden flight on the 4th. *L2158* remained at Rochester till the end of May for auto-pilot and gun-turret tests, but early in June went to Felixstowe to replace *L2159*; the latter had been cleared for tropical use and on 28 May it was collected by a crew from No. 210 Squadron at Pembroke Dock, whence it took-off *en route* for Singapore on 9 June, captained by Flt Lieut Hughes; it flew the 1,250 miles to Gibraltar in 8 hours, and next day reached Malta in $6\frac{3}{4}$ hours, having covered

346

1,200 miles at an average speed of 177 mph, going on the same day to Alexandria in $5\frac{1}{4}$ hours at 181 mph. Hughes and his crew continued in this style via Habbaniyah, Bahrein, Karachi, Gwalior, Calcutta, Rangoon and Mergui, and *L2159* arrived at Seletar on 22 June in record time, to be handed over to No. 230 Squadron in exchange for a Singapore III to be ferried home to Britain. At Rochester *L2160* had flown on 18 May, and on 3 June Parker went to Felixstowe to demonstrate its take-off at 48,700 lb and to test the fuel-jettison system; after this flight it was found that, due to a weighing error, the c.g. was at least 12-in behind the permissible aft limit; yet there was ample elevator control, and Parker's only comment on being told was 'I thought she seemed perhaps a trifle tail-heavy'. *L2160* was then collected by Flt Lieut Watts-Reade and his crew from No. 210 Squadron, who left Pembroke Dock on 22 June and arrived at Seletar on 4 July.

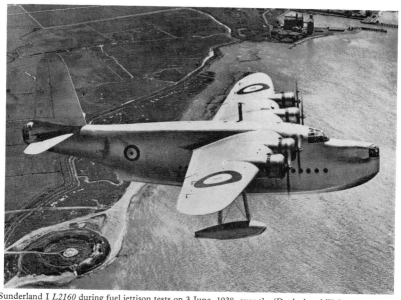

Sunderland I *L2160* during fuel jettison tests on 3 June, 1938, over the 'Dooley' and Walton Battery on the Orwell at Felixstowe; the Dock and M.A.E.E. can be seen at top right.

The rest of the batch were launched at Rochester at regular intervals; Parker flew *L2161* on 23 May, *L2162* on 1 June, *L2163* on 17 June and *L2164* on 30 June; he flew *L2164* for the second time on 6 July with Sir Wilfred Freeman and Ernest Lemon as passengers, accompanied by Oswald Short, Arthur Gouge and W. P. Kemp. *L2165* followed on 12 July, and both *L2166* and *L2167* on the 27th, flown by Piper and Parker respectively; the last of the batch, *L2168*, was launched and flown on 10 August. By the end of September No. 230 Squadron had been completely re-equipped with eight Sunderlands, three of which had been paid for by a gift of £300,000 from the Federated Malay States' Sultans, in whose honour they were ceremonially named *Pahang*,

Perak and *Selangor*. At home No. 210 Squadron had received *L2162* and *L2163*, and in July were based at Invergordon for fleet co-operation exercises. By contrast, the Saunders-Roe A.33, *K4773*, had only just begun flying in August; its life was brief, for its monospar wing collapsed from excessive nacelle nodding when the machine porpoised in the Solent after alighting across the wash of an ocean liner. Thereupon the Air Ministry cancelled the Saunders-Roe development contract and replaced it by one for ten more Sunderlands, S.887–896, *L5798–5807*, the first of which flew on 1 September, the remainder rolling down the slipway at regular intervals until *L5807* flew on 4 January, 1939, with Sqn Ldr E. J. Moreton assisting Parker as co-pilot. Three more Sunderlands, S.897–899, already in progress were covered by contract No. 774293/38 as *N6133, 6135* and *6138*, together with S.1004–1021, *N9020–9030* and *N9044–9050*; the last of these made its first flight just before war began, and *N9021* was launched and flown for the first time by Parker in the presence of the King and Queen when they visited Rochester on 14 March, 1939. After No. 210 Squadron, Nos. 204 and 228 were the next to re-equip with Sunderlands, and all three were operational in home waters early in the war, No. 228 having been recalled from detachment at Alexandria and Malta on 9 September; their Sunderlands were the first to have dorsal mountings for single K-guns on each beam, with the gunners standing on a thwartships platform and being protected by metal windshields.

Sunderland I *L2163* of No. 210 Squadron on patrol in 1940, showing the two dorsal gunners' cockpits provided early in the war. (*I.W.M.—Crown Copyright.*)

Apart from several unsuccessful early attempts to bomb U-boats, the Sunderland's first contribution to the war was the historic rescue of the crew of the torpedoed tramp steamer *Kensington Court*, 70 miles west of the Scillies on 18 September, when three of No. 228 Squadron's boats from Pembroke Dock picked up her SOS during a ten-hour patrol. One of them found the ship sinking by the bows, and her crew of 34 all clinging to a single over-crowded lifeboat; this Sunderland alighted and took 21 of them on board, and then one of No. 204 Squadron's Sunderlands arrived also and picked up the remainder. Though overloaded, both flying-boats took off safely and flew

Sunderland I *P9604* of No. 10 Squadron R.A.A.F. at Mount Batten, showing the F.N.13 tail turret originally installed. (*I.W.M.—Crown Copyright.*)

back to Mount Batten, while a third kept watch for U-boats. This was the first air-sea rescue of the war, and the technique seemed to offer scope for development, but Sunderlands had later to be forbidden to alight to pick up survivors, because too often they became sitting ducks for lurking U-boats, and when overloaded in a rough sea and heavy swell were not always able to take off without sustaining fatal damage.

The next unit to be equipped with Sunderlands was No. 10 Squadron R.A.A.F., whose crews had come to England to take delivery of nine of a batch of 12, S.1028–1039, *P9600–9606* and *P9620–9624*, ordered under contract No. 985038/39, for which the Australian serials *A18-1* to *A18-9* had been allotted; at the beginning of hostilities this squadron was affiliated to the R.A.F. for service in European waters and based at Mount Batten; there it took delivery of its first five Sunderlands, *P9601–9605*, dispatched from

Sunderland II *W3990* at Rochester in December 1941 showing A.S.V. antennae and F.N.7 dorsal turret.

349

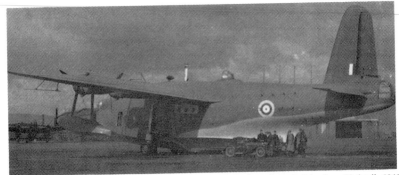

Sunderland II *W6050*, the first produced by Short & Harland, at Queen's Island on 24 April, 1942, before its first flight.

Rochester during November and December, and took its place in the Atlantic patrol early in 1940. Further batches of Sunderlands were ordered from Short Brothers, though never in large numbers at one time, and a second line was set up by Blackburn Aircraft, in conjunction with Denny Brothers at the latter firm's shipyard at Dumbarton on the Clyde.

After Rochester had built 20 more, S.1140–1159, *T9040–9050* and *T9070–9078*, and Blackburn their first 15, *T9083–9090* and *T9109–9115*, performance was improved by substituting Pegasus XVIIIs with two-speed superchargers for the original Pegasus XXIIs, and a Botha-type F.N.7 two-gun dorsal turret took the place of the two open K-gun mountings; at the same time the earlier F.N.13 tail turrets with 500 rounds per gun were replaced by the F.N.4A with 1,000 rpg, a type originally produced in large numbers for the Manchester bomber but superseded in the Lancaster by the roomier F.N.20. All these changes defined the Sunderland Mk II, most of which also sprouted the four vertical dipole masts and 16 transmitting-loops of A.S.V. Mk II radar along the rear of the hull, as well as central and underwing Yagi homing aerials. Rochester built 23 Mk IIs, S.1160–1182, *W3976–3998*, and Blackburn five, *W6000–6004*, while Short & Harland at Belfast began flying-boat production with a batch of 15 Sunderland IIs, *W6050–6064*, of which the first was launched on 10 April, 1942, and flown by Parker on the 24th; future

Sunderland II *W6058* of the first Belfast batch high and dry on a Scottish beach after being blown inshore in a westerly gale in 1942. (*I.W.M.—Crown Copyright.*)

350

production was standardised on the Sunderland III, which differed from the Mk II in having a faired main step to improve speed and range. For many years it had been realised that the main step accounted for a considerable amount of air drag, and experiments at M.A.E.E., Helensburgh, with various fairings on the Scion Senior 'flying-boat' *L9786* and the Sunderland prototype *K4774*, had evolved a compromise 6 : 1 ratio fairing which saved some 10 per cent of the total air drag without appreciably spoiling the hydrodynamic performance of the hull. The prototype Sunderland III was converted at Rochester from *T9042* and was first flown by Parker on 28 June, 1941.

Short Brothers' first production batch of Sunderland IIIs comprised S.1183–1209, *W3999–4004* and *W4017–4037*, which were their last military aircraft to receive constructor's numbers at Rochester, although these were revived briefly after the war to facilitate registration of civil conversions. Parker made the first flight of *W3999* on 15 December, 1941, and thereafter the Sunderland airframe remained virtually unchanged, apart from engines and equipment, for the remaining 25 years of its Service life, a tribute to the excellence of the basic design by Gouge and Lipscomb. However, later

The first production Sunderland III, *W3999*, at M.A.E.E. Helensburgh early in 1942.
(*I.W.M.—Crown Copyright.*)

experience at higher weights was to show the disadvantage of the faired main step, which introduced the new phenomenon of 'bounce porpoising' or 'skipping'; in normal porpoising fore-and-aft pressure fluctuations were confined to the forebody, but, when the main step was faired, suction could develop on the afterbody so that the fluctuations extended the whole length of the planing bottom; in retrospect, it can be seen that the Sunderland III, IV and V (and the Shetland) were much 'dirtier' in the water than the Empire Boat; this was the price to be paid for reduced aerodynamic drag.

The external similarity between the Empire Boat and the Sunderland has already been indicated, the principal differences being the deeper forefoot, tapered rear step, set-back flight-deck to make room for the retractable bow turret, and larger fin area; in spite of its greater weight, the span and overall length of the Sunderland were less than those of the Empire Boat. The

351

Sunderland was built in similar jigs, but to stricter limits and with fuller use of extruded sections; at Rochester, the Sunderland jigs were painted yellow and the Empire Boat jigs red to prevent mistakes, and all details were issued against stores requisitions of the appropriate colour. Forward, the Sunderland had a double-deck layout, with the entrance door and ward-room below the flight-deck, the galley between the main frames under the wing, and the bomb-room aft of the wing, where the upper deck ended in a flare-stowage above the traversing bomb-racks. These were arranged to be loaded inside the hull and to be moved by an electrically actuated rack gear out under the wing through hinged drop-panels in each side of the hull; on the port side a large lower panel could also be removed for loading a complete spare engine or other bulky cargo. Forced-landing flare chutes were mounted in the port side of the hull, and reconnaissance flare chutes were installed in the stern with a vertical camera mounted near by. Folding rest bunks and folding tables were fitted in the ward-room and bomb-room, and there was a small workshop with a fitter's bench and vice above the rear step, where the lower deck ended, giving way to a catwalk to the tail turret. Forward of the flight-deck and entrance door was a raised deck for the spacious bow compartment, which contained the anchor and its winch, also a mooring ladder and one J-type inflatable dinghy, the other being stowed aft below the dorsal turret. The bow compartment also contained the bomb-sight and forward-hinging bomb-aimer's window, above which was the bow turret; this was retractable aft by means of a chain gear to make an open mooring cockpit, with a folding double bollard for towing. The flight-deck was glazed with flat Triplex glass panels, because the Air Ministry were not satisfied that the curved Perspex windscreen of the Empire Boat was free from optical distortion, although it never gave any trouble of this kind; the pilots sat side-by-side with full dual controls, and the navigator and radio operator each had stations, with ample working space, behind them; in addition, the flight engineer had his own station on the starboard side aft of the navigator, with a panel for monitoring engine temperatures, fuel and electrical systems and controls for the engine gills, the exhaust-heated cabin-heating boilers and the auxiliary power unit in the starboard wing-root leading-edge for electrical generation and bilge-pumping when the main engines were stopped. In the early Sunderland there was a catwalk from the engineer's station to the mid-gunners' platform, but when the mid-upper turret was introduced the catwalk was replaced by a companion-way.

Ninety per cent of the Sunderland's duties consisted of ten to twelve-hour ocean patrols, sometimes escorting convoys, but more often plodding out a search pattern alone over a featureless expanse of unfriendly sea, always looking for the tenuous trace of a U-boat or a 'blip' on the radar screen, and always liable to be jumped by enemy Ju 88s or long-range Fw Kuriers, to say nothing of Me 109s based along the French Biscay and Channel coasts. On the eve of the German invasion of Norway a Sunderland of No. 204 Squadron spotted and reported the cruiser *Hipper* and four destroyers heading for Trondheim on 8 April, 1940, and next day another confirmed that *Hipper* was at Trondheim; another of 204's boats sent out to look for German naval activity in the fjords near Oslo failed to return, and no other aircraft available at that time had the necessary 800 miles radius of action. On the 15th a Sunderland of 228 Squadron took Maj-Gen Carton de Wiart, V.C., to Namsos, and another landed Wing Cdr R. L. R. Atcherley at Harstad to look for landing grounds in the Narvik area. During these early sorties the Sunderlands were frequently attacked and could hardly be expected to engage in a dog-fight, but their crews evolved a very successful 'corkscrew' manoeuvre, which enabled them to bring all their guns to bear while presenting a fairly elusive target; they were vulnerable from below and always sought safety as near the sea as possible when attacked. They gave a remarkably good account of themselves, on one occasion shooting down two out of six Ju 88s off Norway and driving the others off, and on another destroying three out of eight Ju 88s over the Bay of Biscay. At one time the Germans believed the Sunderland to be armed with 20-mm cannon, and gave it the respectful nickname *Fliegende Stachelschwein* (*Flying Porcupine*); when the supply of Browning guns improved, the nose turrets were converted from single K-guns to twin Brownings, giving a standard turret armament of eight belt-fed Brownings, soon to be augmented by single K-guns fired from the waist hatches on each side aft of the dorsal turret. Up till April 1940 no U-boat had been sunk by any of the five Sunderland squadrons in home waters, although on 30 January one, already damaged by naval gunfire, was scuttled when attacked by a Sunderland of 228 Squadron; on the other hand, the British submarine *Snapper* had been bombed in error, and a direct hit on her conning-tower with a 100-lb anti-submarine bomb had done virtually no damage, so priority was given to developing a more effective weapon, which eventually arrived in the form of a 250-lb depth-charge filled with Torpex and set to burst at four fathoms.

Until these became available, the Sunderlands were more effective as a threat than in actual attack, but they could often call up naval forces to deal with U-boats, and were instrumental in saving hundreds of lives at sea, either by directing destroyers to the scene, as in the cases of the torpedoed *Arandora Star* and *City of Benares*, or by actually picking up survivors, as from the *Stangrant* on 17 October, 1940, when 21, after three days in a lifeboat, were flown to safety by Flt Lieut Podger of No. 10 (R.A.A.F.) Squadron. This unit remained directly under the control of the Australian Air Board, which gave it more autonomy than Coastal Command might have allowed it; it was thus able to act promptly and account for its actions afterwards, particularly in emergencies when there was no time to 'ask Dad'. Thus when France capitulated on 23 June, 1940, it was a Sunderland of No. 10 (R.A.A.F.) Squadron which flew Lord Gort and Duff Cooper from Mount Batten to Rabat in Morocco to secure Free French co-operation in North Africa. The same squadron was the first to score a confirmed sinking of a U-boat, on 17 July, and repeated this success a month later. But there were still only about 35 Sunderlands available on any day, and no other Coastal Command aircraft could venture more than 500 miles from their shore bases. Soon after Italy entered the war Italian submarines were joining the U-boat packs not only in the Mediterranean but also in the Atlantic. With most of the German pocket battleships either sunk or bottled up by the Royal Navy, Admiral Dönitz put all his resources into the U-boat fleet, and Allied sinkings rocketed drastically all the way from Cape Verde to Iceland. The demand for Sunderlands increased, and several new squadrons were formed early in 1941, including No. 69 at Malta (where detachments of Nos. 228 and 230 were already based), No. 95 at Bathurst and Freetown, and No. 330 (Norwegian) in Iceland, where they had been doing their best with small Northrop floatplanes; the existing home Sunderland squadrons were Nos. 201, 210 and 228 at Pembroke Dock and 204 and 10 (R.A.A.F.) at Mount Batten, with various temporary detachments at Castle Archdale, Stranraer, Oban, Bowmore, Invergordon and Sullom Voe. On 6 January, 1941, a Sunderland of No. 210 sank the Italian submarine *Marcello* 150 miles west of Cape Wrath, and on 22 April another of No. 201 spotted the *Bismarck* in Beisfjord near Narvik, but she escaped under cover of fog and was not located again for a month.

Meanwhile, Italy had invaded Greece and Yugoslavia, and on 16 April, 1941, two of No. 230's Sunderlands flew in to Kotor to rescue King Peter and 48 members of his family and staff, whom they flew to Crete, whence some of them flew on to Alexandria in a third Sunderland two days later. On 20 April No. 228 Squadron joined No. 230 for the Greece-to-Crete airlift, King George II of Greece and ten of his household being flown to Suda Bay on the 23rd; altogether the six aircraft engaged in this airlift carried 782 refugees from Greece to Crete and 314 from Crete to Alexandria, 339 being carried by 228 Squadron alone in the three days 24–26 April, and one Sunderland took off with 84 people on board, all rescues being made at night backed up by reconnaissance by day. The Sunderlands had also rendered valuable assistance in shadowing the Italian Fleet before the Battle of Cape Matapan, but at the end of March had to be based in Egypt because of intensified enemy raids on Malta. At the end of May they returned to Crete to help in evacuating the trapped Allied forces and flew out many of the headquarters staffs, including Grp Capt G. R. Beamish and Maj-Gen Freyberg.

With the end of the Greek campaign and increased U-boat activity in the Atlantic, the main effort of the Sunderland squadrons was switched to Biscay and West Africa; off the latter coast sinkings of Allied ships had increased alarmingly since May, and in September No. 204 Squadron was sent to Bathurst to reinforce No. 95. This caused Dönitz to withdraw his U-boats from the West African coast, but losses to convoys in mid-Atlantic continued to mount in spite of American assistance with convoy protection; the U-boats were virtually unassailable in their heavily armoured and defended pens along the French Biscay coast, and were beyond the range even of Sunderlands once they reached their hunting grounds; they came and went by night, and had proved difficult to detect in spite of the use of A.S.V. radar. Then came the Japanese attack on Pearl Harbour on 7 December and, with America's entry into the war, Allied convoys in her coastal waters became legitimate U-boat targets; by the spring of 1942 losses amounted to 500,000 tons per month and were still rising. By this time Sunderland IIIs were in production at Belfast as well as Rochester and Dumbarton, and were all being equipped with A.S.V. Mk II before delivery; to augment output Short Brothers opened a new flying-boat factory at Windermere, mainly for heavy repairs and overhauls, but including new production of 35 Sunderland IIIs, *DP176–200* and *EJ149–158*, which lasted from September 1942 to May 1944; after the war ended the factory was dismantled by agreement with the Friends of the Lake District.

The Royal Navy and 19 Group Coastal Command (Plymouth) co-operated well in concentrating the search for U-boats on the approaches to Bordeaux, Brest, La Pallice, Lorient and St Nazaire, where their bomb-proof shelters had proved impervious to the utmost effort of Bomber Command. At first the combination of A.S.V. II and Torpex, used at night against U-boats re-charging their batteries on the surface, produced a notable surprise effect, and many U-boats were sunk during the summer of 1942, but then enemy fighter cover over Biscay was greatly increased, and Sunderlands of 10 (R.A.A.F.) Squadron and the newly formed second Australian unit No. 461 found themselves faced with cannon-armed Messerschmitts and Arados on nearly every sortie. In the autumn the number of U-boat radar contacts fell off sharply, and it was later found that the enemy had developed responders which could detect $1\frac{1}{2}$-metre radar transmissions; this was countered by the adaptation of Bomber Command's H2S centimetric radar into A.S.V. Mk III, which restored the ability of aircraft to surprise vessels at night, and against which the Germans had no hope of producing countermeasures in time to be effective. Faced with this situation early in 1943, Dönitz re-armed his U-boats with batteries of 20-mm and 37-mm cannon and ordered his commanders to fight out all aerial attacks on the surface instead of crash-diving; in consequence, the Sunderland crews found the U-boats easily, but were faced with withering fire during the attack, which prevented accurate placing of depth-charges and exposed the flying-boats to damage which was fatal in any subsequent forced landing.

Alighting on the open sea to rescue shot-down survivors had already been forbidden since the death of Wing Cdr Halliday, 461's first C.O., in such an attempt, but on 28 May, 1943, Flt Lieut Dods of the same squadron took the risk of trying to pick up six survivors from a Whitley, only to have his Sunderland's forebody torn off in the heavy swell and to lose his own life. Nevertheless, the ten other members of the crew managed to escape and join the Whitley crew, being found next morning by P/Off Gordon Singleton of 461, who had obtained special permission to search for them. He landed in an 8-ft swell and took all 16 of them on board, knowing that with 27 he could not take off again; later he signalled a Free French destroyer to take charge of 20, but even then the sea was too rough for a take-off to be attempted, so the destroyer took the Sunderland in tow. After severe battering the sea anchor was lost, and one engine was damaged; then the towing bollard was torn out of the bow cockpit. Singleton took the only chance he had, opened the throttles wide on his three good engines and got airborne after three miles of murderous pounding, only to find that the last bounce had punched a hole 7 ft by 4 ft in the planing bottom forward of the main step. He could not alight on water again, so on arrival at Milford Haven he put the boat down on the grass of Angle airfield, with so little further damage that it was salvaged, towed two miles across country, repaired and refloated.

Only three days later another of 461's Sunderlands fought off eight Ju 88s, shooting down three of them. With every member of the crew wounded, Flt Lieut Walker brought this severely damaged boat back on three engines and with no radio; another engine died half a mile from the shore, and with the bottom already holed like a colander, Walker used his two remaining engines to charge through the surf on to the beach at Praa Sands, Cornwall. All the crew got ashore, but the sea pounded the boat to small pieces before next day. There were several instances of Sunderlands being blown inshore by gales and left high and dry without serious damage. The strength of the Sunderland's hull in such emergencies was remarkable, and its apparent vulnerability to being stove-in by water impact seemed inexplicable during the war years, but experimental work at Felixstowe in 1950 and 1951, using low-lag electronic transducers, showed that instantaneous peak pressures above 45 lb/sq in could be generated forward of the main step and that severe damage could also be caused in certain swell conditions by more persistent pressures of no more than 5 lb/sq in.

The Sunderland wrecked on Praa Sands had been the first to be fitted with Vickers K-guns on swivels in the galley hatches as a means of countering beam attacks from below, from either U-boats or aircraft. The idea originated in 461 Squadron and was taken up by Wing Cdr Hartnell, C.O. of No. 10 (R.A.A.F.) Squadron, who had a prototype mounting, complete with 'taboo bar', installed on another Sunderland; this boat on 1 August, 1943, attacked submarine U-454 on the surface and was severely hit in return; nevertheless, Flt Lieut Fry dropped his depth-charges accurately and the U-boat was sunk, but the Sunderland crashed a few minutes later, six survivors being rescued. A revised galley gun-mounting was designed for easier production, and enough sets were made up at Mount Batten to equip all No. 10 (R.A.A.F.)'s aircraft; at the end of 1943 this was officially approved by Coastal Command as a modification for all Sunderlands. Although the galley-guns improved the Sunderland's chances against fighters, they could not be brought to bear forward to force a U-boat's gunners to take cover during a head-on attack; the original single K-gun of the nose turret had already been replaced by twin belt-fed Brownings, but these were not enough by themselves to discourage the enemy gunners, and could not be depressed enough for the final run-in from 50 feet. Eventually Wing Cdr Hartnell and Gp Capt Alexander (O.C. Mount Batten) decided to try the effect of fixed 0·303-in Brownings in the nose, fired by the pilot. After tests of single and twin fixed guns a full four-gun prototype installation was demonstrated to Coastal Command, and certain improvements were agreed with Short Brothers; late in 1943 the fixed nose guns were approved as a production modification in all future Sunderlands. In their first action on 8 January, 1944, they proved their worth when F/Off Roberts of No. 10 (R.A.A.F.) Squadron cleared the decks of U-426 before dropping six depth charges, suffering no damage whatever in return. These four nose guns brought the total armament of the Sunderland III to fourteen 0·303-in belt-fed Brownings, but even this was not the final evolution of the *Porcupine*; German fighters could still open a beam attack at long range with their cannon, and in reply Short Brothers introduced additional beam hatches aft of the mid-upper turret for a pair of 0·5-in Brownings on each side, bringing the total number of guns to 18.

Since early in 1942 it had been realised that a faster variant of the Sunderland could be created by combining it with the Hercules engine installation of the Stirling, at the expense of a heavier structure and a larger planing bottom. This project, defined by specification R.8/42, was called Sunderland IV, and orders were placed at Rochester for two prototypes, *MZ269* and *MZ271*, and 30 production aircraft *NJ200–229*. It was desired to keep as closely as possible to the existing design so as to avoid too many alterations in the assembly jigs and, so far as the wings were concerned, this was achieved, overall dimensions being unchanged apart from the use of heavier-gauge material. In view of the trouble originally experienced in matching the positions of the main step and centre of gravity, great care was taken in designing the new planing bottom, and the beam loading was kept substantially the same by adding 3 ft to the forebody length, $5\frac{1}{2}$ ft to the afterbody length and 1 ft to the maximum beam; the beam was increased by flaring the chines, so that the main frames above the chine line were of standard width. At the same time the main step (which had the same 1 : 6 fairing as the Sunderland III) was deepened by 3-in and the angle between the fore and aft keels was flattened by 1 degree, making the rear step deeper. The overall hull length was increased only by 39-in, all but 3-in of this being in a new frame bay inserted forward of the wing-root leading edge; the wing sweep was unchanged, so that the airscrew thrust-lines retained their characteristic outward cant of $4\frac{1}{4}$ degrees; the tailplane was given just under 5 degrees dihedral to increase spray clearance, and the empty weight rose by 8,000 lb and the maximum all-up weight by 19,000 lb. Armament was also much heavier, with a Bristol B.17 Mk II mid-upper turret mounting two 20-mm Hispano cannon, and a Brockhouse-built F.N.83 nose turret and Glenn Martin tail turret, each carrying twin 0·5-in Brownings; in addition, there were a 0·5-in Browning in a beam hatch on each side of the hull and two fixed 0·303-in Brownings in the nose just above the chines, firing forward. All the turrets were electrically powered, the B.17 having a Ward–Leonard system, the nose turret a Metadyne system and the tail turret an Amplidyne system. The four Hercules XIX engines developed 1,700 hp each and drove 12 ft 9 in-diameter fully-feathering four-bladed D.H. airscrews.

Naturally an extensive revision in a boat of this size involved much re-design of details and offered opportunities for incorporating new types of equipment, so the Sunderland IV was programmed for service in the Pacific against the Japanese and not intended as an urgent replacement for the Mk III; the first Mk IV hull was built at the end of 1943, and assembly of the first prototype was completed by May 1944. Meanwhile the Pegasus XVIIIs

The prototype Sunderland V, *ML765*, at Rochester in November 1944.

of the Mk III were being run almost continuously at combat rating, with consequent deterioration of service life, and Coastal Command recognised the need to substitute engines with a higher reserve of power as soon as possible in their existing Sunderlands. No. 10 (R.A.A.F.) Squadron suggested 1,200 hp Pratt & Whitney Twin Wasps, as widely used in Hudsons and Catalinas, but at first these were thought to be too powerful for the unmodified Sunderland wing; however, Short Brothers investigated this possibility, and Gp Capt Alexander enlisted the support of Gp Capt A. F. Scroggs of the Air Ministry technical staff, with the result that early in 1944 Short Brothers were instructed to convert *ML765* on the Rochester production line to Twin Wasps and also to deliver four new Twin Wasp nacelles to Mount Batten, together with the necessary drawings to convert Blackburn-built *ML839*. *ML765* was completed and flown at Rochester in March, and No. 10 (R.A.A.F.) had *ML839* ready in May; both were successful, and for the first time a fully loaded Sunderland could be flown safely with two airscrews feathered on the same side.

The new variant was designated Sunderland V, and Twin Wasps were adopted in production as soon as possible, beginning at Rochester with *ML796*; at the same time the latest 9-cm radar, A.S.V. Mk VIc, with split scanners under the wing-tips, superseded A.S.V. Mk III with its Yagi antennae; it had already been installed from May 1944 onwards in the final

Sunderland IIIA *ML818* with Pegasus engines and A.S.V. 6c taking off from Belfast Lough

358

Belfast batch of Pegasus-Sunderlands, distinguished as Mk IIIA. Sunderland Vs were first issued in February 1945 to Nos. 228 and 461 Squadrons, both at Pembroke Dock, and proved to have a cruising duration of more than 15 hours, compared with the Mk III's average of $13\frac{1}{2}$ hours. In fact, *ML839* stayed up for 20 hours on test, and much later, in July 1948, one of the 15 Sunderland Vs of No. 35 Squadron S.A.A.F. at Congella, Durban, flew round the Union non-stop from Durban via Port Elizabeth, Cape Town, Luderitz, Walvis Bay and Vaaldam back to Durban, a distance of 2,880 miles, on 2,880 gallons of fuel in 19 hours 57 minutes, alighting with enough fuel left for a further hour's flying.

During 1943 and 1944 the major activity of home-based Sunderlands was hunting U-boats 'to exhaustion' in the Bay of Biscay, while other units patrolled shipping routes from Iceland to Ceylon. The Norwegian squadron, No. 330, covered the northern latitudes from Sullom Voe in the Shetlands

A production Sunderland V of No. 201 Squadron, showing the front guns. (*I.W.M.—Crown Copyright.*)

with assistance from the Canadians of Nos. 422 and 423, based at Oban and at Castle Archdale on Lough Erne in Ireland, which they shared with detachments from No. 201 at Pembroke Dock. No. 423 had been equipped with the first Belfast-built Sunderlands on formation at Wig Bay in August 1942; soon after moving to Castle Archdale it drove off a Ju 88 from a convoy on 21 November, 1942, and its first U-boat kill was in April 1943; one Sunderland from each of Nos. 422 and 201 Squadrons combined on 27 December, 1943, to attack the blockade runner *Alsterufer,* which was finally sunk off Bordeaux by a Liberator; 423 Squadron claimed a 'schnorkel' U-boat off the north coast of Ireland on 11 September, 1944, and made its last attack on 24 April, 1945, while from Castle Archdale, also, a Sunderland of 201 made Coastal Command's final wartime sortie on 4 June, 1945; nearly a year earlier 330 Squadron had scored the first U-boat kill after D-day.

In warmer waters No. 204 Squadron at Bathurst and Freetown had been joined in November 1943 by a new Free French squadron, first called 343 Squadron and later becoming Escadrille 7FE of Aéronavale, which retained its Sunderlands till December 1960, being the last unit to operate them north of the Equator. Farther east No. 230 Squadron at Koggala, Ceylon, sent two

Sunderlands in February 1944 to Assam, where they were the first flying-boats to operate from the monsoon-swollen flood-waters of the Brahmaputra; thence they flew over dense jungle to Lake Indawgyi in Burma, in Japanese-occupied territory west of Moulmein, to bring out 537 wounded Chindits of Wingate's army in an airlift lasting 32 days; these two boats, nicknamed by the troops *Gert* and *Daisy*, barely survived their mission, one being nearly wrecked at moorings by the monsoon and the other being shot at by Japanese fighters during its last day at Indawgyi. In February 1945 Sunderlands of No. 230 Squadron again flew into Burma, this time carrying heavy equipment in loads of 5,000 lb from Calcutta to Shwegyin on the Chindwin river; this was a distance of 1,200 miles and involved crossing mountains at 10,000 ft, where severe turbulence was encountered. By 9 March they had flown 220 hours on this shuttle service and had uplifted 400,000 lb of equipment, being backed up by a similar Sunderland shuttle between Bombay and Calcutta; there was even a scheme to transport midget submarines to the Chindwin by Sunderlands, but this proved impracticable. Before the reoccupation of Rangoon,

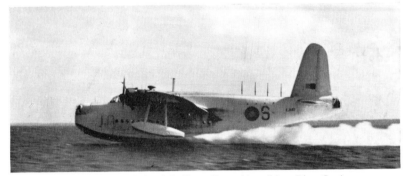

Sunderland III *EJ143* in South Pacific markings taking off from Diego Garcia.
(*I.W.M.—Crown Copyright.*)

Sunderlands gave air cover from Akyab and afterwards they flew from Rangoon to attack Japanese shipping along the Tenasserim coast. After VJ-day production of new Sunderlands was terminated, the last Sunderland V built at Rochester being *TX293*, specially equipped for hydrodynamic experimental work at M.A.E.E., Felixstowe; it was flown on 27 September, 1945, for 97 minutes by John Parker on his last official test flight for Short Brothers. Dumbarton's last new Sunderland, *VB889*, flew on 8 November, 1945, but the Belfast line did not end till 14 June, 1946, with the launching of *SZ599*, also destined for experimental use at Felixstowe.

The prototype Sunderland IV, *MZ269*, was first flown at Rochester on 30 August, 1944, by Parker, but was found to need extra fin and rudder area to control yaw with two engines cut on one side; a new fin 33-in taller was fitted together with a new tailplane of 20 per cent greater area; these were satisfactory in controlling the yaw, but there was some risk of rudder-locking, which was eliminated by adding a forward dorsal extension to the fin leading edge. This arrangement was cleared by Parker on 28 March, 1945, and a few

The prototype Sunderland IV, *MZ269*, at Rochester in May 1944, with standard fin and rudder and original small dihedral tailplane.

In its final state as the Seaford prototype, *MZ269* was used at Felixstowe for the measurement of spray formation and distribution while taxying at weights up to 80,000 lb. (*Crown Copyright.*)

days later *MZ269* was delivered to Felixstowe, being followed in April by *MZ271*; they remained there for extended trials and general experimental duties until July 1947, when both were scrapped after an engine fire in

The fourth production Seaford, *NJ203*, seen here at Rochester in April 1946, became Solent 3 *G-AKNP City of Cardiff* in 1949 and finally went to Australia as *VH-TOB* in 1951 and thence to California as *N9946F* in 1956; it was still extant at San Francisco International Airport in 1967, owned by Howard Hughes.

361

The second production Seaford, *NJ201*, flying at Rochester in April 1946; it was evaluated by Transport Command as *OZZA*, loaned to B.O.A.C. as *G-AGWU*, partly converted to Solent standard as a trainer in 1950 and finally became the Solent 3 flagship *G-ANAJ* of Aquila Airways in 1954.

MZ269. At their maximum weight of 75,000 lb their performance was not a big enough improvement on the Sunderland Vs to warrant entry into squadron service after VJ-day, and only the first eight of the production batch, renamed Seaford and with the new design index No. S.45, were completed for brief operational trials with No. 201 Squadron in April and May 1946; none had their Glenn Martin tail turrets installed, and *NJ201* was delivered as an unarmed trainer/transport variant for evaluation by Transport Command bearing the code letters *OZZA*. Though fast and seaworthy, they were prone to skipping after alighting at high incidence and also suffered from pounding due to resonance of the planing bottom to wave impacts; while not in itself dangerous, this was disconcerting to the crew and was the subject of close investigation at Felixstowe in September 1946; finally, both prototypes were taxied at

NJ201 at Felixstowe in 1950 with Solent-type nose and tail modifications and floats.
(*Copyright E. A. Shackleton.*)

362

an overload of 80,000 lb to measure the distribution of spray patterns in relation to airscrew and tailplane damage. At the end of its trials with Transport Command *NJ201* was modified to have a fully streamlined nose and tail based on the shape of the G-Boat and had earlier been loaned to B.O.A.C. for evaluation as a civil transport, with the registration *G-AGWU*, from December 1945 till February 1946; both *NJ200* and *NJ201* were retained at Felixstowe thereafter, but the other six production Seafords were sent to Belfast in 1948 for conversion into Solent airliners for B.O.A.C., who had already taken delivery of 12 new Solents from Rochester, as described later.

Although no more Sunderlands were ordered after VJ-day and production tailed off in 1946, their career was only one-third run and was not to end until 1967. Of the 28 squadrons equipped with Sunderlands during the war, only Nos. 201 and 228 had received Mk Vs; many were disbanded ɑt the end of 1945, their aircraft being ferried to Wig Bay for disposal, which meant

Sunderland IIIs *ML731* and *ML732* (*above*) and *ML733* (*below*) at Rochester in October 1943 awaiting dispatch to the R.A.A.F. Flying Boat Transport Flight, to become *A26-2*, '*3* and '*4*.

repairing and storing the better ones and cannibalising and scrapping the remainder. Although there was little activity in Europe, Koggala's three squadrons, Nos. 205, 230 and 240, with 36 Sunderlands between them, were at full stretch repatriating prisoners of war and civilian internees from Japan via Penang; during October 1945 alone 457 prisoners of war from Singapore were flown to Koggala and thence to Madras. By May 1946 the rush was over, only ten Sunderlands remained serviceable at Koggala, and Nos. 230 and 240 Squadrons were disbanded; No. 205 was to be reduced to five aircraft only and move to Singapore, while No. 209 was to hold five at Hong Kong and detach five to Singapore. Twelve more were to be made serviceable at Koggala for transfer to the R.N.Z.A.F., but in July 1946 this order was countermanded and six were converted into austerity transports with bench seating for 20 passengers. This task, shared by the R.A.F. with a Short Brothers' working party led by John McFarlane, was completed by August, when the six Sunderlands were flown to Hong Kong to form a new transport squadron, No. 88. This unit began a regular courier service to Iwakuni on 1 September, 1946, and maintained it till 4 April, 1948, in face of severe icing and frequent typhoons; it extended B.O.A.C.'s 'Dragon' route and carried all the mail from Hong Kong for the occupation forces in Japan; in 19 months No. 88 Squadron carried 2,368 passengers and over 200,000 lb each of mail and freight. After April 1948 No. 88 Squadron remilitarised its Sunderlands by reinstalling their nose and tail (but not dorsal) turrets and resumed its normal duties, including air-sea rescue for the R.A.F. station at Kai Tak. On 12 January, 1949, two Sunderlands flew in a salvage party to recover a Vampire which had force-landed in Chinese territory at Bias Bay, and on 21 April another brought a doctor and medical supplies to the besieged frigate *Amethyst*, under shell-fire from Chinese batteries along the Yangtse river; two days later another Sunderland was heavily shelled near *Amethyst* and barely reached Shanghai, where B.O.A.C. made temporary repairs to enable it to fly back to Hong Kong. On 15 and 16 May three Sunderlands evacuated 121 British civilians from Shanghai to Hong Kong, and thereafter No. 88 returned to its routine duties, but a year later, when the Korean War began, the squadron began providing both reconnaissance cover and a ferry service between Iwakuni and the Korean coast. In August 1950, No. 88 was joined by No. 209 from Singapore, hitherto in action against Communist guerillas in Malaya, and on 17 September a Sunderland reconnoitred for mines and submarines as far as Vladivostok. In June 1951 both Nos. 88 and 209 were sent to reinforce No. 205 at Singapore in an all-out attack on terrorists, but left a small detachment at Iwakuni to patrol the Korean coast.

The two home-based squadrons, Nos. 201 and 230 (reformed from 228), had meanwhile been ordered from Pembroke Dock to Calshot in July 1948 and thence to Hamburg to assist in the Berlin Airlift; they operated a shuttle service between the River Elbe at Finkenwerder and the Havel See in West Berlin, carrying in $4\frac{1}{2}$ tons of supplies and bringing out manufactured goods and undernourished refugees on each trip. By good organisation, using DUKW amphibious vehicles for unloading, the turn-round at Hamburg was reduced to 20 minutes and at Berlin to 12 minutes. In spite of frequent fog and danger from floating debris, over 1,000 sorties were made, carrying in 4,500 tons of food and bringing out 1,113 starving children, until ice-floes on the Havel See stopped flying-boat operations on 15 December; Sunderlands were the only aircraft used in the Berlin Airlift whose internal protective treatment permitted them to carry bulk salt, which was urgently needed in

West Berlin, since supplies from Stassfürt had been cut off. In July 1951 four Sunderlands of No. 201 Squadron flew to Jamaica via Iceland, Newfoundland and Bermuda, paying a courtesy visit to the U.S. Navy at Norfolk, Virginia, and arriving back at Pembroke Dock on 7 August. Another flew to Ella Island, Greenland, on 25 July and on to Seal Lake, only 700 miles from the North Pole, three days later; returning via Reykjavik, it brought back a mother and her baby for urgently needed hospital treatment at Dundee. One result of this flight was that five Sunderlands of No. 230 Squadron were allocated to Cdr Simpson's British North Greenland Expedition in July 1952, to ferry supplies between the main base at Young Sound and the advanced base on Britannia Lake; by 22 August over 165 tons of supplies, including teams of husky dogs, had been airlifted for the Expedition, and in return the R.A.F. had gained valuable experience of operation and survival in the Arctic. In August 1953 it was No. 201's turn to airlift a further 70 tons; all went well until on the 17th one Sunderland was holed by a drifting ice-floe and then forced on to rocks; only six days remained in which to escape the onset of winter sea-ice, but by superhuman efforts the bottom was patched and finally sealed with half a ton of sand, cement and calcium chloride; late on the 19th the Sunderland, still leaking fast and very nose-heavy, managed to take off; while airborne the bilges were drained and the holes were caulked with cotton-waste and lanolin, which sufficed for landing to refuel at Young Sound and for taking off for the remaining flight to Wig Bay. Three of No. 230's Sunderlands came to the rescue of victims of the Ionian earthquake in August 1953, and it was their turn again to visit Greenland in 1954 to bring back the North Greenland Expedition.

With the ending of the Korean War in October 1954, No. 88 Squadron was disbanded and its Sunderlands were handed back to Nos. 205 and 209 Squadrons, returning to Wig Bay in rotation for overhaul at the end of each period of 800 hours. On 1 January, 1955, these two squadrons were amalgamated and continued to fly from Seletar on anti-piracy patrols, air-sea rescue and occasional combined naval exercises; at home Nos. 201 and 230 followed a similar routine, but two years later they were finally disbanded, and their ten Sunderlands went into store at Wig Bay, where Short Brothers & Harland maintained a working party for specialised repair and modifications. From 1 January, 1958, the combined No. 205/209 Squadron at Seletar began changing over to Shackletons based at Changi, and two months later the Sunderlands were reduced to a detachment of three, which was finally disbanded after a farewell flight by *ML797* on 20 May, 1959; so ended the Sunderland's 21 years' service with the Royal Air Force, but not its service elsewhere, for, in 1951, 19 had been reconditioned at Belfast for Aéronavale, operating with Escadrille 7FE at Dakar until the last three were withdrawn from service in 1960. Of these the former *ML824* was presented by the French Government to the Sunderland Trust for preservation at Pembroke Dock, whither it was flown from Brest on 24 March, 1961, by Captain Lutherau. After ten years display in the open it was moved to the new R.A.F. Museum at Hendon where it was restored and displayed, initially, outside but later in the

Aéronavale's last Sunderland V, *ML824*, arriving at Pembroke Dock on 24 March, 1961, escorted by Shackletons of No. 201 Squadron, for presentation to the Sunderland Trust. (*Crown Copyright.*)

Battle of Britain Museum which was built around it. *ML824* now carries the 1945 code NS–Z of No. 201 Squadron. A second ex-Aéronavale Sunderland Mk V, *ML796*, was bought in France during 1965 for conversion into a disco and later a restaurant but, in 1976, when threatened with being broken up, it was bought by the Imperial War Museum. Being too large to transport by road it was cut in halves horizontally for its journey to Duxford where, with the help of the Duxford Aviation Society, it was restored for display there.

Meanwhile, in 1953, a further 16 Sunderlands had been reconditioned at Belfast for the R.N.Z.A.F., serving with No. 5 (MR) Squadron at Hobsonville, Auckland and Lauthala Bay, Fiji, five of which (*NZ4107, 4112–4114* and *4116*) remained in service at Hobsonville until early 1967 for mercy flights to island communities too small to have airstrips. In March of that year all five were withdrawn from service and scrapped, the last to remain flying being *NZ4116*. In December 1966 the previously-stored reserve Sunderland, *NZ4115*, was accepted for preservation by the Museum of Transport and Technology at Auckland and is sited on the Sir Keith Park Memorial Airfield. The Museum also has a Solent Mk 4 *ZK–AMO*. Other surviving Sunderlands and its derivatives are one Sunderland GR5, converted

The last Sunderland still in service in 1967 was *NZ4116* of the R.N.Z.A.F. at Hobsonville. (*Courtesy Flt Lt R. C. B. Ashworth.*)

from a Mk III, *ML814/G–BJHS* in Chatham Historic Dockyard; a Solent MK 3 converted from a Seaford, *NJ203* now *N9946F* at Oaklands Airport, San Francisco; and two Sandringhams, a Mk 4 built as a Sunderland Mk III and converted to a Mk V, *JM715/VH–BRC* owned by the Science Museum but displayed in the Hall of Aviation, Southampton; and a Mk 7, similarly built and converted, *JM719/F–OBIP* in the Musée de l'Air, Le Bourget, Paris.

Perhaps the most important experimental modification to any Sunderland was that on *SZ599*, the last to be built, which was given a fully faired main step with natural ventilation of the afterbody, at Felixstowe between 1948 and 1950. With the step fairing ratio as high as 17 : 1, it was shown that severe skipping and instability occurred with the vents sealed, but never with open vents of adequate area close behind the main step. These results shed new light on the mechanism of skipping, and indicated that nearly stepless hulls of very low drag were not beyond the bounds of possibility. Unfortunately this discovery came too late to influence policy decisions already taken to discontinue flying-boat development. Other experimental Sunderlands were

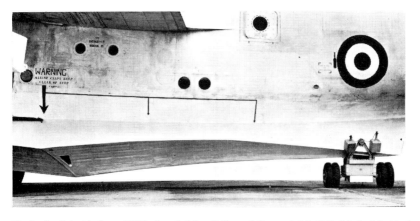

The last Sunderland built was *SZ599*, dispatched from Belfast to Felixstowe in July 1946. It had a fully-faired main step and naturally-ventilated afterbody. (*Crown Copyright*).

PP162 and *TX293*, specially equipped with sensitive pressure transducers for investigating impact loads on planing bottoms at Felixstowe, also those used to test the Swift Synchromo powered controls for the Shetland and later the Boulton-Paul powered controls for the Saunders-Roe Princess; in November 1950 *PP151* was fitted with a Sperrin fin and rudder for full-scale trials of the effectiveness of the proposed full-span servo-tabs. The various civil conversions of the Sunderland and Seaford—Hythe, Sandringham and Solent—are described separately. Including the two Sunderland IV prototypes and eight production Seafords, the total number of Sunderlands built was 749—341 at Rochester, 240 at Dumbarton, 133 at Belfast and 35 at Windermere. In the turbo-jet era they had become as obsolete, but would remain as imperishable in history, as Nelson's *Victory*.

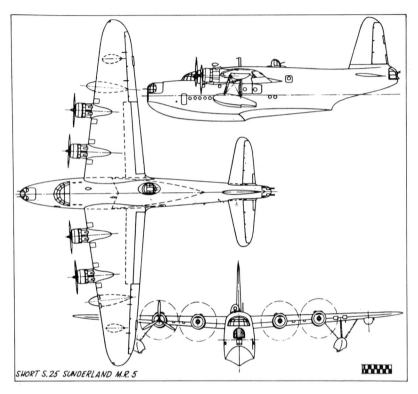

SHORT S.25 SUNDERLAND M.R.5

Sunderland—Span 112 ft 9 in (34·39 m); length 85 ft 4 in (26 m); area 1,487 sq ft (138·1 m^2); empty weight (I) 28,290 lb (12,830 kg), (II & III) 33,000 lb (15,000 kg), (V) 37,000 lb (16,783 kg); all-up weight (I) 50,100 lb (22,750 kg), (II & III) 58,000 lb (26,350 kg), (V) 65,000 lb (29,482 kg); max speed (I) 210 mph (338 km/h), (II & III) 205 mph (330 km/h), (V) 213 mph (343 km/h); duration (normal) 13·5 hr; max range with overload fuel (V) 2,880 miles (4,630 km) in 20 hr.

Seaford—Span and area as for Sunderland; length 88 ft 7 in (27·1 m); empty weight 45,000 lb (20,450 kg); all-up weight 75,000 lb (34,020 kg); max speed 242 mph (389 km/h); range 3,100 miles (4,980 km).

G-AGEV (ex *JM664*), at Rochester on 18 January, 1943, was the fifth of the first six demilitarised
Sunderland IIIs supplied to augment B.O.A.C.'s Empire Boat fleet.

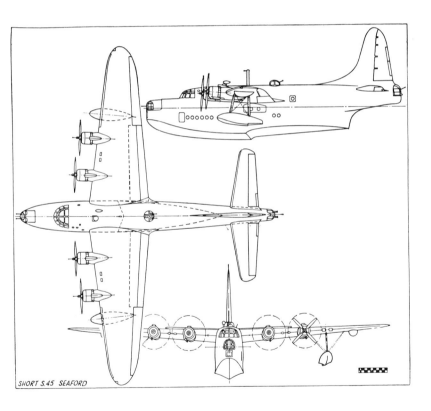

SHORT S.45 SEAFORD

First prototype Stirling, *L7600*, at Rochester Airport on 13 May, 1939, showing original position of undercarriage doors. (*I.W.M.—Crown Copyright.*)

The Short Stirling

For several years before 1934, R.A.F. re-equipment policy was based on an assumption that there would be no major war for ten years. This curious rule, laid down by the Cabinet in 1919 and confirmed by the Committee of Imperial Defence in 1928, allowed the start of the ten-year period to progress with the calendar instead of remaining fixed, and so, although the Salisbury Committee had recommended an increase in the metropolitan strength of the R.A.F. to 52 squadrons after the French occupation of the Ruhr in 1923, any attempt to implement this had always been resisted on grounds of economy; in 1934 the Ten Year Rule was still being invoked in Parliament in spite of Winston Churchill's warnings on the aggressive activities of Adolf Hitler. In March 1935 Anthony Eden and Sir John Simon visited Germany and were blandly informed by Hitler himself that the new German Air Force already equalled the R.A.F. in striking power. At that time the Air Staff were thinking in terms of a twin-engined monoplane as their largest bomber type and had issued specification B.1/35, to which prototypes were later ordered from Armstrong Whitworth and Vickers-Armstrongs, respectively, with new 21-cylinder Deerhound and 24-cylinder Vulture engines in the 1,500 hp class. Hardly were these prototypes begun when further rapid expansion of the Luftwaffe was reported and the Air Staff realised that bigger, as well as more and faster, bombers were going to be needed. In 1936 they issued two new specifications, B.12/36 in July and P.13/36 in September, respectively for a high-speed long-range four-engined strategic bomber and a fast medium-range twin-engined tactical bomber.

Of the many tenders received, the Air Staff selected two designs in each class for construction, awarding contracts for two prototypes each to Short Brothers and Supermarine for the B.12/36, and A. V. Roe and Handley Page for the P.13/36. Both specifications were precisely defined in detail and emphasised that 'design, construction and satisfactory operation of all services must proceed with the greatest possible speed', so that experimental or untried design features had to be avoided. At the same time the pilot was to have an excellent view in all directions, including aft, and armament was to comprise nose and tail multi-gun turrets, together with a retractable ventral 'dustbin'

370

turret for protection against beam and underbelly attacks. For the B.12/36, a crew of six was specified, to share the duties of bomb-aimer, front gunner, navigator, first and second pilots, flight engineer, wireless operator, ventral gunner and tail gunner, although the manner of sharing them was still unresolved; in addition, accommodation was required for a reserve crew with appropriate rest stations, or for 24 fully-equipped troops, for which reason a level floor and an adequate number of push-out emergency exit windows were to be provided; in the P.13/36 only 12 troops were to be accommodated and no flight engineer was required. An important, and as it turned out significant, difference between the two categories was that the largest 'stores' to be carried by the B.12/36 were 2,000-lb armour-piercing bombs, whereas the smaller P.13/36, in its tactical role, had to provide for two 21-in torpedoes. The unforeseen result of this was that the B.12/36 designs had divided bomb compartments suitable for nothing larger than 2,000-lb A.P. bombs, while the P.13/36 designs had uninterrupted bomb cells of maximum length and width. Other requirements included the breakdown of the airframe, by means of bolted or screwed joints, into components no larger than the existing Air Ministry packing-case sizes, which in turn were based on the capacity of standard-gauge railway wagons, and all such components had to be strictly interchangeable. Finally, the bombers had to have short take-off and landing runs matched to existing grass airfields, also good ditching characteristics with ability to float level for several hours after a successful forced landing in a calm sea.

Earlier in 1936, the Air Staff's technical advisers had been pessimistic about the take-off performance of heavily loaded monoplanes and had even predicted that some form of catapult launching (referred to as a 'frictionless take-off' device) would be essential on existing airfields; this had led to the issue of specification B.4/36 for a bomber with assisted take-off, and Short Brothers had submitted a scheme, but expressed the view, based on their experience and expectations of the Gouge flap fitted to the Empire Boat, that such assistance was unnecessary. In due course the first flights of *Canopus* confirmed the earlier results obtained on Scion *M-3*, and Gouge had no hesitation in submitting a B.12/36 tender with a wing of 112 ft span similar to the Sunderland's, which would have given an excellent high-altitude performance at the normal weight of 48,000 lb and acceptable rates of climb at the specified 'increased' and 'maximum overload' weights of 53,000 lb and 65,000 lb respectively. Unfortunately, before ordering any prototypes, the Air Ministry stipulated that the span must not exceed 100 ft, in order to conform to existing hangar dimensions; even this limitation was accepted by Gouge, who increased the flap chord to 48 per cent of the wing chord and hoped to obtain Hercules VI engines in time for production. The two prototypes, design index No. S.29, were ordered under contract No. 672299/37 and received serials *L7600* and *L7605* and c/ns S.900–901. Soon afterwards, successive increases in German air strength led to corresponding revisions in Air Staff planning, and it was decided to place production contracts in advance of the first flights of the prototypes, which was almost equivalent to ordering 'off the drawing board'; the Short B.12/36 was officially named Stirling, and the first production contract was placed for 100 to be built at Rochester; these received c/ns S.902–1001 and serials *N3635–3684, N3700–3729* and *N3750–3769.* The Stirling was the first large landplane undertaken by Short Brothers since *Scylla* and *Syrinx,* and their first ever with a retractable undercarriage, so, following their earlier success in using the Scion Senior as a 'guinea pig' for the Empire Boat, they decided to build a Pobjoy-engined half-scale wooden prototype Stirling in order to gain early experience of its handling character-istics; known as the S.31, this was built very quickly at Rochester Airport, where the new Stirling production line was being set up, and received c/n S.1002. In April 1938 Hitler marched into Vienna, and the Air Staff revised their plans yet again, with the aim of reaching parity with the Luftwaffe within two years at double its 1935 strength; one result of this was a second order for 100 Stirlings, placed with Short & Harland Ltd at Belfast to follow the 50 Bristol Bombays and 150 Handley Page Herefords with which their new factory at Queen's Island had begun manufacture; the serials allotted to this second batch of Stirlings were *N6000–6049, N6065–6104* and *N6120–6129.*

S.31 *M-4* at Rochester Airport before first flight on 19 September, 1938.

Meanwhile the S.31 'little bomber' had flown successfully and paved the way for the Stirling's debut; it was an exact half-size aerodynamic replica of the Stirling, its slipstream being fully representative and its turrets, bomb-doors and landing gear accurately simulated. It accommodated a pilot and observer in tandem, entry being through the sideways-hinged canopy, which gave the pilot adequate, though limited, all-round vision without forfeiting geometric similarity; the less-fortunate observer had to crouch behind the pilot and be content with the daylight from a small round window on each side ahead of the wing-root. The fuselage was a plywood-covered semi-monocoque of orthodox construction, and the wing had a plywood skin and two spars with spruce booms and plywood webs stiffened by vertical spruce blocks; four fuel tanks, slightly larger than the Scion Senior's, were slung between the spars inboard of each nacelle, and the engines at first installed were 90 hp Pobjoy Niagara IIIs driving two-bladed wooden airscrews. Painted aluminium overall, and identified only by the 'B-Condition' mark

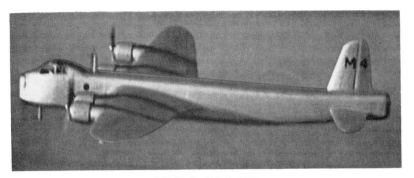

S.31 *M-4* in flight in 1939.

M-4 on the fin and rudder, the S.31 was first flown by John Parker in great secrecy at Rochester Airport on 19 September, 1938, after half an hour's taxying trials on the 14th. Eight more flights, each of about half an hour, were made by Parker between the 21st and 30th and again on 7 and 20 October; next day he flew it to Martlesham Heath in 27 minutes and returned to Rochester later the same day in the same time. The Martlesham test pilots were impressed by its good handling qualities, but considered its take-off and landing runs rather too long in view of unavoidable future growth in the weight of the full-sized Stirling; they recommended an increase of 3 degrees in wing incidence, which had purposely been kept to the optimum ($3\frac{1}{2}$ degrees) for minimum cruising drag, but tooling up on the Stirling production line had already passed the point at which any such change could be made in the wing–fuselage junction design without altering the entire bomb suspension structure; quite apart from the cost of so radical a design change, the delay in delivery would have been totally unacceptable. So Gouge adopted the compromise solution of adding 3 degrees to the ground angle by lengthening the main landing-gear. The corresponding modification was made to the S.31, which flew again with a higher chassis on 22 and 24 November. It was then re-engined with Pobjoy Niagara IVs of larger bore, giving 115 hp, and Parker flew it for 20 minutes with c.g. forward on 10 January, 1939; horn-balanced elevators were fitted to improve longitudinal control before the next flight on the 14th, but were scarcely adequate in tests with c.g. aft on 1 and 11 February, so a larger tailplane with normal elevators was called for, but was not ready by 14 March, when King George VI and Queen Elizabeth visited Rochester and toured both the Seaplane Works and the Airport.

Harold Piper flew the S.31, and to everyone's relief the Pobjoys, usually rather temperamental, started up like clockwork; the Queen was so charmed by the 'little bomber's' display that she asked later in the proceedings for a repeat performance, which caused consternation and despondency, because the engines were much more difficult to start when half-warm, but at the last moment they responded and those in the know breathed freely again. Two days later the large tailplane was fitted and tried out, being accepted by Parker after a final test with c.g. aft on 12 April, only a month in advance of the first trials of the Stirling prototype *L7600*. Thereafter the S.31 was flown regularly by Harold Piper, Geoffrey Tyson and Sqn Ldr E. J. Moreton, to gain familiarity with the Stirling's handling characteristics and to explore its behaviour under various emergency conditions. At a weight of 5,700 lb, the S.31 had a top speed of more than 180 mph and was as manoeuvrable as a fighter; Tyson in particular enjoyed flying it and had a good deal of fun at the expense of Hurricane pilots, who intercepted the 'unidentified bomber' and were nonplussed at close quarters to find it hardly bigger than their own aircraft. The S.31 was camouflaged at the outbreak of war and early in 1940 was lent

S.31 *M-4* in the R.A.E. 24-ft wind-tunnel in June 1940, showing the half-scale Boulton Paul Type O twin-cannon ventral turret; the dorsal Type H turret is not visible in this view.
(*R.A.E.—Crown Copyright.*)

to the R.A.E. for tests of turret drag and torque in the 24-ft wind-tunnel; these tests were made in connection with a proposal to develop a Stirling with 20-mm cannon turrets amidships. At the end of 1941, the S.31 was made airworthy once more, being flown, after rebuilding, by Parker on 13 March, 1942; on 1 June he made its 98th and 99th flights and on 10 August its 110th, but later in the year its engines became time-expired, and as no replacements were available, it was scrapped in 1943.

By contrast, the first Stirling, *L7600*, enjoyed only the briefest of lives. It was rolled out on 13 May, 1939, when Parker did fast taxying runs for half an hour, getting just airborne during one of them. Next day he made a satisfactory first flight of 20 minutes duration, with Moréton as co-pilot and George Cotton as flight engineer, but on landing one brake seized, and in the resultant violent swing the stalky landing-gear collapsed, the aircraft being too badly damaged to be worth repairing. This was hard luck, because its handling in the air was excellent, and without doubt a one-piece forged chassis, like that of the Halifax, would have stood up to the side load; but Gouge, aware of the long delay in obtaining large forgings and castings, and the milling machines suitable for reducing them to final proportions, had insisted on a built-up chassis using separate forged oleo-legs; even so, these forgings were the largest single components in the Stirling; modified oleo-legs machined from the same

Second prototype Stirling, *L7605*, at Rochester in November 1939, showing flaps fully extended.
(I.W.M.—Crown Copyright.)

forgings were put in hand for the second prototype, *L7605*, which also had its undercarriage doors mounted lower to give a simpler and more robust mechanism, but this did not emerge for taxying trials till 21 November. Parker took no chances with it and spent a total of 1¾ hours in taxying, spread over four days, before making a successful first flight of half an hour on 3 December, leaving the chassis locked down. On Christmas Eve he made the second flight, including retraction, and thereafter trials went according to schedule until Moreton, on its eleventh flight, delivered it to Boscombe Down on 22 April, 1940, in 40 minutes. The revised oleo-legs were cleared for initial production, but more trouble developed later when take-off weight rose, and eventually an improved duplex leg was evolved by Turners to replace the Short design.

On 7 May, 1940, Parker flew the first production Stirling *N3635* on a maiden flight lasting 25 minutes despite an engine cut at take-off due to cavitation in the Exactor hydraulic throttle control; this was to be a constant source of frustration, if not actual trouble, for, as on the Empire Boats and Sunderlands, quick movement of the throttle lever was not always matched by engine response because of the inherent lag in the unpressurised liquid column through which the movement was transmitted; several years were to elapse before more precise electrical remote controls were available, and in the official view friction and structural distortion ruled out lengthy mechanical linkages for throttle operation, although American designers succeeded in refining cable and pulley systems to a high degree of precision and reliability; indeed, all the main flying controls, fuel-cock controls and supplementary power plant controls on the Stirling were of this type.

Rochester-built Stirling I *N3638* at Belfast on 13 July, 1940.

375

The next three Stirlings followed quickly, and Parker delivered *N3637* to Upavon on 29 May and *N3638* to Silloth on 8 June and thence to Belfast on 13 July. Five more were flown at Rochester during July, but on 9 August Rochester Airport was the target for a heavy air raid in which six completed Stirlings, *N3645* and *N3647–3651*, were destroyed as they came off the production line. On the 15th a similar attack on Queen's Island destroyed *N6025–6028* and *N6031* during final assembly, and 20 sets of components were moved out to Aldergrove for completion as *N6065–6084*. These raids came during a period of confusion and frustration induced by the rapid shifts of priorities following Lord Beaverbrook's appointment as the first Minister of Aircraft Production and the beginning of the Battle of Britain, in which the Medway Towns were exceptionally vulnerable. The current production programme, 'Plan L', had been introduced after the Munich crisis to bring into being a much larger proportion of heavy bombers, including 1,500 Stirlings, so that while the total number of aircraft remained the same, the total uplift of bombs was to be many times greater. Stirling production contracts already placed at Rochester and Belfast were to be extended, and new contracts were placed with Austin Motors at Longbridge and Rootes in a new shadow factory at Stoke-on-Trent.

To cope with materials and tool ordering, and the organisation of sub-contracts for this greatly increased programme, Short Brothers and the Ministry together set up a mobile group of production engineers, some 600 of whom travelled widely over the whole country to initiate and supervise Stirling component manufacture in more than 20 different factories, supported by a vast army of sub-contractors. Although the component break-down inherent in the Stirling design lent itself to efficient dispersed manufacture, an immense amount of planning and supervision was required, which meant a complete break with the long tradition of shipbuilding methods, still applicable to flying-boats, which had grown up at Rochester. For the first time (discounting a few isolated frames in the Sarafand) Short Brothers had departed from their established principle of always keeping the frames intact and interrupting the stringers at every frame; in the Stirling fuselage, which was constant in section for nearly two-thirds of its length, stringers were continuous between the three main component joints, passing through notches in the frames; all skin joints were joggled and the skin was flush-riveted to maintain a smooth exterior finish. The four fuselage components were manufactured separately for convenient road or rail transport and were finally joined together by tension bolts through the webs of the end frames; the skin joints were then covered by external butt-straps and reinforced internally by T-section extrusions riveted across the joints. The wing structure was similar to the Empire Boat's, except that lattice-braced ribs replaced the earlier tie-rod torsion-box bracing in the spar-truss; the latter, including the top skin, was continuous across the fuselage, having close-tolerance bolted joints at the root-ends; the wing-tips were detachable and there was a manufacturing (and major repair) joint in the spar booms outboard of the outer nacelle; from this point also to the outer end rib the wing was made watertight to provide lateral buoyancy after ditching. The lower centre-section spar booms coincided with the fuselage deck, which was supported by two deep longitudinal girders so as to form three parallel bomb cells 42 ft long; the deck formed the roof of these cells, which were braced by transverse arch-frames and enclosed below by six long doors hinged from the girders and the fuselage sides, each door being made up in three sections bolted together end-to-end; within the cells there were longitudinal beams with 21 strong points for suspending 500-lb bombs; the same attachments could carry racks for seven 2,000-lb armour-piercing bombs, but the cells were only 19 in wide and could not accept any bulkier weapons. The doors were opened and closed by linked torque shafts driven by a single electric motor. There were three bomb cells in each wing inboard of the inner nacelles, each capable of taking a 500-lb bomb; the doors of these cells were also electrically operated, but instead of hinging open were arranged to retract up the cell walls so as not to disturb the airflow at the wing-root.

The navigator's, radio operator's and engineer's stations were grouped above the bomb cells forward of the wing, with the two pilots side-by-side with dual controls in a fully glazed flight-deck above the front end of the bomb cells; in the extreme nose, below the front of the flight-deck, was the bomb-aimer's prone station, with camera and drift-sight adjacent and the twin-Browning F.N.5 front turret above the bomb-sight and release panel; an inclined prone support for the bomb-aimer could be adjusted in height and an auto-pilot steering control was also provided for him. Oxygen bottles were stowed above the wing centre-section and reconnaissance flares, flame floats and smoke floats were carried in racks on the starboard side of the rear fuselage, with their launching chutes near by in the floor aft of the bomb cells. Here there had originally been mounted a twin-Browning F.N.25 retractable ventral turret, but this was too cramped for continuous occupation, increased drag in combat just when it could least be afforded and had a trick of drifting down through leakage of the hydraulic non-return valves when vibrated during taxying, causing the guns to foul the ground; this 'dust-bin' turret was deleted from early production Stirlings and replaced as a temporary measure by beam hatches with pivoted pairs of Brownings on each side; these were incorporated during manufacture in the Stirling I series II, but in series III a dorsal turret was introduced, the model first adopted being the twin-Browning F.N.7 already in production for the Blackburn Botha and also used in the Manchester and Sunderland. The nose and dorsal turrets were powered by a duplex hydraulic pump driven by the port inner engine and had magazines for 1,000 rounds per gun. The starboard inner engine drove a single pump supplying the four-Browning F.N.20A tail turret, which had magazines for 1,000 rounds per gun backed up by a servo-feed from reserve magazines along the port side of the fuselage, giving a total supply of 10,000 rounds; each turret had a hydraulic recuperator in its pressure supply to smooth out pulsations, one of these being in the front turret and the other two aft of the dorsal turret; unfortunately this latter position coincided with the fuselage roundels, which fact was soon discovered by German night-fighter pilots, who used the roundels as aiming targets with disastrous effect until the reason for their success was discovered by British intelligence, and the system was then redesigned to move the recuperators forward to a less-vulnerable position. The final hydraulic system was supplied by two duplex pumps and one single one, and provided also for a low-drag F.N.64 ventral turret mounting two Brownings, periscopically sighted and remotely controlled by a gunner sitting inside the fuselage.

Maximum use was made of the space within the wing, each side of which contained four large fuel tanks within the spar-truss (as in the Sunderland), also two between the spar and the flap shroud and one in the wing-root leading edge; all but the last were encased in laminated sponge-rubber and latex to render them self-sealing if penetrated by enemy fire, and the leading-edge tanks were filled only for maximum-range sorties, when they were used first. For extreme range, the total fixed capacity of 2,254 gallons could be augmented by six ferry tanks totalling 220 gallons, carried in the wing bomb cells; fuel in the two main tanks each side between the inner and outer nacelles could be jettisoned to reduce weight for a forced landing. In early production Stirlings (Mk I series I) Hercules II engines were installed in full monocoque nacelles, but later these were truncated at the firewalls, just ahead of the wing leading edge, the engine mountings forward of the firewalls being welded steel-tube frameworks forming complete power plant assemblies, with detachable cowling panels enclosing the oil tanks and engine-driven accessories; all these had Hercules XI engines with two-speed blowers; aircraft with Short Brothers' own design of power plant were Mk I series II, but when complete Bristol-designed power plants were supplied from Accrington shadow factory, Stirlings equipped with them were known as Mk I series III. The inner nacelles were set slightly below the wing-chord datum so as to provide maximum space for the main undercarriage, whose length and 6-ft-diameter single wheel posed a difficult stowage problem. Originally the oleo-legs had been designed to hinge directly from the front lower spar booms, but when the ground angle was increased an extra forward-folding panel was inserted, bringing the oleo top-hinges a corresponding distance forward of the booms when retracted; this allowed the wheel to be nearly enclosed in the nacelle with minimum shift of its c.g. during retraction or extension. The Stirling's landing-gear, like the bomb-doors and the massive Gouge flaps, was electrically actuated, as were the dual tailwheels, which were compact enough to be completely enclosed below the tailplane, their castoring movement being synchronised by a roller-chain coupling. Originally the main undercarriage retraction motors were mounted in the nacelles, but later they were moved to the fuselage, where they were less liable to damage and more easily declutched when the emergency manual lowering-gear had to be used.

After inevitable delays in obtaining delivery of forgings, extrusions and essential large machine tools such as planer-millers, Stirling production had only just got under way when, in May 1940, Lord Beaverbrook ordered absolute priority for Hurricanes, Spitfires and the three types of twin-engined bombers (Blenheims, Whitleys and Wellingtons) already in squadron service;

no new contracts or priorities were to be given to heavy bombers, at least until the end of September, by when the Battle of Britain would have been lost or won. This gamble paid off, and Fighter Command received more than enough new aircraft to cover its losses, but Stirling production was severely checked and did not recover till the end of the year; not until 18 October was Belfast's first Stirling *N6000* ready for test by John Parker, but then he found it entirely satisfactory, and on its third flight, on the 25th, ferried it to Boscombe Down in $2\frac{1}{4}$ hours. With the immediate threat of invasion postponed, Lord Beaverbrook did his best to make amends for the restriction on heavy bomber production, and the first programme planned by his adviser, Patrick Hennessy of Ford's, aimed at a monthly production of over 2,500 aircraft by the following June and nearly 2,800 by the end of the year; but this was too ambitious and was thwarted by shortage of machine tools resulting from the U-boat blockade, and by the effects of night bombing and factory dispersal, which prevented maximum utilisation of existing facilities by means

The first Belfast-built Stirling, *N6000,* at Sydenham after its maiden flight on 18 October, 1940.

of continuous shift-working. After the August raid on Rochester the Ministry refused to allow Short Brothers to repair their damaged assembly bays immediately, but diverted Stirling components to the newly completed shadow factories at Hucclecote, Gloucester, and South Marston near Swindon; at the same time Short Brothers' main drawing office was evacuated to Kidderminster, where it stayed till the end of 1942, and Austin Motors got under way with their first batch of 150; additional contracts for 100 at Rochester and 50 at Belfast had already followed the original batches, in which losses by enemy action were also made good by orders for *DJ972–977* at Rochester and *MZ260–264* at Belfast; only the first four of these make-weights were assembled at Rochester, *DJ976–977* being diverted to South Marston.

The first few production Stirlings delivered from Rochester in July were issued in August to No. 7 Squadron at Leeming, which thus became the first R.A.F. unit to fly four-engined bombers since 1919, when Nos. 166 and 167 had given up their Handley Page V/1500 biplanes; some of the latter, incidentally, were manufactured by Harland & Wolff at Belfast. Early in 1941 No. 7 moved to Oakington, and its first operation with Stirlings was an attack on oil-storage tanks at Rotterdam on the night of 10/11 February; in April it took part in its first raid on Berlin, and on the 28th made its first daylight raid,

Daily inspection on Stirling I *N3641* of No. 7 Squadron at Oakington in 1941.
(I.W.M.—Crown Copyright.)

the target being Emden; other targets included Brest, Hamburg and Mannheim. Early Stirlings had Dunlop wing and tail de-icing gear, with porous strips along the leading edges for distributing glycol, but these were soon deleted from the wing to make room for armoured leading edges carrying 21 Martin-Baker barrage-cable cutters. Glycol de-icing was retained only for the pilots' windscreen and bomb-aimer's window; the armouring reduced the capacity of each leading-edge fuel tank by 25 gallons, and the twin landing-lights, originally in the port-wing leading edge, had to be rehoused in a retractable mounting under the wing. In spite of the lag of the Exactor throttle controls, the Stirling was very manoeuvrable, with powerful elevators and a phenomenal rate of roll, due mainly to the low aspect ratio of 6·5; for this reason it was tried for a time on daylight raids, as it was felt to be sufficiently heavily armed and agile to be able to look after itself. In one demonstration to a squadron, Tyson pulled a Stirling up vertically until it stalled, to show that it would recover on an even keel without dropping a wing and spinning; it was undoubtedly well liked by its crews in spite of its reduced rate of climb after some 10,000 lb of armour plate and equipment had been added to the empty weight; but later it came to be regarded by the Air Staff as a disappointment, because it was less economical to build, maintain and operate than the Halifax and Lancaster, which were virtually second-generation designs derived from unsuccessful twin-engined P.13/36 projects and had the advantage of the uncluttered bomb cell demanded by their original tactical role. In April 1941, No. 15 Squadron at Wyton was the second bomber unit in No. 3 Group to convert from Wellingtons to Stirlings, making its first attack with them on Berlin on 30 April/1 May. By the end of 1941 over 150 Stirlings had been built, and No. 149 Squadron re-equipped with them at Mildenhall in November in preparation for the first 1,000-bomber raids in 1942; unescorted daylight raids, notably on the *Scharnhorst* at La Pallice on 22 July, 1942, had to be discontinued when they became too costly, and were replaced by 'Circus' operations with fighter escort. Two more squadrons which exchanged Wellingtons for Stirlings were No. 218 at

380

Marham in January 1942 and No. 214 at Stradishall in April, both being largely employed on mine-laying ('Gardening') as well as taking part in heavy raids into Germany; they were reinforced in November by the conversion of two more of No. 3 Group's squadrons, No. 75 at Newmarket and No. 90 at Bottesford. To cope with heavy repairs in No. 3 Group's territory, a Short Brothers subsidiary 'fringe' firm, Sebros Ltd, was set up to operate a Category B repair depot at Madingley, near Cambridge, the repaired aircraft being flown after completion at Bourn; the ponderous passage of a complete Stirling fuselage on a four-wheeled 'Ark Royal' trailer along Chesterton Lane was one of the familiar exasperations of wartime Cambridge.

During 1942 Stirlings were used for long-range attacks on Turin and Milan and, flying at their maximum permissible take-off weight of 70,000 lb, found their terrain clearance marginal across the Alps, particularly in icing weather; nevertheless, their crews found their targets and, having faced extreme peril from the defences, brought their aircraft home through the no less severe hazards of a return across enemy territory with serious battle damage and

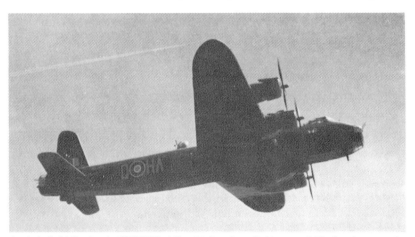

Austin-built Stirling I series III *W7570* of No. 218 Squadron climbing out of Chedburgh *en route* for Germany in 1942. (*I.W.M.—Crown Copyright.*)

casualties. From one such raid on the Fiat works at Turin on 28/29 November, 1942, Flt Sergt R. H. Middleton, R.A.A.F., of No. 149 brought *BF372* safely back to the English coast in spite of very severe head injuries from shell splinters and with extensive damage to the port wing which made lateral control difficult; with only a few minutes' fuel left over the Channel, he ordered his crew to bale out, and five did so safely, but two remained with him and were drowned when he crashed into the sea. For his determination to attack and to bring his crew back in spite of his own wounds he was awarded a posthumous Victoria Cross. Another V.C. was won posthumously on 12 August, 1943, by Flt Sergt A. L. Aaron of No. 218 Squadron, also in an attack on Turin; he, too, was grievously wounded in the face and right arm and, after recovering consciousness, insisted on returning to the controls to fly *EF452* on three engines to a possible landfall in Sicily; after five desperate hours, having missed Sicily, they reached Bône in North Africa and made a crash landing, but Aaron died of exhaustion next day. Two Stirlings of No. 75 Squadron got back to base from Germany with incredible damage, one having collided with a Messerschmitt 109 and lost four feet of starboard wing and the other having had the whole rudder shot away and one engine put out of action.

By this time the Stirling was being superseded in front-line service by Lancasters and Halifaxes, to which the major production effort had been transferred, but before this decision was taken arrangements had been made in 1941 to build Stirlings in Canada and a contract had been placed for 140 Stirling IIs with 1,600 hp Wright Cyclone R-2600-A5B engines instead of Hercules; one version of the Stirling II was to have had twin-cannon dorsal and ventral turrets amidships, with a faired nose and pointed tail; the turrets

The second Stirling II prototype, *N3711*, at Boscombe Down in March 1942. (*I.W.M.—Crown Copyright.*)

would have been Boulton-Paul Type H (upper) and Type O (lower). Two prototypes of the Stirling II were converted at Rochester from *N3657* and *N3711* and flown in August and December 1941, but soon afterwards the Canadian contract was cancelled in favour of a new one for Lancasters, and further projected production of Stirling IIs at South Marston was also abandoned. In 1942 two production Stirling Is, *R9188* and *R9309*, were set aside as prototypes for the Stirling III, which had Hercules XVI power plants complete with underslung 12-in oil coolers; in this form they had succeeded Hercules XI power plants in production at Accrington and gave a valuable improvement in performance and saving in maintenance man-power, so current contracts at Rochester, South Marston, Belfast and Long-bridge were switched to Mk III at the earliest opportunity.

Apart from the power plant, the Stirling III was generally similar to the Mk I series III, but it had the improved F.N.50 dorsal turret of the Lancaster, enlarged fuel tanks and a revised interior layout with fewer windows in the rear fuselage. Stirling IIIs re-equipped existing Stirling squadrons and were also issued in July 1943 to No. 196 Squadron at Witchford and No. 199 at Lakenheath, and in August to No. 622 at Mildenhall and No. 623 at Downham Market; in December 1943 No. 623 was disbanded and No. 622 re-equipped with Lancasters, following the lead of Nos. 7 and 15, but No. 196 moved to Leicester to become part of No. 38 Group, while No. 199 later

Belfast-built Stirling III *BF509* on test over Lough Neagh in March 1943.

undertook special long-range missions to drop arms and supplies to the Maquis in occupied France; in May 1944 it was transferred to No. 100 Group and became a Bomber Support Squadron, employing 'Window' and other electronic countermeasures until March 1945; No. 199 was the last Bomber Command squadron to use Stirlings operationally, No. 214 having changed to Fortresses in January 1944, Nos. 75 and 90 to Lancasters in April and June respectively and Nos. 149 and 218 to Lancasters at the end of August; No. 149 made the last Stirling bombing raid on 7/8 September, 1944, in support of the Allied advance to the Rhine.

Stirling III of No. 138 Squadron (S.O.E.) dropping supplies to Belgian resistance fighters in 1944.

It was inevitable that, with the disadvantages of being the first-born in its family, the Stirling could not survive competition from the later and more versatile Lancaster in the role of heavy bomber. In 1942, the Ministry of Aircraft Production brought very heavy pressure to bear on Oswald Short and Arthur Gouge to discontinue Stirling production in favour of the Lancaster, which the M.A.P. wished to standardise, but Short Brothers were reluctant to do so, and in any case there were still not enough special machine

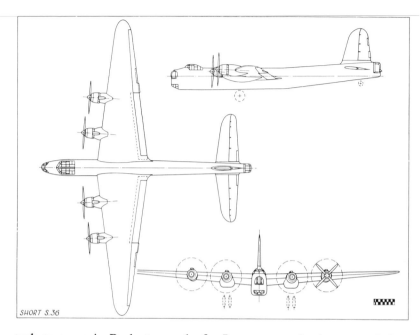

SHORT S.36

tools to re-equip Rochester works for Lancaster production; nevertheless, Austin Motors began changing over to Lancasters after completing 400 Stirlings, and Rootes had already dropped out of the Stirling group many months earlier. Even before war began Short Brothers had tendered, to specification B.1/39 for an 'ideal bomber', an improved Stirling with a larger wing-span and a modified fuselage mounting dorsal and ventral turrets each having four 20-mm Hispano cannon; this design, S.34, would have been powered by high-altitude Hercules 17SM engines, but was not accepted. Two years later Short Brothers proposed their S.36 or 'Super-Stirling' to meet specification B.8/41; this was virtually the landplane counterpart of the contemporary Shetland flying-boat, 17 per cent larger than the Stirling, with four Bristol Centaurus engines and a tapered but unswept wing, having the same sheet-web construction as the Shetland's, of 135 ft 9 in span and 2,145 sq ft area set at $6\frac{1}{2}$ degrees incidence; the fuselage, cranked at $3\frac{1}{2}$ degrees behind the wing, would have been built in ten prefabricated sections on two levels and the main landing-gear would have comprised twin-wheeled units much more compact than the Stirling's; at a gross weight of 104,000 lb, the S.36 would have had a range of 4,000 miles at 300 mph carrying a bomb-load of 10,000 lb; this tender was attractive to the Air Staff, but had been finally rejected in favour of accelerated production of Lancasters.

In March 1943, the new Minister of Aircraft Production, Sir Stafford Cripps, exercised his powers under Defence (General) Regulation No. 78 to take over the full management of all Short Brothers' factories, but agreed to keep the Stirling in production as a glider-tug and paratroop transport, of

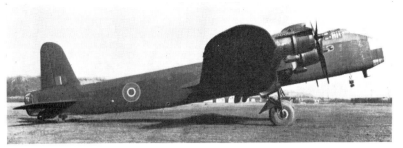

Prototype Stirling IV glider-tug *EF506*. (*I.W.M.—Crown Copyright.*)

which large numbers were needed for the forthcoming invasion of occupied Europe and Germany. The two prototype Stirling IVs, glider-tug *EF506* and paratroop *LJ512*, were converted from Rochester-built Stirling IIIs and flown in the summer of 1943. The glider-tug was basically a Stirling III with front and dorsal turrets removed and a standard M.L. glider-towing coupling installed on a stirrup round the tail turret, which was sometimes removed but often left *in situ*. The paratroop version had a glazed cupola in place of the tail turret and no towing gear, but had a large bath-like paratroop exit hatch in the floor of the rear fuselage aft of the bomb cells. After acceptance trials of the prototypes, most of the remaining Stirlings on the Rochester production line were completed as Mk IVs and the first 12 were delivered to the R.A.F. during the last three months of 1943; thereafter production of both versions of the Stirling IV built up to a steady rate of 30 to 35 per month and was maintained until mid-1945, when 145 had been built at Rochester, 236 at Belfast and 198 at Longbridge. As a glider-tug, the Stirling IV was approved to tow one Hamilcar or two Horsas for assault, or as many as five Hotspurs for ferry or training purposes. Stirling IVs of No. 38 Group (Allied Expeditionary Air Force) were first in action on 6 June, 1944 (D-Day), when Nos. 196 and 299 Squadrons at Keevil and Nos. 190 and 622 Squadrons at Fairford towed Airspeed Horsa gliders to their dropping zones behind the Normandy beach-heads; they also took part in the Arnhem and Nijmegen operations in September and in the final invasion assault across the Rhine in

Prototype paratroop Stirling IV *LJ512*. (*I.W.M.—Crown Copyright.*)

Special Stirling IV *LK589* with H2S radar at Prince Edward Island, Canada, in 1945. (*I.W.M.—Crown Copyright.*)

March 1945. Not all their duties were as assault aircraft, for they also maintained supplies of food and ammunition to paratroops in the front line and fuel supplies to squadrons of the 2nd Tactical Air Force, being continuously engaged on the latter duty from D-Day to VE-Day; their regular load included 120 five-gallon drums of petrol in each aircraft. Stirling IIIs and IVs of Nos. 138 and 161 (Special Duties) Squadrons flew under the Special Operations Executive from Tempsford (and No. 624 similarly from Blida in North Africa) to supply arms and equipment to agents and partisans in occupied areas and later joined with Transport Command Squadrons Nos. 295, 570 and 620 in general supply train operations; Stirling IVs used as glider-tugs in the later actions had fan-cooled engines to reduce overheating at low cruising speeds.

The final variant was the Stirling V, whose prototype *LJ530* was converted on the Rochester production line and first flown by Tyson in August 1944; it was specifically designed as a personnel, cargo and vehicle transport and was entirely unarmed. With a crew of five and accommodation for 40 troops or 20 fully equipped paratroops, or alternatively 12 stretchers and 14 sitting casualties, or two jeeps with trailers or a single jeep with a 6-pounder field-gun, trailer, ammunition and crew, it was a versatile tactical transport in-

Stirling V prototype *LJ530* in August 1945. (*I.W.M.—Crown Copyright.*)

386

tended for use in the Far East campaign in support of 'Tiger Force'; it had an extended nose, hinging open for light cargo, and a large loading door 9 ft 6 in wide by 5 ft 1 in high in the starboard side of the rear fuselage to be used with portable loading ramps. It went into production only at Belfast, where 160 had been built up till November 1945, when all Stirling production finally ended. Stirling Vs went into service with Nos. 46, 48, 158 and 242 Squadrons of Transport Command from January 1945 onwards, finally replacing Stirling IVs in No. 299 Squadron at Shepherd's Grove in March 1946; a detachment of No. 48 was stationed at Cairo West and made many long-stage flights through India and Burma to ferry supplies to the Far East before VJ-Day; during 1946 the Avro York replaced the Stirling V in Transport Command, and thereafter large numbers of Mks IV and V were congregated for scrapping at No. 273 M.U., Polebrook. Only one true civil derivative of the Stirling was ever built, the 'Silver Stirling' or S.37, a fully

The 'Silver Stirling' *PJ958* at Sydenham on 23 May, 1945.

Belgian-owned Stirling V civil transport *OO-XAS* (ex *PK154*) at Blackbushe in 1949.

furnished and insulated transport for 30 passengers to the general requirements of specification C.18/43; this was converted at Belfast from *PJ958*, and flown in May 1945, but could not compete with the similar civil conversion of the Halifax VIII, of which 12 were subsequently rebuilt and furnished at Belfast as Halton airliners for B.O.A.C.'s West African route. However, in May 1947 the 12 most serviceable Stirling Vs at Polebrook were purchased and refurbished by Airtech Ltd at Thame approximately to S.37 standard and supplied to the Belgian charter operator Trans-Air (later Air Transport) of Melsbroek, Brussels, six being fitted out for 36 passengers and six for cargo

387

only; they received the civil registrations *OO-XAK* to *'V* and flew a sporadic service between Blackbushe and Shanghai; in December 1947 one of them crashed on take-off at Kunming at an elevation of 6,000 ft, killing the co-pilot; this appears to have been the only attempt to operate Stirlings as civil transports.

There were no major experimental variants of the Stirling, although standard aircraft were used in the development of various radio and radar installations, including Gee, Trident, Oboe, H2S and Window; no account of this first of Bomber Command's 'heavies' would be complete, however, without recalling that No. 7 Squadron was one of the original five members of Path Finder Force in July 1942, six months before the formation of No. 8 Group, and that its Stirlings played a prominent part in the early development and use of target indicators under the vigorous direction of Gp Capt D. C. T. Bennett, already well known as a pre-war Empire Boat captain and pilot of the record-winning Mayo seaplane *Mercury*. Altogether, 2,381 Stirlings were produced in six years, more than half of them at Queen's Island and its satellite factories at Aldergrove and Meghabery, production flight-testing being shared mainly between Harold Piper, Geoffrey Tyson and George Wynne-Eyton; Wynne-Eyton flew *PW405*, the last of 134 Stirlings from Aldergrove, on 3 February, 1945; Meghabery produced 98, ending with *PW465*, while Queen's Island's last Stirling IV, *PW463*, was its 859th of the type, although production did not end until the final Stirling V, *PK186*, was flown at Sydenham by Piper on 8 December, 1945; this was the main factory's 947th and last Stirling. Incidentally, the above-quoted serials illustrate how, from c/n SH.331 to the end of the three production lines, serials were 'scrambled' and allocated only as each aircraft came up for final inspection, so that no correlation existed between serial batches and factory location.

Stirlings equipped eleven bombing squadrons which made 18,440 sorties, dropped 27,821 tons of bombs, laid some 20,000 mines in enemy waters and lost 769 aircraft, 641 of them by enemy action; to these must be added their massive and gallant contribution to the invasion of occupied Europe and subsequent ferry service across Asia; not one has survived for posterity, but the Stirling's immortality in the annals of the Royal Air Force is assured.

Stirling—Span 99 ft 1 in (30·2 m); length 87 ft 3 in (26·5 m); area 1,300 sq ft (121 m²); empty weight (I & II) 44,000 lb (20,000 kg), (III) 46,900 lb (21,200 kg); all-up weight (I & II) 59,400 lb (26,900 kg), (III) 70,000 lb (31,790 kg); max speed (I) 260 mph (419 km/h), (III) 275 mph (443 km/h); max range (I) 2,330 miles (3,755 km), (III) 2,010 miles (3,240 km), (V) 3,000 miles (4,830 km).

S.31—Span 49 ft 7 in (15·1 m); length 43 ft 7 in (13·25 m); area 325 sq ft (30·25 m²); all-up weight 5,700 lb (2,585 kg); max speed 184 mph (296 km/h).

S.36—Span 135 ft 9 in (41·3 m); length 101 ft (30·8 m); area 2,145 sq ft (199·4 m²); all-up weight 104,000 lb (4,715 kg); max speed 300 mph (483 km/h); range 4,000 miles (6,450 km).

The prototype Stirling *L7600* after its first landing; Rochester Airport, Sunday 14 May, 1939.

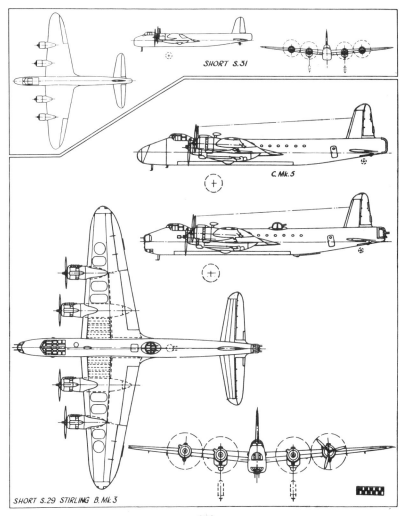

SHORT S.31

C.Mk.5

SHORT S.29 STIRLING B.Mk.3

DX166 being flown by Geoffrey Tyson at Kingsnorth on 15 February, 1945. (*Charles E. Brown.*)

The Short Shetland

In the spring of 1938, with the Sunderland firmly established in production as the standard long-range flying-boat of the R.A.F., the Air Staff began technical studies of a second-generation boat which would embody the experience already gained, and to this end they drew up specification R.8/38 for discussion; this was superseded a year later by R.5/39, virtually a flying-boat counterpart of B.1/39, with similar cannon armament; Short Brothers and Saunders-Roe were invited to submit outline proposals but no prototypes were ordered, although both firms were urged to continue investigation of the various aerodynamic and hydrodynamic problems involved and Saunders-Roe built a half-scale model of their R.5/39 project as a private venture; this was a two-seater with a metal hull and a 50-ft-span plywood wing, powered by four Pobjoy Niagara III engines just as in the half-scale Stirling already flying at Rochester. Registered *G-AFZS* and nicknamed *Shrimp*, the Saro A.37 was completed at Cowes just after the outbreak of war and first flown early in 1940; in May 1941 it was sent to the M.A.E.E. at Helensburgh for further experimental work. By this time the Air Staff had decided on a heavily armed flying-boat to succeed the Sunderland, 50 per cent larger than the R.5/39 and capable of very-long-range reconnaissance together with the ability to carry a heavy load of bombs, mines or depth-charges. This requirement was issued as specification R.14/40 and, since it was the largest project hitherto contemplated, both Saunders-Roe and Short Brothers were asked to collaborate in the design and manufacture of two prototypes, under the overall direction of Arthur Gouge. It was agreed that maximum assistance with wind-tunnel and tank testing would be given by the R.A.E. and N.P.L., that Saunders-Roe would be responsible for the detail design and manufacture of the wing and engine installation and that Short Brothers would undertake the rest of the design and construction and the whole of the final assembly and flight testing; serials *DX166* and *DX171* were allotted for the two prototypes, which took design index No. S.35 and were to be assembled and launched at Rochester; in the event of any further production, this was planned to be done at the Windermere factory.

The preliminary design stage of the S.35 coincided with that of the B.8/41 'Super Stirling' S.36, which was the equivalent landplane bomber; both were to be powered by four Bristol Centaurus engines of 2,500 hp each and to have the same basic wing design, with a high aspect ratio; the wing section was the well-proven Modified Göttingen 436, but the circular-topped Gouge flaps were replaced by Handley Page slotted flaps of higher efficiency and smaller chord. As already mentioned, the S.36 bomber would have had an unswept tapered wing, but the flying-boat design was complicated by the conflicting requirements of aerodynamic and hydrodynamic stability, which dictated an optimum location of the main step which was incompatible with an efficient structural design for the junction of the wing spars and hull main frames. Having learned from the Sunderland prototype the costly results of mis-placing the main step, it was decided to design the wing from the start with a swept leading edge, so that any subsequent adjustments in weight distribution could be made by moving the engines and fuel tanks. This also facilitated the carriage of the 4,000-lb bomb or mine load in the inboard part of the wing and allowed the large overload fuel tank to be placed centrally in the top of the hull right over the centre of gravity. The S.35 was much larger than any previous British aircraft and was to have the highest possible speed (around 275 mph was aimed at), with a correspondingly heavy armament; its three turrets were to carry 0·5-in Browning guns and to be capable of rapid movement and precise control. These requirements pointed to the use of electrical power on a generous scale, and comparative weight analyses showed a strong case for a three-phase alternating-current system supplied from two separate generating sets; this was the first application of three-phase 110-volt a.c. as the primary supply in any British aircraft, and probably the first in the world.

The S.35's hull had a maximum depth of nearly 20 ft at the main step and was too big to be easily assembled in the upright gantries previously employed; moreover, it was desirable to keep components small enough to be manufactured by sub-contractors in workshops of average size and to be handled by normal road and rail transport. Short Brothers had gained a great deal of experience from dispersed production of Stirling components, and the S.35 hull was therefore designed, rather like a Liberty Ship, in ten prefabricated sections, the five lower ones being assembled upside down for easy access to the planing bottom and then rotated for attachment of the four upper ones, the stern being attached later as in the Sunderland. As the shape of the planing bottom and main step was not amenable to theoretical calculation, because

391

of the unpredictable nature of water-flow patterns, which did not follow established scaling laws under hydroplaning conditions, there was a risk that in so large a flying-boat the spray and wave patterns obtained in the water-tank tests might not be reproduced at full scale; to provide an intermediate check on scale effect it was decided to modify the Saro A.37 so as to model the underwater hull lines of the S.35 at a scale of 4/11. The results obtained with the modified A.37 in flight and steady taxying tests at Helensburgh correlated well with the R.A.E. tank tests on a $\frac{1}{19}$ scale model, and in particular the effect of slipstream on spray formation was studied; later the original twin-rudder tail unit of the A.37 was replaced by a single fin and dihedral tailplane representing the S.35 design, and various main step fairings were compared, with and without forced ventilation; thus the best compromise shape was arrived at, although, as with the Sunderland III, the faired step never gave such clean running on the water as the earlier sharp-edged step. Constructionally the hull followed traditional Short practice, with mainly unbroken frames with interrupted stringers cleated to them, the joints between the hull sections being made by riveting or bolting channel members back to back, with the external joint line closed by flush butt straps recessed into corresponding joggles in the skin.

The wing structure was quite different from that used in earlier Short aircraft and aimed at eliminating machined fittings as far as possible, at the same time providing maximum stiffness in bending and torsion to take care of the large concentrated bomb loads. This was achieved by means of a torsion-box leading edge having Wagner shear webs at 5 per cent and 25 per cent of the chord, the latter line having 10·4 degrees of sweepback; the leading-edge skin, back to the quarter-chord web, was relatively thick, and the thinner shear webs were stabilised internally by chordwise diaphragms having large flanged lightening-holes in them, but no attempt was made to utilise the space within this box-spar except to contain an 80-gallon oil tank aft of each engine. The quarter-chord web was in fact doubled out to rather more than half the wing span, outboard of which the 5 per cent web ended and the wing reverted to orthodox two-spar construction; an auxiliary rear spar extended straight across from tip to tip, parallel to the unswept trailing edge, and formed the anchorage for the Frise-type ailerons and untapered slotted flaps. The space between the box-spar and auxiliary spar contained three self-sealing welded magnesium-alloy fuel tanks outboard and one close to the wing-root on each side of the hull, totalling 2,928 gallons, none of which was jettisonable. Between the outer tanks and the root tank, in the area behind the inboard nacelles, were arranged six weapon cells on each side, with internally retracting doors similar to those of the wing bomb cells of the Stirling; the normal weapon load comprised 2,000 lb of bombs, mines or Torpex depth-charges on each side. The outer portions of the wing carried the tip floats on cantilever struts, with A.S.V. Mk 6c radar scanners in radomes on the underside of the wing-tips. The four Bristol Centaurus VII engines were installed as power plants with oil coolers slung below them, although, as already mentioned, the oil tanks were separately installed within the box-spar. At an early stage in the design, consideration had been given to installing low-drag reverse-flow nacelles, with cooling air entering through scoops in the wing leading edge and being extracted through annular exits behind enlarged airscrew spinners, a system promoted by Roy Fedden of Bristols, but wind-tunnel tests showed this scheme to be disadvantageous in other ways. A Dunlop fluid de-icing system was installed along the wing and tail leading edges. The wing torsion-box was carried across the top of the hull by massive high-tensile steel booms built into the braced main frames of the hull, the quarter-chord spar-root attachments having expanding high-tensile steel shear pins 3-in in diameter. In the top of the hull between the quarter-chord and auxiliary spars was a compartment with a strong floor and large removable outer hatch cover, in which was installed a long-range fuel tank of 2,115 gallons capacity coupled to a smaller forward tank of 566 gallons; the fuel in these two tanks could be jettisoned, and for extreme-range operation was to be used first, since this had no effect on trim, but left the outboard fuel intact to relieve the wing-bending moment while the aircraft weight was still high.

The S.35 relied exclusively on three-phase alternating current from its two independent 60 hp Rotol petrol generating sets, installed side by side in a fully protected and ventilated compartment on the lower deck of the forebody. Above this compartment was the flight-deck with stations for a crew of five and two rest bunks; the two pilots sat side-by-side in a fully glazed canopy similar to the Stirling's, giving a good view all round, especially dead astern. Forward of the flight-deck was the massive F.N.66 nose turret, with the bomb-aiming and mooring compartment below; aft of the wing was the F.N.36 mid-upper turret and in the extreme stern the F.N.59 tail turret; all three turrets mounted two 0·5-in Browning guns each, with 500 rounds per gun, and were to be electrically (a.c.) powered with Ward–Leonard controls. The capacious hull contained all the amenities already offered by the Sunderland, but arranged on two full decks, and the normal crew was eleven.

Assembly of the two prototypes, officially named Shetland, went ahead in Shop No. 18, newly built in 1943 upstream of the old works, and the first hull was moved out on to the adjacent hard-standing in February 1944, after which the wings, built and proof-tested by Saunders-Roe at Cowes and brought to Rochester by road, were erected; next the tailplane was attached and the power plants installed; the tanks were inserted in the wing and the fin erected during the first week of April, and at the beginning of May the Shetland was moved to a new position for final installation work; the scaffolding was removed in July, but systems functioning tests and engine runs occupied another three months before *DX166* was launched from the new wide slipway on 24 October; John Parker, with Geoffrey Tyson as co-pilot, made the first take-off from the Medway at Cuxton Reach on 14 December, 1944. After a few adjustments to improve control harmonisation, the Shetland was then flown by Tyson and Piper to moorings off Kingsnorth for the full range of handling and performance tests. Before the first flight the role of the

Shetland I *DX166* moored at Rochester on 6 November, 1944.

Shetland had been revised to that of an unarmed transport, so the turrets were never installed, the mid-upper position being skinned over and the nose and tail cupolas being replaced by sheet-metal fairings of the same shape, pending more sophisticated low-drag fairings. After D-Day, trials continued at a reduced tempo, and in September various changes in equipment were made to suit the transport role, the external finish being changed from sea camouflage to an all-over silver paint scheme, in which it was delivered to M.A.E.E., Felixstowe, early in October 1945. Service trials then began, but had not proceeded far by 28 January, 1946, when *DX166* was burnt out at moorings early in the morning; the cause of this disaster was traced to the duty crew on watch starting up one of the Rotol generators in order to cook breakfast in the galley; the set was inadvertently left running with its cooling intake shutters closed, became overheated, and caught fire.

DX166 in Transport Command silver finish taking off at Kingsnorth on 5 October, 1945.

As soon as the end of the war was in sight it had been decided to complete the second Shetland as a civil transport, with new upper nose and tail sections similar in shape to the original lines of the *Golden Hind*. The new hull thus modified was completed during the summer of 1945 and, with a total internal volume of 8,700 cu ft, offered plenty of scope for furnishing schemes on two full decks for up to 70 passengers, but in fact the official choice was a 3,000 cu ft layout for no more than 40 passengers, representing a maximum payload of under 14,000 lb at an all-up weight of 130,000 lb, which hardly made economic sense. The civil Shetland Mk II (design index No. S.40) never carried the serial *DX171*, but was allotted the final Rochester c/n S.1313 and registered *G-AGVD*. It was launched on 15 September, 1947, and first flown two days later by Harold Piper and Tom Brooke-Smith; after preliminary trials it was ferried to Belfast for completion of interior furnishings; apart from these, differences from the military version included a revised fuel system without any tanks in the hull; the space formerly occupied by the aft hull tank became a mail compartment, while the two Rotol generating sets were moved up to the space in front of the spar vacated by the forward hull tank; aft of the mail compartment the upper deck accommodated the galley and dining-saloon, with a stairway to the saloons below. The total fuel capacity of 6,112 gallons, all in the wing and none of it jettisonable, included

Shetland II *G-AGVD* over Rochester in September 1947. (*Central Press.*)

12 tanks permanently installed in the weapon cells; the civil-rated Centaurus 660 power plants were of improved design, with separate rear-swept exhaust pipes, and the inner engines drove reversible-pitch airscrews to assist manoeuvring on the water. On the first Shetland, all-manual push–pull rods and levers had been used for the flying controls, with a minimum-friction straight run along the level of the upper deck, but in the second aircraft a less direct run had to be taken and friction losses were higher, so both the flying controls and the throttles incorporated Swift Synchromo electric servo assisters, which had previously been installed for development in a Sunderland. Although it could have rendered valuable service either as an airliner or on charter to carry emigrants from the occupied zones of Europe to new life in America, B.O.A.C. showed no enthusiasm to put the Shetland II into service, but reserved it for a time as a possible test-bed for developing the Napier Nomad compound compression-ignition engine, for which a future was foreseen for very-long-range trans-oceanic operation.

    In September 1946 Short Brothers proposed a much improved development

395

of the Shetland, the S.A.8 with four Nomads; at first it was unpressurised, but a later version, offered in May 1947, was to have had a 'double-bubble' pressurised hull to permit cruising at 20,000 to 25,000 ft; the hull retained the 12 ft 6 in beam of the Shetland and the planing bottom was similar, but the overall length was 11 ft 6 in greater; the wing was unswept and of much lighter tapered box-spar construction, with 5,200 gallons of diesel fuel contained in eight tanks within the spar. With 52 passengers the S.A.8 was able to compete on level terms with the Lancastrian and similar interim post-war transport landplanes, and was a great deal cheaper to operate than the short-field Tudor and Hermes, but no match for the Constellations and Skymasters brought into use soon afterwards by American airlines to take advantage of the long paved runways already being built for strategic reasons.

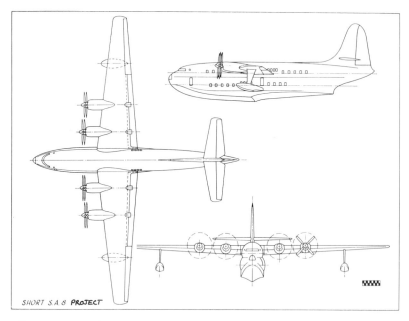

SHORT S.A.8 PROJECT

In a paper read at the 1949 International Aeronautical Conference at New York, David Keith-Lucas, by then chief designer of Short Brothers & Harland, compared flying-boats with landplanes and concluded that though the flying-boat gained the advantage in structure weight at more than 100,000 lb, it could not compete in performance and cost until 500,000 lb was reached; in this paper he referred to a hypothetical F.B.1 flying-boat which closely resembled the S.A.8. Shorts' last flying-boat designs were all military, but only initial layout work was done on them; they comprised P.D.2, a Sunderland replacement to specification R.2/48; P.D.3, a proposed Solent conversion for use in the anti-submarine role; and P.D.5, a water-based jet fighter to specification N.114T. With the cessation of both military and commercial interest in new flying-boats, the Nomad development programme faded out, and in 1951 the Shetland II, bereft of any future, was scrapped at Queen's Island without ever having carried a fare-paying passenger.

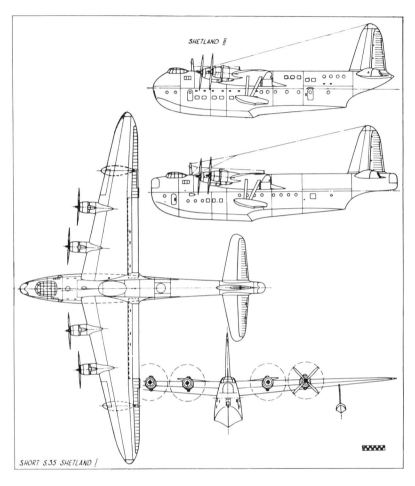

Shetland—Span 150 ft 4 in (46·75 m); length (I) 110 ft (33·5 m), (II) 107 ft (32·94 m); area 2,400 sq ft (223·5 m²); empty weight 75,860 lb (34,440 kg); all-up weight (I) 125,000 lb (56,700 kg), (II) 130,000 lb (59,000 kg); max speed 263 mph (424 km/h); range (I) 4,000 miles (6,440 km), (II) 3,000 miles (4,830 km).

S.A.8—Span 160 ft (48·7 m); length 118 ft 6 in (36·1 m); area 2,262 sq ft (211 m²).

B.O.A.C.'s first civil Sunderland III conversion, *Hythe*, passing the Isle of Wight in 1946.
(*Charles E. Brown.*)

The Short Hythe, Sandringham and Solent

In view of the Sunderland's close relationship to the Empire Boat and its large volumetric capacity, it was an obvious choice as an interim transport to supplement B.O.A.C.'s fleet, which was fully occupied on the Horseshoe Route; in December 1942 six Sunderland IIIs, *JM660–665*, were taken from the Rochester production line, stripped of all military equipment and armament and fitted with austerity bench-and-mattress seating for use on the Poole–West Africa priority passenger and mail service. The first aircraft was flown by John Parker on 26 December and the others followed at five-day intervals until the end of January 1943, by which time all had received civil registrations *G-AGER* to '*W* and certificates of airworthiness. After routine fuel consumption tests and minor modifications by B.O.A.C. at Poole, they went into regular service to and from Lagos in March; they were camouflaged in the standard dark green and grey scheme, with large black registration marks outlined in silver and heavily underlined with tricolour stripes. *G-AGES* crashed on 28 July and was replaced by *JM722*, which became *G-AGHV*, and was followed in August by five more, *ML725–729* (*G-AGHW–'X*, '*Z*, '*IA*, '*B*), of which the last crashed near Sollum on the night of 5 November, soon after entering service on the Poole–Karachi route; this began on 25 October

398

(when the Sunderlands were withdrawn from the West Africa route) after a 5,039 miles proving flight with seven passengers completed in 28 hours flying time. Since the Sunderlands had to operate through military zones in Egypt, they flew under the aegis of R.A.F. Transport Command and temporarily changed their civil markings to roundels and military codes in the group *OQZA–'Z*.

This service prospered as experience grew, and flight times were progressively reduced during 1944; six more Sunderland IIIs *ML751–756* (*G-AGJJ–'O*) were added to the fleet in January 1944 and a final six *ML786–791* (*G-AGKV–'LA*) in July and August; these were followed off the Rochester line by *ML792–795*, which went to the R.N.Z.A.F. Flying Boat Transport Flight as *NZ4101–4104*. On 10 May, 1944, the Poole–Karachi service was extended to Calcutta, and after D-Day it became possible for the Sunderlands to fly across France without calling at Gibraltar, first to Djerba (from December) and later to Augusta (from February 1945). After VE-Day the operation reverted to civilian status under B.O.A.C. with camouflage and military markings discarded, and with the end of the war with Japan the route

The Sandringham 1 *ML788* (later *G-AGKX Himalaya*) at Rochester in November 1945.
(*Aeroplane.*)

continued to Rangoon, the first service being flown by *G-AGHX* on 9 October. The success of the Sunderland as an airliner suggested the incorporation of improved low-drag lines to replace the temporary nose and tail-turret fairings, and *G-AGKX* (*ML788, OQZF*) was returned to Short Brothers at Rochester for remodelling approximately to the nose and tail shape of the Empire Boat; it was relaunched on 28 November, 1945, as the first and only Sandringham Mk 1, retaining its Pegasus engines and furnished internally on two decks with seats and berths for 24 day or 16 night passengers on the lower deck and a dining-saloon and cocktail bar above. It received a C. of A. in January 1946 and after a period of operational trials with Transport Command returned to B.O.A.C. in June.

399

Meanwhile B.O.A.C. had refurnished their Sunderlands to full airliner standard, the pioneer being *G-AGJM*, which received the individual name *Hythe*, which also became the class name of the conversion; all the others were also individually named, continuing the pre-war tradition of Imperial Airways, and the Sandringham 1 became *Himalaya*. The Hythe class was furnished on a single deck, initially for 16 passengers (H.1), but this was soon improved by adding a promenade (H.2) or eight extra seats (H.3); B.O.A.C. retained the front-turret fairing for ease of mooring and considered the new Sandringham tail-cone not worth its cost in delay, as the Hythes were urgently needed to operate the Empire route to Australia; this was extended to Singapore on 31 January, 1946, and between 17 February and 2 April Capt R. C. Parker flew *Hythe*, with Lord Knollys (Chairman of B.O.A.C.) on board, on a 35,313-mile route survey from Poole to Australia, New Zealand, Hong Kong, Shanghai and Tokyo, in a total flight time of 206 hours; on this exercise *Hythe* became the first British civil flying-boat to visit China and Japan. The full Poole–Sydney service, shared with Qantas, commenced outbound on 12 May (*G-AGJN Hudson* to Singapore and *G-AGJL Hobart* thence to Sydney) and inbound on 18 May (*G-AGJK Howard* to Karachi and *G-AGJJ Henley* thence to Poole) on a $5\frac{1}{2}$-day schedule each way. On 24 August B.O.A.C. began their 'Dragon' service to Hong Kong via Karachi, Calcutta, Rangoon and Bangkok, flown by *G-AGIA Haslemere* to Karachi and *G-AGLA Hunter* onwards, with the first return flight flown throughout from Hong Kong to Poole by *G-AGKZ Harwich*; two days later *Harwich* inaugurated a weekly Singapore–Hong Kong link to connect with the courier service operated by No. 88 Squadron's Sunderland Vs for the occupation forces in Japan. The flying-boats were kept very busy, but were already feeling the competition from the 'Kangaroo' landplane service flown from London Airport to Sydney in 63 hours by Lancastrians.

Short Brothers had hoped that B.O.A.C. would take up further Sandringhams, but in fact the first order came from Compañía Argentina de Aeronavegación Dodero of Buenos Aires. Señor Dodero was a ship-owner who believed that flying-boats would be profitable on inter-city services along the Río de la Plata and had been anxious to secure a few Sunderlands even before war ended; shown the Sandringham design, he opted for four Sunderlands converted at Belfast to Sandringham standard, but with Pratt & Whitney Twin Wasp R-1830-92 engines; the first two for local routes were designated Sandringham 2 and accommodated 28 passengers on the lower deck with a further 17 and a cocktail bar on the upper deck; the other two for the longer routes up the Paraguay river to Asunción and the Paraná to Iguazú Falls had seating for 21 passengers below, with a dining-saloon and cocktail bar above, and were called Sandringham 3. The first, *G-AGPZ Argentina*, was ceremonially launched by Señora Dodero on 17 November, 1945, at Belfast, and ferried 7,330 miles from Poole to Buenos Aires in less than 46 hours flying time by Capt Dudley Travers and a B.O.A.C. crew on 25/29 November. The second Sandringham 2, *G-AGPT Uruguay*, was launched on 5 December and arrived at Buenos Aires on Boxing Day, flown by Capt Morton; the two

Dodero's first Sandringham 2, *Argentina*, on Belfast Lough in November 1945.

Sandringham 3s, *G-AGPY Brasil* and *G-AGTZ Inglaterra*, followed on 21 January, 1946, and 26 February respectively, the former making a survey flight in February to Baltimore and back under Capt Gibson. These four became *LV-AAO*, *LV-AAP*, *LV-AAR* and *LV-AAQ* on entering service in Argentina and were joined soon afterwards by a Pegasus-engined Sunderland III similarly furnished for 45 passengers but without structural modifications to the nose and tail-turret fairings; this was *G-AGWX* ordered by the Dodero subsidiary Aviación del Litoral Fluvial Argentina (ALFA) and provisionally registered *LV-AAS*, but transferred before delivery in March to Compañía Aeronáutica Uruguayana S.A. (C.A.U.S.A.) to become *CX-AKF*. C.A.U.S.A. had already ordered a similar Sunderland III *G-AGWW*, which

The first civil Sunderland III for C.A.U.S.A. at Queen's Island in March 1946.

went into service on the River Plate in May as *CX-AFA*; this airline wanted to order Sandringhams to match Dodero, but could not afford the extra cost of the full nose and tail treatment.

The flying-boats performed well in South America, and were augmented later by a further Sandringham 2 for Dodero, *G-AHRE Paraguay*, launched on 12 November, 1946, and entering service as *LV-ACT*, a Sunderland V

C.A.U.S.A.'s second Sunderland III, *G-AGWW*, being launched at Queen's Island in May 1946.

Sunderland V *CX-AKR* in C.A.U.S.A. livery at Belfast in 1948.

conversion for C.A.U.S.A., *CX-AKR Capitan Bosio Lanza*, and in 1947 two more Sunderland Vs, *LV-AHG* and *'H*, for Aerolineas Argentinas, which by 1949 had absorbed the Dodero fleet. *LV-AAP* crashed in fog at Buenos Aires on 29 July, 1948, killing 18 of the 23 passengers and crew, but traffic increased year by year, and in 1955 *LV-AHM* (ex *LN-LMK*) was purchased from Norway; operations continued without further loss till 31 December, 1957, when *LV-AAR* sank after an emergency landing in Buenos Aires harbour, nine being drowned and 40 rescued. It appears that *LV-AAR* was beached and later repaired, although all the boats were laid up in 1962 when Aerolineas Argentinas ceased to operate seaplanes; however, they were stored carefully, and in July 1963 the six survivors (*LV-AAO, LV-AAQ, LV-AAR, LV-ACT, LV-AHG* and *LV-AHM*) were leased by the newly formed Co-operativa Argentina de Aeronavegantes for use as freighters over their former passenger routes, including that to Asunción; although only a few flights were made before operations ceased through financial trouble, all six were still afloat at Buenos Aires in 1966, the oldest being *LV-AAO*, originally built at Rochester in 1942 as *DV964* and finally renamed *Río Aguilera*; nearly as old was *LV-AAR*, built at Dumbarton as *DD841*, resurrected from a watery grave and later named *Formosa*. Many of their engines had been removed for use in other aircraft, and there was a proposal to convert one of the hulls into a hydrofoil ferry-boat, but in January 1967 all were broken up for scrap.

The next order for Sandringhams came from Tasman Empire Airways Ltd for four Mk 4s furnished for 30 day passengers, with a pantry and bar on the upper deck; these were known in TEAL first as the Dominion class and later as the Tasman class, and were replacements for the ageing Empire Boats *Aotearoa* and *Awarua*, which without assistance so faithfully maintained the Sydney–Auckland service from 1940 to 1947. The first Sandringham 4, *ZK-AMB Tasman*, was delivered to TEAL on 17 July, 1946, and was followed by *ZK-AMD Australia, ZK-AME New Zealand* and in 1947 *ZK-AMH Auckland*. In November the domestic airline New Zealand National Airways took over the flying-boat service from Auckland to Fiji previously operated by the R.N.Z.A.F. and their four Sunderlands *NZ4101–4104*, which became *ZK-AMF, 'G, 'J* and *'K*; of these *'F* and *'J* were soon due for major overhauls and were broken up to provide spares for *ZK-AMG Mataatua* and *ZK-AMK Takitimu*; these two maintained regular services from Auckland to Suva and Labasa, and were on call for emergency flights also, in co-operation with the R.N.Z.A.F.; they retained their simple furnishings and Pegasus 38 engines.

N.Z.N.A.C.'s Sunderland III *ZK-AMK Takitimu* (formerly *NZ4104*) at Mechanic's Bay, Auckland, in 1947. (*Courtesy A. J. Jackson.*)

In February 1947 a similar service from Sydney to Lord Howe Island had been inaugurated by Trans-Oceanic Airways Ltd, using three ex-R.A.A.F. Sunderland IIIs *A26-2, '4* and *'5* (originally *ML731, '3* and *'4*) which came on to the civil register as *VH-BKQ Pacific Star, VH-AKO Australis* and *VH-AKP Tahiti Star*; this service continued till July 1952.

Although B.O.A.C. had at first declined to buy Sandringhams, they became seriously short of capacity during 1946 because of delays in delivery of Tudor and Hermes landplanes, and converted three more Hythes from R.A.F. surplus Sunderlands; these were *JM716, DD860* and *PP142*, which became *G-AHEO, 'P* and *'R, Halstead, Hanbury* and *Helmsdale*; the last in fact

403

B.O.A.C. Sunderland III freighter *Helmsdale* on Southampton Water in 1946.
(Courtesy A. J. Jackson.)

remained a cargo-carrier without passenger furnishings or additional windows, as did the only Sunderland 5 in B.O.A.C. service, *G-AHJR*, alias *SZ584*, on temporary loan in 1946–8. However, in January 1947 B.O.A.C. acquired on lease from the Ministry of Civil Aviation nine Sandringham 5s (known as the Plymouth class) furnished on one deck only for 22 day or 16 night passengers, with a pantry on the same level for meals service to passengers in their seats; these were registered *G-AHYY* to 'ZG and named, in order, *Portsmouth*, *Perth*, *Penzance*, *Portland*, *Pembroke*, *Portmarnock*, *Portsea*, *Poole* and *Pevensey*. All were converted from little-used Sunderlands fitted with Twin Wasp R-1830-90D engines, and so were virtually brand-new aircraft. Conversion went ahead fast at Queen's Island, but on 18 January, 1947, the second of the batch caught fire and was gutted while being dragged out of the factory; the remainder were delivered between March and September, and finally a replacement *Perth*, *G-AJMZ* (ex *JM681*), was handed over on 18 December. They began operation on 2 May, 1947, and relieved the Hythes on the routes from Poole to Sydney, Hong Kong and Bahrein and between Sydney and Singapore; after 1 April, 1948, they flew from Berth 50 near the Southampton Docks Ocean Terminal, instead of from Poole; a fortnight earlier they had begun flying through from Hong Kong to Iwakuni, Japan, a total distance of 10,625 miles, for which the scheduled time was 7 days; on 20 November the route was extended from Iwakuni to Tokyo.

Sandringhams proved reliable in B.O.A.C. service, and were well patronised by passengers who were not in too much of a hurry to enjoy the charm of a maritime environment. Early in 1948 three more of an improved 30-passenger version, the Sandringham 7 or Bermuda class, were ordered by B.O.A.C., and followed the three Sandringham 6s ordered by the Norwegian Airline (D.N.L.) for their coastal route from Oslo to Tromsø within the Arctic Circle; these three, *LN-IAU Bamse Brakar*, *LN-IAV Kvitbjørn* and *LN-IAW Bukken Bruse*, were furnished for 37 day passengers on two decks, with a pantry on the lower deck, and were specially equipped for flying in northern latitudes, although of course the service was suspended during winter when sea-ice created an unacceptable hazard in conjunction with several weeks of almost continuous night. As an aid to navigation they retained the full

A.S.V.6c radar installation of the Sunderland V, which was used to avoid mountainsides and cliffs as they flew in and out of the fjords. Conditions were exceptionally difficult even in summer, and all three were eventually lost in crashes, *Kvitbjørn* at Tjelesund on 28 August, 1947, *Bukken Bruse* near Trondheim on 2 October, 1948, and *Bamse Brakar* near Harstad on 15 May, 1950; two more, *LN-LAI Jutulen* and *LN-LMK Polarbjørn*, were supplied as replacements, but in 1951 D.N.L. became part of the Scandinavian Airlines System and these two were put up for disposal, *Jutulen* being chartered to France-Hydro and sunk at Bangui (French Equatorial Africa) in November 1952, while *Polarbjørn* was sold to Aerolineas Argentinas, being ferried as *LV-PAE* and becoming *LV-AHM Almirante Zar* in service.

D.N.L.'s second Sandringham 6, *LN-IAW*, on test at Belfast in May 1947.

In contrast to B.O.A.C.'s success with Sandringhams on the 'Dragon' route, TEAL found their Twin Wasp R-1830-90C engines prone to overheating on the Tasman service, the first failure occurring to *ZK-AME* on 3 December, 1947, when passengers' luggage had to be jettisoned to maintain height on three engines. They were withdrawn from service on 23 February, 1948, pending an official enquiry, but after thorough overhaul at Rose Bay returned to duty on 17 June for a further eighteen months, after which they were superseded by new Solent 4s; the last TEAL Sandringham flight was made by *ZK-AME* on 19 December, 1949, from Sydney to Auckland, after which it was sold to Ansett Airways as *VH-BRD*, together with *ZK-AMH* as *VH-BRC Beachcomber*; in 1953 they took over the Sydney–Lord Howe Island service from Trans-Oceanic Airways. The other Tasman Sandringhams *ZK-AMB* and '*D* became *VH-EBW* and '*X* on Qantas's Sydney–Noumea–Fiji route in May 1950 and were joined a year later by *VH-EBV Pacific Warrior* (ex *G-AHZD Portmarnock*) and *VH-EBY* (ex *G-AHZF Poole*); this service continued until 4 June, 1955, when it was taken over by DC-4 landplanes.

The three Sandringham 7s *G-AKCO Saint George*, *G-AKCP Saint David* and *G-AKCR Saint Andrew* entered service on the Far East routes in 1947 and flew uneventfully till B.O.A.C. retired them after a relatively short life in

1950; the last two were sold to C.A.U.S.A. in 1955 as *CX-ANA* and *CX-ANI*, while *Saint George* was bought in 1954 as *VH-APG* for charter cruises by Capt Sir Gordon Taylor around New Guinea and the islands to the east; in 1958 he sold it to Réseau Aérien Interinsulaire for tourist services between Tahiti and the Society and Tuamotu Islands; re-registered *F-OBIP* and wearing a photogenic livery of green and white, it was still flying a weekly round in 1966, fitted out as a 45-seater, unscathed by the violent storms which

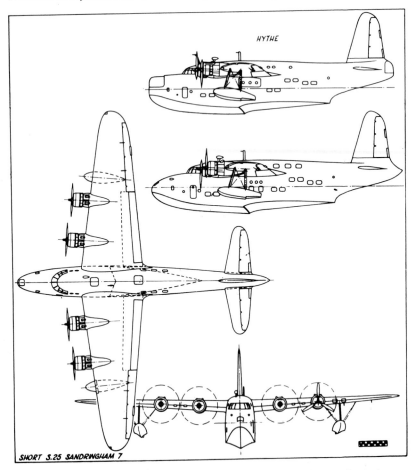

SHORT S.25 SANDRINGHAM 7

had wrecked other Sandringhams in the South Pacific. One such victim was *VH-BRE* of Ansett Flying Boat Services, formerly *VH-EBX*, bought from Qantas to operate the Lord Howe Island route after *VH-BRD* had been written-off at Brisbane on 31 October, 1952. On 3 July, 1963, *VH-BRE Pacific Chieftain*, having just completed a £40,000 overhaul, made an overnight stop at Lord Howe Island before starting on an 8,500-mile charter cruise in Polynesia; during the night an 80-kt cyclone tore the boat from its moorings and wrecked it. With only *VH-BRC* to maintain the service, the Australian Government persuaded the R.N.Z.A.F. to release one of their few remaining Sunderlands; on 19 December, 1963, *NZ4108* was ferried from Hobsonville to Rose Bay in nine hours and after ten months' work emerged as the 'near-Sandringham' *VH-BRF Islander* on 26 October, 1964; like *VH-BRE*, it was fitted out for 43 passengers, but had a more prominent nose fairing than a Belfast-built Sandringham.

Early in 1946 B.O.A.C. took on loan for evaluation the second production Seaford *NJ201*, which was temporarily registered *G-AGWU* in place of its Transport Command marking *OZZA*; it was considered to be a better proposition for development as an airliner than the Sandringham, and Short Brothers had submitted a version, called Solent 1, having three cabins on the lower deck and two on the upper, each cabin being furnished for six passengers by day or four by night; there was also a promenade cabin on the lower deck.

B.O.A.C.'s second Solent 2, *Scarborough*, at Rochester in 1947, with unmodified wing-floats.

M.C.A. agreed to order 12 of this civil variant, S.45A, to be built at Rochester in the jigs made vacant by the cancellation of the rest of the Seaford contract; for this batch of new aircraft without previous identities, Short Brothers revived the system of constructor's numbers abandoned during the war and allotted S.1300–1311 to match civil registrations *G-AHIL* to 'Y and the individual names *Salisbury, Scarborough, Southampton, Somerset, Sark, Scapa, Severn, Solway, Salcombe, Stornoway, Sussex* and *Southsea.* B.O.A.C. wished to carry day passengers only, so the interior was revised as Solent 2, corresponding closely to the Sandringham in their two-deck luxury accommodation for 34 day passengers and a crew of seven, with a dining-saloon, cocktail bar and promenade; the engines were civil-rated Hercules 637s of 1,690 hp, and the fuel tankage was increased by 110 gallons to 3,160 gallons, one of the first British pressure-fuelling systems being installed. *Salisbury* was launched on 11 November, 1946, and first flown by Geoffrey Tyson, who had succeeded John Parker as chief test pilot a year previously. After a long schedule of handling, performance and fuel consumption tests occupying most of 1947, during which five more of the class were launched and flown, a full C. of A. was granted to *Severn* on 10 November of that year and crew training was accelerated in preparation for the introduction of Solents on the Johannesburg route in the following spring. The last of the batch, *G-AHIY Southsea*, launched on 8 April, 1948, was the last new aircraft to be built at Rochester seaplane works, whose gates were to close in the following July. On 14 April, 1948, when Lord Nathan, Minister of Civil Aviation, performed the official opening of B.O.A.C.'s new flying-boat terminal at Berth 50, Southampton Docks, *G-AHIN* was ceremonially named *Southampton* by the Mayoress of Southampton and soon afterwards left on a proving flight over the route to Vaaldam with a party of journalists representing the world's Press; the first normal service commenced on 4 May and was flown by *Severn*.

Although the Solent was cleared to take off at 78,000 lb (3,000 lb higher than the maximum permitted for the military Seaford), it does not seem to have suffered from the pounding experienced with the prototypes at Felixstowe, but its wing-tip float clearance was insufficient at this weight and made precise taxying difficult in choppy water; so on 22 July the eight Solents already in traffic were withdrawn for the floats to be repositioned 18 in forward and 87 in outboard; at the same time these were more robustly mounted on two pairs of inclined struts which eliminated spanwise tie-rod bracing. This modification was first tested on the Seaford *NJ201* at Felixstowe and finally approved on *Salisbury* at Belfast in September, all the Solents being returned to service by 17 October. By this time B.O.A.C. had decided to lease the six Seafords *NJ202–207*, which on completing operational trials with No. 201 Squadron had been declared redundant by the Air Ministry; these were flown to Belfast for conversion to Solent 3s seating 39 passengers, having an extra cabin in the rear of the upper deck. The first of these, *G-AKNO* (ex *NJ202*), received its full C. of A. on 1 April, 1949, and was flown on to the Thames at Limehouse on 5 May, to be ceremonially named *City of London* by Sir George Aylwin at Tower Steps on the 10th; this event formed part of the celebration marking the 30th anniversary of civil aviation in Britain. A fortnight later Solents replaced Sandringhams on the Southampton–Karachi route, but meanwhile an independent British flying-boat operator had emerged; this was Barry T. Aikman, who formed Aquila Airways to take over Hythes and Sandringhams withdrawn from B.O.A.C.'s routes. B.O.A.C. terminated all their Hythe operations on 16 February with the arrival at Southampton from Sydney of *Honduras*; this marked the completion of six years' service by the two dozen civil Sunderlands of B.O.A.C., during which they had carried nearly 80,000 passengers and 2,800 tons of freight, and had flown over 25 million miles.

Barry Aikman had first acquired three Hythes (*Hadfield*, *Haslemere* and *Halstead*) in order to assist the R.A.F.'s Sunderlands on the Berlin Airlift between Finkenwerder and the Havel See; starting on 4 August, 1948, they made 265 sorties and carried over 1,400 tons before ice on the Havel See brought flying-boat operations to an end for the winter on 15 December. With the proceeds of this enterprise Aikman bought up seven more Hythes and the Sandringham 1 *Himalaya* as the nucleus of the Aquila Airways fleet. On 24 March *Hampshire* made the first proving flight to Lisbon and Madeira;

a regular fortnightly service began on 11 June, with an additional weekly shuttle service between Lisbon and Funchal, which proved very popular in Portugal. The Madeira service prospered during the next three seasons, although *Haslemere* had to be broken up for spares in February 1951 and *Hawkesbury* suffered the same fate a year later. Then *Hudson* was written-off after a collision at Funchal on 21 January, 1953, and *Hungerford* sank at Calshot a week later, leaving only *Himalaya*, *Hampshire* and the veteran *Hadfield* serviceable. Aikman then bought Sunderland V *PP162*, a much-rebuilt survivor of the M.A.E.E.'s porpoising and wave-impact flight tests, and got it ferried from Felixstowe to Hamble for conversion into a new Hythe *G-ANAK*, only to have it wrecked by a storm. However, he had seen at Felixstowe the Seaford trainer *NJ201*, already partly modified to Solent standard, and was allowed to buy it; at Hamble it was fully converted into a Solent 3, and in May 1954 became the Aquila flagship *G-ANAJ City of Funchal*.

The last Solent 3, *G-AKNU Sydney*, at Belfast in December 1951 after being purchased by Aquila Airways.

The Solents of B.O.A.C. had cut existing schedules nearly in half when they began work on the South Africa route on 15 May, 1949, but their life was only 18 months, for on 10 November, 1950, B.O.A.C. terminated all its flying-boat operations and the Solents were dispersed to storage at Belfast, Poole and Felixstowe, pending sale by M.C.A., whose property they were. In connection with a proposal (P.D.3) to convert Solents to the anti-submarine role, *G-AKNS City of Liverpool* was loaned to M.A.E.E. for overload rough-weather tests, with the temporary serial *WM759*; it was flown at Felixstowe, Gibraltar and Tangier in swells of various heights and lengths at weights up to 84,000 lb, to determine the relationship between porpoising (especially skipping) and swell length and alighting speed, also the extent of spray damage to airscrew tips and tailplane leading edges under these conditions. While these experiments were primarily intended to obtain data for policy decisions on the future usefulness of military flying-boats, they also cleared the way for approval of a heavier version, Solent 4, ordered by TEAL to replace Sandringhams on the Auckland–Sydney service, as the outcome of a

409

visit to New Zealand by Sir John Buchanan and Bill Hambrook in January 1947. Four of these were built to TEAL's stringent specification, and the first, *ZK-AML*, was launched at Belfast and named *Aotearoa II* by Princess Elizabeth on 26 May, 1949. After completing certification trials it was delivered to Auckland at the end of November, to join *ZK-AMM Ararangi*, *ZK-AMN Awatere* and *ZK-AMO Aranui*, which had gone on ahead.

ZK-AMM Ararangi, the second Solent 4 for T.E.A.L., alighting on Belfast Lough in October 1949.

These four boats (SH.1556–1559) had more powerful Hercules 733 engines with ejector exhausts and fan-cooling, were cleared for take-off at 81,000 lb and were beautifully furnished for 44 passengers, while additional tankage gave them a still air range of 3,000 miles—50 per cent more than the Solent 3; they went into service on 14 November, 1949, between Auckland and Sydney and took over the Auckland–Suva and Suva–Labasa routes from N.Z.N.A.C.'s Sunderlands in June 1950; in October the Solents began a Wellington–Sydney service, and this was extended once every three months to Chatham Island. They were reinforced in August 1951 by Solent 3, *G-AKNR City of Belfast*, ferried out via Lough Erne, Gander, San Francisco, Honolulu and Fiji, to be renamed *ZK-AMQ Aparimu*; at the end of the year they inaugurated the 'Coral Route' to Suva, Cook Islands and Tahiti, later adding a call at Apia, Samoa; the Fiji route was extended to Tonga in August 1953, but between March and June 1954 flying-boats were replaced by landplanes on all TEAL's routes except Fiji–Tahiti, for which *Aranui* was retained until its final 'Coral Route' flight on 14 September, 1960, when it was withdrawn after 14,500 flying hours; it was stored at Hobsonville R.N.Z.A.F. base till May 1966, being then towed round to Herne Bay, Auckland, where it was hauled two miles inland for permanent preservation at the Museum of Transport and Technology, Western Springs.

During the ten years between B.O.A.C.'s cessation of Solent services and TEAL's similar termination, redundant Solents made many long ferry flights as they changed owners. Four, *G-AKNO*, *G-AKNP*, *G-AHIV* and *G-AHIO*, were sold to Trans-Oceanic Airways as *VH-TOA*, *'B*, *'C* and *'D* during 1951 for services linking Sydney with Hobart in one direction and Port

Moresby in the other, but the first was wrecked at Malta on its delivery flight in January; plans for a daily Sydney–Hobart service proved too ambitious, and a proposed extension from Port Moresby across the Pacific, ultimately to Tokyo, was vetoed by the licensing authorities; *VH-TOC Star of Papua* maintained a coastal service weekly between Sydney and New Guinea, and in June 1956 the other two were acquired by an American-owned enterprise, South Pacific Airlines, being ferried to Oakland, California, as *N9945F* and *N9946F*, to join *G-AKNT*, which had already been flown from Belfast via Southampton, Reykjavik, Halifax, Patuxent and Corpus Christi with an extra 800-gallon tank in the cabin, to become *N9947F* in November 1955. Ten years later all three were still in existence, *N9946F* at San Francisco and the others at Oakland, having been refused a CAB licence to operate a projected Honolulu–Tahiti–Fiji route; they had not been flown again, and in 1967 were

Solent 3 *N9946F* (ex *VH-TOB*, *G-AKNP* and *NJ203*) at Oakland, Cal., in South Pacific Airlines livery in 1956. (*Courtesy A. J. Jackson.*)

owned by Howard Hughes, who kept them under armed guard. In a migration in the opposite direction two Solent 4s, *ZK-AML* and *'N*, were ferried back to England in 1955 to join Aquila Airways' fleet as *G-AOBL* and *G-ANYI*. Converted to Solent 3 interiors, they went into service on routes to the Canary Islands, Madeira and Montreux, together with *G-ANAJ* and *G-AKNU*, but the former was wrecked at Santa Margherita on 29 September, 1956, and the latter crashed at Chessell Down, Isle of Wight, on 15 November, 1957, when 46 passengers and crew were killed.

With the ending of British civil flying-boat operation on 30 September, 1958, Aquila Airways closed its regular service to Madeira, but sold its three remaining Solents, *G-AHIN*, *G-AOBL* and *G-ANYI*, to a Portuguese company, Artop, in October, after which they remained beached on the bank of the Tagus at Lisbon, thus suffering the same fate as those in California. They were a sad monument to the enterprise of seafaring aviators overtaken by the invincible combination of 10,000-ft concrete runways and 20,000-lb-thrust turbojets; modern air travel may have become more of a miracle, but some of the magic disappeared when flying-boats ceased to ply.

411

Sandringham 1—Span 112 ft 9 in (34·3 m); length 85 ft 4 in (26 m); area 1,487 sq ft (138·1 m²); empty weight 34,150 lb (15,500 kg); all-up weight 56,000 lb (25,400 kg); max speed 216 mph (348 km/h); range 2,550 miles (4,100 km).

Sandringham 2, 3, 4 & 6—Span and areas as for Sandringham 1; length 86 ft 3 in (26·3 m); empty weight 41,000 lb (18,600 kg); all-up weight 56,000 lb (25,400 kg); max speed 238 mph (383 km/h); range 2,400 miles (3,860 km).

Sandringham 5 & 7—Dimensions as for Sandringham 2; empty weight 39,500 lb (17,920 kg); all-up weight 60,000 lb (27,220 kg); max speed 206 mph (332 km/h); range 2,450 miles (3,945 km).

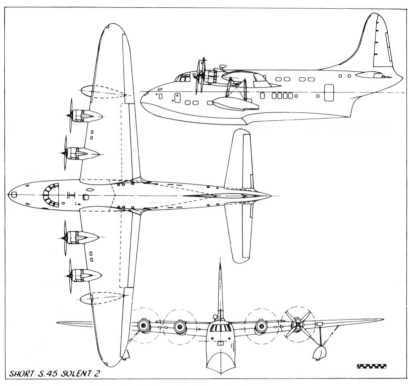

SHORT S.45 SOLENT 2

Solent 2—Span 112 ft 9 in (34·3 m); length 87 ft 8 in (26·7 m); area 1,487 sq ft (138·1 m²); empty weight 47,760 lb (21,670 kg); all-up weight 78,000 lb (35,400 kg); max speed 273 mph (440 km/h); range 1,800 miles (2,900 km).

Solent 3—Dimensions as for Solent 2; empty weight 48,210 lb (21,870 kg); all-up weight 78,600 lb (35,700 kg); max speed 267 mph (430 km/h); range 2,200 miles (3,540 km).

Solent 4—Span and area as for Solent 2 & 3; length 88 ft 7 in (27·1 m); empty weight 49,150 lb (22,352 kg); all-up weight 81,000 lb (36,770 kg); max speed 282 mph (454 km/h); range 3,000 miles (4,830 km).

412

Sturgeon 1 *RK787* at Rochester Airport before its first flight by Geoffrey Tyson on 7 June, 1946.

The Short Sturgeon and S.B.3

Soon after Arthur Gouge left Short Brothers to become Vice-Chairman of Saunders-Roe Ltd, the engineering team at Rochester under C. P. T. Lipscomb began work on a design study for a high-performance naval torpedo-bomber reconnaissance monoplane for use on the new *Ark Royal* and *Hermes* classes of aircraft carrier, to meet specification S.6/43. Two schemes were submitted to the Admiralty during the summer of 1943, one with a single Bristol Centaurus engine and the other with two Rolls-Royce Merlins; the latter design was preferred, and specification S.11/43 was drafted (with the torpedo role deleted) as the basis of a contract awarded in October for three prototypes. The requirements for both performance and space limitations were very severe, and the problems arising demanded considerable ingenuity for their solution; the result was the first high-speed, twin-engined strike aircraft designed specifically for carrier operation with the Royal Navy, the immediate objective being to drive the Japanese naval forces out of the Malayan archipelago. In the event, construction of the new carriers was suspended after the Japanese surrender in August 1945, and the immediate need for the S.11/43 had disappeared before it was ready for flight. So, too, had the enemy fighters and bombers which had hitherto provided live targets for the Royal Navy's gunners, but the latter could not remain efficient in peacetime without some substitute for an enemy; thus it was a logical progression to adapt the new Short monoplane into a fast multi-purpose gunnery training and target aircraft, for which a new specification, Q.1/46, was issued early in 1946. The next vacant numbers in the design index were S.38 and S.39, which were initially allotted to the S.11/43 and Q.1/46 respectively, but in 1945 Short Brothers adopted the universal designation system recommended by the S.B.A.C., and the two designs were re-indexed as S.A.1 and S.A.2; at the same time the official name Sturgeon was adopted, as S. Mk 1 and T.T. Mk 2 respectively.

The Sturgeon 1 was an orthodox mid-wing monoplane of Alclad

413

monocoque construction, with fabric-covered ailerons, elevators and rudder. Although (fortunately for the designers) it did not have to carry a torpedo, its armament in the attack role included two or four fixed forward-firing 0·5-in-calibre Browning guns and either one 1,000-lb bomb or two 500-lb bombs or four 250-lb Torpex depth-charges in the enclosed bomb-cell, plus 16 60-lb rocket projectiles under the wings. The crew of three comprised the pilot in a self-contained cockpit forward of the wing and the navigator and radio operator in a separate cabin aft of the wing; there was no rear turret or other defensive armament, but the crew stations were protected fore and aft by armour plate. Some 500 lb weight of radio and radar equipment was installed, including A.S.V. with its scanner mounted in a nose radome. In the alternative photographic reconnaissance role it carried a crew of two only, with two F.52 cameras and one F.24 camera mounted vertically in the bottom of the rear fuselage, together with a 180-gallon long-range fuel tank in the bomb-cell.

Structurally the fuselage comprised four monocoque sub-assemblies, with notched channel-section frames and continuous stringers; the pilot's cockpit unit was built as a complete sub-assembly enclosed by the front fuselage, and the centre fuselage was built integrally with the parallel-chord centre wing, which extended continuously across the bomb-cell, whose roof it formed; the stern assembly was integral with the fin and two root stubs for attachment of the halves of the tailplane. The wing comprised the centre-section and two outer folding wing panels hinged to it. The wing section was NACA 642215 with a maximum thickness of 15 per cent at 40 per cent of the chord; great care was taken to produce a smooth skin of fairly thick gauge and accurate profile so as to maintain laminar airflow back to 30 per cent or more of the chord over the outer wings. The centre-section contained four flexible self-sealing fuel tanks totalling 410 gallons between the two spars and also carried the nacelles with power plants and main landing-gear units; the engines were Rolls-Royce Merlin 140s of 2,080 hp each, driving six-bladed Rotol contra-rotating airscrews made necessary by the limit of 20 ft on overall folded width; the engines had two-stage superchargers whose intercoolers were mounted in ducts in the lower part of the cowlings, the coolant and oil radiators being installed across the leading edges of the centreplane as in the D.H. Mosquito. The wing spars were simple beams with extruded L-section booms and plate webs, the ribs being pressed from sheet with flanged lightening-holes and draw-sunk stiffening flutes. A peculiarity of the wing geometry was the moderate forward slope of the front spar web and very pronounced backward slope of the rear spar web; this was combined with a similarly raked root-end spar joint to provide an oblique hinge in the rear spar which enabled the wing to fold back with its chord vertical when stowed, so as to occupy minimum space below decks; the very highly stressed spar joints were machined from castings in DTD666 nickel–chrome alloy steel, having an ultimate strength of over 75 tons/sq in. The equally sturdy main under-carriage units designed by Rubery Owen – Messier each comprised a single wheel and oleo-leg folding straight back into the nacelle; the castoring tailwheel was retractable forwards into the rear fuselage, and the deck-landing arrestor hook was mounted just behind it, lying flush with the fuselage when retracted.

The controls were cable-operated with automatic tensioning, the ailerons having spring tabs and the elevators and rudder geared servo-tabs; the rudder had a small horn balance, and the ailerons and elevators were inset from the tips and had shrouded noses and set-back hinges. Split flaps of the sliding Zap type extended across the wing between the ailerons and were actuated hydraulically, as were landing-gear retraction and wing folding; when the first prototype was completed there was a shortage of the specified indicating selector switches, and a push-button wing-folding switch was temporarily fitted that did not show which operation had been selected; consequently, when the engines were first run at Rochester Airport there was momentary alarm when the wings folded back as the hydraulic pressure built up, the selector having been left in that position. The two Sturgeon 1s *RK787* and *RK791* were built concurrently, their jigs being ready in September 1944 and the bare airframes complete a year later. *RK787* was flown by Geoffrey Tyson on 7 June, 1946, at Rochester Airport and first seen in public at Farnborough on 27 June; *RK791* was shipped to Belfast for completion, together with the

The second Sturgeon 1, *RK791*, landing at Sydenham after its first flight by J. S. Booth on 18 May, 1948.

third prototype, originally *RK794*, which was to be modified during construction into the first prototype Mk 2, with the new serial *VR363*. Both were still incomplete when Short Brothers began their move to Belfast and were finally assembled at Queen's Island in the summer of 1948, together with a fourth prototype (second Mk 2) *VR371*; all three made their first flights from Sydenham airfield, adjoining the factory, and the two Mk 2s received the Belfast c/ns SH.1560 and 1561. Jigs already manufactured for Sturgeon 1 production at Rochester were laid down at Belfast and in 1949 a batch of 24 Sturgeon T.T.2s (SH.1576–1599) was ordered for the Royal Navy, using the previously allotted Mk 1 serials *TS475–498*.

Sturgeon T.T.2 *TS486* on test over the Antrim coast in 1950.

The Sturgeon T.T.2 was more than just another target-tug, and was particularly well adapted for the additional roles of 'throw-off' target practice, photographic marking and radar calibration. While retaining the excellent handling qualities of the Sturgeon 1, including the freedom from swing on take-off conferred by cancellation of airscrew torque reaction, it provided for a normal crew of two and had a much extended nose to permit unobstructed use of the special Vinten gunnery marking camera; the nose was arranged to fold down and back to reduce the overall length to the limits imposed by the lift of an aircraft carrier. The Sturgeon 1 had received a very satisfactory assessment in its deck-landing trials on H.M.S. *Illustrious,* and the Sturgeon 2 was seen as a valuable operational training aid which could cruise with the Fleet and always be available for gunnery practice; previously the Royal Navy had had to rely on shore stations to provide target services, which were within range for only a few days at fairly long intervals during a cruise. Apart from the revised nose-shape, the Sturgeon 2 had a deepened centre fuselage to allow the second crew member to crawl beneath the pilot's seat when changing station from the camera in the nose to the Miles hydraulic winch and comprehensive radio in the rear fuselage, where also there was another camera in a turret-like revolving cupola with optically flat panels for target observation. Other minor changes were the tail-unit guard cables stretched between the tailplane and rudder tips to prevent fouling by the winch cables, also Coffman cartridge starting for the engines. Both variants had been stressed and equipped for catapulted or rocket-assisted take-off, and the Sturgeon 2 could tow 32-ft and 16-ft wing targets as well as various patterns of drogue and flag targets.

After handling trials of *VR363* at Boscombe Down between April and July 1949, including deck trials on *Illustrious* on 26 May, the elevator area was enlarged by 20 per cent to improve handling in a 'dead-stick' landing, and after a further check of the modified aircraft at Boscombe Down it was accepted for service in February 1950. Sturgeon 2s were issued to both carrier-borne units and shore establishments, forming the equipment of No. 728 Squadron and the Fleet Requirements Unit based at Hal Far, Malta. In 1951, with improved gun-laying radar available, throw-off target practice was discontinued and Sturgeons were no longer needed for Fleet exercises, although retained at some shore stations; in November 1953 a new variant, T.T. Mk 3 (S.B.9), was contrived by removing all deck-landing aids, including arrestor hook and hydraulic wing-folding; at the same time the nose camera station was deleted, reducing the overall length by 6 ft 9 in, which resulted in the disappearance of the folding portion and rounding off the fixed nose to nearly the shape of the original Sturgeon 1. No new T.T.3s were built, but five T.T.2s were converted to the new variant, *TS475* at Belfast and *TS479–482* at Short Brothers' service department depot at Rochester Airport; further conversions were programmed but cancelled, and although the five T.T.3s served at Hal Far for another five years, the remaining T.T.2s were stored; the second prototype *VR371* was still at Rochester in 1957, the first prototype *VR363* having been used as the tug for the ill-fated S.B.1 experimental glider at Aldergrove in 1951.

Sturgeon T.T.3 *TS475* at Sydenham in November 1953 after conversion from T.T.2.

Meanwhile a further development had resulted in 1949 from a proposal to adapt the Sturgeon to suit the general requirements of specification GR.17/45 as modified for anti-submarine radar search and patrol; for this role specification M.6/49 was drafted, and the last Sturgeon SH.1599 became the first prototype of a new design, S.B.3, being drastically modified before reaching the final assembly jigs; a second prototype, SH.1603, was also laid down, and serials *WF632* and *636* were allotted. Using the basic Sturgeon airframe, the S.B.3 was powered by two 1,475 hp Armstrong Siddeley Mamba turbine engines driving four-bladed airscrews. Its front fuselage was completely revised to accommodate two radar operators in a cabin in front of and below the pilot's cockpit, with a large search radar scanner mounted in a radome under the floor in the nose; the rear fuselage lines were unbroken as in the Sturgeon 1. The S.B.3 could carry a maximum weapon load of 2,620 lb, comprising bombs, mines, depth-charges and sonobuoys in various combinations, and *WF632* was first flown on 12 August, 1950, by Tom Brooke-Smith,

417

The S.B.3 *WF632* on show at Farnborough in September 1950.

who also flew it three weeks later at the S.B.A.C. show at Farnborough. It had been hoped that the S.B.3 would prove competitive with the Fairey Gannet Mk 3, the only other contender for the role, but unfortunately the downward-directed jet-pipes of the Mambas had a serious de-stabilising effect, because the engines were single-shaft turbines whose speed and efflux varied with power demand; consequently, all the Sturgeon's good handling qualities were missing and the S.B.3 was difficult to trim, especially with one engine idling. No full operational assessment of *WF632* was made and *WF636* never flew at all, both being scrapped early in 1951.

The S.B.3 had the same wing-folding mechanism as the Sturgeon. (*Crown Copyright.*)

418

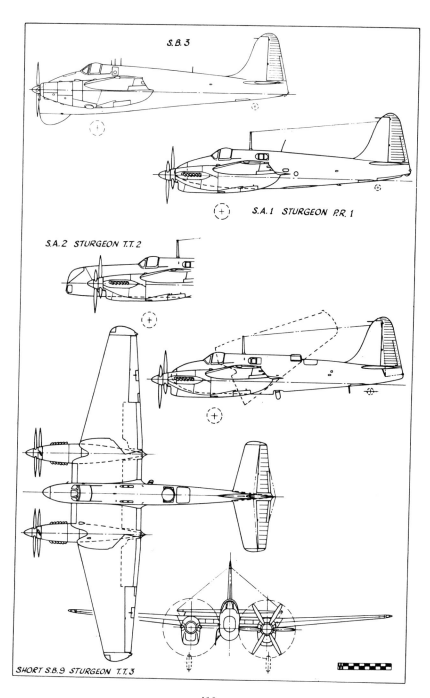

S.B.3

S.A.1 STURGEON P.R.1

S.A.2 STURGEON T.T.2

SHORT S.B.9 STURGEON T.T.3

419

Sturgeon 1—Span 59 ft 11 in (18·23 m); length 44 ft (13·4 m); area 518·4 sq ft (48·16 m²); empty weight 18,126 lb (8,280 kg); all-up weight 21,700 lb (9,850 kg); max speed 352 mph (566 km/h).

Sturgeon 2—Span and area as for Sturgeon 1; length 48 ft 11 in (14·91 m); empty weight 17,647 lb (8,050 kg); all-up weight 22,350 lb (10,136 kg); max speed 366 mph (589 km/h).

Sturgeon 3—Span and area as for Sturgeon 1 & 2; length 45 ft 9 in (14 m); empty weight 16,000 lb (7,255 kg); all-up weight 22,050 lb (10,000 kg); max speed 366 mph (589 km/h).

S.B.3—Span 59 ft 11 in (18·23 m); length 44 ft 9 in (13·7 m); area 520·6 sq ft (48·3 m²); empty weight 15,252 lb (6,925 kg); all-up weight 23,600 lb (10,700 kg); max speed 320 mph (515 km/h); max range 715 miles (1,150 km).

Tom Weekes, with John Stroud as passenger, in the Nimbus during a four-minute flight at Rochester Airport on 1 April, 1947; John Stroud is retaliating with a Leica against *Flight*'s photographer in a Tiger Moth. (*Flight*.)

The Short Nimbus

It had been the lifelong ambition of Oscar Gnosspelius not merely to fly (which he achieved as early as 1912) but to emulate the effortless soaring of the seagull, and his Gull monoplane of 1923 would undoubtedly have been successful as a motorless glider, for its performance on only 16 hp was little short of incredible. He had lived to see the art and science of soaring revived and developed by the Rhön-Rossiten Gesellschaft in Germany in the 1930s, but not to witness the Nazis' degradation of this art in the invasion of his paternal homeland, Denmark, in 1940. When Hitler's war ended, a younger generation of practical aerodynamicists was keen to respond to the technical challenge and aesthetic appeal of soaring, and by the summer of 1946 the revival of gliding as a sport was well under way; naturally a gliding club was soon formed at Rochester, the leading lights being Tom Weekes and Dudley Parkes of Short Brothers' design office.

They could have done what most other clubs were doing and opted to buy one of several efficient training gliders already in limited production for cadets of the Air Training Corps, but they were confident that they could spend their limited cash more effectively by designing and building a prototype to their own ideas. They could not expect Short Brothers, with very heavy overhead expenses, to finance such a project, particularly since the firm was now publicly owned, but the management followed Oswald Short's magnanimous example of 24 years earlier and offered the syndicate drawing-office and workshop facilities for the construction of a prototype; although not an official company product, the final stages of assembly were helped by specialists at the firm's expense, and it was allotted the last but one of the revived constructor's numbers, S.1312. The Government had decided to remove all Short Brothers' activities from the Medway Towns within two years, and plans were already in train for the amalgamation of the parent firm with Short & Harland Ltd at Belfast, with all future design and manufacture centred on Queen's Island. The transfer began in 1947, the design organisation being the last department to move from Rochester, except for a Service Department contingent which stayed on for over ten years before moving to West Malling. Lipscomb was busy with several advanced projects and saw nothing but benefit in allowing his juniors to undertake an enterprise so near to their hearts and at the same time of great educational value. So the last aircraft designed, built and flown from Short Brothers' Rochester works was a motorless sailplane, and a wooden one at that!

Named the Nimbus, but having no design index number, the new craft was a very elegant and efficient gull-wing cantilever monoplane seating two in a neat tandem cockpit enclosed by a one-piece Perspex hood. Its construction followed established sailplane principles, the main novelty being the low-wing position of the upswept two-spar centre-section, which was quite narrow and terminated at the edge of the root fillet, where the outer wings were attached by expanding shear pins in steel-bushed light-alloy fittings. The inner part of each outer wing continued at a steep dihedral angle, while the rear spar converged to join the front one at the 'knuckle', 11 ft from the centre-line, the outer part of the wing being of constant taper and normal dihedral built round a single spar; the spars were of I-section with plywood webs and spruce booms and the wing covering was torsion-resistant thin plywood from the leading edge to the spar and lightweight madapolam fabric thence to the trailing edge; the aerofoil section was Göttingen 535 except at the tips, where it washed out to Clark Y. The plywood-covered spruce-framed monocoque fuselage incorporated a single central landing-wheel partly submerged between the spars, just aft of the centre of gravity, with a rubber-sprung steel-shod skid acting as a forward fairing; the small fin was integral with the fuselage and the tailplane was bolted to a rectangular cut-out, with a detachable fairing, just forward of the fin fillet; there was a small underfin carrying a laminated steel tailskid. The elevators and horn-balanced rudder were madapolam-covered with plywood noses, as were the ailerons, whose differential control circuit included a device for varying upfloat and downfloat during flight. Full dual controls and instruments were installed, including altimeter, A.S.I. and V.S.I. for each pilot; additionally there were a turn-and-bank indicator and a compass on the front panel, while both seats were fitted with Sutton harness and were recessed for back-type parachutes. Spoilers were fitted in the gull-wing upper surface between the converging spar-booms, and the landing-wheel had a trigger-operated brake. The Perspex cockpit cover hinged to starboard for access and incorporated a sliding direct-vision panel on its port side, directly above the Otfur patent towing hook, so that a visual check of release could be easily made. With the rear seat directly above the centre of gravity, no ballast or trim adjustment was needed for flying solo from the front seat, and few two-seaters gave both occupants so excellent an all-round view.

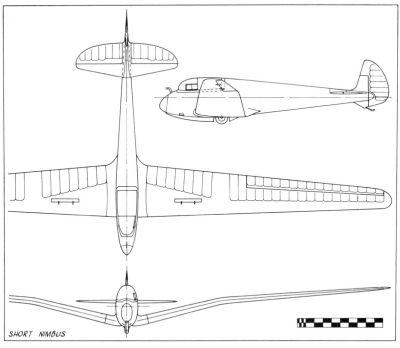

SHORT NIMBUS

After survey by the British Gliding Association, the Nimbus was allotted the registration *BGA470* and quickly attracted interest when first launched by winch on 18 January, 1947, at Rochester Airport, to the extent that Short Brothers were prepared to promote sales and undertake limited production if orders matured. R.A.F. Reserve Command assessed it as rather too exotic for regular use by the A.T.C., but praised its combination of sturdy construction with high aerodynamic refinement. Dr Alan Slater gave it a favourable report after sampling it at Rochester Airport on 1 April, liking its good penetration, which was in some measure achieved by cunning use of the variable-droop ailerons. Espin Hardwick, president of the Midland Gliding Club, was impressed by the Nimbus and provisionally ordered a production model, in which it was hoped to reduce the weight by 100 lb, or 12 per cent of the gross. It was taken to the Long Mynd, where Hardwick and Charles Wingfield soared it to 1,000 ft in one of five half-hour flights made late on 14 April. After winning the second prize for two-seaters in a design competition run by the B.G.A., it was shown at the S.B.A.C. Flying Display at Radlett in September, and on 21 October it took part in the Bristol Gliding Club's 'At Home' at Lulsgate, where it was flown by Philip Wills. Its one defect, unfortunately an incurable one, was that at maximum L/D a slight flow breakdown occurred at the wing 'knuckle' which prevented the best sinking speed from being held; this did not detract from its usefulness as a soaring trainer, but ruined its chances as a championship winner.

The Nimbus being winch-launched at Rochester Airport in January 1947.

In the spring of 1948 Tom Weekes was transferred to Queen's Island, where in due course he re-established Shorts' Gliding Club with encouragement from Professor G. T. R. Hill, who recommended every aircraft factory to run a gliding club 'for promoting design insight'. Conditions at Sydenham were unfavourable for gliding, and the club operated for some years from Bishops-court, Co. Down, but in 1956 it moved to Meghabery, where some excellent performances were obtained; indeed, enthusiasm and talent flourished so vigorously under Bill Erwin and Stuart Morrison that the club was able to enter the Nimbus in the two-seater class at the National Championships at Lasham in 1959. By that time it had survived several heavy repairs during twelve years of club use and had become 'a bit of a barge', so was unplaced. Only the prototype was ever built, as too few orders were offered to make production feasible after the interruption caused by the move from Rochester to Belfast. The Nimbus was later based at R.A.F. St. Mawgan and flew in the 1974 National Gliding Championships at Bicester. In 1989 it was put on display in the Ulster Folk and Transport Museum, Holywood, Co. Down which acquired it in 1985 after restoration by Mike Russell.

Span 62 ft (18·9 m); length 26 ft 10 in (8·2 m); area 230 sq ft (19 m²); empty weight 800 lb (363 kg); all-up weight 1,200 lb (545 kg); sinking speed 2·3 ft/sec (0·7 m/sec) at 38 mph (61 km/h).

Both Sperrins flying over Aldergrove in 1952; *VX161* is the nearer.

The Short Sperrin

The advent of jet propulsion for military aircraft during the later years of the Second World War accentuated the problem of compressibility which had already been encountered with fast airscrew-driven fighters; methods of combating the problem were kept a closely guarded secret on both sides, and the significance of the swept wing in delaying shock-wave formation was not fully appreciated by the Allies until the results of German research had been analysed. Already a specification for a light jet bomber to replace the Mosquito had been finalised as B.3/45, to emerge as the English Electric Canberra, with a thin unswept laminar-flow wing giving excellent stability and control; the same philosophy was applied to the requirement for a four-jet Lincoln replacement, defined a year later by specification B.14/46. Concurrently, the Air Staff had issued specification N.7/46 for a naval jet fighter and 8/46 for a general-purpose four-engined transport. Short Brothers' project design team under C. P. T. Lipscomb were still at Rochester, but knew that their future lay at Belfast, where all the firm's activities were to be concentrated in 18 months' time. They began three projects—S.A.3 for the naval fighter, S.A.4 for the bomber and S.A.5 for the transport—and submitted outline proposals to the Air Staff; the latter realised that any straight-winged design would be limited to a lower Mach number than its swept equivalent, but the risk of postponement at that time was too great to accept in spite of the certainty of early obsolescence. Of the proposals received, the S.A.4 was adjudged to be the best in the bomber class, and Short Brothers were given a contract for two prototypes; the naval fighter order went to Hawkers and resulted in the Seahawk, while the transport, after revision to C.16/46 to take advantage of

424

airscrew–turbine development, emerged as the Armstrong Whitworth Apollo.

The B.14/46 requirements specified a range of 3,350 nautical miles carrying a bomb-load of 10,000 lb at the highest possible speed, with a ceiling over the target of 45,000 ft; for shorter ranges the bomb-load was to be doubled and the aircraft had to accommodate internally either conventional or nuclear weapons; at that date this meant a bomb cell 30 ft long, 10 ft wide and 10 ft high. The crew of five were to be concentrated in a single pressure cabin, since there was no defensive armament and navigation and bomb-aiming were to rely on an advanced version of H2S radar, although a supplementary visual-bombing station in the nose was also specified. Cabin pressure was to be 9 lb/sq in, equivalent to 8,000 ft altitude during cruise at 40,000 ft, reducible to 3·5 lb/sq in (25,000 ft equivalent altitude) over the target to minimise the effects of sudden decompression if attacked; the first pilot was to have an ejector seat, and the other crew members were to be able to bale out quickly before the pilot; finally, the bomber was to be capable of rapid quantity production and easy maintenance, and to avoid novel techniques and unproven materials.

Lipscomb's solution to this formidable demand was essentially a simple and conventional one, albeit attained only by considerable ingenuity. An early difficulty was that Shorts had never had their own wind-tunnel at Rochester and had not yet built one at Belfast; hitherto they had relied on being able to send their models to the R.A.E. and N.P.L., but in 1946 these facilities were in such demand that waiting time became prohibitive, and even firms with their own modern tunnels suffered delays in getting their results confirmed. So Short Brothers relied initially on hydraulic analogy tests in their seaplane tank, using model fuselage shapes with the longitudinal dimension scaled up in accordance with Prandtl's Law; in the case of the S.A.4 this increased the fineness ratio by about 1·9, and tests in water at 2 degrees incidence represented behaviour in air at 3·8 degrees; by this method flow patterns over the nose were plotted and compared. For structural simplicity the wing was uniform in taper and dihedral from root to tip, the trailing edge being nearly straight in plan and the leading edge swept $18\frac{1}{4}$ degrees; the aerofoil chosen was the symmetrical A.D.7 section, having good laminar flow and high-speed control characteristics. The fuselage was somewhat bluff in shape, with the hemispherical windscreen and front wall of the pressure cabin merging into the deck line and the wing intersecting the body in the 'high-shoulder' position as in the Stirling; the tail unit comprised a single fin and rudder and a tailplane with 13 degrees dihedral. Below the pressure cabin the underside of the nose was occupied by a very large area radome which conformed to the fuselage lines, and the stern tapered to a slightly upswept point; the bomb-cell doors extended below the wing along the central parallel portion of the fuselage. By contrast, the arrangement of the four Rolls-Royce Avon turbojets was somewhat startling at first sight, since they were arranged in vertical pairs in nacelles which, in effect, clasped the wing above and below; though apparently bulky in side view, their drag was commendably low, and any extra loss of performance due to their rather extensive wetted area was offset by the weight saved in having an uncomplicated wing structure; servicing was easy and propulsive efficiency was high, as borne out by the later adoption of a similar geometry for the English Electric Lightning; the axes of the engines were parallel to the wing chord at $4\frac{1}{2}$ degrees to the fuselage datum.

Structurally the S.A.4 was straightforward; although a slight risk was taken by using a high-strength aluminium alloy of the 75ST type (DTD687), which was less 'forgiving' when overstressed than the 24ST type (DTD610), peak stresses at cut-outs were avoided and general stress levels were kept low. All skin rivets were flush with milled heads, and stresses round rivet holes were relieved by an ingenious hot-dimpling tool which, being portable, could be used also for repairs. The wing had two spars with concentrated booms milled from massive extrusions, with lightly stiffened plate webs and multiple spanwise channel-section stringers supporting the skin between widely spaced box ribs. The dynamically damped engine mountings were carried on steel-tube space-frames built out from the front spar; each of the two massive British Messier main landing-gears comprised a four-wheeled bogie pivoted to a vertical oleo-leg braced by a drag-strut to a longitudinal forging rotating in trunnions on the front and rear spars inboard of the engine nacelle; the gear retracted sideways to lie flush within the inner wing, the bay being closed by one door mounted on the oleo-leg and another hinged from the lower wing root. The fuselage was built in three portions, the foremost extending from the nose to a butt-joint just aft of the pressure cabin, the long centre fuselage being parallel for most of its length and joined by another butt-joint to the rear fuselage; the fuselage had notched frames and continuous stringers, but the tail surfaces were carried by two massive wheel-like frames whose upper halves were semicircular spoked forgings to which the tailplane and fin spar roots were bolted; the centres of these 'wheels' were connected by a horizontal tube and the lower part of the frames each comprised segmental diaphragms braced by two tubes; the only skin openings aft of the bomb-cell were a maintenance hatch in the underside of the otherwise empty shell and a small camera hatch adjacent. The twin-wheeled nose undercarriage was mounted below the pressure cabin and retracted backwards; between the nose-wheel bay and the front bulkhead of the bomb-cell was the front-hinged crew entry hatch, via a sloping tunnel and floor-level air-lock, which also served as the emergency escape chute. All the fuel tanks were of the self-sealing flexible type, pressurised to prevent their collapsing in a dive; there were seven in each half of the wing—five between the spars and two in the root leading edge— and eight in the fuselage above the bomb-cell, four forward and four aft of the wing spar-box, making a total tankage of 6,170 gallons; an automatic selection system ensured that with tanks correctly loaded the c.g. remained within permitted limits of travel at all times. Inboard of each nacelle in the leading edge was an engine-driven auxiliary gearbox driving a Godfrey cabin-supercharger, a 24-volt generator and two hydraulic pumps for the 4,000 lb/sq in British Messier system, which powered the flaps, air-brakes, dive-brakes, landing-gear retraction, wheel brakes, bomb doors and weapon-loading jacks; these last were later deleted in favour of external crane access through hatches in the fuselage top skin.

The flying controls were the first in Britain to use full-span aerodynamic servo-tabs, with no direct connections between the main surfaces and the pilot. The control runs were cables driving irreversible screw-jacks at each tab; artificial feel proportional to airspeed and a 'g-restrictor' were included in the elevator circuit. To check the effectiveness of the rudder in holding yaw in the engine-cut case, a complete S.A.4 fin and rudder system was installed on a Sunderland V (*PP151*) and flown satisfactorily between November 1950 and May 1951 at Belfast; it was necessary to build up the Sunderland fin attachment with a plinth and dorsal fairing to represent the top of the S.A.4 fuselage, and both flexible and 'wiping' seals were tested on the leading edge of the rudder; as no difference could be discerned in their behaviour, the first S.A.4 prototype was built with a flexible seal and the second with a 'wiper'.

All construction took place from the beginning at Belfast, where three sets of production-type jigs were set up; in these the two prototypes (SH.1600–1601, *VX158, 161*) took shape in 1948, the third set being used to build a fuselage and wing which were exhaustively tested to proof and ultimate structural loading during 1949. The drawing programme was delayed about four months by the removal from Rochester to Belfast, and consequently the first prototype was not completed till the late spring of 1951, and then required a fair amount of ground-running and taxying before first flight. Meanwhile in 1948 Vickers-Armstrongs had come up with their Type 660 project, which was intermediate in performance between the optimum nuclear bomber (B.35/46) and the interim one (B.14/46); this proposal was so attractive to the Air Staff that specification B.9/48 was drafted round it, and two prototypes were ordered; by 1950 the decision had virtually been taken to order it into production in preference to the Short S.A.4, and Vickers-Armstrongs made very rapid progress with the aid of their newly commissioned high-speed wind-tunnel and heavy investment in slab-milling machines; in April 1951 the B.9/48 went into production as the Valiant, the first prototype flying a month later. This was a disappointment to Short Brothers & Harland, but they were assured that the two S.A.4 prototypes were urgently needed for experimental work, and *VX158*, powered by four Rolls-Royce Avon R.A.2 engines, after being taken by road to Aldergrove, was flown for the first time by Tom Brooke-Smith on 10 August, 1951.

Had the political need arisen, there is no doubt that the S.A.4 could have entered service very quickly as a Lincoln replacement, for troubles encountered during flight development were almost negligible; the elevator tab gearing was altered after the first flight to reduce its sensitivity, undercarriage door vibration was cured, the split dive brakes on the flaps were found unnecessary and locked permanently closed, and local buffeting round the nacelles was corrected by adding drooped triangular leading-edge fillets at the nacelle–wing junctions and small boat-tails between the paired jet-pipe exit shrouds. Aileron flutter above 42,000 ft, which was the maximum usable ceiling, prevented the design Mach number of 0·85 being reached at altitude, and for the prototypes the indicated Mach limit was set at 0·78; also high-speed buffeting with the bomb-doors open was troublesome until cured by adding retractable gills about 6 ft ahead of the front edge of the doors. The S.A.4 was delightful to fly and could be dived at a fantastic rate—up to 15,000 ft/min; this at first caused the fuel tanks to collapse, but this was cured by adding small scoops to supply ram air to the vent system, with spring-loaded flaps at the outlets to prevent overpressure. No live emergency escapes were ever attempted, although they had been simulated by volunteers in the R.A.E. blower tunnel and by comprehensive tests on correctly weighted dummies; at an early stage in the design an attempt had been made to provide explosive bolts to release the entire front fuselage as a safety capsule, but model tests showed that severe tumbling would occur in the delayed drop to 12,000 ft before parachutes could be deployed and there would have been a structural weight penalty of more than 1,000 lb.

VX158 using braking parachutes to land at Aldergrove in August 1951.

VX158 appeared in the 1951 S.B.A.C. Flying Display at Farnborough and made a good impression with its evident docility and manoeuvrability, also demonstrating its short landing capability, aided by twin braking parachutes in addition to Maxaret-equipped wheel brakes; its flight trials were begun at Aldergrove, and continued at Sydenham after the runway there had been extended in 1952, being completed in May 1953 and shared by Tom Brooke-Smith and Walter Runciman; then it was delivered to the R.A.E. for operational trials of new high-altitude radar blind-bombing gear scheduled for the later V-bombers. For these trials its bomb-doors were normally not opened, but a small inset door allowed markers to be released; later a visual-sighting station with optically flat panels replaced the original metal nose cap; access to this pressurised station, through a tunnel from the pressure cabin, was an original feature of the design and already existed in both prototypes. *VX161* was completed with up-rated Avon R.A.3 engines and was first flown on 12 August, 1952; after satisfactory contractor's trials at Aldergrove it was delivered on 11 April, 1953, to R.A.F. Woodbridge for dropping trials with concrete dummies of new types of air-to-ground weapons, including 'Blue Danube'; for this purpose its radome had been replaced by a metal skin. On completion of this programme *VX161* was flown to Farnborough for temporary storage pending the next phase of the trials.

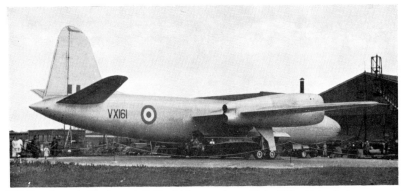

VX161 on view at the Farnborough Golden Jubilee open day on 9 July, 1955, with bomb-doors open and a 10,000-lb bomb in position for loading. (*E. A. Shackleton.*)

In the early spring of 1955, *VX158* was returned to Aldergrove to be adapted as a flying test-bed (P.D.6) for the 15,000-lb static thrust de Havilland Gyron turbojet, with which it was first flown by Jock Eassie on 7 July, 1955, and appeared at the S.B.A.C. show two months later; the Gyron was installed in the port lower position, the independence of the mounting from the wing structure making the S.A.4 (by now officially named Sperrin) particularly suitable for this purpose—indeed, it was the only airframe available which could have been modified in this way. After satisfactory trials at Farnborough

VX158 taking off at Aldergrove on 7 July, 1955, with one Gyron installed.

and Hatfield, *VX158* was flown back to Aldergrove for a second Gyron to be installed on the starboard side. In this form it was flown again from Aldergrove by Jock Eassie on 26 June, 1956, but during this flight the port outer undercarriage door became detached and was lost over the sea, and an immediate landing had to be made at Aldergrove; there was no spare door available, and although one could have been manufactured, it was decided to borrow one from *VX161*, which was flown to Sydenham from Farnborough a few days later and in fact never flew again, being scrapped there early in 1957. *VX158* returned to Hatfield for continued trials and appeared once more at the S.B.A.C. show in 1956, but six months later the Gyron

VX161 at Sydenham after returning from Farnborough in July 1956 to donate an undercarriage door to *VX158*; it did not fly again.

programme was discontinued as an economy measure, and *VX158* was scrapped at Hatfield in 1958. Both Sperrins made a substantial but unpublicised contribution to the efficacy of the R.A.F.'s V-Bomber force; moreover, they pioneered a 4,000-lb/sq in hydraulic system and a four-wheeled Maxaret-fitted bogie in time for their adoption on the Bristol Britannia, which by 1957 was already in production at Queen's Island to supplement the parent company's line at Filton; Shorts' intended manufacture of Comets had been frustrated by cancellation of orders for the Comet 2, of which two completed fuselages had been shipped in 1956 to the de Havilland factory at Chester.

Span 109 ft (33·2 m); length 102·3 ft (31·2 m); area 1,663 sq ft (152 m²); empty weight 72,000 lb (32,650 kg); all-up weight 115,000 lb (52,200 kg); max speed 564 mph (913 km/h); range 3,860 miles (6,050 km).

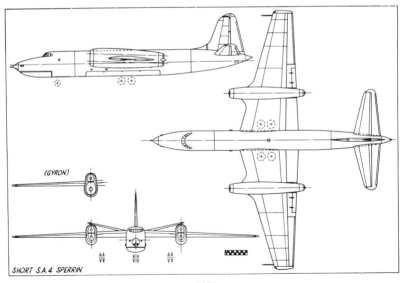

SHORT S.A.4 SPERRIN

430

VX158 taking off at Farnborough in September 1956 with two Gyrons installed.

The prototype Sealand, *G-AIVX*, in its original condition with high nacelles and small rudder.

The Short Sealand

In the early months of 1946 flying-boats were still very much to the fore both at Rochester seaplane works and at Queen's Island. Solents were in production for M.C.A. to lease to B.O.A.C., and Sunderlands were being reconditioned or converted into Sandringhams for operators in many parts of the world; the marine fairway had not yet been ousted by the concrete runway, and Short Brothers were convinced, from the many enquiries they received, that a market existed for a range of commercial flying-boats designed for their purpose rather than adapted from existing stocks of military aircraft. Accordingly, C. P. T. Lipscomb examined the prospects of three sizes of flying-boat, the smallest being designated S.A.6, an intermediate one S.A.7 and the largest S.A.8. The last, developed from the Shetland, has already been described under that heading; the S.A.7 was a tentative project for a general-purpose transport or trainer designed round two 850 hp Armstrong Siddeley Cougar engines; the Cougar was a nine-cylinder single-row radial which never really got beyond the test-bed stage, so the S.A.7 faded out even before the S.A.8. But the little S.A.6 seemed to have plenty of appeal, particularly as an amphibian capable of being flown from the numerous lakes,

431

rivers and harbours forming the traditional communication routes of so much of the world's undeveloped territory.

In June 1946, the firm announced its intention of building the S.A.6, to be named Sealand, as a five/seven-passenger commercial amphibian powered by two de Havilland Gipsy Queen engines; the design task was shared between the Rochester and Belfast establishments, Rochester undertaking the hull and tail unit and Belfast the wing and engine installation. It was a comparatively simple design, almost a half-scale replica of the Solent in hull form, but with the latest improvements in structural methods, particularly in the use of draw-sunk stiffeners in plate webs for ribs and bulkheads. The established 'Short' shape of planing bottom with a faired main step and vertical knife-edge heel was retained, also the Modified Göttingen 436 wing section, although a higher aspect ratio than formerly was chosen to improve rate of climb and cruise economy. To give adequate spray clearance the engines were mounted as high as possible without spoiling the junction of the nacelles with the wing, and the tailplane was located at one-third of the height of the fin. The neat land undercarriage comprised two units swinging up on a parallel linkage to lie flush in sealed recesses on each side of the hull above the static water line, and the wing-tip floats, miniatures of the Shetland's, were of welded Birmabright alloy mounted on streamline cantilever struts; the tailwheel was ingeniously levered from a horizontal oleo-leg protruding from the heel of the planing bottom, the oleo assembly being rotated through 180 degrees in order to raise or lower the wheel; all power for gear retraction, flaps and wheel-brakes was supplied from a 450-lb/sq in pneumatic system, there being no hydraulics. The main undercarriage recesses were in effect box frames forming the front spar attachments for the parallel-chord centre-section; they divided the cabin interior into two compartments with a gangway between them widening from 18 in at floor level to nearly 4 ft at the ceiling formed by the underside of the wing. The cockpit was exceptionally well planned for either a solo pilot or a pilot and navigator; hinged drop panels below the sliding side windows simplified mooring, for which purpose a boat-hook and lanyard were stowed on the port side and an outside step was fitted on the starboard side for access to a mooring hatch in the bow. There were six large windows on each side of the passenger cabin in groups of three separated by the wheel-boxes; on the port side was the main entrance door, with an adjacent extension door for ambulance or freight-loading purposes; in typical layouts there would be either three or four seats in each half of the cabin. Handling on the water was greatly assisted by the provision of reversible-pitch airscrews, which could also be used to shorten the landing run on an airfield, and a water rudder was deemed unnecessary.

The prototype Sealand, c/n SH.1555, registered *G-AIVX*, was launched as a flying-boat on 19 January, 1948, and remained moored till the 22nd, when Harold Piper made two flights totalling 45 minutes from Belfast Lough; subsequently the landing-gear was installed and flying from Sydenham air-field began; the principal modification resulting from the early flight tests was the lowering of the engines and nacelles to reduce the unduly high inter-ference drag. In March Piper resigned in order to return home to New Zealand, and Tom Brooke-Smith succeeded him as chief test pilot, and so was the first to take off from land and alight on water, and vice versa. At first it was intended to build a second prototype with Alvis Leonides engines, in case of difficulty in obtaining Gipsy Queens from de Havillands, who were direct competitors with their Dove; because of its larger airscrews and fuel require-ment, the Leonides variant, S.B.2, known as Sealand II, had its centre-section span increased by 9 ft, with fuel tankage increased from 120 to 150 gallons; a higher top speed and payload capacity were estimated, but the Leonides prototype was not completed as such, becoming the first of four pre-produc-tion Sealands with Gipsy Queens laid down in 1947 with c/ns SH.1562–1565 and registrations *G-AKLM* to ʼ*P*. The first of these received a full C. of A. on 28 July, 1949, and was entered in the King's Cup race on 1 August at Elmdon, where it averaged 169 mph round the course but was unplaced. A further ten, SH.1566–1575, *G-AKLR* to ʼ*MA*, were authorised by the Ministry of Civil Aviation to build up stocks for quick delivery to the export market; a vigorous sales drive was promoted, and in October *G-AKLM* began a demon-stration tour of Scandinavia, but on the 15th it crashed in fog at Lindesnes in Norway, the pilot D. G. McCall and his crew (including George Puddicombe of Shorts' sales staff) being killed. *G-AKLN* was retained as a development prototype and *G-AKLO* replaced ʼ*LM* as the European demonstrator.

Meanwhile *G-AKLP* had been ordered by British West Indian Airways as the first of three needed to operate inter-island services in the Caribbean, and appeared in B.W.I.A. livery as *VP-TBA*, *R.M.A. St Vincent*, at the 1949 S.B.A.C. show at Farnborough. In 1950 Tom Brooke-Smith took it to the West Indies for tropical and route-proving trials, but found that the Sealands were required to operate from open sea at St Vincent and Dominica, where there was no sheltered anchorage; they were, of course, never intended for such conditions, and he had already had experience of making a dead-stick landing into a 3-ft sea in ʼ*VX* in December 1948. On that occasion he had been making partial glides with both airscrews feathered to determine the overall drag with flaps at various settings and decided to finish the series with a dead-stick landing on Belfast Lough; too late he realised that a gale had started to blow since taking off, and on alighting the Sealand took green water over the top of the wing, but there were no leaks into the cabin and he was able to restart the engines and taxy to a lee shore at Holywood, whence he took off and flew back to Sydenham. Although this incident demonstrated the excellent seaworthiness of the Sealand, it also showed that no such risk ought to be taken with fare-paying passengers on board. Consequently, the B.W.I.A. scheme was abandoned and the Sealand reverted to the British register as *G-AKLP*, and in January 1951 was renamed *Festival of Britain* to become the company's American demonstrator. From Trinidad it made a sales tour of North and South America which took it over the Andes into Chile and back again, then via the Bahamas to Toronto and across Canada to Vancouver, then back via Toronto and the United States to Nassau before returning to Montreal for C. of A. inspection in January 1952; flown throughout by Gordon Moulton-Barrett, it had covered 50,000 miles in 350 flying hours and given 250 demonstrations in ten different countries under all conditions of temperature and humidity; only once did it fail to keep a date, on 14 December, 1951, at LaGuardia, when the port starter-motor burned out after a night in the open in 20 degrees of frost.

In Europe and North Africa *G-AKLO* had made a good impression during many demonstrations, resulting in sales to Norway, Yugoslavia and Egypt, but the only dent in the American market was the sale of *G-AKLT* to Capt Al Lewis of the Christian & Missionary Alliance of New York, for use in Indonesia; it was not only the first Sealand to be sold abroad but also the first British post-war aircraft to be sold in America; shipped to Djakarta, it was assembled by a Shorts working party and handed over on 31 December, 1950, for operation from Tandjoengselor, with the appropriate registration *PK-CMA*. The exceptionally difficult terrain with its winding watercourses was a severe test for the Sealand, and steps were taken to improve its handling on the water and at take-off. These stemmed from criticism of *G-AKLN* when it was assessed by M.A.E.E., Felixstowe, in the autumn of 1950, in the air-sea rescue role, for which purpose it was equipped with handrails on the port side of the hull and underwing carriers for A.S.R. pack containers. The

Sealand *G-AKLN* on test with full-span leading-edge slats.

M.A.E.E. pilots recommended a reduction in unstick and alighting speeds, better lateral control to prevent float damage after skipping in rough water, and elimination of the tendency to roll and swing to starboard during take-off from calm water. Between April and October 1951 *G-AKLN* was fitted with modified engine air intakes and with part-span and full-span leading-edge slats; take-off speed and lateral control were improved in exchange for the loss of 8 to 12 kts in top speed, and with wing-tip slats alone there was no real improvement in controlling swing. It was decided to increase the span and wing area by extending the wing-tips of all Sealands by 15-in on each side, at the same time adding wing fences to control stall breakaway; the hull lines and structure were improved to reduce weight and increase buoyancy to compensate for the deeper draught in fresh water, *G-AIVX* being the first to be so

434

G-AKLR with original span and in B.W.I.A. livery as *VP-TBB* being flown in 1950 by Tom Brooke-Smith with starboard airscrew feathered; later it went to Yugoslavia as *YU-CFJ.*

modified, while *G-AKLN* appeared similarly treated at the 1951 S.B.A.C. show. Although the increased wing area lowered the take-off speed, it had no effect on directional instability on the water at moderate speeds, and in December 1951 further trials were started with both *G-AIVX* and *G-AKLN* to attempt to cure the swing on glassy water in zero wind, which made manoeuvring in narrow waterways very difficult. Various devices were tried, including ballasting the port float with 70 lb of water, for which fuel could have been substituted if found beneficial, also a rearward extension of the main step. Neither of these made any difference to the swing, and both introduced new adverse effects; finally, the cure was found by fitting an asymmetric skeg to the planing bottom just ahead of the heel; this caused a strong enough suction to cancel the swing at the beginning of the take-off run, but the effect died away conveniently as speed increased and aileron control took over; this interesting device showed how much hydrodynamic

Sealand III *LN-SUH* (formerly *G-AKLU*) at Bergen in 1951; note the blanking plate covering the landing-gear recess. (*John Stroud.*)

435

Indian Navy Sealand *INS-105* showing extended wing-tips and a skeg at the aft step.

performance depended on unsuspected local flow patterns and suction effects. The root of the trouble was that at low speeds the Sealand's draught was too great, especially in fresh water, but not much could be done to improve matters at a reasonable cost.

With its structure weight reduced by 330 lb, the wing extended, the rudder chord increased and the hull strengthened, the Sealand attracted a better market in 1952. *G-AKLU* had been sold to Vestlandske Luftfartselskap of Bergen in May 1951 and was flown as a pure flying-boat without its landing gear between Bergen, Ålesund and Trondheim, carrying eight passengers, baggage and mail; in this form it was indexed as S.B.7 and called Sealand III; it was re-registered *LN-SUH* and was joined a year later by *G-AKLN* as *LN-SUF*. In September 1951 *G-AKLR* and *'S* were flown by Tom Brooke-Smith and Jock Eassie from Rochester to Zagreb to begin a coastal Adriatic service for Jugoslovenski Aerotransport of Belgrade, as *YU-CFJ* and *'K*. A very special model was the privately owned *Nadia*, equipped as an air-yacht with dual controls, extra leading-edge tanks raising the fuel capacity to 185 gallons, a forward toilet, special ventilation and luxurious furnishings for six passengers in addition to the crew of two; the turquoise hide-upholstered seats were reversible to face either way, and a bookcase and wine cabinet were included in the fittings. This Sealand, *SU-AHY* (ex *G-AKLW*) was ferried to Cairo by Don Tanton and Capt S. Omar, the personal pilot of the owner, Ahmed Abboud Pasha, a director of the Khedivial Mail Line. Another delivery to the East by air was *G-AKLV Pegasus*, bought by Ralli Brothers of London for use on their Bengal jute plantations, where it operated from May

436

1952 till October 1957 as *AP-AFM*; two others followed it in December for service with the East Bengal Transport Commission and became *AP-AGB* and '*C* (ex *G-AKLY* and '*X*); meanwhile in October *G-AKLO* was sold to Shell Petroleum Co for use at Balik Papaan in the Borneo oil-fields as *VR-SDS* (later '*UDS*) and was followed two years later by *G-AKLP* (*VR-UDV*) after its return from America.

In 1952 a contract was obtained to supply ten specially equipped Sealands for the Indian Navy; they had up-rated Gipsy Queen engines, dual control and extra tankage to give six hours' endurance. Accordingly, a further batch of ten Sealands, c/ns SH.1760–1769, was laid down, but to save time the last two of the existing batch were completed as the first two of the Indian Navy contract; so *G-AKLZ* and '*MA* became *INS-101* and *102*, and the first left Rochester for Cochin on 13 January, 1953, piloted by Ray Gough with C. C. (Tubby) Dash as engineer; these two pilots shared all ten delivery flights, the last, with SH.1768 (*INS-110*), being completed in November. SH.1765 was a standard Sealand bought by Shell Petroleum Co for use in Venezuela, whither it was shipped as deck cargo; flown as *YV-P-AEG*, it was well suited to conditions over the extensive waters of Lake Maracaibo and gave excellent

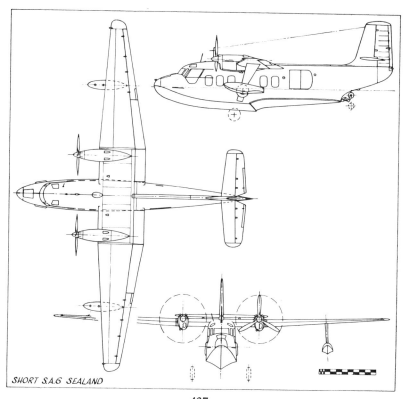

SHORT S.A.6 SEALAND

service for several years. The last Sealand built, SH.1769, was a standard model delivered to the Christian & Missionary Alliance as a replacement for their first one, which had been forced down by a tropical thunderstorm in an inaccessible part of Java, where it had to be abandoned early in 1953. In November that year the new machine, *JZ-PTA*, was dedicated to C.M.A. service before leaving Sydenham for its base at Hollandia, New Guinea, where it was operated into the remote Baliem valley, using a lake 10,000 ft above sea-level as one of its alighting points; it, too, was lost in 1956, and the last civil survivor was Ralli Bros' *Pegasus*, which was shipped back to Rochester for major inspection, but scrapped soon afterwards. The prototype *G-AIVX* was used as a company hack till 1954 and often flown without wing floats and struts, to gain extra payload capacity; after seven years' continuous activity it was scrapped on expiry of its C. of A. in April 1955. At least one Indian Navy Sealand was still being flown at Cochin in December 1959.

Span 59 ft (18 m), later 61 ft 6 in (18·7 m); length 42 ft 2 in (12·8 m); area 353 sq ft (32·8 m²), later 359 sq ft (33·4 m²); empty weight 7,007 lb (3,190 kg); all-up weight 9,100 lb (4,130 kg); max speed 187 mph (300 km/h); duration 3·5 hr (Indian Navy 6 hr).

G-AIVX with wing floats removed to reduce empty weight for land operations only, during a visit to Filton in May 1954. (*E. A. Shackleton.*)

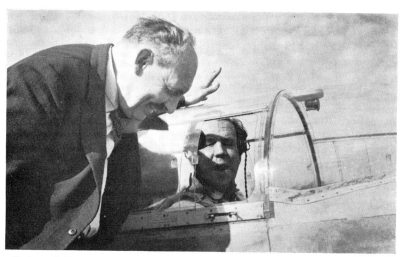

Professor G. T. R. Hill and Tom Brooke-Smith with the S.B.1 glider at Aldergrove in July 1951.

The Short Sherpa

Short Brothers' association with tailless aeroplanes dates quite literally from the dawn of aviation, for it was to the Aero Club at Leysdown that J. W. Dunne migrated in 1909 after the War Office lost interest in his experiments at Blair Atholl in December 1908. At Mussel Manor he met Horace Short and Professor A. K. Huntington, from both of whom he gained new hope of success, despite Wilbur Wright's message, conveyed to him earlier by his father General Dunne, that he would 'never get off the ground in an aeroplane with wheels'. John Dunne had experimented on V-shaped card glider models having a weight distribution and wing twist similar to those of the winged seeds of the Javanese *Zanonia* tree, whose natural mode of dispersion was by steady gliding flight over great distances. At Blair Atholl his sweptback biplane had flown as a glider but had too little power to rise from level ground, and he was convinced that with a better engine he could design an aeroplane that would fly by itself without constant control movements by the pilot. Professor Huntington shared some but not all of his views, and Short Brothers built the curious Dunne-Huntington triplane to their joint design, but it was a disappointment, and Dunne soon returned to his V-shaped biplane, which he detailed as the D.5; this also was constructed by Short Brothers at the end of 1909, before they left Leysdown. After moving to Eastchurch, Horace Short continued to assist the Blair Atholl Syndicate by manufacturing the more difficult components for their later monoplanes and biplanes, but in 1913 Dunne became seriously ill and had to give up active experimentation when on the brink of success.

439

Meanwhile the two sons of Professor M. J. M. Hill of London University, Geoffrey and Roderic, had built themselves a glider (actually in their bedroom) and later, when war broke out, joined the Royal Flying Corps; Roderic took charge of test-flying at Farnborough in 1917 and Geoffrey devoted his talents to improving flight safety and controllability, continuing after the Armistice with private research which in 1923 led him back to Dunne's tailless ideas. Next year he designed and built a light monoplane glider, which the R.A.E. later fitted with a 30 hp Bristol Cherub engine and acquired for experimental purposes, subsequently ordering a larger two-seater version from Westland Aircraft, to whose design staff Hill was then attached. So began the famous Pterodactyl family of tailless swept monoplanes, which had evolved as far as

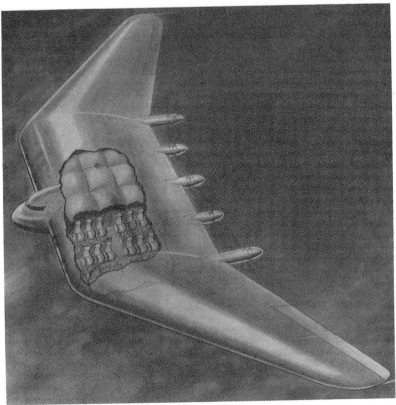

Professor G. T. R. Hill's Pterodactyl VIII transatlantic airliner as proposed in 1944, showing the 'quilted' pressure-cabin and transverse seating within the wing.

the Pterodactyl VII four-engined flying-boat project (R.1/33) during Hill's sojourn at Yeovil, which ended in 1934, when he was appointed Kennedy Professor of Mechanical Engineering at University College, London. When war broke out in 1939 Professor Hill was lent to the Air Ministry to act as consultant to the Canadian National Research Council, which had received a contract to design and test a tailless glider representative of a large high-performance long-range bomber, called Pterodactyl VIII in Hill's series. From 1942 to 1945 he served as Scientific Liaison Officer between the United Kingdom and Canada, and after war ended was appointed consulting engineer to both Short Brothers and General Aircraft Ltd, primarily for tailless aircraft development; when the Brabazon Committee announced its recommendations for British post-war civil transport designs, Short Brothers proposed a large-scale Pterodactyl VIII with five Griffon engines arranged as pushers and the interior of the wing occupied by a 'quilted' pressure cabin, formed of intersecting spherical shells bounded by curved beams which converged into cusps connected by vertical tension-ties; from inside, this cabin appeared as a vaulted chamber with slender pillars and would have afforded very spacious passenger accommodation, but was too unorthodox to be taken seriously by the airlines. On resigning from University College in 1948, Geoffrey Hill settled in Northern Ireland and collaborated with Shorts' project designer David Keith-Lucas, son of Dr Keith Lucas, F.R.S., the gifted Cambridge physiologist who had designed the R.A.F. Mk II Compass, only to be killed while flying at Farnborough in October 1916. David Keith-Lucas was apprenticed to C. A. Parsons & Co Ltd (Horace Short's old firm), from whose design department he came to Short Brothers in 1940, to apply his talents to aviation in time of war as his father had done in 1914; in 1949 he was promoted to Chief Designer of Short Brothers & Harland Ltd, becoming a director in 1953 and Technical Director in 1957.

Short Brothers were briefly concerned in 1947 with another glider project, when they prepared a design, S.A.9, to meet specification X.30/46 for a military transport and assault glider, but this requirement was cancelled before any tender was submitted.

Shorts had tendered both to the interim B.14/46 jet-bomber specification, in which their S.A.4 design had been successful, and also, a year later, to the optimised B.35/46 V-bomber requirement for the best possible performance at the highest possible ceiling; this was P.D.1 (the first of a new series of Preliminary Designs initiated by Keith-Lucas in 1947) and would have retained the S.A.4 front fuselage almost unchanged, with its pressure cabin and radome, together with a broadly similar landing-gear and fuel system adapted to a swept-wing geometry. In view of the narrow limits between the flutter and buffet boundaries of a swept wing, Keith-Lucas was anxious to eliminate the parasitic drag of a conventional tail and fuselage, but the Canadian experiments with the Pterodactyl VIII glider had shown that directional stability was inadequate without fins and rudders which, if made into end-plates, could improve the effective aspect ratio to compensate for their drag but needed a fixed structure to carry them, which in turn precluded the use of rotating wing-tips as elevons; these had given good stability and control on Hill's first Pterodactyl, but hinged elevons could not be made flutter-free, were prone to tip-stalling at low speeds and were ineffective at high speed due

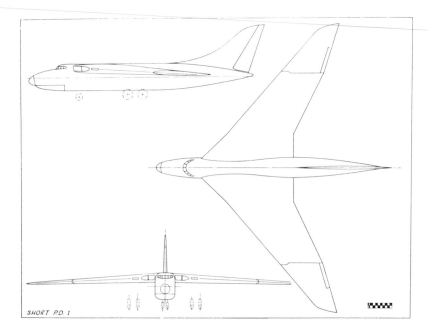

SHORT P.D. 1

to wing twist; the problem was less acute with a low-aspect-ratio wing such as Avro's delta and could be avoided by using a separate tail as in Handley Page's design; in the final assessment, both the Avro and Handley Page proposals were accepted and both firms received contracts to build small-scale powered prototypes to explore low-speed handling problems. Shorts decided to keep up-to-date at their own expense by building a one-third scale glider version of P.D.1, which featured an important structural innovation to ensure that the swept wing would keep its angle of attack unchanged, and thus free from buffet, whatever its deflection under load. In describing this to the 1951 International Aeronautical Conference at Brighton, Geoffrey Hill coined the apt description 'aeroisoclinic wing' for the design jointly contrived by himself and Keith-Lucas, in which the torsional and flexural axes were coincident and the lower skin of the leading edge was separated from the bottom edge of the box-spar to avoid local buckling.

The aeroisoclinic glider, design index S.B.1, c/n SH.1602, was the first aircraft to be wholly designed and constructed at Belfast after completion of Short Brothers' removal from Rochester. It was built as inexpensively as possible, mainly of wood, with a stressed-skin fuselage and a one-piece wing, using spruce framing with plywood covering and light-alloy nose-ribs and local reinforcement by angles and plates; the box-spar had its front beam at 25 per cent of the chord, with additional shear webs at 35 and 60 per cent. The wing had a leading-edge sweep-angle of $42\frac{1}{4}$ degrees, and its large rotating tips acted either in phase as elevators or in opposition as ailerons; they had

442

controllable anti-balance tabs, and there were also pneumatically-operated split landing flaps inset in the undersurface of the wing extending across the inboard half of the span; directional stability and control were provided by a conventional fin and rudder with the same sweep-angle as the wing; by varying the fulcrum position of the tab-control, the relative angles of attack of the elevons and wing in steady level flight could be changed so that the best compromise between maximum lift and freedom from tip-stall could be selected. The cockpit was enclosed by a clear plastic hood, and the landing-gear comprised a pair of narrow-track main wheels under the c.g. with small single bumper-wheels under the nose and tail and a sprung skid under each wing-tip; there was also a long skid from the belly centre-line to the tail for protection in a heavy landing, and an anti-spin parachute in the tail. Marked with prominent stripes to make it conspicuous to other pilots and with the 'B' registration *G-14-5*, the S.B.1 was taken to Aldergrove for its initial flights;

Jock Eassie in Sturgeon *VR363* towing off Tom Brooke-Smith in the S.B.1 at Aldergrove on 30 July, 1951.

after two winched launches on 14 and 17 July, 1951, to check the longitudinal stability margin, the first towed flight behind Sturgeon T.T.2 *VR363* on the 30th went quite well, with cast-off at 10,000 ft, but in the second, with a lengthened tow-line, on 14 October, the glider kept sinking back into the Sturgeon's turbulent wake and Tom Brooke-Smith was forced to cast off the tow before much height had been gained. In recovering from the ensuing nose-up attitude he came down heavily on the runway and crashed; in hospital he was found to have sustained several crushed vertebrae, but he made a good recovery and was able to return to flying duties after six months.

Meanwhile, the damage to the S.B.1 had been assessed and the wing and tail were found to be repairable, but the fuselage was a total wreck; Tom Brooke-Smith objected strongly to making any further flights in the machine as a glider, so the new fuselage was a modified one of light-alloy monocoque construction, with a normal tricycle landing-gear and two Turbomeca Palas turbojets of 350 lb thrust each installed in a false deck above the fuselage and

The Sherpa over Lough Neagh in 1954.

The Sherpa using a braking parachute to land at Aldergrove.

behind the wing; the jet outlets discharged on either side clear of the trailing edge, and a central NACA-type divergent-ramp intake serving both engines proved efficient at all angles of attack. The two 25-gallon kerosene tanks were located within the fuselage, equally balanced about the c.g., and an automatic observer panel occupied the rear fuselage space; electric power for these instruments was supplied by a windmill-driven generator mounted in the extreme nose. As rebuilt, the monoplane was designated S.B.4 and given the new c/n SH.1604 and 'B' marking *G-14-1*. It was first flown by Tom Brooke-Smith at Aldergrove on 4 October, 1953, and quickly proved its good handling qualities, although limited to 250 mph and 5,000 ft altitude. Trials continued throughout 1954, and the S.B.4 was demonstrated by Tom Brooke-Smith at the S.B.A.C. show at Farnborough that year, under its new name Sherpa—an acronym of 'Short & Harland Experimental and Research Prototype Aircraft' having a felicitous affinity with high places after the first ascent of Everest. Throughout the test programme, flight recorder results were analysed and much information was acquired on the probable behaviour of a similar full-sized wing at high speed and high altitude, as well as reassurance on its hand-ling qualities at low speed. It was Keith-Lucas's aim to produce a design of low structure weight capable of being operated safely at all speeds up to low supersonic, with good controllability in the transonic region, but his hopes

444

were not fully realised in practice; apart from P.D.8, a private-venture photo-reconnaissance proposal, Shorts designed an isoclinic wing (P.D.10) for the Supermarine Swift and tendered the isoclinic P.D.13 design for the N.A.39 naval/strike bomber competition to specification M.148T, but the heavier Blackburn B.103 was preferred and became the Buccaneer.

On finishing its flight-test programme at Belfast, the Sherpa was given to the College of Aeronautics at Cranfield for post-graduate research purposes and began flying there, as *G-36-1*, in April 1957 in the hands of Flt Lieut A. J. MacDonald; after some months the programme was brought to a halt by failure of one of the Palas engines, but in 1960 two repaired engines were installed and research into the rolling response of wing-tip controllers continued; in 1964, with both engines finally time-expired, it was transferred to the Bristol College of Advanced Technology for further use as a laboratory test specimen, until in May 1966, having served this purpose, it was presented

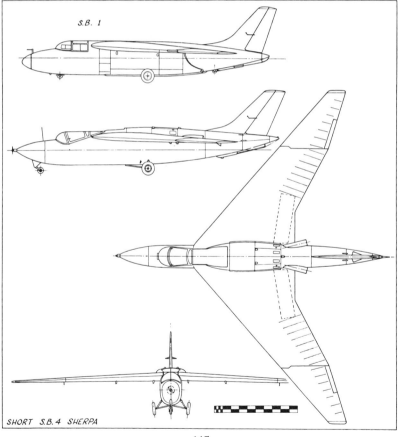

SHORT S.B.4 SHERPA

445

to the Skyfame Aircraft Museum at Staverton, Glos. Like the namesake of its progenitors, the Pterodactyls, it is now extinct in a world of supersonic swing-wings and slender deltas, but for that reason alone its remains are worthy of preservation as an example of evolution in the transonic era. When Skyfame closed in 1979 its aircraft went on loan to the Imperial War Museum at Duxford where, in 1989, the Sherpa fuselage was in store.

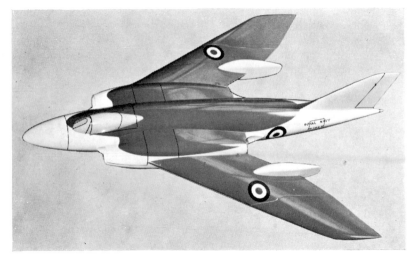

P.D.13, Shorts' proposal for the N.A.39 competition, with jet deflection for quick take-off and an aero-isoclinic wing.

Sherpa—Span 38 ft (11·57 m); length 31 ft 10 in (9·74 m); area 230 sq ft (21·4 m²); empty weight 3,000 lb (1,362 kg); all-up weight 3,300 lb (1,498 kg); max speed 170 mph (274 km/h); duration 50 min.

P.D.1—Span 114 ft (34·7 m); length 95 ft 6 in (29·1 m); area 2,070 sq ft (192 m²); all-up weight 100,000 lb (45,400 kg); max speed $M = 0.87$.

P.D.13—Span 38 ft 1 in (11·6 m); length 51 ft (15·5 m); area 308 sq ft (33·1 m²); empty weight 24,000 lb (10,800 kg); all-up weight 41,000 lb (18,600 kg); max speed $M = 0.95$; range 480 miles (773 km).

S.B.5 with 50 degrees sweep and high tailplane, at Boscombe Down early in 1953.

The Short S.B.5

Contemporary with the Sherpa, the Short S.B.5 was built to specification ER.100 for low-speed trials of the swept-wing configuration proposed for the English Electric P.1 supersonic fighter originated by specification F.23/49. In 1950 there was considerable doubt as to how far sweep-angle could be increased without seriously endangering the low-speed handling of an aircraft, and this information was urgently needed in order to finalise the geometry and structural design of the P.1. Although the S.B.5 was not heavily loaded and was powered only by a single Rolls-Royce Derwent turbojet, it required a very stiff wing whose root attachments could be exchanged to give three different sweep-angles, respectively 50, 60 and 69 degrees; the wing had also to carry the main undercarriage, whose rake had to be adjustable to suit changes in centre-of-gravity position arising from these alterations of sweep-angle. For this reason the wing comprised a very rigid light-alloy box-spar with multiple spanwise stringers attached above and below to sheets so as to form sandwich skin-panels for both upper and lower wing surfaces; this ensured a very smooth outer skin free from buckles or waves under normal loads, and the wing profile was completed by plywood-covered leading- and trailing-edge structures which were easy to modify or exchange. The fuselage was a conventional light-alloy monocoque, with the cockpit well forward above the engine air-intake tunnel and the engine and tanks mounted aft of the wing-root frames. The swept-fin and rudder carried a high delta tailplane, whose incidence was controllable from +10 to −10 degrees, with a one-piece elevator hinged to it. The fuselage terminated in a bluff tail, with the jet pipe in the lower half, and braking and anti-spin parachutes in two separate stowages above.

The S.B.5 (c/n SH.1605, serial *WG768*) was first flown with 50 degrees sweep at Boscombe Down by Tom Brooke-Smith on 2 December, 1952, and within seven months had completed its initial test schedule without incident. The sweep-angle was then increased to 60 degrees, and in this form it flew on 29 July, 1953, and made its first public appearance at the S.B.A.C. show at Farnborough in September. Three months later, the tailplane and elevator, suitably modified, were moved from the top of the fin to the bottom of the

447

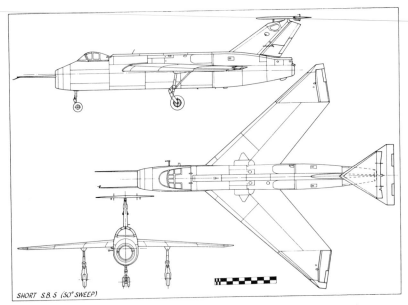

SHORT S.B.5 (50° SWEEP)

rear fuselage; at the same time the inboard leading edges of the wings were modified to a pronounced droop-angle, still with 60 degrees sweep overall. In this form the S.B.5 was first flown at Boscombe Down by Tom Brooke-Smith in January 1954, and the ensuing programme occupied over two years there and at R.A.E., Bedford, the results being correlated with the final develop-

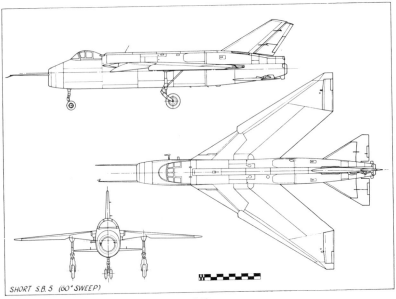

SHORT S.B.5 (60° SWEEP)

448

S.B.5 with 60 degrees sweep and high tailplane, using triple braking parachutes for landing at Boscombe Down in August 1953.

ment of the Lightning supersonic fighter. In 1957, after considering the possibility of attaching an auxiliary turbojet to improve acceleration from near stalling speed, it was decided to install a more compact and powerful Bristol Orpheus in place of the Derwent, concurrently with the final sweep alteration to 69 degrees; at the same time the instrumentation was revised, a zero-level Martin-Baker ejection seat was installed and the aircraft was repainted glossy light blue to enable it to be quickly distinguished from Lightnings of similar appearance but very different performance. The S.B.5 was shipped back to Belfast in 1958 for this quite substantial rebuild and was returned to Bedford

S.B.5 with 69 degrees sweep and Orpheus engine flying near Bedford in October 1960.

in September 1960, the first flight with maximum sweep being made by Denis Tayler of the R.A.E. on 18 October; it remained with Aero Flight for basic handling trials in comparison with wind-tunnel tests. The S.B.5 was then offered to the Australian Aeronautical Research Laboratory, which declined it and it went to the Empire Test Pilots' School which, in 1967, flew it at Farnborough and Boscombe Down for low-speed experience on slender aircraft. It is now in the Cosford Aerospace Museum.

50°—Span 35 ft 2 in (10·74 m); length 45 ft 9 in (13·9 m); area 273·1 sq ft (25·35 m²); empty weight 9,196 lb (4,140 kg); all-up weight 12,000 lb (5,450 kg); max speed 311 mph (500 km/h); duration 35 minutes.
60°—Span 30 ft 6 in (9·3 m); length 45 ft 9 in (13·9 m); area 276·9 sq ft (25·7 m²).
69°—Span 26 ft (7·92 m); length 45 ft 9 in (13·9 m); area 281·7 sq ft (26·15 m²).

Prototype S.B.6, *XA209*, at Queen's Island before its first flight on 23 August, 1953.

The Short Seamew

In 1948, soon after the closure of Rochester works and the transfer of some 400 staff to Belfast had been completed, it was decided that the Managing Director of Short Brothers & Harland Ltd, D. E. Wiseman, should concentrate on production problems and be assisted by a Joint Managing Director (Technical) on the project and development side. This appointment was filled by Rear Admiral Matthew Slattery, who relinquished his position as Chief of Naval Air Equipment at the Admiralty. For some years he had felt concern at the increasing complexity, cost and weight of naval aeroplanes as more comprehensive equipment was added, particularly in the anti-submarine role which was of paramount importance to the NATO countries in view of the Soviet Union's large and increasing underwater fleet; he had campaigned for a re-appraisal of deck-landing requirements with the object of reducing weight and bringing the cost within the reach of the less-wealthy member nations; his arguments had gradually gained acceptance, and in 1951 the Naval Staff invited tenders to specification M.123 for a simple and rugged anti-submarine aircraft which could be operated from the smaller carriers under the most adverse weather and climatic conditions; aided by Admiral Slattery's specialised operational experience, David Keith-Lucas submitted the Short S.B.6 (P.D.4), an ungainly but strictly practical monoplane powered by a single Armstrong Siddeley Mamba turboprop engine, and this was chosen as the best of the designs tendered. Three prototypes officially named Seamew (c/ns SH.1606–1608, serials *XA209, 213* and *216*) were ordered in April 1952 and the first, having been built in the record time of 15 months, was flown at Sydenham by W. J. Runciman on 23 August, 1953, but was badly damaged on landing; in spite of this mishap, intensive night-and-day repair work enabled it to appear at the S.B.A.C. show three weeks later.

Simplicity was the keynote of the Seamew, which carried a crew of two only, pilot and navigator, and no guns. The crew were located high up and well forward in a deep narrow fuselage, giving the pilot an uninterrupted forward and downward view for deck-landing. Since it was primarily intended to 'loiter' on four-hour convoy patrols, its top speed was only 250 mph and it

450

had a long-stroke fixed undercarriage. Ideally this should have been of the nosewheel type for quick take-offs and short landings, but this conflicted with the necessity of locating the large search radar scanner below the crew's stations, so a conventional tailwheel arrangement was adopted, with the difference that the tail-oleo could be lengthened in conjunction with lowering the arrestor hook; this effectively prevented rebound when engaging the arrestor-gear, and a controlled leak in the tail-oleo extension-ram was arranged to lower the tail automatically to the retracted position ready for the next take-off. The Seamew was of straightforward light-alloy construction, using a three-spar wing of laminar-flow section in the NACA 230 series, with an oblique folding hinge at semi-span similar to the Sturgeon's. It had close-pitched flanged-plate ribs with no spanwise stringers, moulded fibreglass wing-tips, slotted flaps and metal-skinned control surfaces, stiffened by shallow chordwise corrugations. Intricate machining operations were avoided, and Redux bonding was used where it cheapened manufacture by reducing drilling and riveting; the main oleo-legs were jettisonable for ditching, and this facility also simplified replacement and servicing. The Mamba turbine engine was very accessibly installed below the pilot's cockpit, with the accessory bay under his floor and the tailpipe swept downwards and to starboard behind the radome. The wing centre-section was built integrally with the centre fuselage, which contained the capacious weapons-bay enclosed by hydraulically operated doors; this could accommodate various combinations of stores, ranging from four depth-charges to 20 sonobuoys, in addition to six rocket projectiles and eight marine markers under the wings, up to a total load of 1,844 lb. The rear fuselage and fin were built as one unit, with the tailplane attached halfway up the fin, and the elevators and rudder, like the ailerons, had inset trim-tabs; there was a sting-type arrestor hook under the tail, and catapult hooks were provided on the front spar at the wing roots. The first prototype had manual wing-folding, but all the rest were hydraulic. All leading edges had fluid de-icing boots, and the pilot's deep windscreen had upper and lower wipers as well as fluid de-icing.

Early flight tests of *XA209* showed all controls to be overbalanced and badly harmonised, also there was a pronounced nose-down attitude with flaps fully down and insufficient elevator power at low speed to correct it; in an attempt to cure this fault fixed leading-edge slats were fitted at semi-span just outboard of the wing-fold joint, and were later reinforced by letter-box slots in the outboard ends of the flaps. Another trouble was a bad breakdown of flow at the fin/tailplane junction, which was alleviated by an inverted slat below the tailplane leading edge on either side of the fin; in production this was replaced by leading-edge vents through the root fillets, exhausting into the elevator nose-gaps. Directional handling was somewhat improved by extending the chord of the rudder and aileron trim-tabs and by adding a horn-balance to the top of the rudder. Very great attention had been paid to weight control during design, and the airframe was stressed for diving at 325 kts, but in practice it was impossible to exceed 280 kts at full power in a vertical dive, and

451

The second prototype Seamew, *XA213*, in a vertical bank, showing buckling of the wing upper skin between the close-pitched ribs.

maximum loading could be realised only on the third prototype, which was used as a structural test-rig and never flew. *XA209* was initially flown without a radome, but this was added at an early stage, and *XA213* was fully representative when it flew early in 1954; both took part in the Farnborough air show that year, giving a speed-contrast demonstration in which *XA209* 'loitered' while *XA213* swept past out of the overcast. A production order for 41 Seamews, c/ns SH.1773–1813, was placed in February 1955, some of which were to be Mk 2s for R.A.F. Coastal Command, having larger wheels with low-pressure tyres, manual wing-folding and no deck-landing gear; this was indexed as a new design, S.C.2, and both variants were produced concurrently, with serials in the range *XE169–210*. In July and December *XA213* underwent satisfactory carrier trials on H.M.S. *Bulwark*, by which time six production Seamews had been completed and flown with up-rated

Seamews at Lossiemouth during operational trials in 1957.

The two prototypes with production Seamews *XE171* and *XE172* in formation at the 1955 S.B.A.C. show. (*Courtesy Flt Lieut R. C. B. Ashworth.*)

Mamba ASM.6 engines; the Seamew's quick take-off, light wing-loading and great strength made it well suited for aerobatics, but only Wally Runciman seemed able to outwit its vicious tendencies and exploit its latent manoeuvrability to the limit.

Deliveries to the Royal Navy at Lossiemouth began in 1956, but soon afterwards the R.A.F. requirement was cancelled, and the total order was reduced to 24 Seamew A.S.1s *XE169–192*; at the same time Shorts were permitted to seek export orders, and Wally Runciman flew *XE175* on sales tours to Italy in March, Yugoslavia in April and Germany in May. After completing some 5,000 miles he had returned to Belfast and was taking part in a local flying display at Sydenham on 9 June, when he 'g-stalled' off a fast roll, lost height

The demonstration Seamew 2 *XE175* in which Wally Runciman was later killed.

453

while inverted, hit the ground during recovery and was killed. Operational trials in progress at Lossiemouth were shared by Jock Eassie with pilots from Boscombe Down, and by the end of 1956 two Seamews had cleared 200 deck take-offs and landings on H.M.S. *Warrior* in a total flying time of 20 hours; catapult trials were also completed, but by the beginning of 1957 only seven out of 19 production Seamews had been accepted by the Royal Navy, and soon afterwards the whole programme was cancelled as part of the 1957 economy drive, and all the rest were scrapped before delivery; only *XE180* survived as an instructional airframe in the company's Apprentice Training School, although the seven stored at Lossiemouth were not broken up for some years. The lesson of the Seamew was that whatever saving in cost might be gained by simplifying the structure, no false economy or optimism in aerodynamic design is ever worth while; more than most Naval aircraft, the Seamew looked like a camel among race-horses; unfortunately it proved to be as difficult to manage as a race-horse among camels.

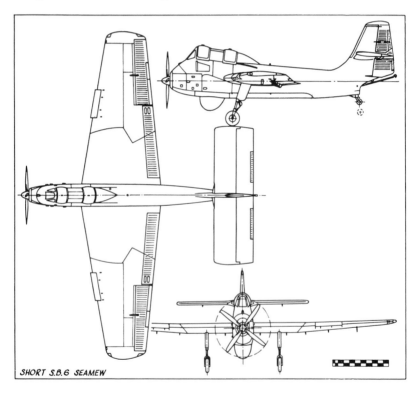

SHORT S.B.6 SEAMEW

Span 55 ft (16·75 m); length 41 ft (12·5 m); area 550 sq ft (59·2 m²); empty weight 9,795 lb (4,440 kg); all-up weight (normal) 14,400 lb (6,532 kg), (overload) 15,000 lb (6,804 kg); max speed 235 mph (378 km/h); range 750 miles (1,200 km).

XG905 with the Rolls-Royce 'Flying Bedstead' at R.A.E. Bedford in April 1960.

Short Vertical Take-off Aircraft

Vertical ascent was no novelty to the three Short brothers long before they began building aeroplanes, but in ballooning, as in aviation, escaping from the ground was much less difficult than a safe return to it. One at least of Oswald Short's descents nearly cost him his life, on 2 October, 1910, when he took up three friends from Battersea Park; all went well until, at 8,500 ft over Epping Forest, the valve rope came away from the valve bridge, and in falling pulled open the rip panel; by urging his passengers, all novices, to jettison the ballast as quickly as possible, Oswald checked their headlong descent just enough to avoid disaster, but the impact knocked them all unconscious, though without breaking any bones. Long before this, in 1893, Horace Short's erstwhile employer Charles Parsons had made and flown a small-scale steam-driven helicopter with a rotor of 11 ft diameter, but experiments with full-size rotorcraft were all failures until Juan de la Cierva produced his Autogiro in 1923; this could climb away very steeply after a short forward run and descend almost vertically under full control, although it could not hover, since its rotor was not power-driven.

In 1926 Short Brothers were asked to investigate the possibility of a flying-boat version of the Autogiro, and specification 31/26 was drafted to cover a project with a metal hull stabilised by sponsons, having a pylon-mounted rotor with hinged blades driven by a Bristol Jupiter engine; Cierva and Arthur Gouge collaborated in this design, C.14, but problems of stability and vibration proved insuperable, and only a few model tests were done in the seaplane tank early in 1927 before the whole idea was given up. In 1938, Raoul Hafner, who had come to Britain from Vienna five years earlier to develop his improved autorotative system, negotiated with Short Brothers to build his A.R. IV Gyroplane, a two-seat side-by-side cabin version of his successful A.R. III open model, to be powered by a Pobjoy Niagara V engine; variants for specific naval and military duties were proposed, and specification A.22/38 was issued as a basis of contract for three army co-operation prototypes on which construction began the following year. By this time Hafner had designed his first true helicopter with a power-driven rotor, which he

455

called P.D.6; this had a similar Pobjoy engine, driving a 39-ft rotor with three steel blades, mounted on top of a very slim aerofoil-shaped fuselage having a hinged flap or 'aileron' inset into its bottom edge; this was movable in the rotor downwash to control yaw and cancel torque reaction, the other controls being collective pitch and throttle for ascent and descent, and cyclic pitch for translation in any horizontal direction. One prototype P.D.6 was begun to specification A.10/39, but at the outbreak of war in August 1939 Hafner, not having acquired British citizenship, was interned under Defence Regulation 18B and his contracts with Short Brothers were cancelled; after some months of enforced idleness he was released to take charge of rotorcraft development at the Airborne Forces Experimental Establishment, where he designed the Rotachute, Rotabuggy and Rotatank, all based on his A.R. III and A.R. IV projects.

Thereafter, no more interest was taken in rotorcraft by Short Brothers until 1952, by which time Igor Sikorsky's classic formula had set the pattern for many successful helicopters, and the R.A.F. and R.N. had gained some

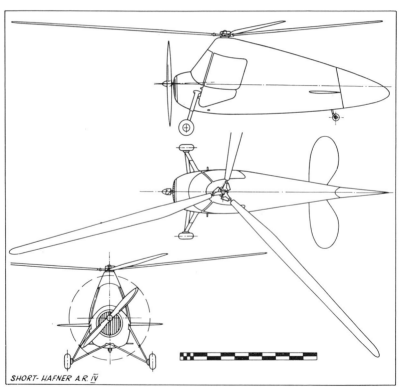

SHORT- HAFNER A.R. IV

A.R.IV—Rotor diameter 32 ft 2 in (11·6 m); length 19 ft 3 in (5·9 m); empty weight 847 lb (384 kg); all-up weight 1,330 lb (603 kg); max speed 115 mph (185 km/h).

456

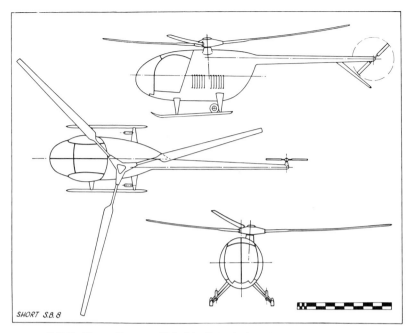

S.B.8—Rotor diameter 30 ft 6 in (9·3 m); length 25 ft 5 in (7·75 m).

operational experience of their capabilities. Seeking to eliminate some of the disadvantages of articulated rotors, with their short fatigue life and heavy replacement costs, Shorts put forward a proposal for a light two-seat helicopter with Frank Robertson's patent rigid rotor, hub-driven by a Gipsy Major engine, which interested the Army enough to promote a new requirement, HR.144T, for a scout helicopter, to which Shorts tendered their S.B.8 design in competition with the tip-jet Bristol 190 and Fairey Ultra-Light projects; only the last received a prototype order. Later rotorcraft proposals by Shorts were the light P.D.66 and two helicopters, P.D.67 and P.D.68, designed in collaboration with the Hiller Corporation of America. Meanwhile turbojet engines had reached the stage where their thrust exceeded their installed weight by a sufficient margin to make experiments with direct jet-lift feasible, the first successful example being the Rolls-Royce Thrust Measuring Rig in 1953, better known as the 'Flying Bedstead'. This used two Nenes mounted horizontally with their effluxes directed vertically downwards close together below the Rig's mass centre, control and stability being obtained by compressed air tapped from the engines and ejected downwards through valves in 'puff-pipes' to produce moments equivalent to those given by conventional control surfaces in forward flight. Having proved the feasibility of jet-lift with the 'Bedstead', Dr A. A. Griffith, Chief Scientist of Rolls-Royce Ltd, initiated the design of a small lightweight turbojet specifically for vertical installation as a lifting engine; this was the RB.108 of 2,000 lb static thrust, with a thrust/weight ratio of 8 : 1; its development was sponsored by the Ministry of Supply, who also issued specification ER.143 for a research aeroplane which could take off vertically by jet-lift alone, then accelerate into forward flight, becoming fully wing-supported in cruise with lift engines inoperative; it had also to decelerate to zero forward speed and alight vertically under full control using jet-lift for support during descent.

In Dr Griffith's opinion the supersonic airliner of the future (as foreseen in 1953) would be a slender delta optimised for high-speed cruise but needing lift engines for take-off and low-speed flight in a horizontal attitude, so Short Brothers & Harland submitted a small tailless delta monoplane with five RB.108 engines, one for propulsion with a normal horizontal jet efflux in the tail, and four grouped vertically in the fuselage round the centre of gravity with their effluxes directed downwards. Just before Hugh Conway's appointment as Chief Engineer in succession to A. W. S. Clarke, who died in April 1954, this preliminary design, P.D.11, was adjudged to be the most promising of the proposals received by M.o.S. and detailing of the design as S.C.1 went ahead; a contract was awarded in August for two aircraft, c/ns SH.1814–1815, serials *XG900* and *XG905*, and a great deal of development effort was devoted to perfecting the automatic-stability control-gear, power controls and specialised landing-gear. The newly established Precision Engineering Division at Castlereagh had already produced their first analogue computer, which was at once put to work on the design of the hydraulic and electronic control mechanisms; in the latter, magnetic amplifiers were used instead of thermionic valves to achieve maximum reliability. A group of hydraulic and electronic specialists was brought in from British Messier to build up an expert design team at Castlereagh under Frank Taylor, and a further notable contribution to the electronic work came from the research team led by E. Lloyd-Thomas. The R.A.E. insisted on quick changeover from manual control to automatic, and vice versa, and the final fail-safe design of the servo-controls incorporated three separate channels in parallel, so that a runaway in any one channel would be overpowered by the other two until cut out by the pilot, and no single fault could be catastrophic. The airframe itself was conventional, with a two-spar delta wing having orthodox ailerons outboard and elevators inboard along the trailing edge and fuel in the leading edge and in interspar bag tanks; there were no flaps, and the tail comprised a swept fin and rudder similar to the S.B.5's. The pilot had conventional controls, plus the lift engines' throttle and tilt levers, and the cockpit was enclosed by a large transparent hood of helicopter pattern giving excellent visibility downwards; a lightweight Folland ejector seat was installed at first, but replaced later by a 'zero-zero' Martin-Baker unit. The middle bay of the fuselage between the spar roots had four main longerons with the top and bottom of the bay open, but elsewhere the structure was composed of close-pitched frames or ribs without stringers, aluminium alloy being used throughout except for the lift-engine bay, which was titanium. In so short a fuselage it was extremely difficult to find space for all the equipment and instrumentation, and not least for the air bleed ducts from the engines; these joined to form a ring-main feeding a four-branched trunk leading to the outlet valves in the nose, tail and wing-tips. The valves were arranged to be half-closed in the neutral position, and were connected to the normal manual controls so that the wing-tip valves operated differentially with the ailerons, and the nose and tail valves with the elevators; in addition, the nose and tail valves were differentially rotatable to deflect their efflux sideways in conjunction with the rudder.

Manufacture of the S.C.1 began in the Experimental Department under Rupert Beaney's management early in 1955, and *XG900* was ready for engine running to commence on 7 December, 1956. Only the propulsion engine was installed, slanted at 30 degrees to ensure proper functioning of its lubrication system, which had been designed for vertical mounting; the top and bottom openings of the lift-engine bay were closed by fairing panels, and the long-stroke oleo-legs of the landing-gear were all raked forward at the same angle, in the best position for conventional take-off and landing; each leg carried a pair of castoring wheels, and the rear wheels had disc brakes; also the angle of the rear oleo-legs could be altered to rake in the opposite direction when required for vertical flight, the change in angle being effected by a simple two-position hydraulic jack acting as a drag strut; in the forward position for normal take-off, the castoring of the rear legs was automatically locked in mid-position. The hydraulic system worked at 2,500 lb/sq in, but the wheel brakes, being exposed to heat from the lift-engines' efflux, were pneumatic. For vertical landing the oleo-legs could cope with a velocity of 18 ft/sec, and the main-oleo castoring action was restrained by weak locking pins designed to shear at a predetermined sideways drift loading. In so small an aeroplane the manual control forces were quite low, and servo-controls were provided solely for the purpose of auto-stabilisation, the total failure of the main hydraulic supply being taken care of by an emergency supply at 1,200 lb/sq in provided by an accumulator giving about 50 seconds' independent servo

XG900 at Sydenham in February 1957 during ground handling trials with only the single propulsion engine installed; in this form it was first flown conventionally on 2 April, 1957, by Tom Brooke-Smith at Boscombe Down.

459

operation, allowing the pilot ample time to switch to manual control after the failure warning.

The engine run on 7 December was satisfactory and taxying began at Sydenham 10 days later; the pilot was Tom Brooke-Smith, who had previously completed a rapid helicopter conversion course with Ronald Gellatly of the Fairey Co and gone on to fly the 'Bedstead' at Hucknall, which he described as 'learning to ride a bicycle again'. After three months he was satisfied with ground handling, and on 6 March *XG900* was loaded on to the S.S. *Copeland* for a stormy two-day voyage round Land's End to Southampton, arriving at Boscombe Down on the 11th and making its first conventional take-off and landing on 2 April, 1957. On completion of its flying tests as a normal aeroplane it could have been returned before the end of the year to Belfast for its lift engines to be installed, but this was postponed in the name of economy, which also slowed down the commencement of hovering trials with the second S.C.1, *XG905*, which had been completed at Belfast and had its installed lift engines run for the first time on 3 September. They were mounted in pairs on two common transverse axes so that they could be tilted fore-and-aft through a range of 35 degrees, to assist transition to level flight when tilted aft and to provide rapid deceleration before vertical descent when tilted forward. The lift engine intakes were protected against ingestion of debris by a wire-mesh guard over the top of the bay ahead of the propulsion engine intake, above which a raised dorsal fin had been added as a result of the flight trials of *XG900*. During the winter a high 'goal-post' gantry was built at Sydenham, mainly from standard Bailey Bridge sections, over a raised platform with an open grid floor to prevent recirculation of exhaust gases, which could cause both rough running and a strong 'anti-lift' effect. Within the gantry was rigged a system of balanced tethering cables designed

XG905 during its initial tethered hovering trials at Sydenham in May 1958.

460

XG905 in free hovering flight away from the grid at Sydenham in November 1958; the noise level is indicated by the white-overalled figure with his hands over his ears.

to follow the aircraft's vertical movements without either restraint or assistance, being intended solely to prevent dangerous translational movements away from the platform or extremes of rolling or pitching attitudes. Thus tethered, *XG905* made its first hover flight on 23 May, 1958, and in the following weeks Tom Brooke-Smith gained experience rapidly in numerous ascents, which he shared with Jock Eassie and with Sqn Ldr S. J. Hubbard of R.A.E. Bedford. By the end of five months he was ready to discard the tethering cables and made the first free hovering flight, clear of the gantry but above a gridded platform, on 25 October. Early in November he landed away from the platform on a football pitch, which was undamaged apart from slight scorching of the grass, and this soon became a regular procedure. *XG905* made its first public appearance at the S.B.A.C. show at Farnborough in September 1959, when Tom Brooke-Smith demonstrated hovering but had to descend hurriedly because the intake debris-guard became clogged with newly mown grass which rose in a cloud as he took off. So he was unable to repeat the sequence followed on 2 June at Sydenham, when he had flown forward for a quarter of a mile, hovered over a road at a height of 30 ft, turned and side-stepped under full control and finally manoeuvred backwards, with lift thrust tilted fully forward, before landing on a metal platform. Finally, he achieved the first complete transition from level flight at 100 ft through vertical descent to 20 ft and vertical climb back to level flight; this was done after a conventional take-off at Bedford on 6 April, 1960. During the intervening months, lift engine power was progressively raised, and lateral speed was increased from 40 kt to overlap the minimum control speed without jet-lift of 134 kt; meanwhile valuable experience had been gained on a fully representative dynamic simulator, originally designed to check the functioning and reliability of the autostabilisation system before

461

hovering began, and continually developed as progress was made towards the ultimate goal of automatic landing in bad weather and darkness.

During the summer of 1960, *XG900* was fully equipped with lift engines and autocontrols and both S.C.1s were fitted with oleo-leg fairings, improved 'puff-pipe' valves and automatic inlet louvres above the lift engines; these comprised a set of longitudinal spring-loaded slats hinged along one edge so that they closed to form a low-drag cowling in level flight but opened immediately the lift engines were spun-up (by ram air from a manually controlled forward-facing gilled scoop) before relighting; on the ground the lift engines were started by air bled from the propulsion engine's compressor. Both aircraft were used to develop rolling take-off techniques from unprepared surfaces, with the dual objects of avoiding erosion and increasing the permissible take-off weight where a steep but not vertical take-off path was adequate. Tom Brooke-Smith demonstrated full transition for the first time in public on *XG905* at the Farnborough show in September 1960, but three months

XG905 with improved autostabiliser being flown at Sydenham by J. R. Green shortly before his fatal accident.

later he retired from test flying and from Shorts, being succeeded as Chief Test Pilot by Denis Tayler of the R.A.E. Bedford, who, together with Alex Roberts of Shorts, had already flown the S.C.1 many times. In April 1961 *XG900* was finally handed over to R.A.E. Bedford and *XG905* was returned to Belfast for the installation of an improved autostabilisation system designed to compensate for gusts and other external disturbances. *XG900* was flown by Denis Tayler at the 1961 Farnborough show, again demonstrating the precision with which it could be handled and the level attitude it could maintain throughout the transitional sequence; in June 1963 *XG905* was ready for tests with its new all-weather control devices, for which purpose another R.A.E. test pilot, J. R. Green, had joined Shorts. During the next three

462

months more than 80 flights were made at Belfast with the revised system, but on 2 October, as Green was returning to his landing point, the buzzer indicated a fault in the gyro input; he immediately reverted to manual control, but the gyros failed to cage, and all three diverged to their stops, giving a false vertical reference which caused the autostabiliser to fly the aircraft into the ground. It was below 30 ft when the runaway began, and Green had no chance of regaining full manual control, as he would have done from a greater height; as it was, the S.C.1 turned over on to its back and he was killed. Recurrence

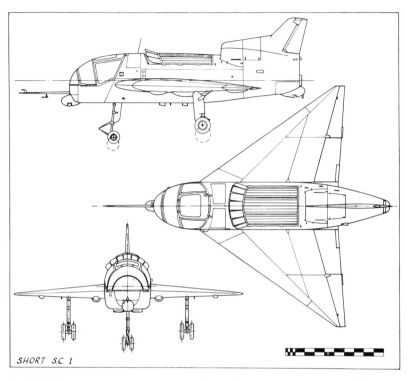

SHORT S.C. 1

of this fault was prevented by modifying the gyro to ensure that it would always cage in any combination of acceleration and attitude, and *XG905* was returned to the factory for repair. It emerged once more in May 1966, equipped with a heading and sideslip control system, director horizon and navigation display, for a further series of trials; tethered flights in the Sydenham gantry recommenced on 17 June, on completion of which a head-up display and ground/air data link were added before going to Bedford in June 1967 for all-weather and night-flying trials by the Blind Landing Experimental Unit; meanwhile *XG900* was still being flown at R.A.E. Bedford to investigate various aspects of VTOL control.

It was extremely unfortunate that Treasury economy cuts, coupled with

463

lack of interest in the higher Service echelons, should have slowed down development of the S.C.1 during 1958 and 1959 almost to the point of extinction. Although narrowly antedated by the American X-14 as the world's first 'flat-riser', the S.C.1 was a brilliant technical achievement and promised to become a valuable tactical weapon; preliminary designs by Shorts

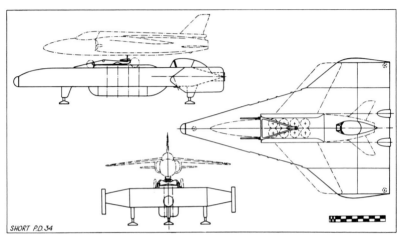

SHORT P.D.34

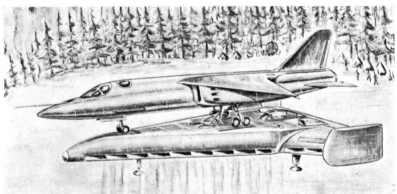

P.D.17 was a joint submission with English Electric Aviation to meet G.O.R. 339 for a Canberra replacement; Shorts' lower component was a VTOL platform for launching English Electric's P.17 strikebomber, which itself developed in collaboration with Vickers-Armstrongs into the more advanced and ill-fated T.S.R.2.

included a tactical transport (P.D.21), a naval strike-fighter (P.D.23), a ground attack fighter (P.D.25), a supersonic transatlantic transport (P.D.29) and a number of NATO submissions; but the most promising development of jet-lift was a series of VTOL launching platforms stemming from the P.D.17 solution to G.O.R.339 and proposed as a means of deploying light jet fighters such as the Folland Gnat (P.D.34) and Fiat G.91 (P.D.40) from hidden airfields of minimum size. Late in 1959 Shorts submitted their S.C.8 (P.D.43) proposal for a two-seat operational trainer version of the S.C.1 with five R.B.108 lift engines instead of four, which could have been built without delay and would have enabled new VTOL applications to be tried out at relatively low cost; but the politicians did not want to know, and the dedicated team who created the S.C.1 had to be content with the spontaneous acclamation of the discerning international audience who witnessed Tom Brooke-Smith's polished performances and the S.C.1's unvarying reliability in successive daily demonstrations at Farnborough in September 1960. Less publicised but equally significant were the first jet-lift crossings of the English Channel to and from the Paris show in 1961, when *XG900* was flown in seven stages from Bedford to Le Bourget between 26 and 30 May, returning to Bedford in five hops between 5 and 7 June; alternate stages were flown by Denis Tayler and Alex Roberts, the off-duty pilot on each stage going on ahead in the firm's Dove; seven of the landings were made vertically, one of them very close to Manston control tower some distance from the runway, to the articulate and profane astonishment of the local air traffic control staff; this exercise took six months to organise and involved the participation of three other aircraft—a Beverley to carry the ground equipment and stores, a Meteor 'chase plane' over the Channel and the Dove. But such elaboration, though wise and necessary in the pioneer stages, was entirely precautionary and could have been progressively eliminated with official backing for a comprehensive development programme.

European aircraft builders, like their American counterparts, were quick to take advantage of the lift engines pioneered by Rolls-Royce and the autostabiliser perfected by Shorts, but official apathy restricted British progress to a limited programme of flying on the two existing S.C.1s for a few more years; the disciples of *Festina Lente* had never heard of Alice's Red Queen, and there was no sign of encouragement for the operational development needing urgently to be done with more advanced flat-risers, such as the P.D.45, P.D.49 and P.D.56 strike fighters, and the P.D.55 and P.D.59 transports, in order to hold on to the ground already gained, but so easily surrendered.

S.C.1 *XG900* went to the Royal Aircraft Establishment at Bedford where it was used until 1971 for VTOL research. It is now part of the Science Museum's aircraft collection at Wroughton having been held in storage at Hayes. The second S.C.1, *XG905*, is in the Ulster Folk and Transport Museum at Holywood, Co. Down.

S.C.1—Span 23 ft 6 in (7·16 m); length 29 ft 10 in (9·1 m); area 141·9 sq ft (13·18 m²); empty weight 6,000 lb (2,720 kg); all-up weight (VTO) 7,700 lb (3,495 kg), (STO) 8,050 lb (3,650 kg); max speed 246 mph (296 km/h); range 150 miles (240 km).

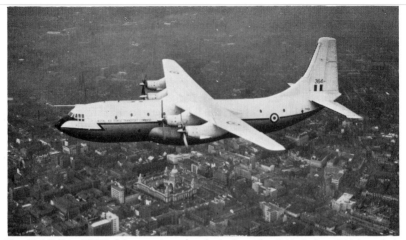

The third Belfast, *XR364*, flying over its native city in September 1964; in June 1966 it made its first entirely automatic landing without intervention by Denis Tayler.

The Short Belfast

In 1953, after a brief flicker of interest in a revival of flying-boats for Coastal Command had died away, Short Brothers & Harland Ltd concluded that the market for large seaplanes had disappeared for ever; the very small demand that still existed in isolated maritime communities in the Indian and South Pacific Oceans could be met for a further ten years by renovating and converting some of the little-used Sunderlands still stored at Wig Bay, of which in that year 16 were supplied to the R.N.Z.A.F. and 19 to the French Aéronavale, these being the last flying-boats to pass through the Queen's Island works, concurrently with the final batch of Sealands. There seemed to be a brighter future for utility transports, including cargo-carriers, and Shorts examined this potential market very carefully, concluding that an attractive project might be a medium-sized four-engined monoplane carrying a payload of four tons over short ranges; to cater for parachute deliveries of cargo to inaccessible sites such as oil-wells, the twin-boom layout of the Fairchild C-119 Packet offered advantages with its clam-shell rear doors which could be opened in flight. So the Short P.D.15 followed this popular pattern, with an unusual variation in having the tail-booms extended from the outer nacelles, which also contained the main undercarriage units, so that the inner nacelles were midway between the booms and the body. With four Alvis Leonides engines and the possibility of substituting turboprops later, the P.D.15 was offered to operators, but nearly all of them, having built up their traffic with war-surplus aircraft, were now looking for something carrying twice the load at much lower cost. By this time also the Air Staff had issued O.R.323 for a medium-range freighter for R.A.F. Transport Command to carry 25,000 lb over 400 miles or 10,000 lb over 2,000 miles. To meet this requirement

Shorts submitted a new project, P.D.16, similar to P.D.15 but larger and with two Bristol Proteus 755 engines, although four Rolls-Royce Darts were a possible alternative; the landing-gear was to be mounted in sponson fairings on the pressurised fuselage, and all the fuel was to be carried externally in pylon-mounted streamlined tanks under the wing. None of the designs tendered by several firms was selected for a prototype contract, although Shorts began detailing the P.D.16 as the S.C.3, but later Armstrong Whitworth went ahead with their design as a private venture which became the Argosy; this was very similar to the S.C.3 in body and tail layout, but had four engines and an orthodox nacelle-mounted landing-gear, and all the fuel was contained in the wing, which was derived from the Avro Shackleton's.

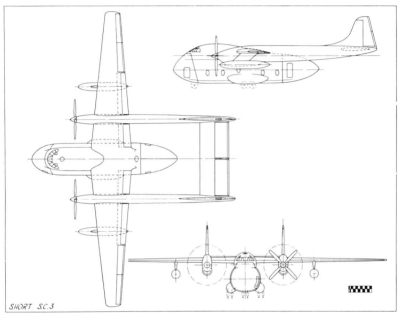

SHORT S.C.3

While the O.R.323 submissions were being prepared, increased demand for Bristol Britannias led to The Bristol Aeroplane Company seeking additional production capacity; already a licence had been granted to Canadair Ltd of Montreal to adapt the basic Britannia design for maritime reconnaissance with the R.C.A.F., who also wanted a long-range transport version with large cargo doors. In July 1954 The Bristol Aeroplane Co became a shareholder in Short Brothers & Harland Ltd, subscribing £360,000 of additional capital to set up a second production line for Britannias at Queen's Island, which came in time to replace the cancelled contract for Comets. As in the Canadair agreement, the collaboration included design as well as manufacture, and Shorts assumed overall responsibility for the large cargo door and heavy duty metal floor required by Transport Command; thus there was complete interchange of all information on Britannia between Bristol, Canadair and Shorts. It was not long before all three firms began considering methods of end-loading to increase cargo capacity and reduce turn-round time. Canadair, who had acquired the manufacturing and selling rights for all Britannia developments in Canada and the United States, developed the swing-tail end-loading version of the CL-44 for American all-cargo airlines, while both Bristol and Shorts explored the possibility of fully exploiting the Britannia wing and power plant in a high-wing freighter with either nose or tail loading by ramp from ground level; these projects were respectively the Bristol Type 195 and the Short P.D.18. Bristol and Shorts had already agreed to co-ordinate their planning of future projects so as to avoid wasteful competition, and in due course it was agreed that the P.D.18 should proceed in preference to the Bristol 195.

Initial studies for the P.D.18 were based on a circular cargo-hold cross-section circumscribing a 10 ft square, with the wing clear of the hold roof, a beaver-tail rear fuselage incorporating the rear loading ramp, the existing Britannia flight-deck and the existing landing-gear contained in sponsons as for the S.C.3. At first an optimised nil-dihedral thin wing with underslung Bristol Orion turboprops was proposed by Shorts, but their Chairman, Sir Matthew Slattery, ruled that this involved more development than they could undertake with existing resources, and a compromise was then evolved which used the existing Britannia wing and tail surfaces almost unchanged and still capable of being built on Britannia jigs; these features were to be combined with a larger fuselage having a hold cross-section circumscribing a 12 ft square and large enough to accept the Blue Streak missile. In August 1957 this was put up to the Air Staff as a strategic freighter named Britannia 553, with a capacity payload of 60,000 lb and a range of 4,860 nautical miles when carrying 13,500 lb, the engines being Orions. Since the all-up weight remained at 180,000 lb, proof and fatigue tests already done for the Britannia were still valid for the wing and landing-gear, and it was considered feasible to test the revised fuselage at Belfast. After careful examination, the Air Staff approved the basic design and undertook to place initial orders with Shorts, the development costs being spread over 30 aircraft; this design was indexed as S.C.5, and in April 1958 named Britannic. By this time the Orion had been cancelled in favour of up-rated versions of the Rolls-Royce Tyne, the latter having been adopted also for the Canadair CL-44D. Development of the Britannic was scheduled to proceed in four stages; Britannic 1 was to fly in 1961 with the standard Britannia wing and nacelles, using Proteus 255 or 765 engines and airscrews and carrying 60,000 lb payload at a gross weight of 180,000 lb; a year later, Britannic 2 was to have Proteus 770 engines with higher activity airscrews, a revised landing-gear with lower runway loading (LCN 40), leading-edge wing fillets at the root and nacelles to raise the Mach limit and a gross weight of 183,500 lb; Britannic 3, due in 1964, would have Tyne 11 engines in new slim underslung nacelles, allowing a payload of 75,000 lb and gross weight of 195,000 lb, while Britannic 4 was a future proposal using fully developed Tynes, to exploit which a high aspect ratio thin wing and a lengthened fuselage were to be combined to permit a payload of 100,000 lb at a gross of 220,000 lb. A possible date for Britannic 4 was 1966, and still more advanced variants, Britannic 5 and 6 with VC10 type swept wings, were foreshadowed. Britannic 3 featured a cargo hold 80 ft long and 12 ft wide, with a removable upper deck forward of the wing, giving a maximum seating capacity of 199 troops and two quartermasters in standard Transport Command seats.

This was too ambitious a programme to be implemented after the economy cuts of 1958, but the need for a strategic freighter capable of airlifting Titan and Blue Streak missiles and many types of heavy and bulky ground equipment from Lyneham to Adelaide, with not more than four refuelling stops, had become more pressing than ever. In March 1959 it was found possible to incorporate enough improvements in Britannic 3 to make it nearly comparable with Britannic 4, and this version was called Britannic 3A. It had a payload of 85,000 lb and gross weight of 218,000 lb, secured mainly by increasing the wing area and installing Tyne 12 engines. The standard Britannia wing of 2,077 sq ft comprised two halves bolted to a central rib; in Britannic 3A this rib was replaced by a parallel-chord centre-section of 16 ft 6 in span built into the top of the fuselage, thus increasing the wing area to 2,454 sq ft and moving all the nacelles outboard by 8 ft 3 in; it was a simple matter to move the inner nacelles 4 ft back towards the wing roots, thus creating the opportunity to fit larger airscrews at a later date if needed. The CL-44 design of 'wet wing', with all fuel tanks integral, and many details of the CL-44's Tyne 12 power plant installation, were also adopted, although the cowling and bearers forward of the firewall were borrowed from the Vanguard. Since the Tyne 12 was cleared for a maximum altitude of 30,000 ft, the former cabin pressure of 8·3 lb/sq in was unnecessarily high for troop-carrying, and a reduction to 6·55 lb/sq in effected a 50 per cent increase in predicted fatigue life; a completely new main landing-gear with eight-wheeled bogies saved weight and kept the LCN down to 44, and hinged forward and upward on a skewed axis, the bogie-beam rotating to lie parallel to the oleo-leg and fuselage skin when retracted; this enabled the sponson fairings to be shortened and their drag reduced. The ailerons remained unaltered, but rolling power was increased by the addition of lift-spoilers similar to those designed for the Canadair CL-28 and CL-44; the flaps were extended inboard, and the electric-motor drive of the Britannia was replaced by twin hydraulic motors. The flight-deck had already been widened, with increased windscreen and window area to meet the latest American (S.A.E.) recommendations on pilot's vision; with so much divergence from the original dimensions it was thought appropriate to drop the name Britannic, and in April 1959 the definitive aeroplane offered to the Air Staff was described simply as the Short S.C.5/10. Late in 1960 a production contract, based on specification C.203, was signed for ten aircraft of this type, serials *XR362–371*, these being the first ten of 12, c/ns SH.1816–1827, the last two being reservations for possible civil orders; concurrently with this contract the type name Belfast C.1 was chosen. Some 12 months before, the detail design of several major components had been sub-contracted, the rear fuselage and loading ramp going to Saunders-Roe and the power plant installation to Vickers-Armstrongs in view of its similarity to the existing design for the Vanguard. The design and manufacture of the Belfast wing was assigned to Bristol Aircraft Ltd and was already under way at Filton when the last Britannia 253 left Sydenham on 2 December, 1960.

The addition of a centre-section with wing-root attachments external to the fuselage shell, coupled with the high wing, made the Belfast assembly sequence much more like flying-boat practice than the Britannia and Canberra had been. The fuselage shell was divided into eight sub-assemblies, five of them being 'barrels', three between the nose and centre-section and two between the centre-section and tail unit; the barrels were built vertically to save space and simplify jigging, as the rigid airship hulls had been at Cardington (and indeed the very first Short metal hull for the F.5 at Rochester) some 40 years before. The fuselage structure, 17 ft 7 in in diameter, was similar in detail to the Britannia, with two heavy frames picking up the centre-plane box-spar; with the centre-plane assembled, the Belfast fuselage was actually 1 ft taller than the Shetland hull had been; the rear spar-frame had extensions at its lower corners through the pressure shell to carry the main landing-gear, so that sealing at these points was straightforward. The nose assembly incorporated an integrated windscreen frame and hemispherical pressure bulkhead as in the Britannia, with an unpressurised fairing containing the nose undercarriage and weather radar; the tail unit comprised two pairs of side panels corresponding to the outward hinging loading ramp and inward hinging rear loading door, connected by upper half-frames and having the tailplane centre-section and fin root-stub built-in. The Belfast's systems were based on those of the Britannia and identical with them in the several localities where developed components could readily be used, but there were a number of major changes. One of these, the integral fuel tankage, has already been mentioned; others were the necessity to supply the air-conditioning system from engine-driven mechanical blowers because there was no provision on the Tyne's compressor for a direct air-bleed; and the use of cables and pulleys with automatic tensioners throughout the flying controls in place of the high-speed torque-shafts of the Britannia; the end drives at the flight-deck and the control tabs, with their non-linear gearing and artificial feel input, were similar to the Britannia's. The flight-deck was wider than the Britannia's, with a larger central console having two separate sets of engine controls for the two pilots, also a full automatic landing system, a ground-run predictor for take-off, a low-speed indicator for taxying and a head-up display for the captain's instruments; an acceptable layout and windscreen were achieved without modification for both military and civil requirements in spite of an inherent incompatibility between these two standards.

Despite determined promotion, particularly in Canada and Alaska, no civil sales for the Belfast could be successfully negotiated, although a good deal of

470

design work was done on a two-deck variant with a side-hinged 'swing-nose' for loading palletised cargo either on to both decks (when the maximum payload would have been 100,000 lb) or on to the lower deck only (60,000 lb) with 141 passengers on the upper deck; this was designated S.C.5/31 and could also have been furnished as an 'air-bus' to carry up to 284 passengers on both decks, with access through separate side doors and additional rapid entry and exit via the rear loading ramp, where baggage racks were to be installed. The swing-nose mechanism was similar to the CL-44D's swing-tail and needed very little further development, while the pallets and their roller-conveyors were the same as those on the CL-44D apart from their greater width.

In 1960 the Air Staff issued O.R.351 for a tactical Beverley replacement capable of carrying large loads into and out of very short and unprepared airfields. To meet this requirement Shorts submitted the S.C.5/21 (P.D.47), a Belfast with blown flaps and control surfaces, giving V/STOL capability equivalent to that of the Breguet 941, for which Shorts later acquired the British agency and offered as P.D.71. The air for boundary-layer control in the S.C.5/21 was supplied from a removable pack of three lightweight Rolls-Royce turbocompressors installed in a fairing behind the centre-plane box-spar; the main landing-gear would have had 12-wheel bogies to permit take-off from grass. As a tactical freighter, the S.C.5/21 would have been somewhat larger than its rivals in the O.R.351 competition, which was won by the Hawker Siddeley HS.681 with vectored-lift engines, only to be cancelled in 1965 after a substantial share of the sub-contract work had been allocated to Queen's Island. In 1964 there was a proposal to revive the Britannic 6 concept, with a swept-wing based on the Lockheed C-141A Starlifter, a high T-tail and four Rolls-Royce R.B.178 turbofans of 25,000 lb static thrust each; this was the S.C.5/41 (originally P.D.53) designed to cruise at Mach 0·75 with a payload of 123,000 lb and gross weight of 420,000 lb; it could have been in service by 1970.

In the long run, no further orders matured, and the first Belfast, initially marked *G-ASKE*, took the air as *XR362* on 5 January, 1964, being flown from

The first Belfast, *XR362*, during its maiden flight from Sydenham to Aldergrove on 5 January, 1964.

471

Sydenham to Aldergrove by Denis Tayler and a crew of six, including co-pilot Peter Lowe. This marked the beginning of an 850-hour flight-development programme aimed originally at simultaneous certification under both military and civil requirements, in which the second Belfast, *XR363*, shared; making its first flight on 1 May, the latter had been fitted with a taller horn-balanced rudder, which just failed to clear the lintel of the Sydenham flight hangar, so an ingenious jacking/towing trolley was devised to lift the nose-wheel and thus lower the tail while being towed in or out of the hangar. In October 1964, the first Belfast, having been granted a restricted C. of A., went as *G-ASKE* to Torrejon near Madrid for take-off tests under temperate high-level conditions, completing 50 hours' flying (including 46 take-offs) between the 15th and the 29th; these tests were a preliminary to full tropical tests at Torrejon planned for the following summer, and included flights at a maximum weight of 225,000 lb; in December 1965 it flew again as *G-ASKE* to Nairobi for a supplementary series of 'hot-high' take-off measurements. Meanwhile at the Farnborough air show in September 1964 the first three Belfasts all flew together, *XR364*, fresh off the production line, disgorging 24 tons of Army vehicles immediately after landing. In June 1965 *XR364*, normally engaged on blind-landing trials at Bedford, made a second public appearance at the Paris air show, when it flew at Le Bourget. By this time *XR365* had been delivered to the A. & A.E.E. at Boscombe Down for tropical trials at Changi, Singapore, whither it left England in October; it was followed in December by *XR366*, which took off from Boscombe Down on 17 January, 1966, to fly to New Zealand and back, carrying as cargo a complete Westland SR.N5 Hovercraft; the arrival coincided with the official opening of the new Auckland airport at Mangere, and the route chosen was via the Azores, Bermuda, United States, Honolulu and Samoa; the flight was completed to schedule and *XR366* arrived back at Boscombe Down on 4

During its operational trials at Boscombe Down in 1966, the fifth Belfast, *XR366*, was flown up to 2¼ *g* with a military payload of 77,400 lb, comprising a Fowler tractor, an Abbot self-propelled gun and two Landrovers; it also flew to New Zealand and back carrying a 12,500-lb SR.N5 hovercraft over maximum-range stage-lengths, on one of which its take-off weight was 230,610 lb; here it is seen at Filton on 31 August, 1966, loading the first Concorde rear fuselage complete with its 60-ft long articulated transporter for rapid delivery to Toulouse. (*E. A. Shackleton.*)

472

The sixth Belfast, *XR367*, before its first flight at Sydenham on 3 November, 1965; this was the first Belfast delivered to No. 53 Squadron at Brize Norton on 20 January, 1966.

February. Later *XR366*, still based at Boscombe Down, assisted in delivering British-built major components of the first BAC–Sud Concorde prototype from Filton to Toulouse on 31 August, 1966, to save time in transit and to avoid disruption of peak tourist traffic on the vehicle ferry from Southampton to Le Havre, the normal transit route for Concorde components.

During their extended flight trials the first five Belfasts had been found to be 10 per cent deficient in maximum payload-range performance due to unpredicted suction drag on the underside of the rear ramp and loading door; this had been aggravated by the addition of yaw-damping strakes along the ramp margins, so the strakes were later to be removed, equivalent yaw-damping being provided electronically via the upper servo-tab of the rudder. With no interest being taken by civil operators, the flight-test schedule was simplified to demonstrate compliance with military requirements only, permitting a further drag reduction by removal of the wing-tip vortex generators and inboard leading-edge breaker strips introduced solely to meet the Air Registration Board's insistence on a positive natural nose-drop in the stall, with wings remaining level; by moving the ventral strakes from the ramp margins to a new position under the tail-cone, which itself was modified in shape to eliminate afterbody suction drag, the contract performance was re-gained in all respects; moreover, this was done without calling on the potential improvement available with up-rated engines driving 19-ft airscrews, which could be installed at any time without structural modification, and would probably be introduced at major overhaul.

The first operational Belfast, *XR367*, was handed over to No. 53 Squadron, R.A.F. Transport Command, at Brize Norton on 20 January, 1966, and was joined soon afterwards by *XR368* and *XR369*. After a period of route-proving and crew-training, including frequent flights to Aden, No. 53's first 'job of work' was to bring back from Atkinson Field, Guyana, the entire equipment of No. 1310 Flight, Transport Command, including three West-land Whirlwind 10 helicopters; this airlift of 5,200 miles, via Barbados and the Azores, was completed by a single Belfast (*XR367*), which arrived back at

473

Fairford on 7 October, 1966. Immediately afterwards XR367 flew out two larger Westland Wessex HC.2 helicopters from Odiham to Akrotiri, Cyprus, then joined the other two Belfasts in ferrying back to Odiham the whole equipment of No. 230 Squadron, including 11 Whirlwinds, from Labuan, Borneo, at the end of the Malaysian–Indonesian 'confrontation'; two Whirlwinds were carried on each of four 10,000-mile sorties and three on the fifth; at the other end of the climatic scale, cold weather trials were completed early in 1967 at Churchill on Hudson Bay. XR370 was delivered on 13 December, 1966, and in May 1967 flew out the French (second) and German (third) stages of the ELDO Europa I satellite-launcher from Munich to Woomera, a distance of 12,000 miles. After retrospective modification to the final standard, all ten Belfasts were expected to be fully operational with No. 53 Squadron on an all-weather basis by the end of 1967. In fact, only one more Belfast was delivered to the squadron by that time; this was XR371, the last to be built, on 3 July, 1967. XR362 was eventually delivered on 8 March, 1968, after a lengthy flight development programme, with XR366 and XR363 following at three-monthly intervals on 27 June and 10 September, after tropical and cold weather trials and handling and performance trials respectively. During 1969 only one aircraft, XR365, was delivered, on 14 January, following extended handling and performance trials at A. & A.E.E. The final delivery was made on 5 November, 1971, when XR364, which had been used for autoland trials at the Blind Landing Experimental Unit at R.A.E. Bedford, arrived at Brize Norton, to where the squadron had moved in May 1967. Belfasts were then the largest aircraft ever to have entered R.A.F. service and could accommodate loads exceeding 11,000 cu ft and up to 77,000 lb weight; they were also the largest in the world to have been equipped with a fully operational automatic landing system.

When No. 53 Squadron was disbanded on 14 September, 1976, as part of the Government's defence cuts, the 10 Belfasts came up for disposal. Eight

Belfast *G–BEPS*, ex-*XR368*, was the second aircraft to enter revenue-earning service with HeavyLift Cargo Airlines on 9 February, 1982. (*HeavyLift Cargo Airlines*).

Three Westland Lynx Mk. 89 helicopters for the Federal Nigerian Navy waiting to be loaded aboard a HeavyLift Cargo Airlines Belfast. (*HeavyLift Cargo Airlines*).

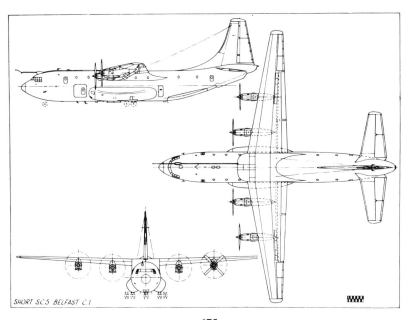

SHORT SC.5 BELFAST C.1

were bought by Rolls-Royce, some having passed through other companies' hands, and were delivered to Hucknall during August 1978. *XR371* went to the R.A.F. Cosford Aerospace Museum in October 1978 and *XR364, 366, 369* and *370* were scrapped at Hucknall during June–August 1979. The remaining three of this batch were ultimately acquired by HeavyLift Cargo Airlines Ltd at Stansted; *XR363*, now *G–OHCA*, is in store at Southend, *XR365* (*G–HLFT*) and *XR367* (*G–BFYU*). HeavyLift also acquired *XR368* (*G–BEPS*) from Pan African and *XR326* (*G–BEPE*) *which is in store at* Southend. Since March 1980 HeavyLift has provided a unique service with these three Belfasts which have been specially modified to transport very heavy and large loads. The maximum length of the cargo hold is 90 ft (27.4 m), height 13 ft 4 in (4.05 m) and width 16 ft 1 in (4.88 m) and the aircraft have an 85,000 lb lifting capability. Typical loads have included drilling equipment, large articulated road vehicles, two Black Hawk helicopters, and a complete Fokker F.27.

S.C.3—Span 122 ft 7 in (37·4 m); length 87 ft 2 in (26·5 m); area 1,500 sq ft (139·5 m²); empty weight 41,500 lb (18,800 kg); all-up weight 69,000 lb (31,300 kg); max speed 316 mph (509 km/h); max range 2,500 miles (4,250 km).

Belfast—Span 158 ft 10 in (48·4 m); length 136 ft 5 in (41·6 m); area 2,466 sq ft (229 m²); operating weight empty 125,000 lb (56,700 kg); all-up weight 225,000 lb (102,220 kg); max cruise speed 358 mph (576 km/h); max range 5,200 miles (8,370 km).

Skyvan on test over Sydenham in 1966, with a Belfast outside the Flight Hangar.

The Short Skyvan

Among the pioneers of aviation have been many families of brothers work-ing together, of whom the two Wrights, the three Shorts, the two Voisins, the three Farmans and the two de Havillands come readily to mind; less common was the husband-and-wife partnership exemplified by Fred and Maxine Miles, who, having started in a small way at Shoreham, Sussex, in 1929, built up their aircraft manufacturing business, under the aegis of Phillips & Powis of Reading, into one of the major producers of wooden trainers during the Second World War. Miles Aircraft Ltd, as it had become in 1943, continued successfully into the post-war era with more advanced designs evolved by Fred's younger brother George Miles, but failed to cope with the vastly increased cost of developing metal aircraft when wood ceased to be acceptable to military and airline customers; after the ensuing financial crisis in 1947, their factory with its Marathon production line, at Woodley, was sold to Handley Page Ltd and George Miles joined Airspeed Ltd, but no ordinary disaster could keep enthusiasts like Fred and 'Blossom' out of avia-tion for long and within three years they were back in business at Shoreham as F. G. Miles Ltd, while the creditors of Miles Aircraft Ltd were repaid out of the profits of manufacturing *Biro* ball-point pens and *Copycat* office dupli-cating-machines, both of which became indispensable and highly productive tools in the aircraft and other industries during the next decade.

After the Magister of early wartime, the most successful Miles aeroplane was the Messenger, ordered for R.A.F. communications in 1944 and produced in peacetime as a four-seat cabin tourer, together with its twin-engined variant

477

the Gemini, for which the demand in 1946 justified a second production line at Newtownards near Belfast. Concurrently George Miles designed the Aerovan, a flying 'one-ton truck' with two Cirrus Major engines and a rear-loading low-level cargo door surmounted by a single 'pan-handle' tail boom. One Aerovan was bought by Lord Londonderry in 1946, and next year a fleet of five more was operated from Newtownards by Ulster Aviation Ltd; these carried tourists to the Isle of Man and ferried Messenger and Gemini components between the Woodley and Newtownards factories. The Aerovan could lift a payload greater than its own tare weight, but could not maintain height on one engine, and one had to be ditched in the Irish Sea when an engine failed.

When the Aerovan first appeared in Northern Ireland Shorts were too preoccupied with their own reorganisation and the closing down of Rochester to take much notice of its activities; besides, they hoped to continue their traditional flying-boat business at Belfast and were about to launch the Sealand. The Newtownards factory was vacated when Miles Aircraft Ltd were wound up in 1948, service support and modification of Aerovans and other Miles types being undertaken thereafter by F. G. Miles Ltd at Shoreham; one of the Aerovans which had survived several years of charter work and joyriding around the Channel Islands and Normandy seaside resorts was converted to incorporate a single-spar strut-braced metal wing of 75 ft span and aspect ratio of 19, designed by Avions Hurel-Dubois of Villacoublay; this was flown at Shoreham from March 1957 to June 1958 as the Miles H.D.M.105, to test the efficiency of the Hurel wing before applying it to commercial projects, the first of which was to be the H.D.M.106 Caravan light freighter of $1\frac{1}{2}$ tons payload capacity.

By this time Short Brothers & Harland had surveyed the air-cargo market very thoroughly and seen their P.D.15 and P.D.16 rejected and the much larger P.D.18 accepted for development into the S.C.5. So when Fred Miles approached Shorts in 1958 suggesting collaboration in developing the Caravan he was cordially though critically received; after examining the Caravan preliminary design, Shorts agreed to purchase it, and a year later F. G. Miles Ltd merged with the Beagle group formed by Peter Masefield and the Pressed Steel Co, while Shorts formed a Light Aircraft Division at Belfast in April 1959, with Frank Robertson as Chief Designer, Light Aircraft; formerly in Miles' design office, he had been Chief Project Engineer at Saunders-Roe before coming to Shorts in the same capacity in 1952. The H.D.M.106 design was rejected in its original form, but its philosophy was commended, and after numerous evolutionary essays on the same theme there emerged P.D.36, an all-metal beaver-tailed rear-loading box-van with a strut-braced rectangular wing of aspect ratio 11, a fixed nosewheel landing-gear and two supercharged flat-six Continental GTS IO-520 engines of 390 hp, of a type scheduled for production under licence by Rolls-Royce at Crewe. Adopted for detailing as the S.C.7, the new project was aptly named the Short Skyvan, and two prototypes, SH.1828 and SH.1829, were put in hand as a private venture on a strictly limited budget. A Treasury grant was applied for to finance a production batch of ten to follow the prototypes, but the long delay in reaching a decision on this at government level seemed likely to jeopardise the Skyvan's chances of catching a large potential market that could not wait indefinitely.

In many respects the Skyvan echoed the Scion of 25 years earlier and was expected to appeal to bush operators in the same way; early interest was shown by Reg Ansett in Australia and Sigurd Wien in Alaska, representing opposite extremes of climatic environment and emphasising the importance of absolute design integrity within rigidly controlled weight and cost limits. There was, however, an almost total breakaway from Shorts' traditional methods of monocoque construction, and the Skyvan was designed to have a stiff non-buckling skin all through the airframe. This was achieved by adopting an improved double-skin technique with a flat or single-curved outer skin attached to a longitudinally corrugated inner skin by continuous bonding between the surfaces in contact; the corrugations were in the form of alternate flats and semicircles, with the flats bonded to the outer skin; after the initial problem of rolling the corrugations dead straight in 30 ft lengths had been overcome (by the Warwick Rim and Sectioning Co) it was found relatively easy to produce the panels in autoclaves. The structural principle, familiar in its application to corrugated cartons for packaging, had been tried in aircraft even earlier than Oswald Short's Silver Streak, by W. T. Reid in the fuselage monocoque for the Bristol M.R.1 of 1917, but had not been entirely successful at that time because of the limited efficiency of the discrete attachments between the two skins by riveting. With modern Redux bonding techniques and inspection procedures, it had become possible to manufacture stiff strong lightweight structural panels of high reliability using very thin sheet alloy which would not in conventional form stand up to handling in normal daily use. The fuselage was a box 6 ft 6 in square internally with a flat floor 16 ft long and the top and side panels extended aft to a horizontal knife-edge at the tail, where the curved rear bottom panel was hinged to open inwards and upwards. The floor panels were of sandwich construction with light alloy faces bonded to an end-grain balsa core and were entirely supported on the transverse frames without addition of longitudinal bearers. Two of the fuselage frames were of heavier box design and picked up with the wing spar roots at their upper corners and the cantilever stub wings at their bottom corners; these carried the main undercarriage units and formed the lower anchorages for the wing struts. In each side panel were five cabin windows (round in the first prototype but rectangular in later aircraft) together with access doors at floor level to enable the lashing down of cargo (particularly wheeled vehicles) to be done from outside when there was too little clearance inside. Forward of the hold was the flight-deck and front fuselage, which was built as a separate unit of conventional stressed-skin design, since it had to conform to double curvature in order to obtain a smooth entry shape. The flight-deck was raised above the hold floor level and was basically laid out for single-pilot operation, although full dual control was available as an option.

The wing was of NACA 63-4-414 section and had two channel-section spars and an auxiliary spar at the leading edge; the upper and lower skin panels were of the same design as the flat fuselage panels, with one-piece spanwise-corrugated inner skins bonded to smooth outer skins of varying gauge, the curvature of the thicker skins being pre-formed before bonding in the auto-clave; in fact, even the flat panels were curved to about 4-ft radius during bonding to ensure their flatness after cooling to room temperature, with the outer skin having a small residual tension; this avoided 'tramlines' due to surface tension at the edges of the Redux layers. The wing struts were com-posed of three channels side-by-side, riveted to upper and lower skins and faired by light-gauge leading and trailing edge; the channels had individual attachments at both ends, to ensure that there were three separate load paths and that no single fatigue crack could cause failure of the whole strut. The tail surfaces were of conventional design with unstiffened single skins attached to front and rear spars and close-pitched ribs; the control surfaces and slotted flaps were similar but with wider rib spacing and the skins stiffened by fluting. The landing-gear was non-retractable, with trailing-arm main units on the ends of the stub-wing spars and a castoring nosewheel unit mounted at the front of the pilot's floor structure; initially there were twin nosewheels, but in the second prototype and all later aircraft a larger fork-mounted single wheel was substituted, together with hydraulic steering. Skis could be attached to the wheeled gear and were hydraulically retractable after take-off from snow for landing on a dry runway, and vice versa; power was supplied by an electro-hydraulic power pack installed in the nose to serve wheel brakes, nosewheel steering and flap actuation, the ailerons being drooped as the flaps were lowered. The electrical system was duplicated, with a 28-volt d.c. supply to a busbar on each side from an engine-driven generator on the same side and a contactor for cross-coupling the busbars in emergency or for engine starting without an external supply; each system included an inverter supplying a.c. for instruments at 115 volts and 400 cps. There were indepen-dent fuel systems for each engine comprising two pairs of bag tanks totalling

Skyvan I *G-ASCN* as first flown with Continental piston engines in January 1963.

480

Skyvan IA, the first prototype re-engined with Astazous in October 1963.

175 gallons installed in a fairing above the fuselage between the wing roots and fore and aft of the main front spar on either side of the centre-line; the forward and aft tanks on each side were coupled to a single collector tank feeding its own engine; there was a balance cock for interconnecting the port and starboard tanks and a cross-feed cock between the collector tanks, so that any tank could feed either or both engines if necessary. Although basically designed to carry freight, including wheeled vehicles of Volkswagen Microbus size, the alternative layout for 15 or 18 passengers in five or six rows of seats proved popular with prospective operators and took priority in the early production orders, the basic flight-deck heating and ventilating system being extended to cater for the cabin.

The first prototype, Skyvan I *G-ASCN*, was first flown by Denis Tayler at Sydenham on 17 January, 1963, with Continental piston engines and completed its handling trials with these in May, but it had been decided in 1962 to adopt Turbomeca Astazou turboprops for all production Skyvans; these had been developed in power plant form, integrated with a special Ratier-Figeac feathering, braking and reversing airscrew with built-in hub and

481

Skyvan IA *G-ASCN* with production-type tail unit, being demonstrated as a paratroop transport in 1965.

detachable blades, by SFERMA of Villacoublay as an exchange unit for piston engines in the 400–500 hp class. *G-ASCN* went back into the works at the end of May to have a pair of 520 eshp Mk II Astazous installed and flew with them as the Skyvan IA (or Turbo-Skyvan) on 2 October, 1963, taking off on only half power and showing such promise that new interest was aroused all over the world. After ironing out some of the early problems stemming from the Astazou's somewhat unorthodox control system and handling characteristics, with power regulated by the pilot via the airscrew pitch-control and fuel flow automatically limited by turbine entry temperature, a special category C. of A. was obtained in April 1964 to permit extension of flight trials overseas, combined with demonstrations to operators but excluding fare-paying passengers.

For its first flight away from Northern Ireland, and its public debut, it was flown by Don Wright and Jack Sherburn to the Hanover air show in April 1964; soon after they took it for two weeks to the Turbomeca headquarters at Pau for engine-matching tests, with encouraging results; meanwhile a sales team had followed up the delayed but favourable Government decision to support limited production with an intensive tour of the United States, New Zealand, Australia, New Guinea, Japan, the Philippines and South America. It was demonstrated by Jack Sherburn to Prince Philip when he visited Queen's Island on 7 May and made its first public appearance in England at the Farnborough air show in September, when it belied its cubist appearance by an impressive display of agility, well contrasted with the more stolid formation of three Belfasts on the same occasion. Immediately the show ended it set off on a rapid sales tour of Lisbon, Madrid, Villacoublay and Jersey, giving demonstrations to the Portuguese and French authorities and to a number of airlines, including Aeralpi. In November it returned to the works again for modifications, including a revised rear fuselage contour to improve performance and save weight, with the tailplane recessed into the stern and lowered in relation to the fins and rudders; at the same time the elevator horn-balances outboard of the fins were deleted and revised one-piece rudders were fitted, entirely above the tailplane. At the other end of the world, the Skyvan was prominently featured at the British exhibition at Sydney on 24 September, where a large model on Shorts' stand carried the livery of Ansett-ANA as an earnest of the future; four weeks later the Skyvan invaded Communist territory in a display at the British industrial exhibition at Peking, an occasion which afforded an unusual opportunity for the Shorts party to see the exotic splendours of the Forbidden City as well as to meet the people of modern China face to face.

On 15 March, 1965, *G-ASCN* re-emerged from the works complete with a production-type rear fuselage and tail, though retaining the original blunt nose with its twin landing-lights and double nosewheels. More important, it now had 666 eshp Astazou X turboprops, which greatly enhanced its short-field performance and permitted the payload to be raised to 4,600 lb and the gross weight to 12,500 lb, the limit for A.R.B. certification in Group C.

The second prototype, *G-ASCO*, and first production Skyvan II, *G-ASZI*, at Pau in May 1966.

Shown in its revised form at the Paris air show in June, its evident STOL capability clinched its first sales with Aeralpi, who operated from Milan into the Italian winter sports resort of Cortina d'Ampezzo, and with a new domestic airline, Emerald Airways of Aldergrove, who ordered four and three Skyvans respectively; it was demonstrated to representatives of Ansett-ANA, Trans-Australia Airlines, Wien Air Alaska and Northern Consolidated Airlines of Alaska, whose President, Ray Petersen, declared, 'There's just nothing like it,' and put its potential world market at between one and two thousand; but the best tribute of all came from the veteran Russian designer Oleg Antonov, who said, 'I am making an aeroplane just like that for Aeroflot—it is almost a copy!' Although the Australians were mainly interested in it as a feeder-liner for up to 18 passengers, the Americans viewed it as a freighter capable of carrying two pre-packed one-ton pallets of the standard 88 in by

483

60 in size, for which Shorts already included a roller-conveyer in their list of optional equipment; a twin-float seaplane conversion set was also available for use on lakes and rivers. The prototype Skyvan II *G-ASCO* was first flown on 29 October, 1965, and was representative of the initial production standard, including a more pointed nose with provision for weather radar, a single nosewheel, fairings for the main landing-gear, separate landing-lights faired into the tops of the wing struts and Astazou X turboprops with automatic feathering. Meanwhile approval had been given for a second batch of ten Skyvans to be started and, in view of the general demand for a passenger version, it was decided to lengthen the cabin floor by 2 ft to 18 ft; the rear loading door was shortened by the same amount and external dimensions were unchanged; with the longer floor and total fuel tankage increased to 225 gallons the second production batch was distinguished as Skyvan II series 2.

G-ASZJ during certification trials in May 1966.

While development flying continued in *G-ASCN* and '*O*, the first two fully-equipped Skyvan II demonstrators, SH.1830–1831 *G-ASZI* and '*J*, emerged with Astazou Xs on 28 January and 3 March, 1966, respectively, and after a visit to the Turbomeca headquarters at Pau in May by *G-ASCO* and *G-ASZI* for engine modifications, fully up-rated 690 eshp Astazou XIIs were approved for production. By this time the Skyvan order book stood at 13 firm sales and five options, the firm customers being Aeralpi, Emerald, Ansett-Mandated Airlines, Papuan Air Transport and Northern Consolidated Airlines of Alaska. While *G-ASCN* made brief trials at Sydenham with ski landing-gear in April, *G-ASZI* was lent to Aeralpi for route-proving on the narrow approach path past the Marmolada to their shut-in terminal airstrip at Cortina d'Ampezzo, and *G-ASZJ* joined in the final certification flight-test schedule at Sydenham. In May the first two Skyvans for customers emerged, SH.1832 *I-TORE* for Aeralpi and SH.1833 *G-ATPF* for Emerald, the former being delivered on 8 June with a special export C. of A. and the

The second prototype, *G-ASCO*, in Ansett-MAL livery flying on one engine during the 1966 S.B.A.C. show. (*E. A. Shackleton.*)

latter on 16 August as soon as an unrestricted C. of A. had been granted; the second for Aeralpi, SH.1834 *I-CESA*, flew on 24 July and was delivered on 8 October; in November it was leased to Alitalia to operate early morning and late afternoon winter services between Venice and Trieste; both Skyvans were called on to assist with flood relief in the Po valley that month and flew ten sorties a day, carrying doctors and medical supplies to the stricken communities and returning with homeless refugees. Emerald's second, SH.1835 *G-ATPG*, first flown on 30 August, was shown in the static park at the Farnborough air show a week later, where the flying display was given by Don Wright in *G-ASCO* repainted in the colourful livery of Ansett-MAL, whose first Skyvan II series 2 (SH.1838 *VH-EJR*) was due to be delivered early in 1967. By September 1966 Shorts had appointed a Skyvan concessionaire for sales in America, Remmert-Werner Inc of St Louis, Missouri, who ordered

Aeralpi's first Skyvan, *I-TORE*, taking off from Sydenham in June 1966.

485

The final Skyvan II series 1, *N4906*, flying over County Antrim in January 1967, in Northern Consolidated Airlines livery.

G-ATPG at Farnborough in September 1966 in Emerald Airways livery; later it became Remmert-Werner's demonstrator in America.

two demonstrators and reserved options for five more; the first Skyvan on the U.S. register and last series 1, SH.1837, flew on 5 November, 1966, as *N4906* for Northern Consolidated Airlines; in February 1967 it became *G-AVGO* for a brief period of F.A.A. certification trials in Belgium. Following the grant of the C. of A. and its validation for American operation, the Government had approved an extension of the production line to a total of 50 Skyvans, with a planned delivery rate by mid-1967 of one per week.

Then came a set-back, for the Astazou XII was found to be temperature-limited for take-off at high ambient combined with altitude; this had first

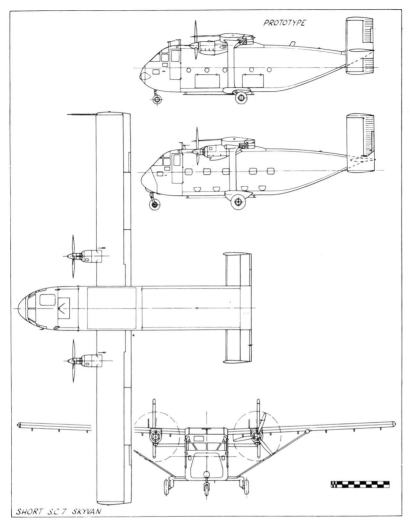

PROTOTYPE

SHORT S.C.7 SKYVAN

Span 64 ft 1 in (19·5 m); length 40 ft 1 in (12·2 m); area 373 sq ft (34·7 m²); operating weight empty 7,350 lb (3,335 kg); all-up weight 12,500 lb (5,670 kg); max cruise speed 210 mph (338 km/h); max range 440 miles (710 km).

become apparent in hot-day take-offs from Cortina during the summer and was seriously restrictive at the tropical mountain airstrips of New Guinea and Papua. Although normal engine development promised a substantially improved performance for the Astazou, this could not be achieved within the delivery programme already agreed. However, Reg Ansett was so keen to have the Skyvan with its exceptional 'quick-change' utility features that he was

487

willing to wait 15 months for delivery with up-rated engines, rather than cancel his order and change to a different aircraft. Concurrently, Shorts and Remmert-Werner studied the possibility of installing an American engine which would give the Skyvan its specified performance in hot and high conditions, and would of course be attractive to U.S. operators; meanwhile Northern Consolidated Airlines and Remmert-Werner agreed to take delivery of their initial orders with modified Astazou XIIB engines, and a North American sales tour by *G-ATPG*, resold to Remmert-Werner, began on 20 April, 1967, when this aircraft and *N4906* took off from Sydenham to fly the Atlantic in convoy via Stornoway, Reykjavik, Sondrestrøm (Greenland) and Frobisher Bay (Baffin Island). Thence *G-ATPG*, flown by Mike Ingle-Finch, turned south via Knob Lake (P.Q.), Albany (N.Y.), Mansfield (Ohio) and Indianapolis to arrive at St Louis, Missouri, on 26 April. Meanwhile *N4906*, piloted by N.C.A.'s Captain Warren Dodson and Tim Woods of Shorts, had flown its longest stage of 900 miles across Hudson Bay from Frobisher to Churchill on 23 April, then westerly via Edmonton, Fort Nelson and Whitehorse to reach Anchorage, Alaska, on 25 April.

A month later Remmert-Werner announced advance orders in North America for 50 Skyvans, to be powered by Garrett AiResearch TP331–201 turboprops continuously rated at 715 eshp; deliveries with the new engines were to begin after clearance of FAA certification in the spring of 1968; meanwhile the initial batch with Astazous commenced delivery at the rate of one a month, and *VH-EJR*, re-registered *G-AVJX*, demonstrated its 'quick-change' feature at the Le Bourget international air show in May; by then, 70 Skyvans were on order and continued Treasury support for the production programme was assured. With only eight Skyvan Series 2s with Astazous being built, re-engining of the third and fourth prototypes, *G–ASZI* and *'ZJ*, began during early autumn 1967; *G–ASZI* first flew with the Garrett engines on 15 December, 1967, and *'ZJ* on 20 January, 1968. Garrett-powered Skyvans became the Series 3. In 1969 a military version modified to carry optional military equipment was prepared, and designated Series 3M. The prototype, *G–AXPT*, first flew during early 1970, to begin a lengthy programme. In 1982 Skyvan 3M–200s were cleared for non-civil operations at 15,000 lb maximum take-off weight, 2,500 lb more than the civil Series 3. Sixty Skyvan 3Ms were built for 17 armed forces, No. 2 Squadron Sultan of Oman's Air Force being the largest user with 16 aircraft. *G–ASZJ* later became the first Skyliner 22-seat all-passenger version, about 12 being produced. Skyvans were sold to civil operators in some 25 countries from Australia, Barbados and Canada to Venezuela and Zaïre. When production ceased in 1985, 154 Skyvans had been built but spares provisioning was still proceeding in 1989.

The first prototype 330, *G–BSBH*, during its first flight on 22 August, 1974, with flaps and undercarriage lowered.

The Shorts 330, Sherpa and 360

Such were the commercial and operational successes of the Skyvan that in 1971, by which time some 70 had been sold, Shorts turned its attention to a successor.

This was originally conceived as a 26-seat aircraft cast much in the mould of a DC-3 replacement, but market surveys had indicated that commuter and regional air service operators were seeking something larger to replace their 18/20-seat aircraft then in their fleets. This became increasingly apparent in the United States where, in July 1972, the Civil Aeronautics Board had changed the rules to allow these operators to fly aircraft with 30 seats or 7,500 lb of payload. Clearly, this was of importance to Shorts marketing experts, whose surveys showed that North America had major sales potential. Thus the design of the new aircraft, originally designated SD3–30, materialised as a 30-seat twin-engined transport which retained many of the Skyvan's features, including a 6 ft 4 in square cross section cabin and the same safe-life concept.

The parallel-sided fuselage was a light alloy structure built in two main portions; the nose portion housed the two-crew flight deck, nose undercarriage bay and the 45 cu ft forward baggage compartment, and the centre and rear portion included the wing main spar attachment frames and lower transverse beams, which carried the main undercarriage and its fairings, plus the 100 cu ft aft baggage compartment and tail unit attachment frames. The nose and rear underfuselage were riveted skin and stringer structures; the remainder consisted of a smooth outer skin Redux-bonded to a corrugated inner skin stabilised by frames. A large passenger/cargo door was fitted in the port side of the nose portion with the normal passenger entry door located aft on the same side. The passenger version of the SD3–30 had two emergency exits in each side of the cabin plus one in the roof. Honeycomb sandwich panels with light alloy faces formed the cabin floor with seat rails to simplify configuration

489

changes and also serve as cargo tie-down points. The floor was flat throughout its 31 ft length.

Where mixed traffic services were flown the cabin could be divided by a partition with cargo forward and passengers aft of it. With all seats removed, which could be accomplished in 20 minutes, there was 1,230 cu ft available for cargo. A galley, toilet and cabin attendant's seat were at the rear of the cabin, large 40 cu ft overhead lockers were fitted and the flight deck and cabin were soundproofed and air conditioned. Pressurisation was considered to be unnecessary for the short stage lengths and low operating altitudes of commuter airliners. Each of the ten rows of seats had a large window. All three of the Menasco undercarriage units retracted hydraulically, the steerable nosewheel retracting rearwards and the main units into fairings carried on the outer ends of the transverse beams. The main wheels did not retract completely, leaving a small portion of the wheel exposed. The initial design of the wing, tip to tip, and of the first tail unit was undertaken by the

A 330 structural test specimen airframe being prepared for testing in the British Aerospace Aircraft Laboratory at Weybridge during 1975. (*British Aerospace–Weybridge*).

British Aircraft Corporation Commercial Aircraft Division Design Office at Weybridge, which was later responsible for the detail design of the centre-section and fuselage top. Detail design of the outer wing panels was done by the Fokker Design Office.

The braced high-mounted wing was built in three sections; the centre-section which was integral with the top of the main fuselage portion, and the strut-braced outer panels which were pin-jointed to the centre-section and were reinforced Skyvan units. The centre-section was a two-spar single-cell box structure of light alloy with light alloy skins and stringers; each outer panel consisted of a two-cell box with skins made up from a smooth outer skin bonded to a corrugated inner skin. All-metal single-slotted ailerons with geared balance tabs and single slotted flaps built in three sections were fitted. The aileron control system was unduplicated push-pull rods. The wing struts

490

embodied three separate tension members to prevent failure through a fatigue fracture in any one member. The wing centre-section/top fuselage fairing housed three fuel tanks forward of the wing and one aft with a total consumable capacity of 560 gallons. The tail unit design followed closely that of the Skyvan, being a cantilever all-metal two-spar fixed-incidence tailplane with twin fins and rudders. Full-span three-section elevators were aerodynamically-balanced by set-back hinges while the rudders each had an unshielded horn aerodynamic balance. Geared balance tabs were fitted on the outboard elevators and the starboard rudder with a trim tab in the port rudder only. Both the rudder and elevator control systems consisted of unduplicated push-pull rods.

With the benefit of hindsight and its experiences with unsuitable engines in the early Skyvans, Shorts took pains to ensure that its choice of power unit for the SD3–30 was definitive. That the choice of the Pratt & Whitney Canada PT6A–45A free-turbine was correct can be judged from the fact that by 1988 more than 20,000 of the PT6A variants had been built and had logged some 100 million flying hours. The use of Hartzell propellers on the Skyvan and on many other PT6A installations undoubtedly influenced the choice of this propeller, in spite of fierce competition from Dowty Rotol.

With the design of the SD3–30 finalised during the early summer of 1973 initial work on the first prototype began in the Skyvan's production area in

The neat installation of the PT6A–45 engine and the five-bladed Hartzell propeller is apparent in this view of a 330. Noteworthy is the upturned exhaust outlet to minimise cabin noise.

491

August. A feature of this prototype's production programme was the setting of firm target dates for the completion of the major assemblies; thus the fuselage, the first of these to be completed on the due date – 15 March, 1974 – was ready for the other sub-assemblies to be fitted. During the next four months every effort was made to meet the many and various deadlines so that the aircraft could be rolled out on 17 July. This was not just an arbitrary date. Shorts' management and sales team were desperately keen to have the SD3–30 ready to make its public debut on 1 September during the Press Preview at the forthcoming S.B.A.C. International Show at Farnborough. This final roll-out deadline was met, allowing just six weeks in which to complete the aircraft, fly it and log the mandatory 10 hours' flying which are demanded by the S.B.A.C. and the C.A.A. before any new prototype can take part in the Farnborough flying display.

Ground running of the engines and ground handling trials began during the second week of August, this important part of the programme coinciding with the receipt of the first order for the SD3–30 on 14 August. This was from Command Airways of Poughkeepsie, New York, and was for three aircraft, with deliveries scheduled to begin early in 1977, and with options on two more. Eight days later, on 22 August, 1974, the first flight, lasting two hours, was made from Sydenham. Registered *G–BSBH*, the aircraft was flown by Don Wright, Shorts' chief test pilot. There followed a week of intensive flying to check the handling characteristics, performance and other aspects of the flight envelope, during which period the C.A.A. issued a 'permit to fly', enabling the still unfinished prototype to go to Farnborough on 29 August for practice flying before the display. During the week of the Show a second order, for two SD3–30s with one option, was received from the Canadian operator Time Air.

On Monday 9 September, the day after Farnborough International '74 closed, *G–BSBH* was flown back to Sydenham to continue its initial test and certification flying programme. A minor set-back occurred at the end of a test flight on 3 October when the port main undercarriage unit failed to come down and Don Wright made a wheels-up landing at Belfast International Airport, Aldergrove. Fortunately, the damage was slight, due partially to the SD3–30's mainwheels protruding below their pod fairing, and the aircraft was flown back to Sydenham a few days later with the undercarriage locked down. The fault was traced and rectified. At the end of the year, by which time 73 test flights and 90 flying hours had been completed and an order for six aircraft had been received from the United States airline Air New England, *G–BSBH* began a series of ground system checks as part of its overall certification programme. Another phase was launched on 10 January, 1975, when one of two special fuselages was despatched to British Aircraft Corporation at Weybridge for structural testing. B.A.C.'s Aircraft Laboratory was responsible for designing and building the test rig and for the two-year programme of structural testing of the complete SD3–30 fuselage. The second specimen airframe remained at Sydenham for fatigue test work. During April

G–BSBH was prepared for a series of temperate-zone peformance trials, flying to Istres in France on 13 May and remaining there for the 12-day trials.

While all these early ground and air tests were being progressed construction of the second aircraft, *G–BDBS*, was proceeding so well that by mid-June it was being readied for its first flight, which took place on 8 July. After preliminary flying this aircraft went for final painting to take part in the flight-test programme. With F.A.A. and C.A.A. certification a vital factor in Shorts' SD3–30 marketing campaign, construction of the first two production aircraft was pressed ahead. Some of the production of early SD3–30s was sub-contracted to British Aircraft Corporation; initially both the centre-section and flaps were produced at Weybridge, but subsequently flap production was moved, first to Hurn then, after closure of that factory, to British Hovercraft Corporation at East Cowes in the Isle of Wight.

The first four SD3–30s were allocated to the certification programme; the two prototypes were to undertake performance and handling checks, noise measurement and a range of systems and engine handling checks and clearances. 'Hot-and-high' trials were also undertaken by *G–BSBH* and were made at Farmington in New Mexico and Marana in Arizona, with noise measurements and certification to meet F.A.R. Part 36 requirements at Fresno in California. *G–BDMA*, the first SD3–30–100 production aircraft, first flew on 15 December, 1975, and was used initially for other certification work and route proving. C.A.A. Type Certification was granted in February 1976 with F.A.A. Certification in June. The second production aircraft, *G–BDSU*, first flew on 15 April to join the three earlier aircraft on the trials programme, while the third production SD3–30, having flown on 14 May, was finished in Command Airways colours and went to join that operator on 27 July. The fourth SD3–30, which first flew on 26 June, was destined to become the first of its type to enter scheduled passenger service. This it did, registered *C–GTAS* in Time Air colours, on 24 August flying a route from Lethbridge to Calgary and Edmonton. It was not until 18 October that Command Airways first flew its SD3–30, registered *N51DD*, on a scheduled passenger service.

A feature of the Shorts 330 history is the rather complex initial registering of the individual aircraft as they were produced and the many changes of registration and owners in their subsequent operational lives. Many 330s first flew carrying Class B markings before a national registration was applied. Once in service there were, too, registration changes to prevent the aircraft being sequestrated by the creditors of airlines which had gone into liquidation.

C–GTAM, in Time Air colours and fully furnished, was used as the demonstration aircraft during the first six days of Farnborough International '76, registered *G–BEEO*, being replaced by *G–BDMA*, the first production aeroplane, for the last two public days of the Show. Immediately afterwards it went on a sales tour of 11 European and Near East countries, which lasted two weeks, and a month later undertook a similar tour of North America. The last three months of 1976 saw the delivery of Time Air's second and third aircraft and the receipt of the first order from a European operator, Deutsche

Luftverkehrsgesellschaft (D.L.T.) for one aircraft and an option on another. Deliveries of these aircraft (the option was exercised) were in February and June 1977.

Although Shorts' management and sales team had hoped for good results from the two sales tours, orders were much slower in arriving than they had hoped. Even so, it was only some five months after the North American tour that Golden West Airlines in California ordered two 330s. These were delivered in July and August, and Golden West later took delivery of three more during 1979 and 1980. With still only a handful of 330s in service the order intake during the remaining nine months of 1977 continued slowly; however, during 1978 the tide began to turn as new and repeat business began to appear from D.L.T. (repeat 3) Suburban Airlines in Pennsylvania (4), Hawaiian Air (3), Metro Airlines in Houston (5) and Chautaqua Airlines (1). By the year's end the 330 order book was 36 with two options.

With the production line now firmly established and a growing number of 330s in service with 10 airlines, 1979 was to provide some new milestones. On 9 February *G–BFZY*, the 26th aircraft, was the first to fly with the improved PT5A–45B engines, this 330 going to Hawaiian Airlines on 5 June, registered *N373HA*. Of major importance was the first order from a United Kingdom airline, received in March. This was from Loganair for two aircraft with scheduled delivery of the first one, *G–BGNA*, in July. Before that date, however, it went to the Paris Air Show from 5–13 June. A few weeks later Mississippi Valley Airlines in Wisconsin ordered three 330s. The strong saleability of in-service 330s was evidenced by the first Loganair aircraft, which subsequently had at least six owners. This sale and re-sale pattern was very much in evidence in the log books of most of the U.S.-registered aircraft. By the end of 1979 another trend was becoming evident: it was that the success of the 330 in service was not only bringing repeat orders but was also encouraging operators of leased aircraft to buy their own. Aircraft on the production line during the last months of 1979 were for Air North, Metro Airlines, Mississippi Valley Airlines, Royale Airlines and Suburban Airlines. It was a Suburban 330 which, ultimately, made a major contribution to Shorts' regional aircraft development work. Originally flying as *G–14–3041 G–BHCG* during February 1980 before being registered *N844SA*, it was written off after being severely storm-damaged on the ground. The fuselage was returned to Sydenham during October and formed the basis for the first prototype of SD3–60, *G–ROOM*.

New orders received during 1980 included the first from Venezuela by Aeronaves del Centro (3), Líneas Aéreas Privadas Argentinas (1), Jet Charter (4), which recorded the first Australian success, Pennsylvania Commuter Airline (1), Olympic Airways (2 plus 4 options), with repeat orders from Mississippi Valley (1) to bring its 330 fleet to six, Suburban Airlines (2) and Crown Airways (1). The Pennsylvania, Jet Charter, L.A.P.A., Crown and Suburban orders were announced during Farnborough International '80 in September at which Aeronaves del Centro's second 330–100, *YV–374C*,

Named *Isle of Patmos*, SX–BGA was the first of six 330s delivered to Olympic Airways during 1980–82.

appeared in the static aircraft park.

January 1981 marked the final planning and the beginning of the most wide-ranging sales tour made by Shorts with the 330, lasting some 10 weeks. *G–BDBS*, the second production aircraft, toured through Southeast Asia and the Pacific Basin demonstrating in many locations en route to Australia and New Zealand, before returning home in early April. As with the first tour, there was no immediate response and both the 330 order book and the production line were comparatively slow-moving in the early part of the year. However, on 23 March a 330, which had first flown on 20 February with Class B markings *G–14–3064*, was delivered to Coral Air in the Virgin Islands, registered *N4270A*, not as a sale but on a short-term lease. The registration was subsequently changed to *N280VY* while the aircraft was still with Coral Air; it then returned to Shorts and was converted to become the first 330–200 during early 1982, powered with more powerful PT6A–45R engines.

Then followed a series of small but vital orders, including one from Eastern Airways (2) based at Humberside. This airline put its second 330, *G–EASI*, into service on 3 August, 1981, on the Humberside–Heathrow route, to become the first 330 commuter service into London's principal airport. An order from Avair (1), the first from an operator in Eire, was also historic, being reputed to be the first sale of a Shorts aeroplane into that country. On 3 April *G–BITV*, the 69th aircraft, became the first 330–200 off the production line to fly. It was delivered to Inter City Airlines two weeks later.

A major achievement, on 1 June, 1981, was the first flight of *G–ROOM*, the prototype Shorts SD3–60, some six months ahead of schedule which was, in part, due to the use of a 330 fuselage in its construction. This was closely followed by its appearance at the Paris Air Show. While Shorts was, no doubt, pleased with this early completion of its new regional airliner in time for it to go to Paris, this pleasure could also have been a bit ambivalent as potential customers' interests appeared to be concentrating on the 360 to the detriment of orders for the 330. However, Mississippi Valley took up its options for two more 330s which kept the production line occupied. Total deliveries during 1981 were 18 aircraft.

495

This view of Guernsey Airlines' 330, *G–BMKU*, at Eastleigh Airport, Southampton, in June 1987, shows the tail unit and the access door to the rear baggage compartment. (*Gordon Roberts*).

If 1981 had appeared to herald the beginning of the end of the Shorts 330 production run, 1982 marked the advent of two new 330 variants, the Utility Tactical Transport (UTT) and the Sherpa. In May orders for seven 330s ended a seven-month period without any, and all were delivered by the end of July, at which time total sales of 330s were announced as being 111 to 34 operators in 14 countries with more than 80 in service. They had logged 325,000 flying hours and carried eight million passengers. Shorts' determination to keep the 330 well publicised was underlined by the appearance at Farnborough International '82 on 5–12 September of Eastern Airways' *G–BKDO* in company with a 360 and a Skyvan. The year ended on a high note with the first flight of the Sherpa, *G–BKMW*, on 23 December.

G–BNYA Corbière, a British Air Ferries 330, taxies for departure from Eastleigh. (*Gordon Roberts*).

496

An early 330 sale in 1983 was a single aircraft, *EI–BEG*, later to become *EI–BEH*, to Aer Lingus for a year's trial use on its Dublin–Liverpool route which was revitalised by the increased frequency and cost-effectiveness of the service with this aircraft. The one-year trial period extended into November 1984 when '*BEH* was returned to Shorts and was re-registered *G–BKMU*. During the next 30 months it flew, on lease, in the colours of three operators before being sold to Syd Aero at Oskarshamn in Sweden at the end of August 1987 to be registered *SE–IYO*. This is a classic example of the way in which many 330s were leased, sold and resold many times during their operational lives. This was particularly apparent in North America where an important element of Shorts' presence there was Short Brothers (USA) Inc., which was established in 1978 and, at various times, has had offices and facilities at Logan International Airport at Boston, in Irvine, California and Arlington, Virginia. This subsidiary is responsible for commercial and technical services and sales support in all of the United States.

In the United States one of several operators which were experiencing financial difficulties during late 1983 was Golden West Airlines, two of whose 330 fleet, *N330GW* and *N331GW* were repossessed by the F.A.A. and stored at Moline in Illinois. Two more 330s, *N332GW* and *N334GW* followed them in early 1984, also going into storage until February 1985 when all four aircraft went to Field Aviation in Calgary, Canada, for overhaul, modification to military standard and respraying, having been bought by the U.S. Army. During July they were delivered to the Kwajalein Missile Base in the Marshall Islands in the Pacific for inter-island transport of personnel. Designated C–23Bs, they were serialled *85–25342–45* respectively. Earlier, on 16 May, 1984, the first Shorts 330 UTT variant first flew, initially with Class B markings *G–14–3098* but then registered *G–BLJA*.

The order intake from civil operators slowed markedly, only orders from the United States Air Force for Sherpas and a small number of UTTs from Thailand kept the 330 variants on the production line during 1985–86. By the end of 1988 the 330 order book was 129 of which 120 had been delivered, 48 options and four letters of intent.

330–UTT

Throughout the 330 programme before 1982 there had been only limited interest evinced either in military or freighter variants, either by customers or Shorts (which was wholly committed to producing and supporting the civil commuter version). However, during that year, when the end of the programme appeared more imminent, some more thought was given to the military variant for the tactical transport role. That thoughts had turned into hardware became apparent on 7 September when Shorts announced at Farnborough International '82 that production of a prototype military utility tactical transport (UTT) version of the 330 had begun. At the same time a freighter version, the Sherpa, was revealed.

The new version was designed as a multi-purpose transport for rear area operations, and the basic 330 airframe and power plant remained unchanged; however, the maximum payload was increased to 8,000 lb (3,630 kg) and the maximum operational necessity take-off weight increased to 24,600 lb (11,158 kg) which was 1,700 lb (771 kg) more than the civil 330–200. Other modifications included a strengthened cabin floor with strong points to which military equipment could be secured, the fitting of two rear inward-opening doors in place of the standard outward-opening passengers' door, and the use of a reconfigured avionics panel to meet military requirements. These new-style doors could be opened in flight for fast despatching of paratroops or for supply dropping. Accomodation in the 30 ft long cabin could be provided for up to 33 troops, or 30 paratroops plus a jump-master, in quickly-installed sideways-facing seats. When operating in the casualty evacuation role the aircraft had provision for 15 stretcher cases and four seated personnel, while the standard 30 passengers could be accommodated in the troop/personnel transport configuration.

The production programme to which the 7 September, 1982, announcement had referred was, in fact, the conversion of the pre-production 330 prototype *G–BDBS*, and this work, having begun in the spring, was sufficiently advanced to enable the first flight of what was the UTT prototype to take place at Sydenham on 10 September, only three days after the Farnborough announcement had been made. There followed a long period of flight testing which included operational trials of supply and paratroop dropping plus ground loading and unloading. At the conclusion of this part of the UTT programme the aircraft faced a bleak future as no orders for it had been placed. It was not until 1983 that the first positive interest in the UTT was shown, and this by a Thai military mission visiting Shorts. As a result of this and, no doubt, the success of Thai Airways' four 330s, which had given reliable service for some 18 months, Shorts received an order for two aircraft during early 1984, one for use by the Royal Thai Police and the other by the Royal Thai Army. The Army's UTT, registered *G–BLJA*, was the first to fly and be delivered on 16 May; the Police aircraft, *G–BLJB*, first flew on 14 August and appeared at Farnborough International '84 between 2 and 9 September before returning to Sydenham to be prepared for delivery on 26 September.

Only two months after the Royal Thai Army put its UTT into service, a second aircraft was ordered and, registered *G–BLLL*, was delivered on 22 February, 1985. A similar follow-on order for a single UTT for the Royal Thai Police was received a short time afterwards, finally departing on its delivery flight as *G–BLRR*; on 23 March. A fifth UTT was ordered during late 1985 for service with the Emiri Guard Air Wing of the United Arab Emirates. Initially this aircraft, c/n SH.3121, carried the markings *AGAW–131* but for its first flight and its subsequent delivery, on 23 March and 16 May, 1986, respectively, it was registered *G–BMGX*. It reverted to its initial markings once in service. Three more UTT variants were built, the second of which first

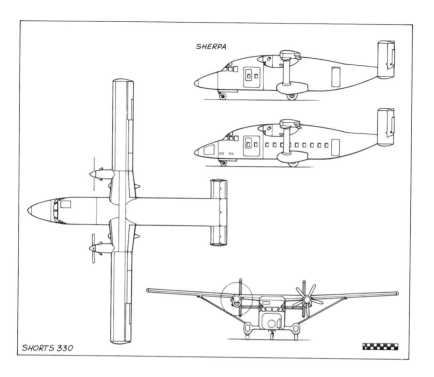

SHERPA

SHORTS 330

flew on 29 May, 1986, and was sold to Industria Venezolana de Aluminio CA in Venezuela, being delivered during August and registered *YV–O–GVR1*.

Sherpa

The Sherpa, designed as a freighter version of the 330–200, retains many features of the all-passenger version to enable utility transport of passengers to be undertaken. Thus, the forward freight door and the constant-width hold of the 330 are unchanged but the Sherpa's design embodies a hydraulically-operated full-width rear cargo door which also serves as a ramp to allow through-loading of bulky cargo. This door, which can be controlled from outside or inside the aircraft, can be raised or lowered to a variety of positions to simplify loading or unloading with ground vehicles of different heights. High value cargo can be locked inside a forward baggage compartment, one of the retained features. The specially-strengthened floor can carry international standard containers where the Sherpa is required for short-haul cargo feeder services. Typical loads include two LD3 containers and nine passengers; four LD3 or seven CO8 containers; two half-ton vehicles such as Land Rover types or other bulky cargo. The seat rails can be used as cargo lashing-down points

The second C–23A, serialled *83–513*, for the United States Air Force Europe, landing after a demonstration in the 1984 S.B.A.C. Flying Display. (*Michael Hall*).

and roller conveyor systems with pallet locks, which pick up on the seat rails, can also be installed in the hold.

The prototype Sherpa, c/n 3194, *G–BKMW*, was flown for the first time on 23 December, 1982, and flight testing, allied to ground checks of the loading techniques and internal equipment, continued through the early months of the following year. It was during 1983 that the United States Air Force was planning a cost-effective programme to provide optimum spares support of its combat aircraft in Europe, and to reduce aircraft-on-ground time to a minimum. The European Distribution Systems (EDS) which was conceived had three elements aimed at enhancing the wartime capability of the USAFE Fighter Force. They were a tactical aircraft capable of carrying spares to wherever they are needed, a programme of in-theatre positioning of critical spares, and a logistics Command, Control and Communications (C^3) System to locate and effect distribution decisions. Several aircraft were considered for this task including the CASA C–212, DHC Dash Seven and the Sherpa. The first element ultimately was provided by the USAFE's choice of the Sherpa, designated C–23A, and in March 1984 eighteen Sherpas were ordered for use by the 10th Military Aircraft Squadron of Military Airlift Command in the European Distribution System Aircraft (EDSA) role.

This fleet is based at Zweibrücken Air Force Base in West Germany for the transport of high priority spares among some 20 peacetime USAFE bases. The initial contract, worth some £115 million, included ten years' logistic support and servicing of the C–23As and options on 48 additional Sherpas.

The first production Sherpa, c/n 3100, *G–BLLJ*, designated C–23A for the EDSA role and to be serialled *83–512*, first flew on 6 August, 1984. It was delivered with the second C–23A in November. Production of the succeeding 16 Sherpas proceeded steadily through 1985 with all being delivered by 6 December. That the Sherpa proved a success in this specialised role was proved on many occasions during the first four years' service. The reliability and performance of the aircraft was regularly referred to as 'outstanding' which enabled the operating squadron to receive many awards for its

500

achievements. In addition, Shorts' Contractor Logistics Support in support of the USAFE Sherpas was consistently similarly graded.

This record undoubtedly led to another order worth £35 million, announced on 26 October, 1988, for 10 Sherpas for the United States Army National Guard. These aircraft, designated C–23s, replace a number of ageing C–7 Caribous at various locations throughout the United States, their prime role being to transport Army Aviation spares and components between National Guard bases and Aviation Classification Repair Activity Depots. The Sherpa's ability to carry complete combat aircraft engines or a substantial volume of smaller spares made it eminently suited to the National Guard role.

The prototype 360, *G–ROOM*, in Allegheny Commuter livery, over Belfast Lough.

360

On 10 July, 1980, Shorts announced the first details of a stretched development of the 330. With six additional seats in a lengthened fuselage, the new aircraft, designated the Shorts SD3–60, could carry 36 passengers. The major structural changes, apart from the longer fuselage produced by the insertion of a 3 ft (0.91 m) plug forward of the wing, were strengthened outer wing panels and bracing struts, a tapered rear fuselage and new tail unit featuring a single swept fin and rudder, plus more powerful and fuel-efficient versions of the Pratt & Whitney Canada PT6A propeller-turbine.

Designed, like its predecessors, for short-haul airline operations over typical commuter stage lengths averaging some 140 miles (225 km), the aircraft did not require the sophistication of cabin pressurisation; thus, the 6 ft 4 in (1.93 m) headroom and 'wide-body' square-section interior, the seat comfort and air conditioning of the 330 were retained. The changes to the tail end were not purely cosmetic but show advantages by providing increased baggage capacity

The narrow chord of the 360's wing is apparent in this July 1983 view of one of Imperial Airlines' aircraft.

This 360, carrying Class B registration *G–14–3620* and photographed during its first flight on 24 August, 1983, became *VH–MVX* in service with Murray Valley Airlines in Australia.

G–ISLE, Manx Airlines' second 360, seen at Belfast in March 1984. (*Gordon Roberts*).

502

coupled with reduced drag and improved fuel-efficiency. The 360's under-carriage, though similar in design to the Menasco units of the 330, are of Dowty design to cater for the increased operating weights.

Rolled out in May 1981, the prototype 360, c/n 3600 *G–ROOM*, made its first flight on 1 June, six months ahead of schedule, powered by 1,156 hp PT6A–45 engines. It seemed that there was not the same impetus behind the production of the second 360 which, with a similarly descriptive registration, *G–WIDE*, did not fly until 19 August, 1982. However, little time was lost in preparing it for delivery to Suburban Airlines in the United States on 11 November, registered *N3605A*. On 1 December the first 360 ordered by Simmons Airlines was delivered to become the forerunner of some 30 operated by this Chicago-based airline. One more 360 was delivered before the end of the year, *G–BKKT* going on 20 December to Genair, the first United Kingdom operator of 330s to move up to the 360.

The new year quickly got under way with a first delivery to Air Ecosse on 6 January, 1983, and production of 360s gathered momentum during the ensuing months with aircraft being built at the rate of one every two weeks. New customers' names appearing on the flight line were British Midland Airways, Newair and Imperial Airlines. Production and deliveries were stepped up slightly during the second half of the year with 14 first flights and 13 deliveries. Among them were two for Australia's Murray Valley Airlines, two for Pennsylvania Airlines and one for Sunbelt Airlines.

A new European operator of 360s was Maersk Air's Air Business based at Esbjerg, Denmark, which took delivery of the first, *G–BLCP/OY–MMA* on 12 January, 1984, to begin Shorts' deliveries for that year. By then the production had settled back to one aircraft every two weeks; however March saw 11 first flights and nine deliveries, including two for Aer Lingus and one each to British Midland and Dash Air of Santa Ana, California. During the second half of 1984 an interesting long-range delivery was that of *G–BLJR/*

G–BLPY, an AirUK 360, seen at Eastleigh Airport during April 1986. (*Gordon Roberts*).

503

9M–KGN for the Kuala Lumpur-based Malaysia Air Charter Company. An important order secured during 1984 was one for eight aircraft for the Civil Aviation Administration China. All of these 360s were produced as a batch during May–July 1985 for delivery by the middle of August. A name absent from Shorts' order for a decade was Time Air which had operated the first 330 scheduled passenger service on 24 August, 1976; however, two 360s were delivered to this Canadian operator during September and October.

A new chapter in the 360 story opened with the introduction of an enhanced variant, know as the Shorts' 360 Advanced, with more powerful and economical 1,424 shp Pratt & Whitney Canada PT6A–65AR engines. These were introduced from the 80th aircraft which, as *HS–TSE*, was the first of two bought by Thai Airways Company of Bangkok. The following 11 months up to 17 October saw the production and delivery of 20 of the 360 ADV variants to six airlines. These were followed during 1987 by another 20 deliveries. By the end of 1988 there were 150 orders and options for the 360 with 144 having been delivered.

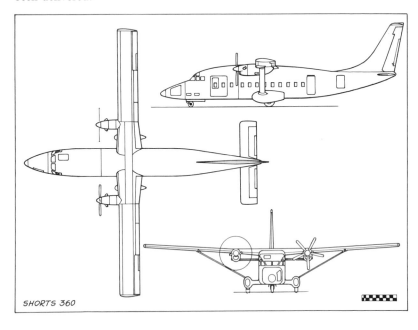

SHORTS 360

Shorts 330–200—Span 74 ft 8 in (22.76 m); length 58 ft 0½ in (17.69 m); area 453 sq ft (42.1 m²); operating weight empty 19,207 lb (8,712 kg); all-up weight 22,900 lb (10,387 kg); max cruise speed 218 mph (352 km/h); max range 544 miles (876 km).
Shorts 330 UTT—Span, length, area and operating weight empty as for 330–200; all-up weight 24,600 lb (11,158 kg); max cruise speed 231 mph (372 km/h); max range 691 miles (1,112 km).

504

Sherpa—Span, length, area and operating weight empty as for 330–200; all-up weight 22,000 lb (9,855 kg); max cruise speed 218 mph (352 km/h); max range 770 miles (1,239 km).

Shorts 360—Span 74 ft 10 in (22.81 m); length 70 ft 10 in (21.59 m); area 453 sq ft (42.1 m^2); operating weight empty 20,740 lb (9,407 kg); all-up weight 26,453 lb (11,999 kg); max cruise speed 245 mph (394 km/h); max range 1,036 miles (1,667 km).

Appendix A

Construction for other Manufacturers

From their earliest days Short Brothers undertook occasional construction of aeroplanes or parts thereof to the designs of private individuals, syndicates or firms. In 1907, before Horace joined them, Eustace and Oswald Short had made up a few parts for J. T. C. Moore-Brabazon's abortive glider which he tried to fly at Brooklands; two years later at Leysdown Horace Short had built the Dunne-Huntington triplane and the D.5 tailless biplane to J. W. Dunne's order and designs, and after the move to Eastchurch Short Brothers manufactured major assemblies of the D.6 and D.7 monoplanes and D.8 biplane for Dunne's Blair Atholl Syndicate, of which C. R. Fairey was engineer before becoming Shorts' works manager in 1913.

During 1918 Short Brothers built 100 D.H.9 biplanes under contract No. AS.34886; these were manufactured at Rochester and delivered with 230 hp Siddeley Puma engines, although Fiat A-12s had been originally specified. Their serials were *D2776–2875* and their constructor's numbers were probably S.428–527; some of them were equipped with buoyancy bags in the rear fuselage and frontal D.H.4-type radiators for deck-flying trials from H.M.S. *Eagle* and *Argus*, the standard underslung radiators being dangerous for ditching. Concurrently with D.H.9 production, Short Brothers manufactured 50 Porte-type flying-boats, as already described in the Cromarty chapter; of these *N4000–4035* were F.3s, the last few having various improvements such as horn-balanced ailerons, while the rest were F.5s; this batch had c/ns S.588–637, suggesting that several intermediate batches of unspecified types were cancelled in 1918, their c/ns being re-allotted at once, because a second batch of 50 F.5s, *N4830–4879*, had c/ns S.528–577; all after the first ten were cancelled at the Armistice, but by then over 20 were well advanced in construction and after delivery of S.528–537 to the R.A.F. as *N4830–4839*, a further nine, S.546–554, were completed for Japan in 1920, followed by three more, S.555–557, with Napier Lion engines in 1922.

During the lean years following the Geddes 'Axe', Short Brothers received a contract to overhaul and repair 24 F.5s, and it is believed that these were c/ns S.640–643 and S.645–664; they were followed by modification contracts for D.H.9As, both unused ex-Air Ministry Stores and time-expired from R.A.F. units; the former included S.671–676 (*J7823–7828*), S.693–705 (*J7829–7834, J7884–7890*) and S.714–731 (*J8154–8171*), while 29 repaired and overhauled airframes accounted for c/ns S.679–692, S.706–709, S.732–735 and S.737–743. Of the many aircraft of all types and sizes that came to Rochester seaplane works to be equipped with float undercarriages, only A. E. Guinness's D.H. Moth amphibian *G-AAVC* received a Shorts c/n,

S.761; this was because a substantial amount of modification was done, including the substitution of a Hermes engine for the original Gipsy II, installation of the central-float amphibian gear and, by no means least, enlargement of the access door to the front cockpit for the owner, who was both elderly and portly. This was the last 'foreigner' to receive a Rochester constructor's number.

At Belfast, Harland & Wolff had undertaken aircraft manufacture as early as 1916, when they delivered 300 D.H.6 trainers, *C5451–5750*, under contract No. AS.19062; of these *C5527*, *C5533* and *C5547* continued flying after the war as *G-EARA*, '*B* and '*C*. They were followed on the same contract by 300 Avro 504J trainers, *C5751–6050*, of which the later deliveries were to 504K standard; a further 300 504Ks, *E301–600*, were built under contract No. AS.4291, *E449* surviving to be converted in 1925 into the first Avro 548A, *G-EBKN*, by the Aircraft Disposal Co. After their successful debut in the aircraft industry, Harland & Wolff received one of the two major production contracts for the large four-engined Handley Page V/1500 bomber in 1918, the other contractor also being a shipbuilder, William Beardmore & Co of Dalmuir on the Clyde. Each contract was for 20 aircraft, Harland & Wolff's batch being *E4304–4323*, to contract No. 35A/185/C.74. The completed components of the first machine were delivered to Handley Page Ltd for erection at Cricklewood, where it was flown by Capt V. E. G. Busby in May 1918; at least three more were completed before cancellation of the contract after the Armistice, and thereafter Harland & Wolff dropped out of aviation until the formation of Short & Harland Ltd in 1936.

Short & Harland began manufacture with two 'learning' contracts, the first being for 80 Bristol Bombay bomber-transport monoplanes to specification 47/36; these received c/ns SH.1–80 and serials *L5808–5887*, and the first was flown at Sydenham in March 1939. After war began, the last 30 Bombays were cancelled in order to accelerate production of the parallel line of Handley Page Hereford bombers to specification 44/36, the first batch of 100, SH.81–180, *L6002–6101*, being followed by another of 50, SH.181–230, *N9055–9081* and *N9084–9106*; by this time the Napier Dagger engines of the Hereford had proved so unreliable in service that the airframe standard was revised to Hampden I with Bristol Pegasus XVIIIs; 11 aircraft from this batch were delivered as Hampdens, the last, *N9106*, becoming the prototype torpedo-bomber version for Coastal Command. At the end of the war, Short & Harland Ltd, in addition to all civil conversion of Sunderlands, undertook the complete modification and furnishing of 12 Handley Page Halifax C.10s as Haltons for B.O.A.C.'s West Africa route, delivered between July 1946 and June 1947 with registrations *G-AHDL* to *G-AHDX* (excluding *G-AHDQ*); two more Halifaxes were similarly modified for the French Government. They also converted and furnished for BEA's internal routes ten ex-Luftwaffe Junkers-Ju 52/3mg8e transport monoplanes, registered *G-AHOC* to *G-AHOL*; known as the *Jupiter* class, these commenced airline service between Croydon and Nutts Corner in November 1946 and were scrapped in

1948 after being replaced by DC-3s. No Lancasters were converted into Lancastrians at Belfast, as was proposed at one time, but 94 Lancasters were overhauled between 1945 and 1947, and 50 Lincolns in 1947–8; the latter included 12 for export to the Argentine Air Force.

After the formation of Short Brothers & Harland Ltd, sustained efforts were made by Admiral Slattery, the new Managing Director, and George Gedge (who, entering Short Bros as an apprentice in 1926, had won steady promotion to Production Manager by 1948) to utilise the large production capacity available at Queen's Island; to this end they secured contracts from the Admiralty to modify, overhaul and maintain large numbers of Hawker Seahawks, Vickers-Armstrongs Scimitars and de Havilland Sea Venoms for the Royal Navy, who operated an Aircraft Yard at Sydenham; similar work was done in 1954 on Harvards and Sabres for the U.S. Air Force in Europe. In addition, manufacturing sub-contracts were obtained for 150 English Electric Canberras, c/ns SH.1610–1759; of these, 60 were delivered as B.2s, 49 as B.6s and 23 as P.R.9s, but the remaining 18 were cancelled by the Government economy cut of 1957. Shorts undertook a major redesign programme in producing the Canberra P.R.9, since English Electric's own prototype *WH793* was little more than an adaptation of their B(I).8 variant, and Shorts had to redesign the hydraulic system to incorporate power-operated controls and also to modify the forward navigator's station to take an ejector seat, with a hinged nose for access. The first Short-built Canberra P.R.9 was test-flown by Peter Hillwood on 26 July, 1958, and flight development was continued by Alex Roberts, who had just previously been responsible for the high-altitude phase of the acceptance trials of a new Canberra variant, the U.10, developed entirely by Shorts as an unmanned target drone mainly for use at the Weapons Research Establishment, Woomera, South Australia.

Canberra U.10 *WD961* making this variant's first unmanned take-off at Woomera on 25 June, 1959.

The Canberra U.10, design index S.C.4 (originally P.D.31), was basically a conversion of time-expired B.2s into fast high-flying bomber targets controlled entirely from the ground by a VHF radio link and containing a 24-channel telemetry transmitter which sent back continuous information about the

508

drone's own performance and the track and miss-distances of missiles aimed at it. The auto-pilot control system was self-sustaining in the absence of command signals, and would maintain a fixed altitude with automatic control of heading and airspeed; it also included such structural safeguards as automatic landing-gear retraction on reaching 160 kt after take-off. The prototypes were converted from Handley Page-built *WJ624* and Avro-built *WJ987*, their low-altitude initial handling being monitored by D. R. Turley-George at R.A.E. Bedford and A. & A.E.E. Boscombe Down early in 1958; later the high-altitude trials were conducted by Alex Roberts, who took *WJ624* up to 56,700 ft in one series of flights. Twenty-four production U.10s, flown in 1959, were followed by six of an improved version, U.14 (S.C.6), having P.R.9-type hydraulic servo-controls; these were sent to Hal Far, Malta, as targets in naval Seacat trials. Finally, a single Canberra P.R.9, *XH132*, was converted in 1960 to carry an infra-red installation in a much-modified nose for trials of the 'Red Top' missile; this was indexed as S.C.9 (formerly P.D.48) and was first flown by Alex Roberts at Sydenham on 2 May, 1961, being later delivered to Turnhouse for use by Ferranti Ltd. In 1967 a Canberra P.R.3 (*WE146*) was adapted as a launch vehicle (S.D.1) for the American-built Beech AQM-37A supersonic target drone modified by Shorts for British use as S.D.2. Other Canberra variants proposed by Shorts, but not built, were P.D.32, a G.P.V.-carrier, and P.D.33 with increased span.

The S.C.9 *XH132* flying at Sydenham in May 1961; basically a Canberra P.R.9, its overall length was increased by the conversion to 70 ft 10 in (21·6 m).

In addition to the production of Canberras, arrangements were made in 1954 for Shorts to build Comet 2s for de Havilland, and in fact two fuselages were completed and delivered to Chester before the programme was cancelled; in 1956, having furnished the first two Bristol Britannia 102s *G-ANBA* and *'BB* to full airline standard after their return from C. of A. trials, Shorts began manufacture of two Britannia 300s, five Britannia 305s and five Britannia 314s on sub-contract to Bristol Aircraft Ltd, and were then given a direct contract for three Britannia 252s and 20 Britannia 253s for R.A.F. Transport Command; for both the latter variants Shorts designed the forward freight door, and for the 253 they also evolved an all-metal 'floating' freight floor and an associated air-portable loading lift; arising from this exercise, a proposal to convert existing Britannia 312s for freighting was later put forward as P.D.57. Deliveries of Britannia 253s from Queen's Island occupied most of 1959 and 1960, but by this time Bristols themselves had become underemployed, and five sets of Belfast-made components were shipped to Filton for final assembly there; all Britannias built at Belfast had Bristol constructor's numbers. As agents till 1966 for the range of Beech executive and light transport monoplanes, Shorts had proposed manufacture of a five-seater (P.D.52) based on the Beech Baron and of the French development of the same model with Turbomeca Astazou engine known as the SFERMA Marquis (P.D.54); the Beech Queen Air adapted for R.A.F. communications

PH-JHG, the prototype Fokker F.28 seen on its first flight near Schiphol on 9 May, 1967. (*Fokker.*)

duties was tendered as P.D.58 and a further development of it as P.D.64, but none of these was actually built, nor was an offer to manufacture the Breguet 941 STOL transport under licence as P.D.71 taken up by operators. In 1965 Shorts delivered the first of 13 complete VC10 fuselages to the British Aircraft Corporation's Weybridge factory for incorporation in R.A.F. Transport Command's new jet aircraft; similar component manufacturing contracts were obtained for the McDonnell Phantoms ordered for the Royal Navy, and from the European consortium building the Fokker F.28 Fellowship turbojet airliner, and were in progress in 1967; deliveries of Phantom outer wings began ahead of schedule in February 1967, concurrently with the first sets of complete F.28 wings to Amsterdam; having undertaken the detail design of the F.28 wing, Shorts became the sole manufacturer of wings for both the European-built F.28 and its American derivative, the Fairchild–Hiller F-228. For the latter they also undertook production of pod nacelles for its Trent turbofan engines under contract from Rolls-Royce Ltd.

During the ensuing years these sub-contract manufacturing programmes grew to embrace a range of airframe components and engine nacelle systems. Shorts' Aerostructures Division took over responsibility for the production of all airframe components, specialising in the design and manufacture of jet engine nacelles. Large areas of the Belfast complex were made available for the manufacture of major components in advanced composites and other special materials. In 1969 the company was awarded a contract to produce ailerons, wingtips, spoilers and main undercarriage doors for the Lockheed TriStar, and this was followed by a sole-source contract with Boeing Commercial Airplane Co to manufacture main undercarriage doors for the 747 aircraft. More recently Shorts collaborated with many manufacturers in Europe and the United States; their projects ranged from quite small structures to complete wings. When the Fokker 100 programme was launched in 1983 Shorts became responsible for the design and development of the wing for this successor to the F–28, the ailerons and flaps being produced in carbon fibre. In 1986 the company became a Programme Associate on the advanced technology Boeing 7J7 jetliner while in 1989 work in hand included the continuing supply of Boeing main undercarriage doors, wing flaps for the 757 and all-composite rudder assemblies for the 737–300.

During mid-1967, when Shorts was going through a particularly difficult period of financial constraint and reorganisation, Anthony Wedgwood Benn, then Minister of Technology, announced in the House of Commons that Shorts was entering an arrangement with Rolls-Royce to build 'engine pods' for the RB.211 turbofan. This statement came to fruition in May 1968 when the company won an initial £6 million order for nose cowls for these engines installed in the Lockheed TriStars. In early 1979 British Aerospace awarded a £20 million contract to Shorts for the design and production of complete nacelles for the AVCO–Lycoming ALF502R turbofans in the BAe. 146. Shorts was also chosen to produce the nose cowls on RB.211 turbofans in the Boeing 747, 757 and 767, but a contract from Pratt & Whitney for prototype cowls for its PW2037 third-generation turbofan failed to win a production order. But success was not long in returning, however, for in the spring of 1985 Shorts, working in collaboration with Rohr Industries in the United States, secured a contract to build complete nacelle systems, including the thrust reversers, for International Aero Engines' advanced V2500 turbofans to power Airbus Industrie's A320 Airbus.

To meet the demands of these and other contracts a subsidiary company, Short Brothers (Dunmurry) Ltd., was established near Belfast to specialise in the production of advanced composite components.

The Short S312 Tucano

During the early 1980s it was apparent that the Hunting Percival/British Aerospace Corporation family of Jet Provost two-seat basic trainers, widely used by the R.A.F. flying training schools, was in need of replacement. Cost of procurement and ownership were major features for consideration with maximum performance for minimum cost being the major aim. To this end Ministry of Defence Air Staff Target (AST) 412 was issued in June 1983 calling for a propeller-turbine trainer with a performance higher than any other existing aircraft of this type.

Originally the AST's essential requirement was for a speed of 242 mph (389 km/h) with 276 mph (444 km/h) being desirable. This was later changed to make the higher speed essential, much to the chagrin of the manufacturers who claimed that 'the goal posts had been moved' by the MoD. Other features of the AST were a 12,000 hours fatigue life to enable the aircraft to withstand the arduous life of an R.A.F. trainer; stepped tandem seating to simplify the pupil pilot's later transition to the Hawk; an assisted escape system (*i.e.* ejector seats); a rapid rate of climb to training airspace above the weather, and sufficient internal fuel for two training sorties with adequate reserves. Of major importance was the in-service date requirement which was set for 1989, the year when the Jet Provost was to be phased out of R.A.F service. This time-scale meant that the aircraft ordered would be an existing type rather than a completely new design.

By November 1983 no less than 17 proposals, some powered by turbofans, had been submitted by 15 manufacturers, all attracted by the promise of an order for 130 aircraft and an option on 15 more for the successful contender. Four months later, on 17 March, 1984, a statement in the House of Commons confirmed earlier rumours that a short list of four types had been prepared; they were Australian Aircraft Consortium's A–20, the EMBRAER EMB–312 Tucano (Toucan), Britain's Norman Aircraft Co Firecracker and the Swiss Pilatus PC–9.

During the next three months each of the four companies established partnerships with other United Kingdom manufacturers in order to meet the requirements of an offset programme. By June, when invitations went out for tenders to Specification T301 D & P, the contenders were partnered thus: Westland Group with the Australian Aircraft Consortium, Short Brothers and EMBRAER, Hunting supporting the Firecracker and British Aerospace the PC–9.

The issue of a new short list on 18 November revealed that, following the change to the maximum speed requirement, there was a performance shortfall in the Westland–AAC A–20 and the Hunting Firecracker and both had been eliminated. Their high costs also contributed to this elimination from the list. This brought two more, presumably improved, submissions from these companies, which appeared to prompt the MoD to invite 'best and final offers' from each of the four partnerships for submission by 31 January, 1985. Shorts seized the opportunity to offer, in partnership with EMBRAER, several alternative engine installations ranging upward from the original 750 shp Pratt & Whitney Canada PT6A–25C, through the 850 shp PT6A–25C/2 and the 930 shp PT6A–25C/3 to the 1,100 shp Garrett TPE331–12B, this last engine offering a top speed of 310 mph (500 km/h) to the Tucano. Again, the submissions were examined and, again, the A–20 and Firecracker were

The Garrett-engined EMBRAER/Shorts Tucano prototype. (EMBRAER).

eliminated, both on performance plus the facts that the A–20 was not an 'off-the-shelf' aircraft and the Firecracker because it was too small and its handling characteristics in no way approximated to those of a jet aircraft.

Although the companies' 'best and final offers' had been made on 13 March, the MoD invited both Shorts and British Aerospace to submit revised-downward offers – by noon the following day. Shorts responded immediately with an offer to supply 130 Garrett-engined Tucanos, modified to meet Specification T301, for £125 million; however, nothing was received from British Aerospace until 19 March when an offer of £120 million for the same number of PC–9s was made. Two days later Michael Heseltine, then Defence Minister, announced in the House of Commons that as Shorts' bid was the lower cost tender to be received before the noon deadline, it had been accepted. Apart from meeting the R.A.F's requirements, subject to a substantial number of modifications being embodied, there was no doubt that the choice of the Tucano was influenced by other political factors. These included the desire to provide much-needed employment in Northern Ireland, to help repay Brazil for its support to Britain during the 1982 Falklands campaign and to assist the Government's plans for the privatisation of Shorts.

The significant modifications made in the Shorts Tucano compared with the basic EMBRAER EMB–312 included the engine of much increased power to improve speed, particularly at low altitude, and to improve the rate of climb; a hydraulically-operated ventral air-brake to control speed during the descent; structural strengthening for increased manoeuvre loads and fatigue life; strengthened wing and tailplane leading edges to withstand bird-strikes; a new

513

cockpit layout to meet R.A.F. requirements; a wide use of British equipment plus an optional armament and strike capability.

Re-engining of a Tucano with a Garrett engine as chosen for the R.A.F. version was done by EMBRAER and the first flight of this aircraft, *PP–ZTC*, took place in Brazil on 14 February, 1986. Having completed some six hours test flying during six flights, the aircraft was dismantled and moved to Belfast where it was re-assembled to continue the flight-test programme. Its first flight carrying Shorts Class B markings *G–14–007* was made on 11 April, 1986. During this flight the aircraft achieved a sea level speed of 308 mph (496 km/h). The first production Tucano, serialled *ZF135*, first flew on 30 December, 1986, and was officially 'rolled out' on 20 January, 1987. During that year this aircraft plus *ZF136*, the second production Tucano, went to the A. & A.E.E. at Boscombe Down for evaluation. The first delivery of a Tucano to the R.A.F. took place on 1 September, 1988, when *ZF135* went to the Central Flying School at R.A.F. Scampton.

Span 37 ft 0 in (11.28 m); length 32 ft 0 in (9.84 m); area 208.08 sq ft (19.33 m^2); operating weight empty 4.447 lb (2,017 kg); all-up weight 5,842 lb (2,650 kg); max speed 322 mph (518 km/h); endurance (30 min reserves) 5 hr 12 min.

Appendix B

Airship Manufacture by Short Brothers (1910–21)

As already related, Eustace and Oswald Short first began their partnership in 1900 for the purpose of manufacturing spherical balloons. No complete record of their output has survived, but the account given at the beginning of this book summarises their activities in this field up to the outbreak of war in 1914. While their designs were based on those of Édouard Surcouf of Billancourt and were not original, they introduced many refinements in rigging and valve construction, and Horace Short's project for a high-altitude balloon with a pressurised gondola, complete with a 'boot-strap' ventilating system, in 1904, has already been mentioned; this was his sole contribution in the lighter-than-air field, since he saw no future in unsteerable vessels and distrusted any kind of airship having a petrol motor in dangerous proximity to a large container of inflammable gas. This did not prevent Eustace and Oswald from undertaking contracts suited to their skill and high standard of workmanship, such as gas-bags, valves, outer covering and control surfaces for the ill-fated Vickers-built *Naval Airship No. 1* in 1910. An important advance in balloon design was the equatorial suspension band suggested by Griffith Brewer and incorporated in the 18,000 cu ft *Bee* which Short Brothers built for him in May 1911; this was one of the last new balloons they made, and it gave valuable wartime service at Roehampton, where Brewer used it to teach the principles of free ballooning to R.N.A.S. airship pilots; after August 1914 the supply of rubberised balloon fabric from Continental Gummiwerke at Hanover ceased, and thereafter no more free balloons were made at Battersea; later, a satisfactory proofed fabric was developed by Vickers Ltd in collaboration with the Ioco Company at Glasgow, but by then large production contracts had been given to George Holt Thomas's new company, Airships Ltd at Merton, Surrey, for both free and tethered observation balloons.

When the U-boat menace first became serious early in 1915, the First Sea Lord, Admiral Lord Fisher, called urgently for small non-rigid Submarine Scout airships, and after the successful conversion of the 28,000 cu ft *Naval Airship No. 2* (Willows IV) into *SS1* on 18 March, 12 more trial 'blimps' were ordered; although the *SS2* built by Airships Ltd was a failure, Shorts' *SS3* did well in her acceptance trials at Kingsnorth; in spite of this, most of the 50-odd 60,000 cu ft 'blimps' constructed during 1915–16 were supplied by Airships Ltd, and Shorts' contribution to the programme was restricted to the supply of valves and instruments. As an alternative to participation in 'blimp' production, Short Brothers were invited in January 1916 to build two 23-class rigid airships of Admiralty design derived from the Vickers-built *No. 9*, which

515

Short Brothers' only complete 'blimp' was *SS3* of 60,000 cu ft (1,700 m³); the twin vertical surfaces were later modified to a single fin and rudder.

was itself based on Zeppelin experience and had multiple elevators and rudders designed and supplied by Shorts. After various changes of programme, the Admiralty awarded a contract for *R31* and *R32*, which were to be wooden rigids to a new design by the Royal Corps of Naval Constructors using methods recommended by a former Schütte-Lanz employee of Swiss nationality named Müller; an independent design by Short Brothers for a wooden airship 700 ft long, 67 ft diameter and 2,077,000 cu ft capacity, with a disposable lift of 20 tons and an estimated endurance of 20 hours at 70 mph, had been rejected in favour of the official design, which began as 594 ft long and 64 ft diameter but was finalised as a 1,547,000 cu ft ship, 615 ft long and 65½ ft diameter. To enable these two to be built, a new 700-ft-long double-bay airship shed was erected and equipped at Cardington, near Bedford, by Short Brothers, who received a Government loan of £110,000 for this purpose. The hull was of an improved low-drag shape and had 20 longitudinal girders of triangular or rectangular cross-section made up of slotted plywood webs glued to spruce flanges, fire-proofed and varnished to resist weathering, carried on ring-frames of similar construction and wire-braced in the standard Zeppelin manner; there was a forward control cabin directly attached to the hull and leading into a walkway inside the bottom of the hull, extending to the tail and giving access to ladders to three pairs of boat-built engine gondolas, each containing a 275 hp Rolls-Royce Eagle engine driving a 17-ft two-bladed propeller through a Hele-Shaw clutch, with reversing gear also on the two midships propellers. There were 21 gas-bags of rubberised cotton lined with gold-beater's skin, giving a gross lift of 47 tons and disposable lift of 16½ tons; machine-guns were mounted on top of the hull (reached by a vertical ladder in a canvas tube from the control cabin) and under the tail-cone just aft of the bottom rudder, and at various points along the walkway and in the gondolas. The horizontal and vertical tail fins were externally-braced flat surfaces, each carrying a control surface on set-back hinges to give partial aerodynamic balance.

516

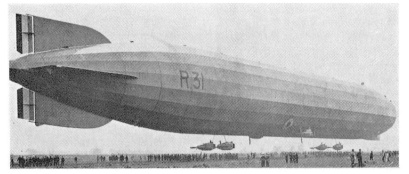

R31 at Cardington in August 1918, with six engine gondolas and original long fins. *(Courtesy S. Swayland.)*

R31 was launched for her first flight in August 1918 and achieved a top speed of 70 mph, the fastest of her day and better than estimated, but as her fuel consumption was also higher than expected, it was decided to delete one of the rearmost gondolas and to place the other under the centre-line; even with five engines, she still reached 65 mph on her second trial on 16 October, but on that occasion the top fin collapsed sideways, and it was then decided to reduce the area of all four fins by cutting back their leading edges. Having flown four hours on these two trials, *R31* was commissioned on 6 November and began her delivery flight to East Fortune the same day, but after two hours some of the joints in the girders, for which gelatin glue had been used because the correct casein cement (kaltleim) was not at first available, began to crack and she had to be docked three hours later in the spare shed at

R32 at Cardington in 1919, showing the five engine gondolas and cut-back fins, together with the control car in line with the internal catwalk; the hull was so flexible that a man at the aft end of the catwalk, when viewed from the control car, would disappear and reappear as the ship yawed; note the upper gun platform. *(Courtesy S. Swayland.)*

517

Howden, whose roof had been destroyed by fire; her subsequent abandonment and demolition have been referred to earlier. *R32* was completed to the same final standard as *R31*, with cut-down fins and five engines, and after commissioning on 3 September, 1919, flew 84 hours on experimental duties for the N.P.L. till October 1920, then becoming the training ship for the U.S. Navy crew assigned to *R38* until the new Vickers-built *R80* became available; she had flown a total of 260 hours when tested to destruction (intentionally) at Howden on 27 April, 1921, to the disappointment of Sir Hubert Wilkins, who had hoped to borrow her later for polar exploration, since her still-air range on two-thirds power was more than 2,000 miles.

R38, with *R37* on the left, under construction at Cardington early in 1919.

While *R31* and *R32* were under construction, Short Brothers were asked to take over the final erection of the duralumin *R37*, originally ordered in November 1916 from Vickers Ltd, who had fabricated the girders but were unable to complete the ship in September 1917 because their Walney Island shed was too small and no steel was available for building their proposed new 700-ft shed at Flookburgh. Assembly of *R37*'s frames in floor jigs began at Cardington in November 1917, and the sections were turned over and joined up as soon as *R31* departed a year later. Like her Beardmore-built sister *R36* (before being modified for passenger-carrying), *R37* was derived from the Zeppelin *L48*, and was 675 ft long and 78 ft 8 in diameter, with 13 main and 12 secondary longitudinals; her 20 gas-bags totalled 2,101,000 cu ft, giving a gross lift of 74 tons and disposable of $32\frac{1}{2}$ tons; she had four 350 hp Sunbeam Cossack engines arranged in single gondolas fore and aft with a pair amidships, the front one being faired into the rear of the forward control cabin although separate from it. Erection continued more slowly after the Armistice, and the

518

structure was nearly complete by February 1921, but then all further work on her was stopped and she was dismantled soon afterwards.

The last airship built by Short Brothers, *R38*, originated in June 1918 as the Admiralty 'A' design, required to have a radius of action of 3,000 miles and an ultimate cruising endurance of 211 hours. Commander C. I. R. Campbell's first proposal in reply to this demand was a 3,000,000 cu ft ship 750 ft long, but, as there were no sheds longer than the 700-ft one at Cardington, the contract was awarded to Short Brothers in September, and the dimensions were altered to 699 ft long, $85\frac{1}{2}$ ft diameter and 2,750,000 cu ft; this airship had a gross lift of 84 tons, disposable $45\frac{1}{2}$ tons, maximum speed 70·6 mph, ceiling 22,000 ft and duration 65 hours at 65 mph; the forward control cabin was directly attached to the hull and six 350 hp Sunbeam Cossack engines were installed separately in three pairs of power gondolas. Though based on Zeppelin practice, the hull had two intermediate rings between each main frame instead of the usual one, a trapezoidal keel containing a full-length corridor from nose to tail with nose access to a mooring-mast, and cantilever fins of symmetrical aerofoil section carrying horn-balanced control surfaces. The main frames were pitched 15 metres apart, thus saving a certain amount of structure weight but, as events were to prove, rendering the ship weak in bending when subjected to the high manoeuvring loads made possible by the powerful balanced controls; it was not appreciated that in previous rigid airships, both German and British, catastrophic manoeuvres had been prevented by the heaviness of the controls at maximum speed. Short Brothers undertook much of the detail design work with a team of designers, stressmen and draughtsmen under C. P. T. Lipscomb, while the General Manager in charge of manufacture was E. H. Mitchell, formerly a Tyneside shipyard manager.

In December 1918 Short Brothers put forward a design by Mitchell for a commercial airship of 4,450,000 cu ft to carry a payload of 20 tons (including first-class liner accommodation for 50 passengers) at 60 kt over a still-air range of 6,000 nautical miles. This airship would have been 694 ft long with all the accommodation in a central bottom keel and three-lobed gas-bags of 'inverted triple-teardrop' section (patent No. 134,684 of 24 December, 1918) and two extra-deep longitudinals fitting into the cusps in the top of the gas-bags; these members were connected to the main keel by suspensory cables, and the shape of the bags, with curvature proportional to the local pressure, ensured that tension in all parts of the fabric and circumferential rigging wires remained uniform, even when some bags were partly deflated. The height was to be 115 ft and the width 120 ft, giving a gross lift of 128 tons and a disposable lift of 64 tons, of which 44 tons were taken up by fuel; the intended power plants were five Rolls-Royce Condors of 550 hp each, disposed in two pairs of wing gondolas and a central terminal nacelle built into the after end of the main keel. This was one of several proposals for a long-range civil airship for the Empire and Atlantic routes during a period of optimism just after the Armistice, and it could have been built without enlarging the Cardington shed, but no Treasury support was forthcoming, and in the end only the addition of a 50-passenger saloon to Beardmore's *R36* was sanctioned.

The circumstances in which Short Brothers were deprived of the *R38* contract and turned out of Cardington works have already been detailed, but even after the Air Ministry take-over in April 1919 Lipscomb and about 20 draughtsmen stayed on until the ship was launched to assist the staff of the Royal Airship Works, as it had become. *R38*'s first flight on 23 June, 1921, occupied seven hours and brought various troubles to light, in particular control overbalance combined with backlash in the long control cables, whose tension varied with temperature, as there was no adequate means of compensation. After the second flight on 28 June all the control surface areas were reduced by 10 per cent; at the same time the fins were strengthened and the fuel system was modified to prevent flooding of the service tanks in the gondolas. On the third flight on 17 July (the first with U.S. Navy emblems and the mark *ZR-2* applied), speed was increased to 50 kt for the first time, but longitudinal hunting developed with an amplitude of 500 ft and two girders failed amidships; more serious damage would probably have resulted had the elevator wheel not been taken from the coxswain by Flt Lieut Pritchard, who managed to reduce the amplitude to 100 ft and brought *R38* safely back to Howden, where repairs were made. On 23 August she left Howden on her fourth flight with Flt Lieut Wann in command, and after manoeuvring for some hours arrived over Pulham in poor visibility and could not find the mooring mast before dusk, so she stood off over the North Sea all night and crossed the Suffolk coast at Thorpeness next morning; after making a 15-minute full-speed run at 60 kt in the afternoon she arrived over Hull at 5.20 pm at a height of 2,500 ft and began yawing manoeuvres at 54 kt, but 17 minutes later she broke in half between frames 9 and 10 and fell into the Humber, the forward half being destroyed by explosion and fire; of the 49 personnel on board, only Flt Lieut Wann, three others of the crew and N.P.L. observer H. Bateman (in charge of the recording cameras in the stern) survived. After the formal R.A.F. Court of Inquiry had reported on 5 September, the A.R.C. Accidents Sub-Committee was convened under Mervyn O'Gorman as chairman to investigate the technical causes of the disaster; they concluded that failure was due to structural weakness accentuated by the high control forces exerted, but the technical evidence was incomplete, since Commander Campbell was one of the victims; it was established that all the design and construction work carried out by Short Brothers had been fully in accordance with the specification requirements, and a later comparison with the surrendered Zeppelin *L71* showed *R38* to have been the stronger ship of the two, but *L71* was protected from overstress in turning by the heavy build-up of control-wheel force as speed increased, so limiting the rate of manoeuvre attainable by the coxswains.

The loss of *R38* at a time of national financial stringency deprived the Treasury of the sale price of £500,000 agreed on handing over to the United States Navy, and brought all current plans for commercial airship operation to a halt, although *R33* and *R36* were allowed to survive in storage until new plans for the 5,000,000 cu ft *R100* and *R101* emerged in 1926. By that time Short Brothers, having learned at Cardington how to make the best use of duralumin, were firmly established as builders of all-metal flying-boats, whose destiny was to forge the links of Empire where airships had failed.

Appendix C

Francis K. McClean's Private Fleet List (1910–14)

1. Short No. 1
2. Short-Wright No. 3
3. Short Biplane S.26 ('The Dud')
4. Short S.29 (lost with C. Grace)
5. Short S.28 (ex Moore-Brabazon No. 6)
6. Short S.34 (became RNAS *1*)
7. Short S.27 (ex C. Grace No. 2)
8. Short S.32 (used by Territorials) later rebuilt as No. 14
9. *Birdling* Monoplane
10. Short Triple-Twin S.29 (became RNAS *3*)
11. Short Tandem-Twin S.27 (rebuilt No. 7)
12. Short Tractor Biplane S.36
13A. Short S.33 (used by Territorials)
13B. Short S.33 floatplane (Thames flight)
14. Short S.32 (as rebuilt with 70½ ft span) (later RNAS *904*)
15. Short Tractor Circuit Seaplane S.68 (Green)
16. Short Nile Seaplane S.80 (later RNAS *905*)

Appendix D

Short Design Index Numbers (1921–89)

S.1	Stellite—later Cockle
S.2	Metal Hull for F.5
S.3	Springbok I (19/21)
S.3a	Springbok II (8/24)
S.3b	Chamois (A.30/24)
S.4	Satellite
S.5	Singapore I (R.13/24)
S.6	Sturgeon biplane (1/24)
S.7	Mussel
S.8	Calcutta (14/26)
S.8/2	Calcutta (French Navy)
S.8/8	Rangoon (R.18/29 & 19/31)
S.9	Single-Jupiter Monoplane project
S.10	Gurnard (O.22/26)
S.11	Valetta (21/27)
S.12	Singapore II (R.32/27)
S.13	Not used
S.14	Sarafand (R.6/28 & R.10/30)
S.15	K.F.1 (for Kawanishi)
S.16	Scion (prototype)
S.16/1	Scion (production)
S.17	Kent (L.17 *Scylla/Syrinx*)
S.18	Monoplane F.B (R.24/31)
S.19	Singapore III (R.3/33 & R.14/34)
S.20	Mayo Upper Component ⎫ (13/33)
S.21	Mayo Lower Component ⎭
S.22	Scion Senior
S.23	C-class Empire Boat (Pegasus)
S.24	Coastal Reconnaissance (4 Pobjoy) project
S.25	Sunderland (R.2/33 & R.22/36)
S.26	G-class Flying-boat
S.27	Catapult F.B. (35/36) project
S.28	Intermediate Landplane (4 Terriers) project
S.29	Stirling (B.12/36)
S.30	L.R. Empire Boat (Perseus)
S.31	Half-scale Stirling (Pobjoy)
S.32	Long-Range Civil Landplane (14/38)
S.33	Empire Boat (Strengthened Hull)
S.34	Cannon-armed Bomber (B.1/39) project
S.35	Shetland I (R.14/40)
S.36	Super-Stirling (B.8/41) project
S.37	Stirling Civil Conversion (C.18/43)
S.38	= S.A.1 Sturgeon 1 (S.11/43)
S.39	= S.A.2 Sturgeon T.T.2 (Q.1/46)
S.40	Shetland Civil Conversion
S.41	= S.A.3 F.A.A. Jet Fighter (N.7/46) project
S.42	= S.A.4 Sperrin (B.14/46)
S.43	= S.A.5 4-engined Transport (8/46) project
S.44	= S.A.6 Sealand 1 (Gipsy Queen)
S.45	Seaford (ex-Sunderland IV) (R.8/42)
S.46	= S.A.7 Twin-Cougar Flying-boat project
S.47	= S.A.8 Civil Flying-boat—4 Nomads
S.48	= S.A.9 Military Glider (X.30/46) project
S.B.1	Aeroisoclinic Glider (⅓ scale B.35/46)
S.B.2	Sealand 2 (Leonides) project
S.B.3	Sturgeon A.S. development (M.6/49)
S.B.4	Sherpa (rebuilt from S.B.1 with 2 Palas)
S.B.5	Low-speed Lightning Test Vehicle (ER.100)
S.B.6	= P.D.4 Seamew 1 (M.123D)
S.B.7	Sealand 3 (F.B.—Gipsy Queen)
S.B.8	Light 2-seater Helicopter (Gipsy Major) project
S.B.9	Sturgeon T.T.3
S.C.1	= P.D.11 Jet-Lift Single-seat (ER.143)
S.C.2	Seamew 2 (Coastal Command)
S.C.3	= P.D.16 Freighter (2 Proteus)
S.C.4	= P.D.31 Canberra U.10 (conversion from B.2)
S.C.5	= P.D.18 Belfast C.1
S.C.6	Canberra U.14 (conversion from B.2)
S.C.7	= P.D.36 Skyvan and Skyliner
S.C.8	= P.D.43 2-seat version of S.C.1 (6 R.B.108)
S.C.9	= P.D.48 Canberra P.R.9 converted for 'Red Top' development.
S.D.1	Canberra P.R.3 modified to launch S.D.2.
S.D.2	Supersonic target drone: modified Beech AQM–37A.
S.D.3–30	= 330 Transport.
S.D.3–60	= 360 Transport.

Appendix E

Preliminary Designs—Belfast (1947–89)

P.D.1	V-Bomber (B.35/46)
P.D.2	M.R. F.B. (R.2/48)
P.D.3	Solent M.R. version
P.D.4	= S.B.6 (M.123D)
P.D.5	Water-based Fighter (N. 114T)
P.D.6	S.A.4 Gyron Test-bed
P.D.7	Rocket Fighter (F.124T)
P.D.8	P.V. Photo-Recce (isoclinic)
P.D.9	L.A. Bomber (B.126T)
P.D.10	Isoclinic Wing for Swift
P.D.11	= S.C.1 (ER.143)
P.D.12	L.R. Supersonic Bomber
P.D.13	NA.39 Naval Strike (M.148)
P.D.14	Executive (2 400 hp Turboméca Marcadau turboprops). Span 46 ft.
P.D.15	Freighter (2 Darts or 4 Leonides). Span 87 ft.
P.D.16	= S.C.3 Freighter (2 4,200 hp Eland turboprops). Twin boom. Span 104 ft
P.D.17	G.O.R.339 VTOL (with E.E.)
P.D.17/3	VTOL Launching Platform
P.D.18	= S.C.5 (Britannic) = Belfast
P.D.19	Agricultural Twin
P.D.20	Transatlantic (4 Orions or Olympus)
P.D.21	VTOL Tactical Transport
P.D.22	SST for BEA (M = 1·3)
P.D.23	VTOL Naval Strike (4 schemes)
P.D.24	Air-Bus (2 Tynes)
P.D.25	VTOL Ground Attack (5 schemes)
P.D.26	⎱ Short-Range Feeder-Liner studies
P.D.27	⎰ (2 Gazelles or 2 G.E. T58)
P.D.29	L.R. SST (M = 1·8)
P.D.30	SST studies (STAC)
P.D.31	= S.C.4 (Canberra U.10)
P.D.32	Canberra (GPV-carrier)
P.D.33	Canberra (incr. span)
P.D.34	VTOL Launcher (Gnat)
P.D.35	SS Target Drone (based on Gnat)

P.D.36	= S.C.7 Skyvan
P.D.39	Recce Drone
P.D.40	VTOL Launcher (G.91)
P.D.41	Towed Targets
P.D.43	= S.C.8 (VTOL: 6 RB.108)
P.D.44	Naval Strike F.R.
P.D.45	VTOL Low Level Strike
P.D.46	'Jumping Jeep'
P.D.47	S.C.5 STOL
P.D.48	= S.C.9
P.D.49	VTOL Light Strike (NATO)
P.D.50	S.C.7 VTOL Test-Bed
P.D.51	= Skyvan 2
P.D.52	5-seater based on Baron
P.D.53	S.C.5 with C-141 wing
P.D.54	SFERMA Marquis (licence)
P.D.55	NATO V/STOL Tactical Transport (NBMR4)
P.D.56	NATO VTOL Fighter (NBMR3)
P.D.57	Britannia 312 Freight Conversion
P.D.58	Beech Queen Air for R.A.F.
P.D.59	V/STOL Skytruk Light Transport
P.D.60	Short-Range Civil Transport
P.D.62	Skyvan with B.L.C.
P.D.63	Inflatable Ground Effect M/c
P.D.64	Light Communication
P.D.65	Feeder Liner (2 Darts or turbofans – 4 schemes)
P.D.66	Light Rotorcraft
P.D.67	Hiller-Short twin-turbine 4 seat Helicopter
P.D.68	Hiller 12-E development
P.D.69	Maritime Recce (O.R.357)
P.D.70	2 seat Ground Effect M/c
P.D.71	Breguet 941/942 (licence)
P.D.75	200 seat Air-Bus for BEA
P.D.77	Strategic Transport study
P.D.78	COIN study
P.D.80	Feeder-Liner (2 turboprop)

Note: P.D.28, 37, 38 and 42 not used; P.D.61 and 74 not released; P.D.72–73 and 76 non-aircraft.

Most of the Preliminary Designs listed above remained as layouts or tenders; where further work was authorised, Design Index numbers were allotted as shown in the table, and these have already been described in their proper context. An exception on which a substantial design effort was expended was P.D.65, which deserves special mention.

In 1961 a private venture investigation was undertaken by Frank Robertson into requirements for a DC-3 replacement and world-wide interrogation of

The P.D.65 feeder-liner in the turbofan version proposed in July 1965 as a joint VFW-Fokker-Short venture.

existing DC-3 operators indicated that, for an established service, they would next re-equip with larger aircraft; on the other hand, operators intending to start a new service would not want anything bigger than a DC-3, so it was decided to concentrate effort on this size of aircraft. At first turboprops were preferred, but a year later opinion veered in favour of turbofans, if available at the same cost. During 1962 two layouts in the 25,000–30,000-lb class were examined, one with twin Darts having a cruise speed of 270 kt and the other with two Lycoming turbofans having a cruise speed of 400 kt at a direct operating cost 10 per cent higher.

Following an optimisation programme in which high- and low-wing configurations were examined together with a variety of engine positions both on wing and on fuselage, in 1963 a low-wing configuration was chosen with turbofan engines in long duct nacelles above the wing; since the general specification for the design appeared to be similar to the proposed D.H.136, a meeting was called to discuss collaboration between Shorts and de Havilland, but divergence of opinion on field length and certain features of geometry ended these discussions. Shorts then sought collaboration with Fokker, and it was discovered that Fokker and Vereinigte Flugtechnische Werke were already discussing the VFW-614 project. This was aimed at almost the same specification as P.D.65, but had certain features, such as a T-tail and engines within separate pods above the wing, which Shorts disliked.

At the Paris show in June 1965, VFW suggested tripartite collaboration with Shorts and Fokker on the lines already established for the Fokker F.28; by November 1965 the only design difference remaining was the nacelle

524

shape, the P.D.65 fuselage having been enlarged slightly to match VFW's proposals and VFW having revised their wing and tail geometry to agree with P.D.65. The German Federal Government had undertaken to contribute 60 per cent of the capital needed by the consortium, and the British Government was asked to put up 25 per cent, leaving 15 per cent to be found by the Netherlands and already promised. For some reason the British Government directed Hawker Siddeley to take Shorts' place in the consortium, with the inevitable result that the D.H.136 and VFW-614 designs were found to be totally incompatible; VFW declined to collaborate unless Shorts were reinstated, and when this was refused, decided to continue the project with Fokker alone. So P.D.65 died, but its ghost was just discernible to VFW–614 passengers as a shadow on the clouds beneath them.

Span 69 ft 9 in (21·25 m); length 67 ft 2 in (20·5 m); area 685 sq ft (63·6 m²); all-up weight 32,500 lb (14,750 kg); max cruise speed 457 mph (735 km/h); range 1,000 miles (1,610 km).

Following the success of the 330 and 360, Shorts' market studies indicated a continuing growth in the 20–130 seat bracket into the twenty-first century. This stemmed from the development of major and secondary hub airports served by large airlines and fed by regional airlines operating along ever-extending spoke route networks. Shorts' design work on a twin-turbofan commuter began in 1986 and was revealed to U.S. operators in March 1988. Designated the FJX, it is a low wing 44-seat design powered by under-wing pylon-mounted turbofans.

Span 73 ft 9 in (22.49 m); length 81 ft 11 in (24.96 m); max take-off weight 40,400 lb (18,325 kg); max cruise speed 492 mph (791 km/h); range 1,000 miles (1,610 km).

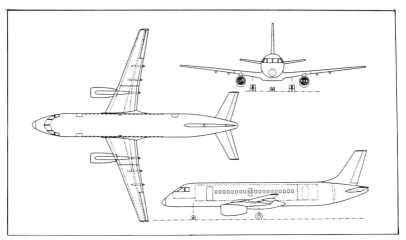

FJX Project (*Shorts drawing*)

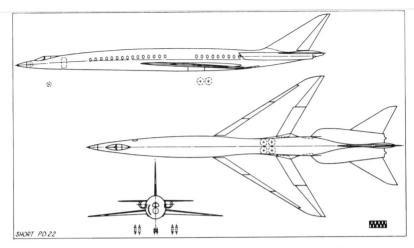

SHORT PD.22

In 1957, Shorts' first investigation into the feasibility of a supersonic transport resulted in P.D.22, a medium-range airliner suitable for BEA's longer routes and designed to cruise at M = 1·3. Concurrently the transatlantic SST problem was studied, and P.D.29 and P.D.30 included several layouts, both with and without lift engines, for operation at M = 1·8, but no definite designs emerged.

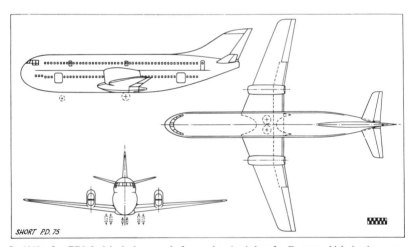

SHORT P.D. 75

In 1965, after BEA had invited proposals for a subsonic air-bus for European high-density routes, Shorts submitted P.D.75, a 200-passenger double-decker with four turbofan engines arranged in vertical pairs above the wing.

526

Appendix F

Constructor's Numbers—Eastchurch and Rochester (1910–48)

(All except those marked with an asterisk have been confirmed by documents or photographs)

S.26	Farman-Sommer type Biplane 'The Dud'	S.82–85	Enlarged S.65, RNAS *119–122*
S.27	Farman-Sommer type Biplane 'C. Grace No. 2' (later rebuilt as Tandem-Twin)	*S.86	As S.82, torpedo, 180 hp Gnome, RNAS *186*
S.28	Farman-Sommer type 'Moore-Brabazon 6'	*S.87–88	Tr. S/p, N/F, 135/200 hp Salmson, *135, 136*
S.29	Extended Farman-Sommer type (lost with Grace)	*S.89	Torpedo S/p Type B, 200 hp Le Rhône, *178*
*S.30–31	No record	S.90–95	Tr. S/p, Folder, 200 hp Salmson, *161–166*
S.32	School Biplane, side-by-side, F. McClean 8 (later rebuilt to 70½ft span, *904*)	*S.96–103	Tr. S/p, Folder, 100 hp Gnome, *811–818*
S.33	As S.32, later rebuilt as seaplane	*S.104–105	No record
S.34	Long range, as S.29, RNAS *1* (*T1*)	S.106–107	Torpedo S/p Type 184 (P), *184, 185*
S.35	As S.29 plus nacelle, Maurice Egerton	*S.108–110	Type 830, 135 hp Salmson, *819–821*
S.36	Tractor Biplane, 70 hp Gnome, F. McClean 12	*S.111–116	Type 827, 150 hp Sunbeam, *822–827*
*S.37	Tractor Monoplane, 50 hp Gnome, *M2 (14)*	*S.117–119	Type 830, 135 hp Salmson, *828–830*
S.38	Replacement for S.26, RNAS *2* (*T2*)	*S.120–128, 130	Type 184, 225 hp Sunbeam, *841–850*
S.39	Triple-Twin, RNAS *3* (*T3*), (later rebuilt as improved pusher)	S.129	Type 184 spare airframe (*Benmy-Chree*)
*S.40	No record (spare for S.38, RNAS *8*?)	*S.131–142	Type 830, *1335–1346*
S.41	Tractor Biplane, 100 hp Gnome, RNAS *10*	S.143–172	Type 827, *3093–3112, 3063–3072*
*S.42	No record (spare land fuselage, S.41?)	S.173–247	Type 184, *8031–8105*
S.43–44	As S.32, for C.F.S., *401, 402*	*S.248	Type 184 Landplane Bomber (P), *3706*
S.45	Tractor Biplane, 70 hp Gnome, RNAS *5* (*T5*)	S.249–298	Bomber, 250 hp Rolls-Royce, *9306–9355*
*S.46	Twin-Gnome Monoplane, RNAS *12*, 'Double-Dirty'	S.299–300	Type 310-A (P), *8317–8318*
S.47	Triple-Tractor, RNAS *4* (*T4*) 'Field Kitchen'	S.301–310	Training S/p, 140 hp Salmson, *9781–9790*
S.48–50	As S.45, for C.F.S., *413, 423, 424*	S.311	Type 310-B North Sea Scout, *8319*
*S.51–52	Improved S.41, RNAS *20, 21*	*S.312	Type 310-A4 (P), *N1480* (ex *8320*)
*S.53	P.V. improved S.41, 80 hp Gnome, RNAS *42*	*S.313	N.2A Scout No. 1 (later No. 2), *N36*
S.54–58	S.38 nacelle type, RNAS *19, 28, 34, 62, 63*	S.314–333	Type 184 (Eastchurch), *N1080–1099*
S.59	S.38 for Egerton, later RNAS *190*?	S.334–353	Type 310-A4, *N1300–1319*
S.60–62	As S.54, RNAS *64, 65*, CFS *448*	S.354–363	Type 310-A4, *N1150–1159*
S.63–64	Tr. S/p, Folder 2-bay, 160 hp Gnome, *81, 82*	S.364	N.2A Scout No. 3
*S.65–66	Tr. S/p, Folder 3-bay, 160 hp Gnome, *89, 90*	S.365–388	Type 310-A4, *N1481–1504*
*S.67	No record (RNAS *145*?)	S.389–398	Type 184, *N1580–1589*
S.68	Tr. S/p, Folder, 100 hp Green, C. of B.*4* F. McClean 15	S.399–418	Type 310-A4, *N1390–1409*
S.69–75	Tr. S/p, N/F, 100 hp Gnome, RNAS *74–80*	S.419–420	N.2B (P), *N66–67*
*S.76–79	Tr. S/p, N/F, 100 hp Gnome, RNAS *180–183*	S.421–423	Shirl (P), *N110–112*
S.80	Nile Seaplane, 140 hp Gnome, F. McClean 16, later *905*	*S.424–427	No record (N.2Bs *N68–71*?)
		*S.428–527	D.H.9, *D2776–2875*
S.81	Gunbus Seaplane, 160 hp Gnome, RNAS *126*	S.528–537	F.5 (Eagle), *N4830–4839*
		S.538	Atlantic (*Shamrock*) (no mark)
		S.539	Cromarty, *N120*
		S.540–542	Sporting Type Seaplane, *G-EAPZ, G-EAUA, 'UB*
		S.543	Silver Streak, *J6854* (*G-EARQ*)
		*S.544–545	Cromarty, *N121–122*
		S.546–554	F.5 (Eagles) for Japan
		*S.555–557	F.5 (Lions) for Japan
		S.558–577	F.5 (cancelled)
		*S.578–583	No record
		*S.584–585	D. of R 3A (cancelled)
		S.586–587	Springbok I, *J6974, J6975*

S.588–623	F.5 (Eagles), *N4000–4035*
S.624–637	F.5 (Eagles), *N4036–4049*
S.638	Stellite (Cockle), *G-EBKA* (*N193*)
*S.639	F.5 (metal hull), *N177*
*S.640–643	F.5 (reconditioning?)
S.644	Satellite, *G-EBJU*
*S.645–664	F.5 (reconditioning?)
*S.665–667	Springbok II, *J7295–7297*
*S.668–670	Springbok III–V, (*J7298–7300*) (cancelled)
*S.671–676	D.H.9A (new), *J7823–7828*
S.677	Singapore I, *N179* (*G-EBUP*)
S.678	Mussel I, *G-EBMJ*
S.679–709	D.H.9A (including new: *J7829–7834, J7884–7890*)
S.710–711	Sturgeon (1/24), *N199–200*
S.712–713	Calcutta, *G-EBVG, G-EBVH*
S.714–731	D.H.9A (new), *J8154–8171*
S.732–735	D.H.9A (reconditioning)
S.736	Crusader (7/26), *N226*
S.737–743	D.H.9A (reconditioning)
S.744–745	Gurnard (O.22/26), *N228–229*
S.746	S.9 Civil Mono. (not completed)
S.747	Valetta, *G-AAJY*
S.748	Calcutta, *G-AADN*
S.749	Singapore II, *N246*
S.750	Mussel II, *G-AAFZ* (*M-1*)
S.751	Calcutta (Fr.), *F-AJDB*
S.752	Calcutta, *G-AASJ*
S.753	K.F.1, *M-2*
S.754	Calcutta, *G-AATZ*
S.755–756	Rangoon, *S1434, S1435*
S.757	Rangoon, *S1433* (*G-AEIM*)
S.758–760	Kent, *G-ABFA* to *G-ABFC*
S.761	Hermes-Moth Amphibian, *G-AAVC*
S.762	Calcutta (for Breguet) unmarked
S.763	Sarafand, *S1589*
S.764–765	Rangoon, *K2134, K2809*
S.766	Scion (P), *G-ACJI*
S.767	R.24/31 (Knuckleduster), *K3574*
S.768–769	Scylla, Syrinx, *G-ACJJ, G-ACJK*
S.770–773	Singapore III, *K3592–3595*
S.774–777	Scion I, *G-ACUV* to *G-ACUY*
S.778	Scion II (P), *G-ACUZ*
S.779	Scion Senior, *VT-AGU*
S.780	Rangoon, *K3678*
S.781–784	Singapore III, *K4577–4580*
S.785–794	Scion II, *G-ADDN* to *G-ADDR,†* *VH-UUT* *G-ADDT,* *VH-UVQ,* *G-ADDV,* *VH-UTV,* *G-ADDX*
S.795	Empire Boat (S.23), *G-ADHL*
S.796	Mayo Upper Component, *G-ADHJ*
S.797	Mayo Lower Component, *G-ADHK*
S.798–802	Singapore III, *K4581–4585*
S.803	Sunderland (P), *K4774*
S.804	L.R. Empire Boat (S.23), *G-ADHM*
S.805–809	Singapore III, *K6907–6911*
S.810	Scion Senior, *VT-AHI*
S.811–822	Empire Boat (S.23), *G-ADUT* to *G-ADVE* inc.
S.823–833	Singapore III, *K6912–6922*
S.834–837	Scion Senior, *G-AECU, G-AENX, L9786, VT-AIJ*
S.838–851	Empire Boat (S.23), *G-AETV* to *G-AEUI* inc.
S.852–859	Singapore III, *K8565–8568, K8856–8859*
S.860–870	Sunderland I, *L2158–2168*
S.871–873	G-Boat (S.26), *G-AFCI* to *G-AFCK* inc.
S.874–875	Catapult Boat (S.27) cancelled

S.876–878	Empire Boat (S.23), *VH-ABA, VH-ABB, VH-ABF*
S.879–886	Empire Boat (S.30), *G-AFCT* to *G-AFDA* inc.
S.887–899	Sunderland I, *L5798–5807, N6133, N6135, N6138*
S.900–901	B.12/36 (P), *L7600, L7605*
S.902–1001	Stirling I, *N3635–3684, N3700–3729, N3750–3769*
S.1002	Half-scale Stirling, *M-4*
S.1003	Empire Boat (S.30), *G-AFKZ*
S.1004–1021	Sunderland I, *N9020–9030, N9044–9050*
S.1022–1024	14/38 (S.32), *G-AFMK* to *G-AFMM* (cancelled)
S.1025–1027	Empire Boat (S.33), *G-AFPZ, G-AFRA,* (*G-AFRB* canc.)
S.1028–1039	Sunderland I, *P9600–9606, P9620–9624*
S.1040–1139	Stirling I (series 1), *R9141–9170, R9184–9203, R9241–9290*
S.1140–1159	Sunderland I, *T9040–9050, T9070–9078*
S.1160–1182	Sunderland II, *W3976–3998*
S.1183–1209	Sunderland II, *W3999–4004, W4017–4037*

Hereafter no more constructor's numbers were used by Short Bros until after VJ-Day; all Stirling production was dispersed to other factories until the end of 1942; during this period the following were built:

Stirling I (series 2), *DJ972–977, EF327–369, EF384–400, EF413*
Stirling II, *EF401–412, EF425–470, EF488–518* (later conversions to IV(GT) were *EF404, 429, 435, 446, 470, 506*)
Sunderland III (at Rochester), *DV956–980, EJ131–145, JM659–689, JM704–722*
Sunderland III (at Windermere), *DP176–200, EJ149–158*

In 1943 production restarted at Rochester Airport, where the following were built:

Stirling III & IV, *LJ440–483, LJ501–544, LJ557–596, LJ611–653, LJ667–670, PW255–266*
Sturgeon 1 (P), *RK787, RK791*

Production at Rochester seaplane works, 1943–5, comprised:

Shetland I (P), *DX166*
Sunderland III, *ML725–774, ML777–795, PP103–132*
Sunderland IV (P), *MZ269, MZ271*
Sunderland V, *ML796–801, RN264–273, TX293* (conversions: *ML765* to Sunderland V (P), *ML788* to Sandringham 1 (P))

On 1 January, 1946, allotment of constructor's numbers was resumed, as follows:

S.1292–1299	Seaford 1, *NJ200–207*
S.1300–1311	Solent 2, *G-AHIL* to *G-AHIO, G-AHIR* to *G-AHIY*
S.1312	Nimbus, *BGA470*
S.1313	Shetland II, *G-AGVD* (ex *DX171*)

Notes: Seaford *NJ201* was *G-AGWU* from December 1945 till February 1946 and became *G-ANAJ* in April 1954; Seafords *NJ202–207* were converted to Solent 3s (*G-AKNO* to *G-AKNU*)† at Belfast in 1949. Sturgeon *RK791* did not fly at Rochester, but was first flown at Sydenham by J. S. Booth on 18 May, 1948. Maker's numbers consisting of 'SB' followed by four digits are not constructor's nos., but Shop Order Nos., and do not identify airframes; c/ns between S.1210 and S.1291 inclusive were not used.

† Excluding *G-ADDQ* and *G-AKNQ*.

Appendix G

Constructor's Numbers—Belfast (1936–66)

SH.1–50 Bristol Bombay, *L5808–5857*
SH.51–80 Bristol Bombay, *L5858–5887* (cancelled 1939 and reallotted, viz.:)
SH.51–65 Sunderland II, *W6050–6064*
SH.66–80 Sunderland III, *W6065–6068, W6075–6080, DV985–989*
SH.81–230 Handley Page Hereford & Hampden, *L6002–6101, N9055–9081, N9084–9106*
SH.231–330 Stirling I (series 1), *N6000–6049, N6065–6104, N6120–6129*
SH.331–379 Stirling I (series 2), *R9295–9308, R9310–9334, R9349–9358*

SH.380–395,
SH.397–488,
SH.490–493, } Stirling I (series 3), *BF309–358,*
SH.497, 503, *BF372–416, BF434–454*
SH.504, 515
SH.396, Stirling III (P), *R9309*

SH.489, 494–496,
SH.498–502, Stirling III, *BF455–483,*
SH.505–514, *BF500–534,*
SH.516–569, 587, } *BF561–570,*
SH.570, 581–583, 589, *MZ260–264,*
SH.571–580 *BF571–580*

SH.584–586, 588,
SH.590–604,
SH.606–614,
SH.616–618, 620–624, Stirling III,
SH.626–631, 633–638, } *EE871–975*
SH.640–646, 648–660, 662,
SH.664–670, 672–677,
SH.680–688, 690–699

SH.625, 661, 678,
SH.700–705, 707–713,
SH.715–720, 722–729, Stirling III,
SH.731–743, 745–749, *EF114–163,*
SH.751–761, 763–773, } *EF177–217,*
SH.775–792, 794–817, *EF231–277,*
SH.819–823, 825–832, 834, *EF289–316*
SH.836–846, 848–856,
SH.860–863, 873–874

SH.619 Stirling IV (P), *LJ819*

SH.835, 857–859, } Stirling IV, *EF317–323*
SH.864–866

Later conversions, III to IV:
*EE889, 900, 960, 962, 966,
EF141, 213, 214, 234, 237, 241–244, 248, 256, 260,
EF261, 263–265, 267–270, 272–277, 292–293,
EF295–298, 303, 305–306, 309, 311, 314, 316*

SH.867–868, 871–872,
SH.875–881, 883–898, Stirling IV,
SH.900–914, 916–917, *LJ810–818,*
SH.919–927, 929–939, } *LJ820–851,*
SH.941–966, 968–973, *L864–899,*
SH.975–987, 989–1003, *LJ913–956,*
SH.1005–1015, 1017, *LJ969–999*
SH.1019–1029, 1031–1035

SH.1037–1040, 1042–1054,
SH.1056, 1057, 1059–1070,
SH.1072, 1074–1094, 1096–1103,
SH.1105–1114, 1116–1125,
SH.1127–1129, 1131–1138,
SH.1140, 1142–1158, 1162–1170, Stirling IV,
SH.1172, 1174–1180, 1182–1190, *LK114–156,*
SH.1192–1194, 1196, 1197, } *LK169–211,*
1199–1210, *LK226–257,*
SH.1213–1216, 1218–1222, *LK270–313,*
SH.1224–1228, 1230–1234, *LK326–370*
SH.1236–1240, 1242, 1244–1247,
SH.1249, 1251–1254, 1256,
SH.1261–1262, 1264–1268,
SH.1271, 1272, 1274, 1275,
SH.1277–1281, 1283, 1284

SH.1286, 1288, 1289–1292, } Stirling IV,
SH.1294, 1295, 1298, 1300, } *PK225–237*
SH.1303, 1305, 1306

SH.1297, 1302, 1308, 1309,
SH.1311, 1312, 1314–1316,
SH.1318, 1321, 1322, 1324,
SH.1326, 1330, 1334, 1337,
SH.1340, 1341, 1345, 1347,
SH.1348, 1350, 1352, 1355,
SH.1356, 1359, 1360, 1363,
SH.1364, 1367, 1368, 1370, Stirling IV,
SH.1373, 1376, 1377, 1380, } *PW384–425,*
1381, *PW438–465*
SH.1383, 1385, 1386, 1389,
SH.1391, 1393, 1395, 1397,
SH.1399, 1409, 1412, 1413,
SH.1415, 1416, 1425, 1431,
SH.1434, 1435, 1437, 1443,
SH.1447, 1451, 1455, 1460,
SH.1468, 1472, 1478, 1482,
SH.1489, 1495, 1502, 1509

SH.605, 615, 632, 639, 647 Sunderland III, *DV990–994*

SH.663, 671, 679, 689, 706, }
SH.714, 721, 730, 744, 750 } *DW104–113*
SH.762, 774, 793, 818, }
SH.833, 847, 860–870 } *EJ163–165, EJ167–172*

(N.B. *EJ166* burnt out, c/n reallotted).

SH.882, 899, 915, 918, 928,
SH.940, 967, 974, 988, 1004,
SH.1016, 1018, 1030, 1036,
SH.1041, 1055, 1058, 1071, } *ML807–831*
SH.1073, 1095, 1104, 1115,
SH.1126, 1130, 1139, 1160

SH.1159, 1171, 1173, 1191, 1195 *NJ253–257*

SH.1212, 1243, 1259, 1270, 1296,
SH.1320, 1331, 1338, 1342, 1351, } Sunderland V,
SH.1371, 1390, 1400, 1414, 1417, } *NJ258–277*
SH.1422, 1430, 1432, 1438, 1456

(N.B. Post-war Sunderland conversions from III to V and later rebuilds at Belfast totalled 300 aircraft.)

529

SH.1141, 1161, 1181, 1198,
SH.1211, 1217, 1223, 1229,
SH.1235, 1241, 1248, 1255,
SH.1260, 1263, 1269, 1273,
SH.1276, 1282, 1285, 1287,
SH.1293, 1299, 1301, 1304,
SH.1307, 1310, 1313, 1317,
SH.1319, 1323, 1325, 1327–1329,
SH.1332, 1333, 1335, 1336,
SH.1339, 1343, 1344, 1346,   Stirling V,
SH.1349, 1353, 1354, 1357,   *PJ878–923,*
SH.1358, 1361, 1362, 1365,   *PJ935–959,*
SH.1366, 1369, 1372, 1374,   *PJ971–999*
SH.1375, 1378, 1379, 1382,
SH.1384, 1387, 1388, 1392,
SH.1394, 1396, 1398, 1401–1408,
SH.1410, 1411, 1418–1421,
SH.1423, 1424, 1426–1429,
SH.1433, 1436, 1440–1442,
SH.1444–1446, 1448–1450,
SH.1452–1454, 1457

SH.1458, 1459, 1461, 1463–1466,
SH.1469–1471, 1474–1481,
SH.1484, 1486–1488, 1490–1494,   Stirling V,
SH.1497–1500, 1505–1508,   *PK115–158,*
SH.1510–1514, 1516, 1519,   *PK171–186*
SH.1521–1526, 1528–1532,
SH.1534–1541

SH.1462, 1467, 1473, 1483,
SH.1485, 1496, 1501, 1503,
SH.1504, 1515, 1517, 1518,   Sunderland V,
SH.1520, 1527, 1533,   *SZ559–584*
SH.1542–1552.

SH.1553, 1554   „   *SZ598, SZ599*

Note: For security reasons, wartime SH constructor's numbers were not allotted until the aircraft were ready for final inspection, at which stage the next available serial was applied regardless of which production line the aircraft came from; consequently there is no individual correspondence between c/ns and serials between SH.331 and SH.1541, although the groups of c/ns correspond with the serial blocks shown beside them. SH.1250, 1257, 1439 and 1609 were not used.

SH.1555	Sealand (P), *G-AIVX*
SH.1556–1559	Solent IV, *ZK-AML* to *ZK-AMO*
SH.1560, 1561	Sturgeon 2 (P), *VR363, VR371*
SH.1562–1575	Sealand 1, *G-AKLM* to *'LP, YU-CFJ, YU-CFK, PK-CMA, LN-SUH, G-AKLV, SU-AHY, AP-AGB, AP-AGC, INS101, INS102*
SH.1576–1598	Sturgeon 2, *TS475–497*
SH.1599, 1603	S.B.3, *WF632, WF636*
SH.1600, 1601	S.A.4, *VX158, VX161*
SH.1602	S.B.1, *G-14-5*
SH.1604	S.B.4, *G-14-1* (later *G-36-1*)
SH.1605	S.B.5, *WG768*
SH.1606–1608	S.B.6 (P), *XA209, XA213, XA216*
SH.1610–1644	Canberra B.2, *WH853–887*
SH.1645–1669	Canberra B.2, *WH902–925, WH944*
SH.1670–1709	Canberra B.6, *WH945–984*
SH.1710–1718	Canberra B.6, *WT205–213*
SH.1719–1741	Canberra PR.9, *XH129–137, XH164–177*
SH.1742–1759	Canberra B.6 (cancelled), *XH138–151, XH158–163*
SH.1760–1769	Sealand 1, *INS103* to *INS107, YV-P-AEG, INS108* to *INS110, JZ-PTA*
SH.1770–1772	Sealand (cancelled)
SH.1773–1796	Seamew, *XE169–196, XE205–210*
SH.1797–1813	Seamew (cancelled)
SH.1814, 1815	S.C.1, *XG900, XG905*
SH.1816	Belfast C.1, (G-ASKE) XR362, G-BEPE
SH.1817–1825	Belfast C.1 XR363, G-OHCA; XR364 (scr. 11.6.79); XR365, G-HLFT; XR366 (scr. 8.8.79); XR367, G-BFYU; XR368, G-BEPS; XR369 (scr. 10.7.79); XG370 (Scr. 4.7.79); XR371 (Cosford Aerospace Museum).
SH.1826, 1827	Belfast C.1 (reservations cancelled)

Skyvan, 330, Sherpa and 360 production details in Appendix H.

Appendix H

Skyvan, 330, Sherpa and 360 Production

Skyvan 1/1A

SH.1828	G–ASCN	Shorts	wfu 15/8/66

Skyvan 2

SH.1829	G–ASCO	Shorts	wfu 10/72
SH.1830	G–ASZI	Shorts	
SH.1831	G–ASZJ	Shorts	Skyvan 2/3
			Skyliner mock-up
SH.1832	I–TORE	Aeralpi	
SH.1833	G–ATPF	Emerald Airways	bu
SH.1834	I–CESA	Aeralpi	G–AXCS BU 10/72
SH.1835	G–ATPG	Emerald Airways	N731R
SH.1836		Not completed	
SH.1837	G–AVGO	Northern Consolidated Airlines	N4906

Skyvan 3

SH.1838	G–AVJX	Australia	VH–EJR
SH.1839	G–AWCS	South West Aviation Ltd	N33VC
SH.1840	VH–PNI	Australia	VH–PNI
SH.1841	N725R	Caribbean Air Services	N725R
SH.1842	G–AWCT	Compania dos Diamantes de Angola	CR–LJF
SH.1843	N729R	Caribbean Air Services	N20DA
SH.1844	G–14–1	Caribbean Air Services	N723R
SH.1845	N734R	Caribbean Air Services	CF–GSC
SH.1846	N4916	Caribbean Air Services	P2–BAG
SH.1847	N735R	Remmert-Werner Inc	G–AWKV
SH.1848	6Y–JFL	Continental Air Services	N3201
SH.1849	VH–PNJ	Australia	N64AC
SH.1850	N4917	Wien Alaska	wo
SH.1851	G–AWSG	P T Suryadirnow, Hong Kong	PK–PSE
SH.1852	G–AWVM	Sadia Sa	PP–SDO
SH.1853	G–AWJM	Forrester Stephens	VH–FSH
SH.1854	G–AWWS	Pan Alaskan Airlines	CF–VAN
SH.1855	G–14–27	Austrian Army (3M)	5S–TA
SH.1856	G–AWYG	Loganair	N28TC
SH.1857	G–AXAD	Cherokee Airlines	N20CK
SH.1858	G–AXAE	Cherokee Airlines	N21CK
SH.1859	G–AXAF	Cherokee Airlines	N22CK
SH.1860	G–14–32	Austrian Army (3M)	5S–TB
SH.1861	G–AXAG	Pan Alaskan Airlines	N123PA
SH.1862	G–AXCT	Selkirk Air	CF–YQY
SH.1863	G–AXCU	Alaska Leasing	N100LV
SH.1864	CF–TAI	(G–AYYR) Malaysia Air Charter	9M–AQG
SH.1865	G–AXFI	Alaska Leasing	N200LV
SH.1866	G–AXWU	(SX–BBT) Oman Air Force	912
SH.1867	G–AXPT	Oman Air Force (3M)	911
SH.1868	G–AXNV	Ecuador Army Air Service	SAE–T–100
SH.1869	G–AXLB	Olympic Airways	SX–BBN
SH.1870	G–AXLC	Olympic Airways	SX–BBO
SH.1871	G–AMXO	Indonesian Air Force (3M)	T–701
SH.1872	G–AXLD	Nordair	CF–NAS

SH.1873	G–AXLE	Delaware Air Freight	N10DA
SH.1874	G–AXDO	Indonesian National Oil Co	PK–PSA
SH.1875	G–14–47	Sultan of Oman Air Force (3M)	902
SH.1876	G–AYCS	Sultan of Oman Air Force (3M)	903
SH.1877	G–14–19	Sultan of Oman Air Force (3M)	904
SH.1878	G–14–50	Sultan of Oman Air Force (3M)	905
SH.1879	G–AYDP	Sultan of Oman Air Force (3M)	901
SH.1880	G–14–52	Sultan of Oman Air Force (3M)	906
SH.1881	G–14–53	Indonesian Air Force (3M)	T–702
SH.1882	G–14–54	Indonesian Air force (3M)	T–703
SH.1883	G–14–55	Canada	CF–QSL
SH.1884	G–AYIX	Royal Flight of Nepal	9N–RAA
SH.1885	G–AYJN	Gulf Aviation Ltd	A40–SN
SH.1886	G–AYJO	Gulf Aviation Ltd	A40–SO
SH.1887	G–14–58	Argentine Naval Prefecture (3M)	PA50
SH.1888	G–14–59	Argentine Naval Prefecture (3M)	PA51
SH.1889	G–14–60	Argentine Naval Prefecture (3M)	PA52
SH.1890	G–14–61	Argentine Naval Prefecture (3M)	PA53
SH.1891	G–14–62	Argentine Naval Prefecture (3M)	PA54
SH.1892	G–AYZA	Indonesian National Oil Co	PK–PSD
SH.1893	G–AYZB	Indonesian National Oil Co	PK–PSC
SH.1894	G–AYZD	Royal Nepal Air Force (3M)	9N–RF14/RAN–14
SH.1895	907	Sultan of Oman Air Force (3M)	907
SH.1896	908	Sultan of Oman Air Force (3M)	908
SH.1897	G–AZKL	Royal Thai Police (3M)	21897
SH.1898	G–AZHP	Royal Nepal Air Force (3M)	9N–RF15/RAN–15
SH.1899	909	Written off (3M)	
SH.1900	910	Sultan of Oman Air Force (3M)	910
SH.1901	G–AZRY	Shorts (Skyliner) demonstrator	LN–NPA
SH.1902	G–AZSR	Royal Thai Police (3M)	21902
SH.1903	G–AZYW	British European Airways (Skyliner)	LN–NPG
SH.1904	PK–PSF	Indonesian National Oil Co	OE–FOL
SH.1905	PK–PSG	Indonesian National Oil Co	
SH.1906	G–AZWX	Thai Highways	U–01
SH.1907	G–BAHK	Gulf Aviation (Skyliner)	A40–SK
SH.1908	G–BAIT	British European Airways (Skyliner)	LN–NPC
SH.1909	G–BAID	Mexican Government	XC–GAY
SH.1910	PK–PSH	Indonesian National Oil Co	PK–DSV
SH.1911	G–BAIE	Mexican Government	XC–GAZ
SH.1912	703	Republic of Singapore Air Force (3M)	703
SH.1913	700	Republic of Singapore Air Force (3M)	700
SH.1914	701	Republic of Singapore Air Force (3M)	701/9V–PNJ
SH.1915	702	Republic of Singapore Air Force (3M)	702
SH.1916	704	Republic of Singapore Air Force (3M)	704
SH.1917	705	Republic of Singapore Air Force (3M)	705
SH.1918	G–BBEZ	Japan (Skyliner)	JA8793
SH.1919	G–BBFA	Royal Thai Police	21919
SH.1920	G–BBPL	Mexican Air Force (3M)	TP–0213
SH.1921	G–BBRR	Yemen Arab Republic Air Force (3M)	1153
SH.1922	G–BBRU	Yemen Arab Republic Air Force (3M)	1155
SH.1923	G–BBUR	Pelita Air Services	PK–PSI
SH.1924	G–BBUS	Pelita Air Services	PK–PSJ
SH.1925	G–BBYC	Pelita Air Services (Skyliner)	PK–PSK
SH.1926	G–BBYD	Pelita Air Services (Skyliner)	PK–PSL
SH.1927	G–BBYF	Pelita Air Services (Skyliner)	PK–PSM
SH.1928	G–BCFG	Ghana Air Force (3M)	G451
SH.1929	G–BCFH	Ghana Air Force (3M)	G452
SH.1930	G–BCFI	Ghana Air Force (3M)	G450
SH.1931	G–BCFJ	Ghana Air Force (3M)	G453
SH.1932	G–BCFK	Ghana Air Force (3M)	G454
SH.1933	G–BCFL	Ghana Air Force (3M)	G455
SH.1934			

SH.1935			
SH.1936			
SH.1937			
SH.1938	G–BCMI	Angola (3M)	CR–LOD
SH.1939	G–BCIB	Japan	JA8800
SH.1940	913	Sultan of Oman Air Force (3M)	913
SH.1941	914	Sultan of Oman Air Force (3M)	914
SH.1942	915	Sultan of Oman Air Force (3M)	915
SH.1943	5T–MAM	Mauritanian Air Force (3M)	5T–MAM
SH.1944	G–BDBT	Sultan of Oman Air Force (3M)	916
SH.1945	5T–MAN	Mauritanian Air Force (3M)	5T–MAN
SH.1946	G–BDVM	Mexican Government	XC–BOD
SH.1947	G–BDSV	Correos de Venezuela	YV–O–MC–8
SH.1948	G–BDVN	Correos de Venezuela	YV–O–DAC–3
SH.1949	G–BDVO	Correos de Venezuela	YV–O–MC–9
SH.1950	G–BDVP	Mexican Government	XC–BOT
SH.1951	G–BEHZ	Mexican Air Force	TP–0215
SH.1952	G–BELY	Mexican Air Force	TP–0216
SH.1953	G–BELZ	Mexican Air Force	TP–0217
SH.1954	G–BEOL	Japan	JA8803
SH.1955	G–BEOM	Correos de Venezuela	YV–O–MC–10
SH.1956	G–BERZ	Saudi Arabia	HZ–ZAL
SH.1957	G–BFHZ	Saudi Arabia	HZ–ZAP
SH.1958	G–BFIA	Kingdom of Lesotho Defence Force (3M)	7P–AAB/SC7–PMU1
SH.1959	G–BFUI	Fuerza Aérea Panamena	FAP300
SH.1960	G–BFUJ	Kingdom of Lesotho Defence Force (3M)	7P–ACC/SC7–PMU2
SH.1961	G–BFUL	Oman	A40–SM
SH.1962	G–BFUM	Botswana Defence Force	OC–1
SH.1963	G–BGEP	Oman	A40–SP
SH.1964	G–BGFR	Botswana Defence Force	OC–2
SH.1965	G–BGRY	South Africa	ZS–KMY
SH.1966	G–BGWB	Guyana	8R–GFF
SH.1967	G–BHHS	Malaysia Air Charter	9M–AXM
SH.1968	G–BHPH	Air Malawi	7Q–YMB
SH.1969	G–BHCH	Saudi Arabia	HZ–ZAS
SH.1970	G–BHHT	Saudi Arabia	HZ–ZAT
SH.1971	G–BHPI	Air Malawi	7Q–YMB
SH.1972	G–BHVJ	Air Malawi	7Q–YMU
SH.1973	G–BHVK	Air Malawi	7Q–YAY
SH.1974	G–BIFL	Guyana (3M)	8R–GFK
SH.1975	G–BIOH	Maldives (3M)	8Q–CA001
SH.1976	G–BJDA	Guyana (3M)	8R–GRR
SH.1977	G–BJDB	South Africa	ZS–LFG
SH.1978	G–BLDC	Royal Nepal Air Force (3M)	RAN–23
SH.1979	G–BJDD	Colombia	HK–3011X
SH.1980	G–BLLI	Barbados	8P–SKY
SH.1981	G–BMHH	Amiri Guard Air Wing -Sharjah (3M)	AGAW–121

Shorts 330–100

SH.3000	G–BSBH	Shorts	
SH.3001	G–BDBS	Shorts (became UTT prototype)	
SH.3002	G–BDMA	Golden West Airlines	N330US
SH.3003	G–BDSU	Deutsche Luftverkehrsgesellschaft	D–CBVK
SH.3004	G–14–3004	Command Airways	N51DD
SH.3005	G–14–3005	Time Air	C–GTAS
SH.3006	G–BEEO	Time Air	C–GTAM
SH.3007	G–GTAV	Time Air	C–GTAV
SH.3008	G–BENB	Deutsche Luftverkehrsgesellschaft	D–CDLT
SH.3009	G–14–3009	Command Airways	N52DD
SH.3010	G–BETN	Golden West Airlines	N330GW
SH.3011	G–BEWT	Golden West Airlines	N331GW
SH.3012	G–BEZX	Henson Airlines	N696HA

SH.3013	G–BFDX	~~Deutsche Luftverkehrsgesellschaft~~	~~D–CODO~~
SH.3014	G–BFDY	Henson Airlines	N796HA
SH.3015	G–BFHY	Deutsche Luftverkehrsgesellschaft	D–CDLA
SH.3016	G–BFMA	Deutsche Luftverkehrsgesellschaft	D–CDLB
SH.3017	G–BFMB	Antillean Airlines	PJ–DDA
SH.3018	G–BFMD	Antillean Airlines	PJ–DDB
SH.3019	G–BFSW	Golden West Airlines	N332GW
SH.3020	G–BFSX	Hawaiian Airlines	N371HA
SH.3021	G–BFTP	Deutsche Luftverkehrsgesellschaft	D–CDLC
SH.3022	G–BFUH	Hawaiian Airlines	N372HA
SH.3023	G–BFZW	Deutsche Luftverkehrsgesellschaft	D–CDLD
SH.3024	G–BFZX	Suburban Airlines	N724SA
SH.3025	G–BFZY	Hawaiian Airlines	N373HA
SH.3026	G–BGEY	Chautauqua Airlines	N330L
SH.3027	G–BGEZ	Golden West Airlines	N334GW
SH.3028	G–BGMZ	Henson Airlines	N896HA
SH.3029	G–BGNA	Loganair	G–BTJR
SH.3030	G–BGNB	Mississippi Valley Airlines	N330MV
SH.3031	G–BGNC	Suburban Airlines	N799SA
SH.3032	G–BGNE	Metro Airlines	N935MA
SH.3033	G–BGNF	Henson Airlines	N996HA
SH.3034	G–BGNG	Mississippi Valley Airlines	N331MV
SH.3035	G–BGNH	Chautauqua Airlines	N331L
SH.3036	G–BGNI	Metro Airlines	N936MA
SH.3037	G–BGNJ	Air North	N50AN
SH.3038	G–BGZV	Chautauqua Airlines	N332L
SH.3039	G–BGZU	Air North	N51AN
SH.3040	G–BGZT	Metro Airlines	N937MA
SH.3041	G–BHCG	Suburban Airlines	N844SA
SH.3042	G–BHHU	Mississippi Valley Airlines	N332MV
SH.3043	G–BHJM	Olympic Airways	SX–BGA
SH.3044	G–BHHV	Command Airways	N53DD
SH.3045	G–BHHW	Suburban Airways	N846SA
SH.3046	G–BHJJ	Metro Airlines	N938MA
SH.3047	G–BHSH	Metro Airlines	N939MA
SH.3048	G–BHVL	Olympic Airways	SX–BGB
SH.3049	G–BHWT	Mississippi Valley Airlines	N333MV
SH.3050	G–BHWU	Aeronaves del Centro	YV–373C
SH.3051	G–BHWV	Crown Airways	N140CN
SH.3052	G–BHYJ	Pennsylvania Airlines	N304CA
SH.3053	G–BHYK	Suburban Airlines	N847SA
SH.3054	G–BHYL	Aeronaves del Centro	YV–374C
SH.3055	G–BHYM	Crown Airways	N141CN
SH.3056	G–BIFG	LAPA	LV–OJG
SH.3057	G–BIFH	LAPA	LV–OJH
SH.3058	G–BIFI	Suburban Airlines	N848SA
SH.3059	G–BIFJ	Command Airways	N54DD
SH.3060	G–BIFK	Jet Charter Airlines	VH–KNN
SH.3061	G–BIGA	Aeronaves del Centro	YV–375C
SH.3062	G–BIOD	Egypt (registration not taken up)	SU–BCP
SH.3063	G–BIOE	Jet Charter Airlines	VH–KNP
SH.3064	G–BIOF	Coral Air (converted to 330–200)	N4270A
SH.3065	G–BIOG	Olympic Airways	SX–BGC
SH.3066	G–BITU	Olympic Airways	SX–BGD
SH.3067	G–BIRN	Loganair	

Shorts 330–200

SH.3068	G–BITV	Inter City Airlines	
SH.3069	G–BITX	Inter City Airlines	
SH.3070	G–BITW	Eastern Airways	G–EASI
SH.3071	G–BIYA	Atlanta Express Airlines	N330AE
SH.3072	G–BIYD	Comair	N2678G

SH.3073	G–BIYE	Jet Charter Airlines	VH–KNQ
SH.3074	G–BIYF	Atlanta Express Airlines	N26288
SH.3075	G–BIYG	Mississippi Valley Airlines	N337MV
SH.3076	G–BIYH	Mississippi Valley Airlines	N338MV
SH.3077	G–BJFK	Inter City Airlines	G–BJFK
SH.3078	EI–BLP	Avair	N5369X
SH.3079	G–BJLL	Mississippi Valley Airlines	N2629P
SH.3080	G–BJLM	Mississippi Valley Airlines	N2629Y
SH.3081	G–BJUJ	Comair	N2630A
SH.3082	G–14–3082	Casair	G–BJUK
SH.3083	G–BJUL	Olympic Airways	SX–BGE
SH.3084	G–BJWA	Olympic Airways	SX–BGF
SH.3085	G–BJXF	Thai airways	HS–TSA
SH.3086	G–BJXG	Thai airways	HS–TSB
SH.3087	G–BJXH	Thai Airways	HS–TSC
SH.3088	G–BKDL	Thai Airways	HS–TSD
SH.3089	G–BKDM	Shorts Inc	N330CA
SH.3090	G–BKDN	Eastern Airways	G–BKDN
SH.3091	G–BKDO	Eastern Airways	G–BKDO
SH.3092	G–BKMU	Aer Lingus	EI–BEG
SH.3093	G–BKMV	Command Airways	N155DD
SH.3094	G–BKMW	Shorts (Sherpa demonstrator)	
SH.3095	G–BKSU	AirUK	G–BKSU
SH.3096	G–BKSV	Fairflight/Air Ecosse	G–BKSV
SH.3097	G–BLGG	Syd-Aero	SE–INZ
SH.3098	G–BLJA	Royal Thai Army (UTT)	3098
SH.3099	G–BLJB	Royal Thai Police (UTT)	43099
SH.3100	G–BLLJ	United States Air Force (C–23A)	83–512
SH.3101	G–BLLK	United States Air Force (C–23A)	83–513
SH.3102	G–BLLL	Royal Thai Army (UTT)	3102
SH.3103	G–14–3103	United States Air Force (C–23A)	84–458
SH.3104	G–14–3104	United States Air Force (C–23A)	84–459
SH.3105	G–BLRR	Royal Thai Police (UTT)	43105
SH.3106	G–14–3106	United States Air Force (C–23A)	84–460
SH.3107	G–14–3107	United States Air Force (C–23A)	84–461
SH.3108	G–14–3108	Royal Thai Army (UTT)	3108
SH.3109	G–14–3109	United States Air Force (C–23A)	84–462
SH.3110	G–14–3110	United States Air Force (C–23A)	84–463
SH.3111	G–14–3111	United States Air Force (C–23A)	84–464
SH.3112	G–14–3112	United States Air Force (C–23A)	84–465
SH.3113	G–BLZG	United States Air Force (C–23A)	84–466
SH.3114	G–14–3114	United States Air Force (C–23A)	84–467
SH.3115	G–14–3115	United States Air Force (C–23A)	84–468
SH.3116	G–14–3116	United States Air Force (C–23A)	84–469
SH.3117	G–14–3117	United States Air Force (C–23A)	84–470
SH.3118	G–14–3118	United States Air Force (C–23A)	84–471
SH.3119	G–14–3119	United States Air Force (C–23A)	84–472
SH.3120	G–14–3120	United States Air Force (C–23A)	84–473
SH.3121	G–BMGX	Amiri Guard Air Wing (UTT)	AGAW.131
SH.3122	G–BMLF	Shorts (UTT)	G–BMLF
SH.3123	G–BMLG	Industria Venezolana de Aluminio CA (UTT)	YV–O–GVR1
SH.3124	G–14–3124	Shorts	

Shorts 360

SH.3600	G–ROOM	Shorts	
SH.3601	G–WIDE	Suburban Airlines	N360SA
SH.3602	G–BKJC	Simmons Airlines	N360MQ
SH.3603	G–BKKT	Genair	G–BKKT
SH.3604	G–BKKU	Air Ecosse	G–RMSS
SH.3605	G–BKKV	Mississippi Valley Airlines	N342MV
SH.3606	G–BKKW	Air Ecosse	G–DASI
SH.3607	G–BKKX ،	Simmons Airlines	N361MQ

SH.3608	G–BKMX	Loganair	G–BKMX
SH.3609	G–BKMY	Mississippi Valley Airlines	N343MV
SH.3610	G–BKMZ	Newair	N715NC
SH.3611	G–BKPO	British Midland Airways	G–BMAJ
SH.3612	G–BKPP	Simmons Airlines	N362MQ
SH.3613	G–BKPR	Imperial Airlines	N601A
SH.3614	G–BKSL	Simmons Airlines	N363MQ
SH.3615	G–BKSM	Mississippi Valley Airlines	N344MV
SH.3616	G–BKSN	Mississippi Valley Airlines	N345MV
SH.3617	G–BKUF	Fischer Brothers	N617FB
SH.3618	G–BKUG	Imperial Airlines	N691A
SH.3619	G–BKUH	Simmons Airlines	N364MQ
SH.3620	G–BKWJ	Murray Valley Airlines	VH–MVX
SH.3621	G–BKWK	Simmons Airlines	N365MQ
SH.3622	G–BKWL	Fischer Brothers	N622FB
SH.3623	G–BKWM	Pennsylvania Airlines	N601CA
SH.3624	G–BKWN	Sunbelt Airlines	N912SB
SH.3625	G–BKZN	Pennsylvania Airlines	N4498Y
SH.3626	G–BKZO	Murray Valley Airlines	VH–MVW
SH.3627	G–BKZP	Imperial Airlines	N701A
SH.3628	G–BKZR	Genair	G–BKZR
SH.3629	G–BKZS	Sunbelt Airlines	N913SB
SH.3630	G–BLCN	Sunstate Airlines	VH–SVU
SH.3631	G–BLCO	Sunbelt Airlines	N914SB
SH.3632	G–BLCP	Maersk/Air Business	OY–MMA
SH.3633	G–BLCR	British Midland Airways	G–BMAR
SH.3634	G–BLCS	Dash Air	N132DA
SH.3635	G–BLED	Air Lingus	EI–BEK
SH.3636	G–BLEE	Aer Lingus	EI–BEL
SH.3637	G–BLEF	Manx Airlines	G–LEGS
SH.3638	G–BLEG	Manx Airlines	G–ISLE
SH.3639	G–BLEH	Simmons Airlines	N366MQ
SH.3640	G–BLGA	Simmons Airlines	N367MQ
SH.3641	G–BLGB	Loganair	G–BLGB
SH.3642	G–BLGC	Aer Lingus	EI–BEM
SH.3643	G–BLGD	Wright Airlines	N631KC
SH.3644	G–BLGE	Wright Airlines	N632KC
SH.3645	G–BLGF	Wright Airlines	N633KC
SH.3646	G–BLIJ	Wright Airlines	N634KC
SH.3647	G–BLIK	Wright Airlines	N635KC
SH.3648	G–BLIL	Maersk/Air Business	OY–MMB
SH.3649	G–BLIM	Mississippi Valley Airlines	N346MV
SH.3650	G–BLIN	Mississippi Valley Airlines	N347MV
SH.3651	G–BLJR	Malaysia Air Charter	9M–KGN
SH.3652	G–BLJS	Pennsylvania Airlines	N124CA
SH.3653	G–BLJT	Pennsylvania Airlines	N151CA
SH.3654	G–BLJU	Simmons Airlines	N369MQ
SH.3655	G–BLJV	Simmons Airlines	N370MQ
SH.3656	G–BLPU	Aer Lingus	EI–BPD
SH.3657	G–BLPV	Air UK	G–BLPV
SH.3658	G–BLPW	Simmons Airlines	N371MQ
SH.3659	G–BLPX	Simmons Airlines	N372MQ
SH.3660	G–BLPY	Shorts	G–BLPY
SH.3661	G–BLRT	Fairflight	G–BLRT
SH.3662	G–BLWA	Suburban Airlines	N362SA
SH.3663	G–14–3663	Westair Commuter	N360SE
SH.3664	G–BLTO	Fairflight	G–BLTO
SH.3665	G–BLUC	Atlantic Southeast	N190SB
SH.3666	G–BLUD	Atlantic Southeast	N191SB
SH.3667	G–BLRU	Civil Aviation Administration China	B–3601
SH.3668	G–BLUR	Atlantic Southeast	N360SY
SH.3669	G–BLUU	Civil Aviation Administration China	B–3602

SH.3670	G–BLWJ	Civil Aviation Administration China	B–3603
SH.3671	G–BLWK	Civil Aviation Administration China	B–3604
SH.3672	G–BLWN	Civil Aviation Administration China	B–3605
SH.3673	G–BLYF	Civil Aviation Administration China	B–3606
SH.3674	G–BLYG	Civil Aviation Administration China	B–3607
SH.3675	G–BLYH	Civil Aviation Administration China	B–3608
SH.3676	G–BLZT	Air UK	G–BLZT
SH.3677	G–BLZU	Time Air	C–GTAU
SH.3678	G–BLZV	Westair Commuter	N342SB
SH.3679	G–BMEN	Time Air	C–GTAX

Shorts 360 ADV

SH.3677	G–BLZU	Time Air	C–GTAU
SH.3678	G–BLZV	Westair Commuter	N342SB
SH.3679	G–BMEN	Time Air	C–GTAX
SH.3680	G–BMEO	Thai Airways	HS–TSE
SH.3681	G–BMEP	Thai Airways	HS–TSF
SH.3682	G–BMER	Simmons Airlines	N373MQ
SH.3683	G–BMES	Simmons Airlines	N374MQ
SH.3684	G–BMHV	Simmons Airlines	N375MQ
SH.3685	G–BMHW	Simmons Airlines	N376MQ
SH.3686	G–BMHX	British Midland Airways	G–BMHX
SH.3687	G–BMHY	British Midland Airways	G–BMHY
SH.3688	G–BMLC	Loganair	G–BMLC
SH.3689	G–BMLD	Aer Lingus	EI–BSP
SH.3690	G–BMLE	CC Air/Piedmont Commuter	N690PC
SH.3691	G–BMNG	CC Air/Piedmont Commuter	N360PC
SH.3692	G–BMNH	CC Air/Piedmont Commuter	N693PC
SH.3693	G–BMNI	CC Air/Piedmont Commuter	N695PC
SH.3694	G–BMNJ	CC Air/Piedmont Commuter	N694PC
SH.3695	G–BMNK	Shorts	G–BMNK
SH.3696	G–BMUV	Stateswest Airlines	N711PK
SH.3697	G–BMUW	Stateswest Airlines	N711HJ
SH.3698	G–BMUX	Stateswest Airlines	N711MP
SH.3699	G–BMUY	Simmons Airlines	N377MQ
SH.3700	G–BMXP	Simmons Airlines	N378MQ
SH.3701	G–BMXR	Simmons Airlines	N379MQ
SH.3702	G–14–3702	Simmons Airlines	N380MQ
SH.3703	G–14–3703	Simmons Airlines	N381MQ
SH.3704	G–BMXU	Simmons Airlines	N382MQ
SH.3705	G–BNBA		SE–IXE
SH.3706	G–BNBB	Simmons Airlines	N383MQ
SH.3707	G–BNBC	Simmons Airlines	N385MQ
SH.3708	G–BNBD	Connectair	
SH.3709	G–BNBE	Simmons Airlines	N386MQ
SH.3710	G–BNBF	Simmons Airlines	N387MQ
SH.3711	G–BNBG	Simmons Airlines	N384MQ
SH.3712	G–BNDI	Jersey European Airways	G–OBLK
SH.3713	G–BNDJ	Jersey European Airways	G–OBOH
SH.3714	G–BNDK	Jersey European Airways	G–OBHD
SH.3715	G–BNDL	Stateswest Airlines	N711PM
SH.3716	G–BNDM	Capital Airways	G–BNDM
SH.3717	G–BNFA	GPA Jetprop	EI–BTH
SH.3718	G–BNFB	GPA Jetprop	EI–BTI
SH.3719	G–BNFC	GPA Jetprop	EI–BTJ
SH.3720	G–BNFD	GPA Jetprop	EI–BTK
SH.3721	G–BNFE	CC Air/Piedmont Commuter	N121PC
SH.3722	G–BNMB	CC Air/Piedmont Commuter	N722PC
SH.3723	G–14–3723	Command Airways	N160DD
SH.3724	G–14–3724	Command Airways	N161DD
SH.3725	G–14–3725	Command Airways	N162DD
SH.3726	G–14–3726	GPA Jetprop	EI–BTO

SH.3727	G–BNYE	CVG Edelca Venezuela	YV–O–GUR–2
SH.3728	G–BNYF	GPA Jetprop	EI–BTP
SH.3729	G–BNYG	CC Air/Piedmont Commuter	N729PC
SH.3730	G–BNYH	CC Air/Piedmont Commuter	N730PC
SH.3731	G–BNYI	CC Air/Piedmont Commuter	N360CC
SH.3732	G–BOEF	Fortis International	
SH.3733	G–BOEG	CC Air/Piedmont Commuter	N133PC
SH.3734	G–BOEL	CC Air/Piedmont Commuter	N134PC
SH.3735	G–BOEI		
SH.3736	G–BOEJ	Shorts	
SH.3737	G–BOFG	Capital Airlines	G–OLBA
SH.3738	G–BOFH	Capital Airlines	G–OLTN
SH.3739	G–BOFI	Capital Airlines	G–CPTL
SH.3740	G–BOFJ	Command Airways	N165DD
SH.3741	G–BOFK	Capital Airlines	G–OLGW
SH.3742	G–BOWF	CC Air/Piedmont Commuter	N742CC
SH.3743	G–BOWG		
SH.3744	G–BOWH		
SH.3745	G–BOWI		
SH.3746	G–BOWJ		
SH.3747			
SH.3748			
SH.3749			
SH.3750			

Appendix I

Conversion Numbers—Belfast (1945–50)

SH.1C	Sandringham 2	*DV964/G-AGPZ*	Dodero
SH.2C	,, 2	*DD834/G-AGPT*	,,
SH.3C	,, 2	*DD841/G-AGPY*	,,
SH.4C	,, 2	*EJ170/G-AGTZ*	,,
SH.5C	Sunderland 3	*EJ156/G-AGWW*	CAUSA
SH.6C	,, 3	*ML876/G-AGWX*	,,
SH.7C	Not used		
SH.8C	Ju 52/3mg8e	*VN723/G-AHOE*	BEA
SH.9C	,,	*VN729/G-AHOF*	,,
SH.10C	,,	*VN740/G-AHOD*	,,
SH.11C	,,	*VN741/G-AHOL*	,,
SH.12C	,,	*VN742/G-AHOK*	,,
SH.13C	,,	*VN744/G-AHOI*	,,
SH.14C	,,	*VN746/G-AHOH*	,,
SH.15C	,,	*VN756/G-AHOJ*	,,
SH.16C	,,	*VM923/G-AHOC*	,,
SH.17C	,,	*VM979/G-AHOG*	,,
SH.18C	H.P.70 Halton	*PP310/G-AHDU*	BOAC
SH.19C	,, ,,	*PP315/G-AHDW*	,,
SH.20C	,, ,,	*PP228/G-AHDM*	,,
SH.21C	,, ,,	*PP314/G-AHDV*	,,
SH.22C	,, ,,	*PP277/G-AHDS*	,,
SH.23C	,, ,,	*PP224/G-AHDL*	,,
SH.24C	,, ,,	*PP234/G-AHDN*	,,
SH.25C	,, ,,	*PP268/G-AHDP*	,,
SH.26C	,, ,,	*PP269/G-AHDR*	,,
SH.27C	,, ,,	*PP308/G-AHDT*	,,
SH.28C	,, ,,	*PP316/G-AHDX*	,,
SH.29C	,, ,,	*PP226/G-AHDO*	,,
SH.30C	Sandringham 4	*ML761/ZK-AMB*	TEAL
SH.31C	,, 5	*ML838/G-AHYY*	BOAC
SH.32C	,, 4	*NJ255/ZK-AMD*	TEAL
SH.33C	,, 4	*NJ179/ZK-AME*	,,
SH.34C	,, 5	*ML783/G-AHZA*	BOAC
SH.35C	,, 5	*ML784/G-AHYZ*	(burnt)
SH.36C	,, 5	*ML818/G-AHZE*	BOAC
SH.37C	,, 5	*ML828/G-AHZG*	,,
SH.38C	,, 5	*NJ171/G-AHZB*	,,
SH.39C	,, 5	*NJ253/G-AHZC*	,,
SH.40C	,, 5	*NJ257/G-AHZD*	,,
SH.41C	,, 5	*NJ188/G-AHZF*	,,
SH.42C	*Golden Hind*	*G-AFCI* (refit)	,,
SH.43C	Sandringham 2	*ML843/G-AHRE*	Dodero
SH.44C	D.H. Hornet Moth	*W5775* (ex impress.)	
SH.45C	H.P. Halifax 8	(French)	
SH.46C	,, ,,	,,	
SH.47C	Sunderland 3	*ML750*	
SH.48C	Sandringham 6	*ML809/LN-IAV*	DNL
SH.49C	Lockheed 12A	*LA620/G-AGWM*	(export)
SH.50C	,, ,,	*LA623/G-AGWN*	(export)
SH.51C	Sandringham 6	*ML807/LN-IAU*	DNL
SH.52C	,, 6	*JM720/LN-IAW*	,,

SH.53C	Sandringham 3		*LV-AAQ* (SH.4C refit)	
SH.54C	,,	3	*LV-AAR* (SH.3C ,,)	
SH.55C	,,	4	*JM715/ZK-AMH*	TEAL
SH.56C	,,	5	*JM681/G-AJMZ*	BOAC
SH.57C	,,	7	*JM719/G-AKCO*	,,
SH.58C	,,	7	*EJ172/G-AKCP*	,,
SH.59C	,,	7	*ML840/G-AKCR*	,,
SH.60C	Sunderland 5		*DP195/CX-AKR*	CAUSA
SH.61C	,,	5	(reservation-not used)	
SH.62C	Sandringham 6		*W4037/LN-LAI*	DNL
SH.63C				
SH.64C				
SH.65C				
SH.66C	reservations—not used (Solent 3?)			
SH.67C				
SH.68C				
SH.69C	Sunderland 5		*EJ171/LV-AHH* ⎫	⎧ Aerolineas
SH.70C	,,	5	*EK579/LV-AHG* ⎭	⎩ Argentinas
SH.71C	Sandringham 6		*JM714/LN-LMK*	DNL

Appendix J

Short Brothers Aircraft Built by Other Manufacturers (1915–45)

Manufacturer	Type	Quantity	Identification
Austin Motors Ltd, Long-bridge, Birmingham	Stirling I (series 3)	191	*W7426–7475, W7500–7539, W7560–7590, W7610–7639, BK592–628, BK644–647*
	Stirling III	429	*BK648–667, BK686–727, BK759–784, BK798–818, EH875–909, EH921–961, EH977–996, EJ104–127, LK375–411, LK425–466, LK479–521, LK535–576, LK589–624* (37 later converted to IV)
Blackburn Aircraft Ltd, Dumbarton	Sunderland II	20	*T9083–9090, T9109–9115, W6000–6004*
	Sunderland III	160	*W6005–6016, W6026–6033, DD828–867, EK572–596, ML835–884, NJ170–194, PP135–144*
	Sunderland V	60	*PP145–164, RN277–306, VB880–889*
S.A. des Ateliers d'Aviation Louis Breguet, Le Havre, France	Calcutta	4	(Aéronavale)
Brush Electrical Engineering Co Ltd, Loughborough, Leics	Type 827	20	*3321–3332, 8230–8237*
	Type 184	190	*N1660–1689, N2600–2659, N2790–2819, N9060–9099, N9260–9289*
Fairey Aviation Co Ltd, Hamble, Hants	Type 827	12	*8550–8561*
Kawanishi Kokuki Kabushiki Kaisha, Naruo, Kobe, Japan	K.F.1	4	(Imperial Japanese Navy Type 90-2)
Mann, Egerton & Co Ltd, Norwich, Norfolk	Type 184	22	*8344–8355,* (Type B) *9085–9094*
	Bomber	20	*9476–9495*
Parnall & Sons, Bristol	Type 827	20	*8218–8229, 8250–9257*
	Bomber	6	*9771–9776*
Phoenix Dynamo Manufacturing Co Ltd, Bradford	Type 184	62	*8368–8379, N1630–1659, N1740–1759*
	Bomber	6	*9831–9836* (one became *A3932* for R.F.C.)
Pobjoy Airmotors & Aircraft Ltd, Rochester, Kent	Scion II	6	*VQ-PAA, VQ-PAB, G-AEIL, G-AEJN, G-AETT, G-AEZF.* (C/Ns *PA1001–1005, 1008*)
Robey & Co Ltd, Lincoln	Type 184	256	*9041–9060, N1220–1229, N1260–1279, N1820–1839, N2820–2849, N9000–9059, N9140–9169, N9290–9305*
Frederick Sage & Co Ltd, Peterborough, Northants	Type 184	72	*8380–8391, 9065–9084, N1130–1139, N1590–1599, N1780–1799*
S.E. Saunders & Co Ltd, Cowes, Isle of Wight	Type 184	80	*8001–8030, N1140–1149, N1600–1624, N1760–1774*
Sunbeam Motor Car Co Ltd, Wolverhampton, Staffs	Type 827	20	*8630–8649*
	Bomber	15	*9356–9370*
	Type 310-A4	50	*N1360–1389, N1690–1709*
Supermarine Aviation Works, Woolston, Southampton	S.38-type	12	*1580–1591*
	Type 184	15	*N9170–9184*
Westland Aircraft Works (Petters Ltd), Yeovil, Som	Type 184	12	*8356–8367*
	Type 166	20	*9751–9770*
J. S. White & Co, Cowes, Isle of Wight	Type 184	110	*N1240–1259, N2950–2999, N9100–9139*
White & Thompson Ltd, Middleton-on-Sea, Sussex	S.38-type	24	*3143–3148, 8434–8439, 8530–8541*

541

Index—General

(For Aircraft and Engines see pp. 558–60)

554

Sourabaya, 331
South African Air Force, 359
Southampton, 70, 119, 224–9, 270, 309–25, 332, 404, 408, 460
Southdown, 19
Southend-on-Sea, 289–93
Southern Airways, 291
South Pacific Airlines, 411
Southwold, 104
Special Operations Executive, 386
Speke, 297
Spence, Robert, 322
Spencer, Percival, 3, 8
Spezia, 231
Sphere, The, 87
Spottiswood, First Off, 322
Spottiswoode, J. Herbert, 63, 66, 224
Spratt, E. D., 293
Squadrons:
  Aéronavale Escadrille 7FE, 365
  RAF
    7, 379–80
    15, 380
    46, 387
    48, 387
    53, 473–4
    69, 354
    75, 381
    88, 364–5
    90, 381
    95, 354
    116, 293
    119, 329, 338
    138, 386
    149, 380–1, 383
    158, 387
    161, 386
    190, 385
    196, 382, 385
    199, 382–3
    201, 354, 359, 362–3, 366
    203, 234–6, 253–4
    204, 348, 352, 354
    205, 253–4, 364–5
    209, 254, 284, 364–5
    210, 236, 253–4, 346–7, 354
    214, 381
    218, 380–1, 383
    228, 254, 348, 353–4, 359, 363
    230, 253, 347, 359–60, 364, 474
    240, 254, 364
    242, 387
    272, 338
    295, 386
    299, 385, 387

    320 (*Neth*), 311
    330 (*Nor*), 359
    343 (*FF*), 359
    413 (*RCAF*), 329
    422 (*RCAF*), 359
    423 (*RCAF*) 359
    461 (*RCAF*), 355–6, 359
    570, 386
    620, 386
    622, 382, 385
    623, 382
    624, 386
  R.A.A.F.
    10, 338, 349, 353–6, 358
  R.N.A.S.
    2 *Wing*, 102
    3   " 127–8
    5   " 128
    7   " 127
    8 (GEA *Sqn*, 104–5
  R.N. (*F.A.A.*)
    728, 417
  R.N.Z.A.F.
    5 (*M.R.*), 254, 365–6
  S.A.A.F.
    35, 359
Stangate Creek, 289
Stangrant, 353
Stanleyville, 330–1
Stansted, 476
Stanton-by-Dale, 1
Stephenson & Co., Robert, 1
Stevenson, Robert Louis, 1
Stocken, Rex H., 178–9
Stockholm, 201
Stocks, Mrs. de Beauvoir, 92
Stonehaven, Lord, 188
Store, Capt A. Gordon, 319, 327
Stornoway, 298, 486
Stradishall, 381
Stranraer, 228, 329, 337–8, 354
Strood, 152, 156, 259
Stroud, Glos, 97
Suburban Airlines, 494, 503
Suda Bay, 229, 231, 354
Sueter, Cdr. (later Sir) Murray, F., 17, 110–15, 123, 127, 129, 144
Sullom Voe, 354, 359
Sultan of Oman's Air Force, 488
Sunderland Ltd, x
Sunbelt Airlines, 503
Surcouf, Édouard, 3, 492
Sutherland, Duke of, 175, 177
Swale, 57, 340
Swift Synchromo, 367, 395

556

Index—Aircraft and Engines